Aging, the Individual, and Society

Seventh Edition

Susan Hillier
Sonoma State University

Georgia M. Barrow

Wadsworth Publishing Company
I(T)P® An International Thomson Publishing Company

Belmont, CA • Albany, NY • Boston • Cincinnati • Johannesburg
London • Madrid • Melbourne • Mexico City • New York
Pacific Grove, CA • Scottsdale, AZ • Singapore • Tokyo • Toronto

Sociology Editor: Halee Dinsey
Assistant Editor: Barbara Yien
Editorial Assistant: Jennifer Jones
Marketing Manager: Christine Henry
Project Editor: Jerilyn Emori
Print Buyer: Karen Hunt
Permissions Editor: Robert Kauser
Production: Karen Slaght & Associates
Interior and Cover Designer: Carolyn Deacy
Copy Editor: Karen Slaght
Illustrator: Publishers' Design and Production Services, Inc.
Cover Image: Jon Riley/©Tony Stone Images, Inc.
Signing Representative: Christine Henry
Compositor: Publishers' Design and Production Services, Inc.
Printer: Webcom Limited

Printed in Canada
1 2 3 4 5 6 7 8 9 10

For more information, contact Wadsworth Publishing Company, 10 Davis Drive, Belmont, CA 94002, or electronically at http://www.wadsworth.com

International Thomson Publishing Europe
Berkshire House
168-173 High Holborn
London, WC1V 7AA, United Kingdom

International Thomson Editores
Seneca, 53
Colonia Polanco
11560 México D.F. México

Nelson ITP, Australia
102 Dodds Street
South Melbourne
Victoria 3205 Australia

International Thomson Publishing Asia
60 Albert Street
#15-01 Albert Complex
Singapore 189969

Nelson Canada
1120 Birchmount Road
Scarborough, Ontario
Canada M1K 5G4

International Thomson Publishing Japan
Hirakawa-cho Kyowa Building, 3F
2-2-1 Hirakawa-cho, Chiyoda-ku
Tokyo 102 Japan

International Thomson Publishing Southern Africa
Building 18, Constantia Square
138 Sixteenth Road, P.O. Box 2459
Halfway House, 1685 South Africa

Library of Congress Cataloging-in-Publication Data
Hillier, Susan.
Aging, the individual, and society / Susan Hillier, Georgia M. Barrow. — 7th ed.
p. cm.
Rev. ed. of: Aging, the individual, & society / Georgia M. Barrow. 6th ed. 1996.
Includes bibliographical references and indexes.
ISBN 0-534-55242-0 (pbk.)
1. Gerontology. 2. Aged. 3. Aged—United States. I. Barrow, Georgia M. II. Barrow, Georgia M. Aging, the individual, & society. III. Title.
HQ1061.B37 1998
305.26—dc21

This book is printed on acid-free recycled paper.

Dedication

In memory of three of the twentieth century's great women—Grandma Battles, Mama Bea, and Elaine. Also to my students—the shapers of political value for the twenty-first century.—SH

To three of my Kansas kin with love: My Mom Edna Coleman; her sister, my Aunt Georgine Coleman; and in memory of my Dad's sister, Aunt Georgia Sales.—GB

Contents

4 / Theories in Social Gerontology

5 / Friends, Family, and Community

6 / Intimacy and Sexuality

7 / Physical Health and Well-Being

8 / Work and Leisure

9 / Finances and Lifestyles

10 / Living Environments

11 / Mental Health

12 / The Oldest-Old and Caregiving

13 / Special Problems

14 / Women and Ethnic Groups

15 / Death and Dying

Preface

The dawn of the 21st century is an exciting time to explore the relationship of human aging, individual processes, and our American society. The study of aging has changed dramatically since the late 1960s when a handful of scholars began seriously to explore the human and social meanings behind longevity and the demographic shift from a nation of youths to one of adults. This text, too, has grown and stretched with grace and vision in its history.

The seventh edition benefits from the strength of the previous editions, and moves on to address many of the recent changes in the field of gerontology. For starters, the new edition is a product of the collaboration between Georgia Barrow, a sociologist, and me, Susan Hillier, a psychologist with a specialty in later life development. We think that this interdisciplinary perspective adds an exciting and valuable dimension to the text and lends itself to a fuller description of the *meaning* of aging in individual and social terms.

The tone of the text reflects the current understanding that aging is a powerful process and that growth and development do continue in later life. Indeed, as long as an individual lives, personality continues to develop in complexity and richness. Perhaps no previous edition of *Aging, the Individual, and Society* so directly addresses the impact on society of increasing adult populations that are living longer.

The dramatic impact of advances in science and technology on our story of human aging is woven into this edition. Longevity research has moved from a fringe pursuit to a major industry as laboratories around the world identify genes and genetic mechanisms impacting aging. Likewise, the impact of computer technology on the lives and community of the current elderly and the future elderly—Baby Boomers—is discussed.

The new edition presents a multidisciplinary perspective for viewing the ways biology and psychology affect social structures. It also provides strategies for understanding the ways in which social systems impact an individual's long life now and in the future. In short, changes included in this edition have been designed to fully describe the spectrum of aging into the 21st century. A cursory review of the bibliography, which has been expanded to include a depth of scientific and professional literature as well as popular literature, will attest to these extensive revisions.

Psychologists and sociologists are especially attuned to the need to address different learning styles and various pedagogical approaches. Accordingly, each chapter begins with a familiar news story providing a real-life illustration of a basic chapter concept. These stories are intended to help students make the connection between theory and life-as-lived. Summaries of research discoveries and snippets of information are provided in boxed sections throughout the text. These bits and pieces are designed to promote critical thinking by presenting ideas that can be explored further through library research, lecture, and group discussion.

Questions for discussion, for exploration on the Internet, and for experiential learning end each chapter. Each set of activities is integrated topically, theoretically, and pedagogically. They require a personal interaction of the student with material representing specific chapter concepts, thereby reinforcing the content of each chapter. The text includes an appendix of Internet addresses to assist students and faculty to seek further information on a broad range of topics.

NEW TO THE SEVENTH EDITION

Several changes have been made to the seventh edition of the text. They include:

- New chapters on:
  Psychosocial development in later life
  Community and friend networks
  Intimacy and sexuality
- Reorganization of subject matter
- Emphasis on the interdisciplinary overlap of issues
- Issues presented to enhance critical thinking
- Topics tightly linked to policy making and implementation
- Greater emphasis on theory
- Chapter-by-chapter integration and discussion of research methodology
- Emphasis on aging in the future—Baby Boomers; technological change
- Summary tables and figures of theoretical material as learning aids
- Extensive use of literature representing research and professional writing
- Chapter-based Internet exercises for research and analysis of resource material
- Enhanced bibliography
- Appendix on Internet Addresses relevant to issues in aging

ACKNOWLEDGMENTS

I am so gratified to be part of the exciting process of developing teaching and learning material for the field of gerontology. I am indebted to Georgia Barrow who graciously invited my participation in this seventh edition of her excellent undergraduate text on gerontology. I am indebted also to the many students in my gerontology classes whose questions, experiences, personal styles, and intellectual energy have challenged me and provided inspiration for the style and content of the text.

The seventh edition of *Aging, the Individual, and Society* would not have happened without the skill, good humor, support, and friendship of my two research collaborators, Christopher Kelly and Pamela McCullogh. Given an extraordinarly tight schedule, these two wonderful souls joined me for hours of intense library and Internet research, reading and editing, philosophical and political argument, and overall tension-relief. The additional organizational skills of Kathleen Kelly iced the cake and put us over the top.

Most special acknowledgment goes to Donald Dixon for his loving support during the production of this text. Also a sincere and loving thanks to Brian Gore and Jennifer Parks; to my parents, Kenneth and Alouise Hillier; and to those friends whose words of encouragement and acts of kindness are forever treasured.

The seventh edition reflects the thoughtful contributions of the following reviewers: Jeffrey A. Burr, State University of New York at Buffalo; Karen Conner, Drake University; Jean E. Daniels, California State University, Northridge; David Jorgenson, Southwest Texas State University; Dale Lund, University of Utah; and George F. Stine, Millersville University.

Our deep appreciation is extended to Wadsworth Publishing Company and to Denise Simon, former Senior Editor, our tactful, consistent, patient, trustworthy editor; Angela Nava, former Editorial Assistant, for persistence and good cheer; Eve Howard, Publisher; Jerilyn Emori, Senior Project Editor; and Production Coordinator Karen Slaght. Finally, a special word of gratitude is extended to the scholars, writers, activists, and practitioners whose works are referenced herein, and to those whose experiences have provided grist for our thinking and writing.

1

Aging in America

Riding the "Age Wave"

David R. Gergen

Howard Baker, who has moved beyond his distinguished career in politics but will always keep his good humor, tells the story these days of an older couple watching TV. The man stretches and says, "Honey, I think I'll go to the kitchen and get some ice cream. Would you like some?"

"Believe I would, thanks." "Would you like some chocolate sauce on it?" "Yes, I would . . . but now be sure and write that down so you won't forget." Her husband glares, shakes his head, and marches off to the kitchen.

Twenty minutes pass as the husband rustles about. Finally, he reappears, carrying a plateful of scrambled eggs. "Why," exclaims his wife, "I told you to write it down. Here you've come back and forgotten my bacon!"

It's almost as much fun to watch Baker tell his tales as to hear them. At 72, he's acting like a young pup after a year of marriage to another former senator beloved by colleagues, Nancy Kassebaum, not many years his junior. And together, they are just the opposite of the couple in search of ice cream: They head up commissions trying to improve our national life, jet hither and thither, read good books, and keep plenty of time for each other.

They are riding the top of a new wave in America—the "age wave," as author Ken Dychtwald calls it in his popular book by that title. In a country where 1 out of 5 will soon be over 65, people everywhere are finding a fresh lease on life just when it's least expected.

Billy Graham (left) and Nelson Mandela (right) are remarkable examples of elders who continue to grow in spiritual and political leadership.

Delight. Word that former publisher Katharine Graham, at age 80, had won a Pulitzer Prize for her recent autobiography brought whoops of delight across the newsroom of *The Washington Post* last week. Hard-edged veterans of the paper had watched with admiration as this woman of quiet courage had flowered over the years and has now become a role model for women everywhere.

Celebrations were also underway last week for George Mitchell, four months shy of 65, for his stunning success in negotiating a peace agreement in Northern Ireland. He and President Clinton joined in a textbook case of American leadership. It was especially poignant for Mitchell, who in 1994 had turned down the president's offer of a seat on the Supreme Court so he could attempt to win passage of health care reform. That was a debacle; this was a fitting climax to his years of public service.

Last week, too, 76-year-old John Glenn was in training in Texas for his space launch this fall, while 72-year-old Alan Greenspan was keeping the economy humming. For him, like Baker, a recent marriage has brought a wave of irrational exuberance. Meanwhile, 79-year-old Billy Graham—a man who is said to have preached to greater multitudes than anyone else alive—recently opened his own Web site. A 79-year-old Nelson Mandela is moving his nation into the sunlight. And a 77-year-old pope is nudging open the doors to freedom in Cuba. Who has greater moral authority than these men?

At 58, Jack Nicklaus hardly qualifies as an oldster, but in sports, he's darn close to Methuselah. Returning to the Masters Golf Tournament this spring for his 40th appearance (!), Nicklaus came within four strokes of the top. He even whipped Tiger Woods. Over in Baltimore, another group of "old men" is on fire, too. The Orioles have 21 players over the age of 30—Cal Ripken is a full 37—but the oldest team in baseball is off to a soaring start.

What we are seeing all about us are men and women who are practicing "successful aging." This is the title of a brand-new book that, according to health writer Jane Brody of the *New York Times*, should be featured in every newspaper and on every talk show in the country. In a project sponsored by the MacArthur Foundation, Doctors John W. Rowe and Robert L. Kahn summarize a decade of research by doctors in the United States and Sweden proving it's possible to realize the Greek ideal—as Brody puts it, "to die young, as late in life as possible."

It's the best news of the spring: Most older Americans, they find, are in reasonably good health and generally doing well; a great many are learning how to operate a computer, surf the Net, and communicate by E-mail. And they never forget the bacon.

Who is growing old? We all are! In many people's minds, however, growing old is something that happens only to others and only to individuals older than themselves. If you have not yet reached your sixties, can you imagine yourself to be 65, 75, or 90? With reasonable care and a bit of good luck, you will live to be 75 or more. With advances in medical science and technology, we all can anticipate long lives.

But what will be the quality of our lives? As we advance through life, aging may bring either despair or enhanced vitality and meaning. Indeed, at the dawn of the new millennium many social and medical issues of aging focus more on postponing **senescence** (age-related loss of function) and on ensuring a good quality of life than on ensuring old age itself. For example, research for the past 30 years on the health risks of environmental factors like cigarette smoking or air and water quality; on genetics and genetic engineering; and on biochemical and pharmaceutical factors in health—all combine to increase our longevity. Concern with living well in our old age is now at least as great an issue for many people as concern with living a long life.

An Interdisciplinary Study

The study of aging is exciting and complex and can be examined from many perspectives. It can be viewed through emotional, physiological, economic, social, cognitive, or philosophical lenses, for example. **Gerontology** is the study of the human aging process from maturity to old age, as well as the study of the elderly as a special popu-

Racial and ethnic diversity in the population will continue to increase. The proportion of white, non-Hispanic elders is expected to decline from 87 percent in 1990 to 67 percent in 2050.

lation. Each viewpoint in gerontology adds a dimension to the broader understanding of what it means to age personally, socially, and globally. This understanding, in turn, allows us to plan for our own well-being in later life and to consider quality of later life issues on a social level.

Gerontology as a scholarly field has changed markedly since its fledgling beginnings in the early 1950s. Gerontologist John Rowe now describes a "new gerontology" in which the focus goes "beyond the prior preoccupation with age-related diseases...to include a focus on senescence...and physiological changes that occur with advancing age and that influence functional status as well as the development of disease" (Rowe, 1997, p. 367). To his concept of "new gerontology," we might add a focus on the social issues that are inherent in any society undergoing social and interpersonal change as rapidly as the United States and other industrialized countries are now doing because of their changing demographics.

Three primary disciplines dominate gerontology: (1) biology, (2) sociology, and (3) psychology. Perhaps the most basic discipline in the study of aging is *biology*. Without the biological aging process, we could all theoretically live forever, but the causes of biological aging are still not clearly understood. The term *aging* is wildly nonspecific: wine ages, babies age, galaxies age, we each are aging right now regardless of our chronological ages. Clearly that does not imply a common biological process. **Aging** in the context of this text refers to progressive changes during adult years, but these changes are not necessarily negative nor do they necessarily reduce an individual's viability. For example, gray hair is a result of aging, but it does not impair a person's functioning. Because of negative stereotyping, however, gray hair might have negative *social* meaning in some cultures. On the other hand, mutations that may accumulate over time in certain genes in cells in the reproductive system describe age-related loss of function, which is referred to as **senescence** (Ricklefs & Finch, 1995; Peto & Doll, 1997).

The biological approach to aging includes studies of all kinds of animals, including detailed analyses of the human body. The effects of diet and exercise (lifestyle effects) on longevity are an important focus of study, and the cutting-edge field of genetics is dramatically changing our understanding of the complexity of the human organism.

Second, the *sociological perspective* examines the *structure of society*—its norms and values and their influence on how a person perceives and reacts to the aging process. A society that gives the aging person high status can expect more positive outcomes for its aging population, whereas a society that accords the aged a low or marginal status can expect a more negative outcome. Within the sociological circle are anthropologists, who find that cultures around the world offer elders enormously varied roles. Also in the circle are political scientists, social policy experts, and historians, who all have an interest in the aged. Demographic and population experts provide information on the numbers and distribution of older persons in countries around the world and provide projections of population trends to be considered by policymakers.

A third lens from which aging is viewed is that of *psychology*. Psychologists focus their inquiry on the *individual* and the network of relationships, personal and institutional, that impact that individual's life. They are additionally interested in the aging mind—how perception, motor skills, memory, emotions, and other mental capacities change over time. Motivation, adaptability, self-concept, and morale have an important influence on how we age. Psychologists bring a perspective to solving social problems by considering individuals in terms of their life span, rather than at one particular point in time. They view individuals as being dynamic and interactive, existing in multiple webs of relationships, history, and culture, and they focus on identifying the connections between psychological and social aspects of the individual's life (American Psychological Association, 1997).

Studies of older people cannot be complete without considering *philosophy, spirituality, and ethics*. Virtually all theories of human development suggest that the psychological task of later life is to gain a greater understanding of the life we have lived and of our own approaching death. We seem to gain greater clarity of the meaning of our lives by asking the very questions that have been asked throughout the history of humankind: What was this life all about? What is the relationship of the people I am connected with to the meaning of my life? How should I view my eventual death? In the same vein, *ethical issues* are central in the care of the elderly. Families are the major care providers for America's frail elders, and issues regarding competence and decision making, or autonomy and family relationships, are central to families and therefore to the larger society of which they are part (Hope, 1997; Nelson & Nelson, 1995).

Gerontologists, then, are multidisciplinary. They examine aging from a **chronological perspective** (age on the basis of years from birth), and they study biological and psychological processes and individual meanings of aging. **Social gerontologists** examine the social meaning of aging, including changing roles and relationships brought about by moving through the life course. Gerontologists can apply their specialty in many fields—medicine, dentistry, economics, social work, mental health, religion, education, and recreation.

A SOCIAL PROBLEMS APPROACH

This text considers aging from a social problems approach, relying heavily on information from social gerontologists. A social *issues* approach targets widespread patterns of behavior that affect quality of life indicators, and a social *problems* approach tries to identify and remedy those patterns with negative outcomes for people. The causes and solutions do not remain solely at the individual, or microlevel, but must ultimately be found at a greater level—they require macrolevel response. The problems lie with large numbers of people; the causes and solutions may be at a group, societal, or global level. Although it is people who create social problems, it is people who can also find solutions.

In this text we address social situations that are problematic or undesirable for a large proportion of older adults as well as those that promote vitality, connection, and well-being. Chapter by chapter, the text addresses problems that older people face—issues about status, roles, income, transportation, housing, physical and mental health care, work, leisure, and sexuality and relationships. The text not only describes problems, but also suggests solutions.

History of Aging

Nature has always been harsh with old age. Among humans, however, the ways in which the old are treated has been related to the culture of their society (Beauvoir, 1973; Crandall, 1980). Early in the study of aging, sociologist Leo Simmons pointed out that in all cultures it takes both cultural values and environment to provide for the aged. According to his analysis, the culture must state that aging is a positive achievement and must value the aged *as individuals* in

Today's elders are different than elders of the past. Here a 94-year-old man responds to interview questions (posted on board) from a fourth-grade classroom.

order for the aged to have status and value (Simmons, 1945, 1960).

In the United States, old age has not always been viewed as a social problem (Brown, 1990). Until 1900 or so in the United States, only the debilitating illnesses related to old age, not growing old in itself, were defined as problems. With the industrialization that began in the late 1800s, problems associated with growing old were reconceptualized, not just on a physical level but on social, economic, and psychological levels as well. By the 1930s and 1940s this new conceptualization of the aged by society and by individuals themselves had created an identifiable group with problems that called for collective action. For example, the "right" to a decent income at retirement was at issue. Applying the phrases of sociologist C. Wright Mills, a family's "private troubles" had become "public issues" (Mills, 1959). Responsibility for aging individuals now fell not only to family members but also to society. Older people had more public attention paid to their needs, but in the process they began to be viewed as helpless and dependent. These negative images were universally applied for many years in spite of improvements in the health of the "young-old" aged 65 to 74, and in spite of the countless people aged 75 and over who remained active and involved in society.

This view of the aged as a social problem has been tempered, but it still continues today. Most social problems textbooks, for example, include a chapter on the status of older persons. The caution to be exercised in using the social problems approach is not to "blame the victim" when the blame may lie in the way our society is structured. A further caution is to avoid the pessimist's "half-empty" perspective when approaching the study of a tremendously dynamic developmental and social time of the life course.

We must be careful not to view older people as more dependent and helpless than they are. That perspective is a negative stereotype. We need to understand both the strengths and the vulnerabilities of the older person and to identify and give positive support for institutions and social structures that foster those strengths and self-reliance.

The **critical perspective** in sociology is an excellent example of a social problems approach. It draws sharp attention to inequities in U.S. society, attacking broad and fundamental structures such as the class system, capitalism, sex roles (sexism), and age roles (ageism). It is the most radical sociological approach in the strength of its attack and in its suggestions for completely new structures to replace failing ones. Gerontologists have recently made use of the critical perspective to understand the problems of aging in a broad political, social, and economic content (Hendricks & Leedham, 1992; Minkler & Estes, 1991). Reference will be made to this perspective throughout the text, especially in the chapters on finances, women and minorities, and senior power.

Any social problems approach, including the critical perspective, considers ageism in our society as a major problem. Aversion, hatred, and prejudice toward elders, and the manifestation of these emotions in the form of discrimination on the basis of age, is **ageism**, a term coined by Robert Butler in 1975. Sister Rose Therese Bahr defined ageism in the United States as "the process of systematic stereotyping of and discrimination against people because they are old" (Bahr, 1994, p. 4). The critical perspective looks to the class system and capitalism for root causes of ageism. Before we can consider ageism we will define and describe the older population and its tremendous growth.

The Aging Revolution

What was once referred to as the "graying of America" might now more accurately be called a *revolution*, and the social meaning of that revolution profoundly permeates American culture. The population of Americans 65 years and older has greatly exceeded the growth of the population as a whole, and the "oldest-old" (85 years and over) are the most rapidly growing elderly age group. Between 1960 and 1994, the 85-plus age group rose by 274 percent, whereas the elderly population in general increased by 100 percent and the entire U.S. population grew only 45 percent (Hobbs & Damon, 1996).

The total number of people in the United States under age 65 has tripled in the past century; however the number of people aged 65 or older has increased by a factor of 11 (U.S. Census Bureau, 1996). Projections indicate the elderly population will more than double between now and the year 2050, to 80 million, when one in five Americans will be over the age of 65 (Figure 1.1). A huge growth jump will occur from 2010 to 2030, when the leading edge of the **Baby Boom generation** (those born between 1946 and 1964) reaches 65. Because of the presence of "Boomers," the elderly population will grow by an average of 2.8 percent annually, compared with annual growth of 1.3 percent during the preceding 20 years (Hobbs & Damon, 1996). By midcentury, there will probably be more people over the age of 65 than there are people 14 years or younger. This shift will profoundly affect national and regional policies on education, health, recreation, economics, role of government—indeed the national self-concept will experience a shift from being a youth-oriented nation to one of mature citizenry.

The 1990 Census Bureau findings also indicated the strong growth and growth projection of the older population from 1900 to 2030. Figure 1.1 reflects these changes. The old as a group are becoming much older, and the numbers of the very old will continue to mushroom. The population aged 95 to 99 nearly doubled in 10 short years. The centenarian group (those reaching 100 years of age) grew 77 percent in the same time period. The 1990 census reported 3.1 million people age 85 and over in the United States, including slightly more than one million 90 and over. Of these, 213,000 were 95 and over, 37,000 aged 100 and over, and 6,259 people were 105 and older.

The dramatic increase in number and proportion of elderly is increasing worldwide. In 1994, the world population age 65 and over was 357 million. Twenty percent of this proportion (61 million) is age 80 and older. By 2020, the numbers of the oldest-old are expected to more than double to about 146 million (Hobbs & Damon, 1996).

FIGURE 1.1

Growth of elderly population in the United States, 1910–2050

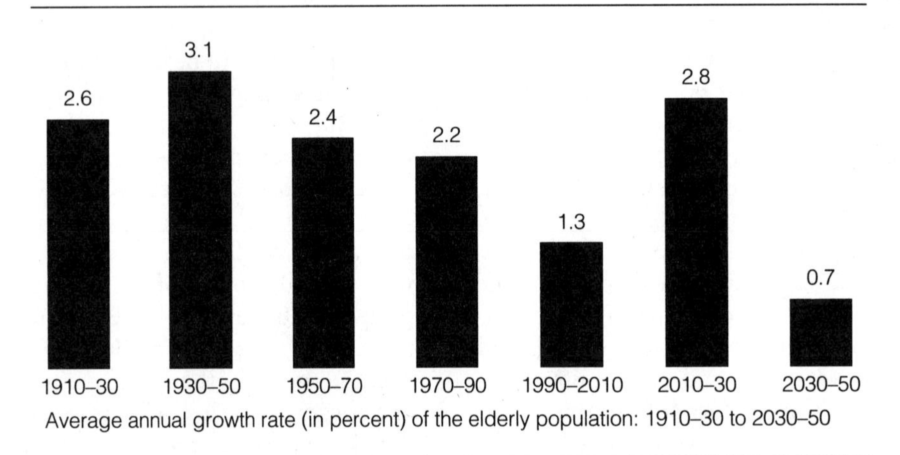

Source: U.S. Bureau of the Census. (1995). Estimates of the population of the U.S. Current Population reports, Series P-25. U.S. Department of Commerce, Washington, DC.

Two major reasons for the increasing proportion of older people are increased life expectancy and a declining birthrate. We will consider each topic separately.

INCREASED LIFE EXPECTANCY

Life expectancy in the United States has consistently increased throughout the 19th and 20th centuries. A dramatic increase in life expectancy occurred in the 1920s as a result of reduced infant mortality, health-care advances, and improved nutrition, although the increase is characterized by ethnic disparities. Overall, estimated life expectancy in 1995 was just under 76 years (National Center for Health Statistics, 1996). White males born in 1920 could expect to live to 54; white females, to 56. The life expectancy at birth in 1995 for white males was 73; for white females, nearly 80. White males, however, live more than six years longer than African-American males, whose life expectancy in 1995 was just over 65. The life expectancy for African-American females in 1995 was 74. We will examine this gap in the chapter on women and ethnic groups.

The mean life expectancy today of women at age 65 is another 20 years. Fully half of all women today in the United States who are 65 will survive to 85 (Smith, 1997). Women at every age, regardless of race or ethnicity, have longer life expectancies than do men. This discrepancy levels out somewhat among those who have made it to the oldest-old age group.

In 1991, a 60-year-old person could expect to live to age 81, and an 85-year-old person could expect to live past 91. Table 1.2 shows life expectancies for persons of various ages 60 and beyond. Notice that African Americans have a shorter life expectancy at all ages, but at the ages of 80 and 85 the differences between whites and African Americans become negligible. The elderly are gradually becoming more ethnically and racially diverse, however. In 1994, 1 in 10

TABLE 1.1

Rank order of states in the United States of people 65 and over; and of people 85 and over

	Percent 65 Years and Over
United States	12.7
1 Florida	18.6
2 Iowa	15.5
3 Rhode Island	15.5
4 West Virginia	15.3
5 Arkansas	15.0
6 North Dakota	14.8
7 South Dakota	14.7
8 Missouri	14.2
9 Nebraska	14.2
10 Massachusetts	14.0
11 Kansas	13.9

Source: U.S. Bureau of the Census. (1995). Estimates of the population of the U.S. Current Population reports, Series P-25. U.S. Department of Commerce, Washington, DC.

TABLE 1.2

Life expectancies in 1991 in the United States by sex, by ethnicity

		Years Expected to Live			
		White		African American	
Age	Average of Total	Male	Female	Male	Female
60	20.8	18.7	23.0	15.9	20.5
61	20.1	18.0	22.2	15.4	19.8
62	19.4	17.3	21.4	14.8	19.1
63	18.6	16.6	20.6	14.3	18.5
65	17.2	15.9	19.1	13.2	17.2
70	13.9	12.1	15.4	10.7	14.1
75	10.9	9.4	12.0	8.6	11.2
80	8.3	7.1	9.0	6.7	8.6
85 and over	6.1	5.2	6.4	5.0	6.3

Source: U.S. Census Bureau, *Statistical Abstract of the United States*, (Washington, DC: U.S. Government Printing Office,, 1994), p. 88, table 116.

older persons were of a race other than white; in 2050, this proportion should rise to 2 in 10 (Hobbs & Damon, 1996).

The longer a person has lived, the greater is that person's statistical life expectancy. The reasons for this have to do with **selection for survival** (Holliday, 1996; Olshansky, 1995), meaning that members of a population are selected for survival based on their resistance to common causes of death. Those causes might be intrinsic or environmental, but studies on the genetics of long-lived people and of twins suggests that genes probably affect longevity by altering the risk of death at different ages, rather than by directly determining age at death (McGue et al., 1993; Yashin & Iachine, 1995). In other words, our genetic programming seems more aimed at the level of "protection" we have against mortal illness than at setting age-at-birth.

Over the years there have been dramatic reductions in the death rates for diseases of the heart, cerebrovascular disease, and pneumonia. Even though life expectancy for males is not as high as for females, both genders' expectancies have increased considerably over the last several decades. This increase has been driven overwhelmingly by changes in environmental factors causing death, rather than factors intrinsic to the aging process itself. In addition to having long-lived grandparents (genetic factors), being near an ideal weight for one's stature, having low blood pressure and low cholesterol, not smoking, consuming alcohol moderately, exercising vigorously four to five times a week, eating a healthy diet, and living a relaxed and unstressed lifestyle are central predictors to a long life.

Heart disease remains the leading cause of death for older Americans; however, the proportion of death due to coronary heart disease has fallen in the past 10 years. Now death rates from cancer take a third of lives between 65 to 75, especially among African Americans (NCHS, 1996). The age-adjusted death rate for coronary heart disease declined by 16 percent from 1987 to 1993, and the death rate for stroke dropped by 12 percent. Older Americans are living longer, and they are less frail than their parents and grandparents were.

Studies comparing the longevity of men and women show that the top causes of death kill more men than women. Heart disease, lung cancer, homicide, suicide, accidents, and cirrhosis of the liver all kill men at more than twice the rate as they do women (Dolnick, 1991). Each of these causes of death is linked to behaviors that our culture either encourages or finds more acceptable in males than in females: using guns, drinking alcohol, smoking, working at hazardous jobs, or appearing fearless. Such cultural expectations seem to contribute to males' elevated mortality. Men suffer three times as many homicides as women and have twice as many fatal car accidents (per mile driven) as women. Men are more likely to drive through an intersection when they should stop, are less likely to signal a turn, and are more likely to drive after drinking alcohol. But behavior does not entirely explain the longevity gap.

FIGURE 1.2

Causes of death for persons in the United States aged 85 and older, 1993

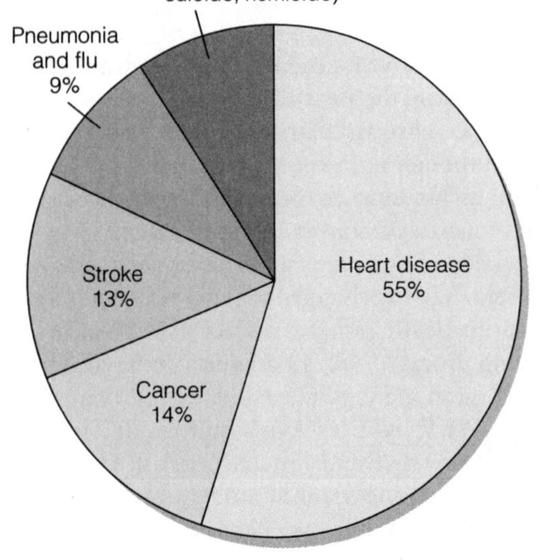

Source: U.S. Bureau of the Census. (1995). Current Population Reports, Series P-25. U.S. Department of Commerce, Washington, DC.

Women seem to have a genetic makeup that "programs" them to live longer. Some scientists think that the longevity gaps may be due to chromosomal or hormonal differences. Whatever the reasons, elderly women outnumbered their male counterparts in 1994 by a ratio of three to two—20 million to 14 million—and the difference grew with advancing age. One consequence of this gender discrepancy is that elderly women are much more likely than men to live alone. Eight of 10 noninstitutionalized elderly living alone in 1993 were women (Hobbs & Damon, 1996).

The leading causes of death for men and women over age 65, ranked in order from most to least common, are: (1) diseases of the heart, (2) malignant neoplasms (tumor), (3) cerebrovascular disease (stroke), (4) chronic obstructive pulmonary disease, (5) pneumonia and flu, (6) chronic liver disease, (7) accidents, (8) diabetes, and (9) suicide. Men have higher death rates in all the categories, except diabetes.

DECREASING BIRTHRATE

When the birthrate declines, the number of young people decreases in proportion to the number of old people. The birthrate has gradually declined since public record keeping began in the eighteenth century. A baby boom in the 1940s and 1950s increased the birthrate temporarily, but did not reverse its long-term trend.

In 1972, we witnessed a near zero population birthrate (2.1 children born for every couple): the number of live births nearly equaled the number of deaths, stabilizing the population. The birthrate then dipped lower until it rose slightly in the early and mid-1980s. According to the Population Reference Bureau in Washington, D.C., the 1991 birthrate evened out at 2.1 children. If the United States maintains a lower birthrate, the proportion of older people will further increase. With no increase in the total population, the relative proportion of older persons will grow each year.

The post–World War II babies, born between 1946 and 1964, are one of our largest age groups. Now in midlife, this age group will begin to reach age 65 in 2011, massively increasing the over-65 population. If we assume continued low birthrates and further declines in death rates, the older populations will jump tremendously by the year 2030. As we saw earlier, their numbers will double and their percentage of the population will rocket to over 20 percent.

A controversy rages as to whether medical science can do anything further to extend life expectancy at birth to more than 85 years. In the past 125 years, the life expectancy of Americans has almost doubled: from 40 to nearly 80 years. But these gains in life expectancy, most of which have come through a combination of reducing deaths of the young (particularly infants) and mothers in childbirth, may have been the "easy" ones.

The population that is presently the oldest-old has had unique life experiences. They are a **cohort** (born in the same grouping of years) that survived infancy when the infant mortality rate was about 15-20 times the present rate and the infectious diseases of childhood when medical practice did not have much to offer. They survived at least one world war, and the females survived childbearing at a time when the maternal mortality rate was nearly 100 times its present level (Smith, 1997). The next generation of elderly will have lived their adult years with many of the advantages that were only emerging for the previous older generation, so mortality rates will continue to be lower in later life. That does not, however, appear to change the maximum human life span, which seems to have fixed limits (Finch & Pike, 1996).

Some medical experts and laboratory scientists say that the period of rapid increases in life expectancy has come to an end. They argue that advances in life-extending technologies or the alteration of aging at the molecular level, the only ways to extend life expectancy, will be either improbable or long, slow processes. And, though they do agree that eliminating cancer, heart disease, and other major killers would increase life expectancy at birth by about 15 years, cures for these diseases are not in sight. Other scientists are more positive about extending life expectancy.

The longest documented human life span on record is that of Frenchwoman Jeanne Calment, who lived to be 122. There are some generally

Frenchwoman Jeanne Calment, who died in 1997 at the age of 122, was the world's oldest person with verifiable birth records.

accepted records of people throughout history who have died between 110 and 120 years of age, but few that are extensively documented. The most extreme claims come from populations with the least reliable records. There is no evidence, either current or historical, that there has been much change in the rate of aging. Increases in life expectancy have been driven overwhelmingly by reductions in environmental causes of mortality (Austad, 1997). It appears that the maximum human life span has not increased; however, the mean life expectancy in developed countries has done so tremendously.

Aging America and the Aging World

Figure 1.3 illustrates the percentage of people 65 and over in each state in the United States.

FIGURE 1.3

Percentage of population aged 65 and over, by state: 1996

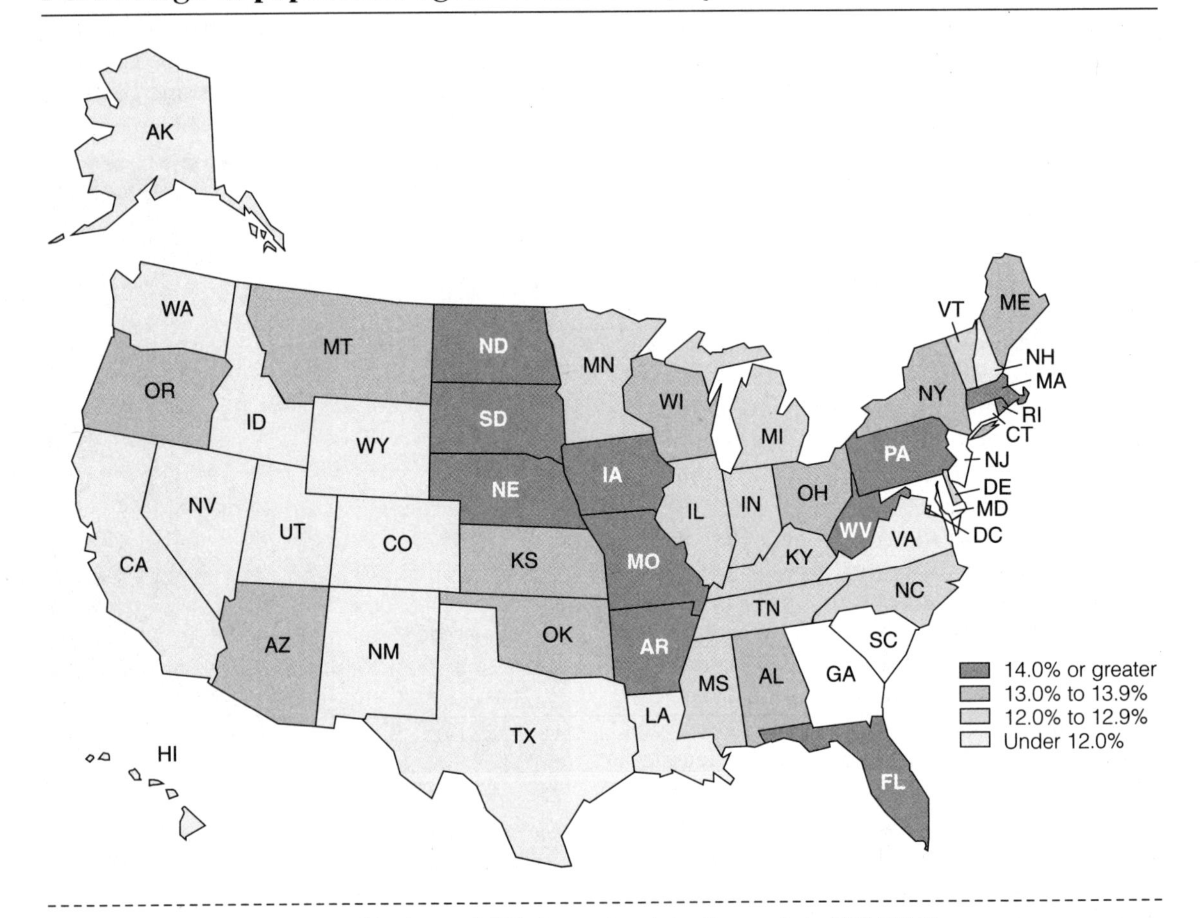

Source: U.S. Bureau of the Census. (1995). Current Population Reports, Series P-25. U.S. Department of Commerce, Washington, DC.

Although California has the largest *number* of elderly, Florida has the highest *percentage*. In several states, 14 percent or more of the population is 65 or older.

Florida, a retirement haven, ranks first in the nation with the largest over-65 proportion, as shown in Figure 1.3. Many of the states with the largest over-85 population are farm belt states where younger people are leaving farms for jobs in cities, whether those cities are in the same state or not, and where the oldest generation has traditionally aged in place, that is, at home on the farm.

The social implications of these demographics are broad. The increasing percentage of older people means that more and more families will be made up of four generations instead of two or three. Currently whites are more likely than African Americans to live in married-couple-only households, and African Americans are more likely than whites to live in multigenerational households (Coward et al., 1996), although these differences balance out somewhat as people age. In the next 20 years it seems clear that more children will grow up with the support of older relatives, and more people in their sixties will be called on to care for 80- and 90-year-old parents.

Population pyramids illustrate the effects of a population's age and gender composition on the structure of a nation's population. In Figure 1.4, the horizontal bars in the pyramid represent **birth cohorts** (people born in the same year) of 10 years. The effect of the Baby Boomer cohort on the U.S. population can be clearly observed. Note the relationship between lower birthrates and lower death rates, indicating fewer young people and more older people. This trend effectively reshapes the pyramid into a more boxlike image, illustrating the more balanced proportion in the population of each of the age cohorts.

Developed countries throughout the world are experiencing an aging boom. Comparative data can illustrate the rapid global increase of people over 65 and show differences between countries of greater or lesser development.

The shape of the population pyramid for a less-developed country like Nigeria, for example, would be a large base, indicating high birthrates, and a small top, indicating a high death rate with few people surviving into old age. This pyramid was typical of the United States as a developing nation in the early 1800s, and it is typical of most developing nations. Countries with this pyramid form have difficulty caring for all their young, and as a result, social policy is directed toward youth.

Countries like Sweden and Japan, on the other hand, have an even higher proportion of elderly than the United States. They have achieved virtual zero population growth and thus would have a "stationary," or boxlike, pyramid. The social implications are that the needs of a society change with a changing age structure, as must social policy that directs national resources to various segments of the population. Housing, health care, education, and other services for elders must be balanced with services targeting more youthful age groups, as the population shifts in age.

Ageism as a Social Problem

We have defined a social problem as a widespread negative social condition that people both create and solve. Ageism is such a problem. We know that the number of older persons is large and growing larger, and ageism directly affects the older population.

Ageism, discrimination on the basis of age, has been called the third "ism," after racism and sexism. Whereas racism and sexism prevent racial minorities and women—and in what is called "reverse sexism," men—from developing full potential as people, ageism limits the potential development of individuals on the basis of age. Ageism can oppress any age group, young or old. If you are young, you may have been told that you are too inexperienced, too immature, too untested. If you are elderly, you may have been told you are out-of-date, old-fashioned, behind

FIGURE 1.4

Population pyramid summary for the United States, 1997, 2025, 2050

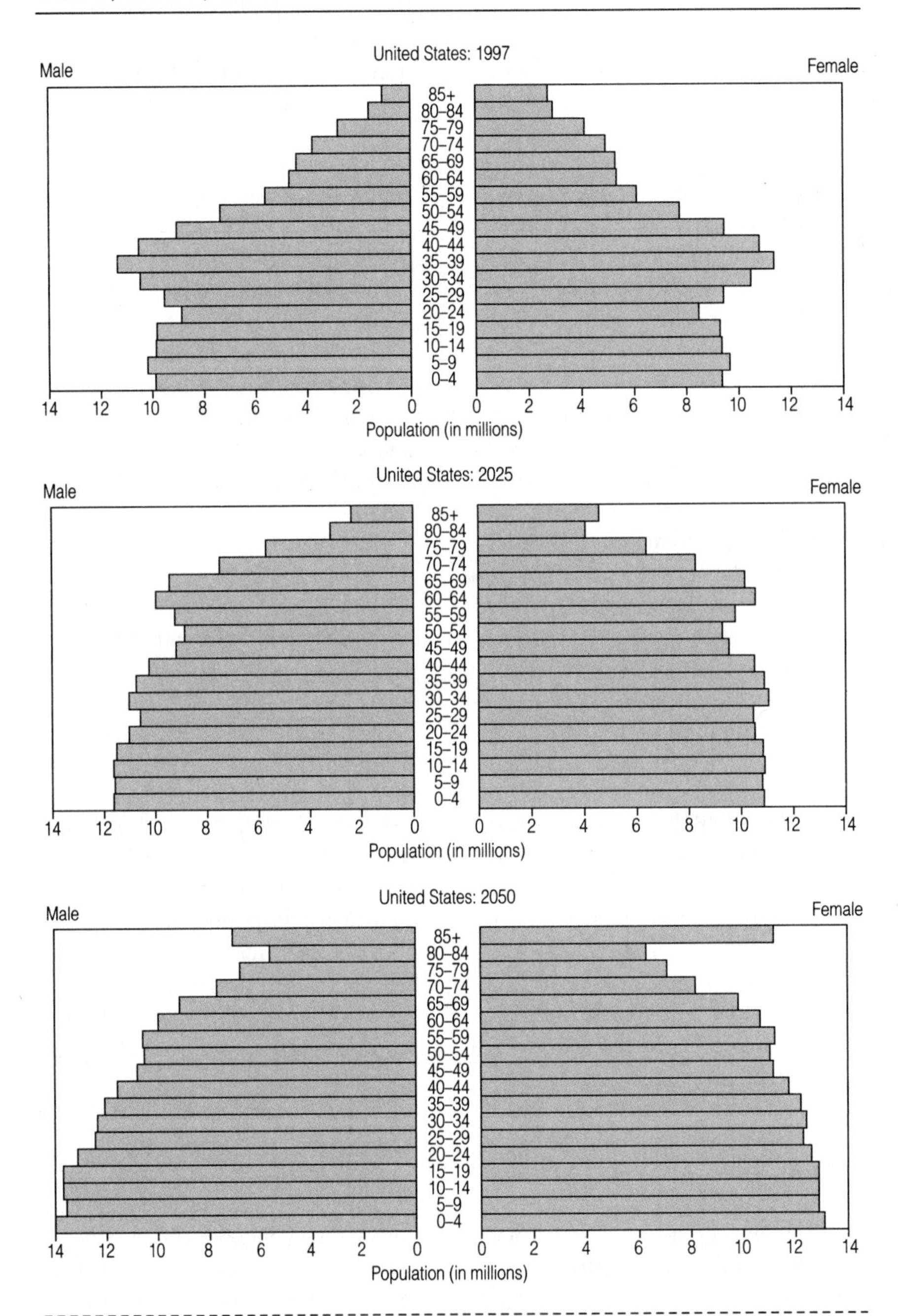

Source: U.S. Bureau of the Census. (1994). Population pyramid summary for the U.S. *International data base*. U.S. Bureau of the Census. U.S. Department of Commerce, Washington, DC.

the times, of no value or importance. At both ends of the scale, young and old, you may be the victim of ageism. Although ageism may affect the young as well as the old, our concern here is with the senior members of society. Robert Butler noted, "The tragedy of old age is not that each of us must grow old and die, but that the process of doing so has been made unnecessarily and at times excruciatingly painful, humiliating, debilitating, and isolating" (Butler, 1974, pp. 2-3).

Ageism is a complex phenomenon affected by technology, industrialization, changing family patterns, increased mobility, demographic changes, increased life expectancy, and generational differences. A discrimination leveled by one group against another, ageism is not an inequality associated with biological aging alone. It is created and institutionalized by many forces—historical, social, cultural, and psychological.

AGEISM TODAY

Our Western cultural heritage decrees that work and financial success establish individual worth. Industrialization has reinforced the high value of productivity and added further problems for the aging worker. The speed of industrial, technological, and social change tends to make skills and knowledge rapidly obsolete. Most people must struggle to keep abreast of new discoveries or skills in their fields. The media have used the term **Detroit Syndrome** to describe older people in terms of the obsolescence that exists for cars. When younger, stronger, faster workers with newly acquired knowledge are available, employers tend to replace, rather than retrain, the older worker. Within the workforce, older persons have often been considered a surplus population. As such, they suffer the potential for being managed much like surplus commodities: devalued and discounted.

Social change can create a generation gap that contributes to ageism. Rapid social change can cause our values to be somewhat different from our parents' and significantly different from those of our grandparents. Those who grew up in a given time period may have interpretations of and orientations toward social issues that differ from those who grew up earlier or later. For example, the person who matured in the 1940s and experienced the patriotism of World War II may be unable to understand the behavior and attitudes of those who matured in the 1960s and protested the wars in Vietnam or the Persian Gulf. Further, people maturing in the 1990s may not understand the historical rationale for the United States intervening in small countries like Panama or El Salvador. For another example, these young people, many of whom are postponing marriage and childbearing, may be unable to grasp the reasons for early marriage and large families held by the now-elderly generations. The study of intergenerational relations, which provides insights into similarities and differences in values across generations, reveals that communicating and understanding across generations are difficult when values are different.

Ageism also appears in the many euphemisms for old age and in the desire to hide one's age. The elderly themselves do not want to use the term *old*, as the names of their local clubs show: Fun After 50, Golden Age, 55 Plus, and Senior Citizens Club. Some forgo their "senior citizen discounts" because they do not want to make their age public. Fear of aging is apparent when men and women want to keep their age a secret. They hope that their appearance denies their age and that they project a youthful image. Many people suffer a crisis of sorts upon reaching age 30 and repeat it to some extent when entering each new decade. Some even experience an identity crisis as early as their late twenties, because they are entering an age that the youth culture considers "old." Many counselors recognize the "over 39" syndrome as a time when young adults come to terms with the fact that youth does not last forever but blends gradually with the responsibilities of maturity.

Greeting-card counters are filled with birthday cards that joke about adding another year. Despite their humor, they draw attention to the fear of aging that birthdays bring. Some birthday cards express the sentiment that to be older is to be better, but then add a note that says, in effect, that no one would want to be better at the price of aging. Though birthday cards often joke about physical or sexual decline, that fear in the minds of many is no joke at all. Fear of aging can damage psychological well-being and lead us to shun older people. Ageism is a destructive force for both society and the individual.

Ageism as a concept in literature has been described in a general sense, but it also has been measured in more specific ways. Alex Comfort (1976) used the term *sociogenic* to imply ageism in a broad sense. He described two kinds of aging: *physical,* which is a natural biological process; and *sociogenic,* which has no physical basis. **Sociogenic aging** is imposed on the elders by the folklore, prejudices, and stereotypes about age that prevail in our society. Thus, age prejudice, as it exists in our minds, has become institutionalized in many sectors of our society.

We can find more specific evidence of ageism in our laws, particularly those dealing with employment, financial matters, and legal definitions relating to "competency" as an adult. Income differences, occupation differences, and education differences vary by age. One aspect of ageism is age inequality in education and occupation, caused by the fact that newer generations receive an education attuned to a highly technical and computerized society and are therefore better qualified for jobs. Elders are easily left behind on the "information highway" as the "high tech" knowledge of younger age groups rises. Income inequality based on age is caused not only by younger age groups having more extensive formal or technical education, but also by age discrimination in employment. Gerontologists believe that ageism in employment dates back to the early 1800s. This age prejudice will be covered in more detail in the work and leisure chapter.

AGEISM YESTERDAY: THE EARLY AMERICAN EXAMPLE

A look at older people in earlier times, when age relationships were different, provides us with a clearer view of ageism now and in the future. Generalizing about ageism in the past is not easy. Some historians believe the status of older people was elevated in the colonial period—the time during which early settlers, especially the Puritans, founded America and formed the 13 colonies. In contrast, other historians point to ageism and neglect of older persons in the colonial days.

EARLY COLONIAL DAYS

According to David Fischer, author of *Growing Old in America* (1977), the power and privilege of old age were deeply rooted in colonial times, when age, not youth, was exalted. To be old was to be venerated by society and to be eligible for selection to the most important positions in the community. Meetinghouse seats were assigned primarily by age, and the elderly sat in positions of highest status. According to Fischer, the national heroes were "gray champions." Community leaders and political officeholders tended to be older men, and the elderly were honored during ceremonial occasions.

Older adults were believed to be in favor with God. Their long life was thought of as an outward sign they would be "called" or "elected" to heaven. Biblical interpretation suggested that good persons would be rewarded with long life: "Keep my commandments, for length of days and long life shall they add unto thee." The Puritans pictured Jesus as an old man with white hair, even though, according to most theologians, Jesus died in his early thirties. Respect for age was also evident in manner of dress. Increase Mather, the president of Harvard College from 1685 to 1701, wrote that old men whose attire was gay and youthful, or old women who dressed like young girls, exposed themselves to reproach and contempt. Male fashions during the 1600s, and even more in the 1700s, flattered age. The styles made men appear older than they were. Clothing was cut specifically to narrow the shoulders, to broaden the waist and hips, and to make the spine appear bent. Women covered their bodies in long dresses. Both sexes wore white, powdered wigs over their hair. Not until the 1800s did clothing styles begin to flatter the younger man or woman.

Fischer studied other historical data that indicate age status. American literature, for example, emphasized respect for old age from the 1600s until after the American Revolution. A careful examination of census data shows that in the 1700s individuals tended to report themselves as older than they actually were in order to enhance their status. (In the mid-1800s this tendency reversed itself.)

The tradition of respect for the elderly was rooted not only in religious and political ideology, but also in legal and financial reality. The elders owned and controlled their own land, which did not pass to their sons until they died. The sons, therefore, had financial reason to show respect for and deference to their fathers. In these conservative times, the young had little choice other than to honor, obey, and follow the ways of the old.

A word of caution must guide our consideration of the older person's status in colonial times. "Status" is a multidimensional concept, measurable in many ways, that indicates one's social ranking in society. Deference, respect, health, economic resources, material possessions, occupation, education, and political power are all possible indicators of social status. By some measures, the colonial elders had high status. They were shown deference and respect, and they had political power and financial control of their land. But not all elderly colonial citizens had financial and political power. Indeed, financial and political power was held by only a very few. Colonial legal records show that widows who had no means of support wandered from one town to another trying to find food and shelter. Older lower-status immigrants, and most certainly older Africans, had an especially difficult time because of their low economic status; many were indentured servants or slaves.

Additionally, most old people suffered from health problems that medical science was unable to cure or alleviate. Benjamin Franklin, for example, was wracked with pain in his later years because of gout and "the stone" (gallstone). Yet the old, in spite of their infirmities, were expected to be models of service and virtue to their communities. The very veneration that brought older persons respect kept them from enjoying close, intimate relationships with younger people. Youth/elder relationships were distant and formal, causing the old to suffer loneliness in their elevated position.

A number of historians take exception to Fischer's rosy picture of colonial days. Haber (1983) described old age in colonial times as more dire than Fischer's work indicates. Haber believes that although select, well-to-do elderly had high status in the Puritan days, they did not live in a golden era of aging. Too many not so well-to-do fared badly; they were viewed with scorn and contempt. Haber advises that a careful sociologist or historian must try not to idealize the past, but to recapture reality by examining all of its facets: political, historical, economic, and social. Quadagno (1982) and Cole (1992) share Haber's point, emphasizing that multiple forces, some positive and some negative, shaped life in colonial times.

Changing Age Status

According to Fischer, change throughout the 1800s altered the system of age relationships in a negative way, leading to social problems for the aged. The most fundamental change took place in political ideology. The principles formulated in the Declaration of Independence became stronger: equality for all in legal, social, and political matters. This trend affected older persons because "lovely equality," in Jefferson's words, eradicated the hierarchy of age, and hence the respect automatically accorded the old. A study of word origins shows that most of the negative terms for old men first appeared in the late 1700s and early 1800s. *Gaffer,* originally an expression of respect, changed from a word of praise to one of contempt. Before 1780, *fogy* meant a wounded soldier; by 1830 it had become a term of disrespect for an older person. *Codger, geezer, galoot, old goat,* and *fuddy-duddy* came into general usage in the early 1800s.

The preeminence of religious elders began to wane as doctors and other technologists replaced preachers as the custodians of virtue and learning. The United States became more industrialized. In the 1800s, the city became a means of escape from both farming and parental control. Instead of waiting for his father to provide him with land, a young man could move to the city and find work in a factory. As long as America remained a traditional agricultural society, in which parents controlled property until their advanced years, older adults exercised considerable power. Urban and industrial growth led to diminished parental control over family, wealth, and possessions (Haber, 1983). By the late 1800s, the young pioneer and the young cowboy had become popular heroes; Teddy Roosevelt was young, rough, and ready. The youth cult began to replace the age cult.

The older population grew rapidly during the 1800s and 1900s because of advances in the medical sciences. Retirement gradually became more and more common. However, many of the older people who retired had no source of income and were often neglected. Old age became a burden to those who lived it and a social problem to those who analyzed it.

Fischer (1977) divided U.S. history into two general periods:

1. 1600 to 1800: an era of growing **gerontophilia.** Old age was exalted and venerated, sometimes hated and feared, but more often honored and obeyed.
2. 1800 to present: an era of growing **gerontophobia.** Americans increasingly glorified youth instead of age, and the elderly often became victims (self-victims as well as social victims) of prevailing attitudes and social arrangements.

Fischer states that we may eventually enter another period of age relations, one that will create better conditions for older adults. The goal, he stages, should be to make a new model—a fraternity of age and youth, and a world in which "the deep eternal differences between age and youth are recognized and respected without being organized into a system of inequality" (Fischer, 1977, p. 199).

The example of colonial America shows that the position of elders in our society can be something other than what it is now. We can be aware of various age relationships and possibilities that are more positive than the situations we have created.

Ageism in the Future

For many years our society has suffered from **gerontophobia.** The term comes from the Greek *geras*, "old," and *phobos*, "fear, " and refers to fear of growing old or fear or hatred of the aged. To conceive of any status for elders other than that to which we are accustomed is difficult. We have accepted tension between youth and age. As a nation, the United States clearly identifies itself as youth oriented. Respect by the young for the old in our society is not a given. It is not deeply imbedded in the fabric of our society.

Some people view the increasing number of older adults as a burden on society, referring to the economic burden of providing care for the unemployed elders who depend on society for financial aid. The number of people 65 and older relative to the working population (those 18-64) is called the old **age–dependency ratio.** If the population age 65 and older grows faster than the working population, the cost to the taxpayer of providing for the elderly population rises. The percentage of elders to the working population has increased steadily, so there are proportionally fewer employed people to support older, retired people today. In 1910, there were 10 working people per older person; in 1980, 5 or 6. If the trend continues, by the year 2010 a ratio of .22, or about 4.5 workers per retired person is expected (U.S. Bureau of the Census, 1994).

A larger proportion of seniors requires more Social Security and Medicare payments and, consequently, higher taxes. Indeed, Social Security taxes have slowly increased over the years.

The reasons are multiple; however, one reason is the increase of retirees in that system. This will be addressed more fully elsewhere in the text. The prospect for the future rests on one simple fact: if you go to work at a young age, you will have to live a very long time to receive in benefits what you have paid into Social Security, because resources for that "enforced savings plan" will have been spent on people who are *presently* retired. If we view elders solely as an economic burden, ageism may increase as the number of retired, sick, or frail elderly increases.

Some gerontologists believe that we have become an age-segregated society, with separate schools for the young and separate retirement communities for the old. Undeniably, segregation further generates misunderstandings and conflict. Other gerontologists, alternatively, maintain that ageism is declining. They point to the improved health of seniors and to retirement communities composed of increasingly younger retirees who seem happy and content. In such contexts the image of older persons is improving. In addition, the increasing numbers of elders may be leading to a psychological shift away from a youth-oriented culture, toward a more life-course inclusive identification.

The increasingly large number of older persons is eroding the youth cult. The Baby Boomers of the 1940s, 1950s, and 1960s had a major impact on the economics of the 1980s. Young adults of the 1980s, many of them "yuppies," prospered from a relatively inexpensive college education and the economic expansion of the times. These same Baby Boomers will age in unprecedented numbers and continue to influence our lifestyle and our economy.

Older people are not a burden either to themselves or to the nation. The senior boom "is not a chance to be old longer but a chance to live longer" (Boynton 1993). As "Boomers" make demands on the market, our nation will modify our culture to accommodate an older population—from changing how long it takes a traffic light to turn from green to red, to clothing styles, to increased services at airports (Dychtwald, 1989).

Business will stop discriminating on the basis of age when it becomes apparent that there are not enough young people to maintain commerce single-handedly and that older workers are good, solid employees, who, if treated well, will not choose to retire. Indeed, employers in the future may well pay to update the education of older employees, rather than contend with inexperienced applicants from younger workforce. There is support for these predictions in Japan, whose economy depends on the work and experience of its older workers, despite rapid changes in technology (Carr, 1997).

Old age can be an exciting time of contributing to others and of self-fulfillment.

Chapter Summary

Gerontology is a multidisciplinary study of the human aging process from maturity to old age, as well as the study of the elderly as a special population. The key perspectives in gerontology are *biological, sociological,* and *psychological* processes. The text uses a *social problems approach*, examining patterns of social behavior and institutional structures that negatively affect the quality of life of the aging individual.

America has always been a youth-oriented nation; however increased longevity and lowered birthrate have transformed the population to an older one during the last half of the 20th century. Social problems such as ageism, changing economic burdens, and the need for changes in social policy have resulted. The need to address the issues of an aging nation is upon us. Gerontologists believe that ageism can be ameliorated through education and the changing health and lifestyle of the "new" elderly, who are more healthy and vigorous than the population of elders preceding them.

Key Terms

age–dependency ratio
ageism
aging
Baby Boom generation
birth cohorts
chronological perspective
cohort
critical perspective
Detroit syndrome
gerontologists
gerontology
gerontophilia
gerontophobia
life expectancy
population pyramids
selection for survival
senescence
social gerontologists
sociogenic aging

Questions for Discussion

1. Explore ageist attitudes within yourself, using some specific topics to focus on, such as your reaction to older drivers or your own fears of aging.
2. What are some social implications of the "aging revolution" not covered in this chapter? How will they affect advertising, fashion, or music?
3. What are some implications of increased longevity for family interactions?
4. How long do you expect to live, and how long do you want to live? Why?
5. There are different ways of looking at age. How old are you in your mental outlook on life? How old are you spiritually? Chronologically? Physically? How old are your parents in each of these categories? Your grandparents? What basis did you use for assigning the ages?

Fieldwork Suggestions

1. Browse several card shops—one at a local grocery store, and another at a stationery store—and develop a list of the number and type of birthday cards that you find. How many do you find that joke about physical health? Memory? General negativity about age? How would you characterize the general tone of the greeting card sections? Find an example of a birthday card directed to adults that is particularly meaningful to you, and one that is particularly offensive.
2. See how many people know the meaning of the word *ageism.* Talk with some younger people as well as some middle-aged and older people in your investigation.
3. Survey several people about 15-25 years old to see how many come in contact with an elderly person daily. Survey several people 35-50 to see if there are differences. Determine how age-segregated we are as a society.
4. Describe a chronologically young person who meets your criteria of being old.
5. Describe a chronologically old person who meets your criteria of being young.

Online Activities

1. Using the Internet, locate the home page for the U.S. Bureau of the Census. Go to Bureau of the Census Current Population Reports, and locate data on the number of people over 65 in your home state. How does this compare with the number over 65 for your state in the 1980s? What would the population pyramid look like for your state?

2

Stereotypes and Images

Stop the Mission, I Want to Get Off

Andrew Herrmann

John Glenn. American.

As American as the 60-hour workweek.

As American as the nightly dinner without daddy.

As American as the exhausted mom poring over her office work after the kids have been put to sleep.

As American as workaholism.

Since news broke that former astronaut Glenn, at age 77, will be returning to space, we've seen countless gee willikers! stories about how wonderful his trip is.

Oh, there are some gripes here and there about whether Glenn has clouted his way onto the space shuttle. But, overall, the idea of a guy three-quarters of a century old heading into the Great Wide Open has been vigorously applauded. Plucky!

Senior citizens aren't just sitting around in their retirement anymore, so the stories go. They're raising packs of homeless kids. They're teaching Martians English. They're doing brain transplants, and writing books about it, and winning the Nobel Prize.

May I interrupt this "Up With Old People" rally for a moment to ask one simple question? Don't we ever get to stop? I mean, before they put us in the pine box, that is.

From where I sit, Glenn's space mission is not something to cheer but bemoan. It's the latest assault on leisure in this country. Workaholism is sloshing over into old age, poisoning what are supposed to be our Golden Years. One in five American men are now working past age 65.

John Glenn, the first American to orbit the Earth, speaks to reporters about his role in the Space Shuttle Discovery scheduled to launch in 1998.

Uh, hooray?

I am fully aware that the space mission is Glenn's idea. Some 36 years ago he became the first American to orbit Earth, and I'm sure it was a thrill he would like to relive. "I'm excited to be back," he told reporters last week.

But the larger impact he is having on society is that, once again, the bar is being raised for the rest of us.

What self-respecting 77-year-old now will be able to beg off playing catch with the grandson because, well, he just doesn't feel like it? "Grandpa needs his rest" once was a sufficient explanation for "no." Now, "But John Glenn went to space" lingers over us like rocket exhaust.

And the Big Sixty Five as the true age of emancipation dissolves.

For many of us, Congress already has raised Social Security benefits to age 67. Now there are proposals floating to push the carrot even further: The retirement age could be extended to 70. Supporters note that advancements in medical technology are allowing people to live longer, but is that the way we want to use these extra years? Working?

Here are some sobering figures: If the typical American woman reaches 65, she can expect to live 19 more years. A typical man, if he reaches 65, can count on 15 more years. Figure in another additional five years on the job to reach 70 and, by my calculations, that means 1,825 midmorning naps unslept, 1,305 long lunches uneaten, 260 matinees missed and about a million frames un-bowled.

Other nations don't have this approach. Late last year, after months of anguish and teeth-gnashing, Italy raised its minimum age of retirement—to 54.

I understand that some people have a problem with retirement. They're bored, feeling useless, depressed. But what is not needed is public support for equating work with personal worth—but instead, some kind of effort to teach Americans how to enjoy themselves. I'm a writer by trade, but the only writing I plan to be doing at age 77 is scratching in the starting lineup on a scoreboard.

At the announcement of Glenn's selection, a NASA official said that Glenn "is now poised to show the world that senior citizens have the right stuff."

I've got a counter to that: Nobody's deathbed regret was ever, "I should have worked more."

Have you ever heard the following statements or made them yourself? "Old people are narrow-minded." "They are set in their ways." "Old people are terrible drivers!" These statements are stereotypes. This chapter explores stereotypes based on age and provides information to explain why they exist.

Stereotypes of Aging

Stereotypes are generalized beliefs or opinions based on individual experience, often produced by irrational thinking. Stereotyping and labeling seem to fulfill our need to structure and organize situations in order to minimize ambiguity and to clarify where we stand in relation to others. Because of the complexity of our society, we need to be able to make quick assessments of situations and of people, based on our beliefs or previous experience: This is a person I can trust . . . this situation makes me uncomfortable . . . this person is probably not reliable, and so forth. These assessments are our "people skills," and form the basis for making judgments and shaping many of our interactions in the larger society. However, when observations become categorized—I cannot trust this person because she looks like someone else I could not trust—then we have fallen into making assessments based on stereotypes.

Stereotyping, whether direct or subtle, is usually inaccurate. When we generalize by putting people into categories, we tend to oversimplify reality. We ignore inconsistent information and emphasize only a few characteristics. Thus, the statement "old people sit around all day" is a generalization that does not apply to the many active older individuals who still work, write, paint, are physically active, or are involved in community affairs.

Although stereotypes can be positive, many are negative. Whether positive or negative, they are impressions that are not based on objective information, and they categorize people. Stereotypes also can arouse strong and often negative emotions, such as hatred. Hating any person or group of people for any reason, but especially on the basis of a single trait such as age, is both ignorant and unfair.

POSITIVE AND NEGATIVE STEREOTYPES

Tuckman and Lorge (1953) were among the first gerontologists to study stereotypes. Using a list of statements with which subjects were asked to agree or disagree, they found that old people were perceived as being set in their ways, unproductive, a burden to their children, stubborn, grouchy, lonely, "rocking-chair types," and in their second childhood. Since the Tuckman and Lorge study, gerontologists have continued to find that society stereotypes older persons.

Palmore (1990) summarized the **negative stereotypes** of aging as including (1) illness, (2) impotency, (3) ugliness, (4) mental decline, (5) mental illness, (6) uselessness, (7) isolation, (8) poverty, and (9) depression (grouchy, touchy, cranky). He countered all these stereotypes with factual information disproving these stereotypes for the majority of older persons. Stereotypes, however, are no longer as negative as they were in the 1950s (Palmore, 1990). Palmore and others (Luszez & Fitzgerald, 1986; Schwald & Sedlacek, 1990) have cited studies showing increasingly positive attitudes toward elders over the last several decades. This is due in no small part to the shifting demographics discussed in Chapter 1, which result in more exposure by the general population to older individuals as well as the better general health of elders in the final decades of the 1900s.

Despite this positive shift in social attitude, negative stereotyping such as that described by Palmore remains a significant social issue. Two other kinds of negativism are common enough to have been given separate labels. One is an ageism that focuses only on the least capable, less healthy, least alert aged. This focus on the sick takes attention away from the healthy aged who defy negative stereotypes (Estes & Binney, 1989; Estes, 1993). The biomedicalization of aging emerged over a century ago with the growth of scientific inquiry and subsequent breathtaking advances in medical sciences. **Biomedicalization of aging** is defined as the belief that problems associated with aging are biological rather than social and behavioral. The "problems of aging," therefore, can only be addressed by medical technology, if at all (Vertinsky, 1991).

A second kind of negativism is called **compassionate stereotyping.** Binstock (1983) coined this term to describe images that portray elders as disadvantaged on some level (economic, social, psychological), in need of help, and deserving help by others. This may sound harmless. But consider the reaction of disabled activists to posters of the Easter Seal Child—a poster designed to invoke pity for those with disabilities. Activists, including the elderly, do not want pity; rather, they want the tools for being independent and self-reliant. Compassionate stereotypes perpetuate dependency and low self-esteem and unnecessarily lower expectations of what older people can achieve.

A **positive stereotype** is a generalized belief that categorizes all older people in a favorable light, whereas a negative stereotype categorizes old people in demeaning ways. The extent to which different stereotypes elicit positive versus negative attitudes has now been studied by a number of social scientists (Crockett et al., 1987; Heckhausen et al, 1989; Hummert, 1993, 1994, 1995; Hummert et al., 1994; Linville, 1982). Hummert (1995) found that the two most frequently cited positive stereotypes of older people were the "Golden Agers" (lively, adventurous, active, sociable, witty, independent, well-informed, successful, well-traveled, etc.) and "Perfect Grandparents" (kind, loving, family-oriented, generous, grateful, supportive, understanding, wise, knowledgeable, etc.). She found the most prevalent negative age stereotypes to be "Severely Impaired" (slow-thinking, incompetent, feeble, incoherent, inarticulate, senile) and "Despondent" (depressed, sad, hopeless, afraid, neglected, lonely). Her "Despondent" stereotype finding illustrates compassionate stereotyping, whereas the "Severely Impaired" stereotype reflects biomedicalization of aging. The mass media are a profoundly important source of stereotypes about the aged in the United States. Media influences shape the attitudes of children as well as the self-concepts of adults. The public believes that there have been significant improvements in television portrayals of older people (Ferraro, 1992), however analyses of fictional television show that the older generation continues to be invisible or negatively portrayed. When they are visible, it is seldom (less than 10 percent of the time) in major roles (Robinson & Skill, 1995). Old women are even less likely to appear than are old men, and when they are present they are more likely to be characterized in negative stereotypes (Hilt & Lipschultz, 1996; Robinson & Skill, 1995; Vasil & Wass, 1993). Negative stereotyping and sexism continue as major themes in portraying the elderly in the electronic media.

To many older people, television is a companion: a window on the world. Repeated exposure to negative images or few images with which they can identify can be neither psychologically productive for the elderly nor in the long run economically productive for television networks, yet the trends continue. For example, despite numerous findings that viewers aged 50 and older were significantly more likely than younger viewers to be consumers of television news (Wurtzel, 1992; Usdansky, 1992), a study of television station management described the struggle within news management regarding stories of interest to an "older" audience. In terms of the consumer elders' interest and ability to understand social issues, news directors had a significantly more positive image than did station general managers; however, both groups agreed strongly with the statement that "exciting video helps a story" (Hilt & Lipschultz, 1996). It is difficult to cover many social issues of interest to an older audience with action-oriented television news. If local television were to report more stories of interest to an older audience, viewers of all ages would have a more well developed perspective of social issues affecting a broad age range. In that way we all will be less likely to have our stereotypes and biases reinforced through this powerful medium.

Who Is Old?

Stereotypes would have us believe that the label *old* is a term that can be unequivocably and universally applied to all people once they reach a certain point. This section, "Who Is Old?" calls that into question. It's very difficult to say who is old or the age that it happens. First, legal definitions of old are presented, which imply that aging is experienced by all people in uniform fashion. But the topics that follow are presented to introduce the idea that "who is old" varies by individual mental and physical functioning, self-concept, society's judgments, and even by the occupation of any given individual. We must be aware of the tremendous diversity in the aged population. Only then can we break down the labels and stereotypes that are so judgmental and constricting.

When is a person old? Do the words *old, elderly, senior, mature adult, or senior citizen* mean the same thing? Or do they mean different things to different people, under different circumstances? No definition of an older person has been universally agreed upon. "Old age" means different things, and is assigned on the basis of chronology (age 65, for example), of biology (how well one functions), and by social standards (the point at which, for example a woman is considered "too old" to wear revealing clothing on the beach). Sweeping statements about a category of people ("the elderly," "the

30-somethings," "teenagers," etc.) stereotype the individuals within that category because they bypass the vast individual differences that exist. Some old people are frail; some are wise; some are cranky; and some are jolly, or patient. We age just as we have lived—we do not become a different person because we have reached a chronological marker that makes us "old." Aging is a gradual process with many influences. The reality is that people age differently. In part, longevity is behind the need for more precise descriptions of just who are the "old": those who are relatively young, about 65 to 75, are referred to as the "young-old." They tend to be vigorous, fit, and healthy and have been labeled as "able elders." Those 75 and older are variously called the "old-old," or labeled the "frail elderly" depending on their health and the focus of the gerontologist's work. Those 85 and older have been labeled the "extreme aged."

THE LEGAL DEFINITION OF "OLD"

In the 1890s, Germany's Otto von Bismarck established a social security system for German elders that benefited citizens 65 years or older. Life expectancy in the late 1800s was approximately 48 years for men and 51 years for women, so the political advantage of addressing the emerging Positivist social thought by establishing social security programs far outweighed any economic disadvantages.

Nearly 60 years later, in 1935, the United States passed the Social Security Act under President Franklin D. Roosevelt. In that act, according to a tradition by then established in Europe, 65 was named as the onset of old age. In line with Social Security standards, most companies as well as state and local governments developed pension programs beginning at age 65 for retiring workers.

This legal definition has become a social definition: on retirement, a person's lifestyle generally changes dramatically, creating a point of entry from one phase of life to another that has become a social event for celebration and congratulations. Retirement, in fact, is one of the few life course transitions that is celebrated throughout the United States. Age 65, or the age of retirement, has become somewhat standardized legally, socially, and psychologically as initiation into "old age."

Since the 1930s, however, medical science has extended longevity and improved general health. The 65-year-old today is not the same physically or psychologically as the 65-year-old in 1935. That person today is likely to be healthier and better educated, for starters, and to be more intimately connected with the larger world through the medium of television and radio than was his or her counterpart in 1935. Social scientists now question whether 75, 80, or 85 might more accurately mark the beginning of old age. Whatever the age, any *chronological* criterion for determining old age is too narrow and rigid, for it assumes everyone ages in the same ways and at the same time.

Biology: The Function of Age

Some authorities say aging begins at the moment of conception. Others reserve the term *aging* to describe the process of decline following the peak in the biological characteristics of muscle strength, skin elasticity, blood circulation, and sensory acuity. Peak functioning in most capabilities occurs at relatively early ages. After the mid-twenties, for example, hearing progressively declines, and muscle strength reaches its maximum between 25 and 30 years of age.

We spend approximately one-fourth of our lives growing up and three-fourths growing old. Biological decline, a gradual process beginning in young adulthood and continuing gradually throughout the life span, varies among individuals in its speed and extent. One person may be biologically old at age 45; another may be physically fit at 80. All organs do not decline at the same rate either. Someone may have a 30-year-old heart, a 60-year-old response rate, 80-year-old eyes—and be only 20 years old! That everyone ages in the same way and at the same pace is totally erroneous; however, the dominance of the medical model (the biomedicalization of aging) has shaped public perception to view aging as a decremental process, based solely on our age.

Psychology and Mental Functioning

Mental functioning includes the capacities to create, think, remember, and learn. Although we often assume that mental functioning declines with age, studies now show that this belief is too simplistic to adequately describe mental functioning in later life. Though older students enrolling in college after raising families or retiring are often concerned that they cannot keep up with younger students, most professors know that older, non-traditionally-aged students as a group prove to be outstanding in their classroom work. Most of us have known some men or women in their 80s or 90s whose minds are clear and alert and others who have memory lapses or confuse facts. The wide variations in the mental functioning of older people may be caused by disease, genetic makeup, or the effects of stress. We are only just beginning to realize how the aging process affects people psychologically. But, like body functioning, mental functions do not automatically decline with age.

Studies of mental functioning in adulthood show tremendous **heterogeneity** (variability) and emphasize the need to distinguish between normal, optimal, and pathological aging. Psychologists have identified a "developmental reserve capacity" in later life, demonstrated, for example, by the ability of older people to develop in their professional lives, or to profit from practice and engage in new learning (Featherman et al., 1990; Willis, 1987; Baltes & Lindenberger, 1988; Perlmutter, 1990; Baltes, 1991). Newer psychological studies indicate there is generally a loss in the mechanics of the mind with aging, but that **pragmatic knowledge** (information-based knowledge) forms the basis of new ways of learning in later adulthood (Holliday & Chandler, 1986; Baltes & Smith, 1990; Sternberg, 1990). Psychologists are now focusing research on the identification and meaning of *wisdom* as a select area of knowledge and problem solving.

The Social Construction of Aging

Self-concept is the way in which a person sees him- or herself as being. It is how individuals define themselves *to themselves*, and it forms the basis for the way people maintain a sense of continuity even as their bodies age and change. Early in the study of gerontology, Bernice Neugarten (1977) referred to chronological age as an "empty variable," stressing that it is the importance of the *events* that occur with the passage of time that form the basis for the study of identity development, not time itself (Vertinsky, 1991). Perhaps more importantly, self-concept dictates the way in which people interpret, or make meaning of, the events that occur in their lives.

The **social construction of self** addresses the idea that the way we interpret events in our lives is partially a reflection of how we are treated and partially the extent to which we have internalized the way society has defined or categorized us. So, for example, it might not be unexpected for a 60-year-old woman to believe that it is improper for her to wear a bikini on the beach. Her self-concept precludes that behavior: She sees herself, perhaps, as too dignified *at her age* to publicly expose her less than youthful body.

Those people who see themselves as old and accept as true the negative characteristics attributed to old age may, indeed, *be* old. As sociologist W. I. Thomas (1923) stated, "If people define situations as real, they are real in their consequences" (p. 42). Current research on self-concept emphasizes the knowledge base, or structure, that helps individuals maintain a consistent sense of who they are throughout their life experiences (Schaie & Willis, 1996). Those people who have a good sense of continuity of who they are appear to be better adjusted in later life. They are less likely to identify themselves as being "old," because they identify as being who they *always* have been. The dimensions of an individual's self-concept that deal with self-esteem and a sense of social worth are the very dimensions that our society is most likely to treat harshly.

A current focus in gerontology is to move away from attempting to measure "hard, scientific" data and to listen to the voices of aging people themselves. This methodology is referred to as **phenomonology**, in which the meaning of an event is defined by the person experiencing that event (or phenomenon), not a researcher's hypothesis. Sharon Kaufman's skillfully developed study *The Ageless Self: Sources of Meaning in Later Life* (1987) is an excellent example of using the voices of elders to develop a description of their self-concept. "I wanted to look at the meaning of aging to elderly people themselves, as it emerges in their personal reflections of growing old" (Kaufman, 1994, p. 13). Kaufman documented the finding that many older people do not see themselves as old, but see themselves as being ageless, living *in their old age.*

The voices of older people, documented by Kaufman (1987) and in a second study by Tandemar Research, (1988), best describe this ageless self:

> *I don't feel 70. I feel about 30. I wear my hair the way I did then. . . . I just saw some slides of myself and was quite taken aback. That couldn't be me . . . (Kaufman, 1987, p. 8).*
>
> *The only way I know I'm getting old is to look in the mirror . . . but I've only felt old a few times—when I'm really sick (Kaufman, 1987, p. 12).*
>
> *I'm always telling my children I'm still the same inside. I just have to walk for the bus now instead of run (Tandemar Research, 1988, p. 23)*

Kaufman summarized the process by which people maintain a solid sense of self in later life, even as their bodies, their relationships, and their social circumstances changed over time:

> *[The ageless self] draws meaning from the past, interpreting and recreating it as a resource for being in the present. It also draws meaning from the structural and ideational aspects of the cultural context: social and educational background, family, work, values, ideals, and expectations. . . . [Elders] formulate and reformulate personal and cultural symbols of their past to create a meaningful coherent sense of self, and in the process they create a viable present. In this way, the ageless self emerges. Its definition is ongoing, continuous, and creative (Kaufman, 1994, p. 14).*

OCCUPATION AND ACHIEVEMENT

The age at which a person becomes old depends to some extent on the nature of his or her job. In his classic work, *Age and Achievement* (1953), Harvey Lehman studied the age at which superior productivity tends to occur in different occupations. He found that in most fields, the productivity of adults peaked in their thirties. Only for a few fields did it peak in those in their forties or older. Researchers have been challenging and refining his work ever since. More recent studies show the forties and beyond to be highly productive for a number of professions, including sales and marketing, and fields requiring special skills and knowledge (Landau & Werbel, 1995; Day, 1993). Productivity in family farming requires physical endurance as well as historical knowledge of plants, soils, and weather patterns. Because it requires such physical endurance, farmer productivity usually peaks at midlife—around the time children in the family begin to take more central roles in the business. It seems that the older family farmer, if possible, moves to the role of mentor, as the younger generation takes over (Tauer, 1995). Novelists peak in their fifties and sixties; botanists and inventors, in their sixties; and scholars such as historians, humanists, and philosophers, in their sixties and seventies. If we can truly define old age as a time of reflection, we can understand why scholars are able to make major contributions in later life (Kramer, 1987).

Although many people who give peak performances in early adulthood continue top-notch performances throughout their lives, productivity rates do depend on the type of work an individual performs. Studies of blue-collar workers indicate that they reach their highest productivity at an earlier age than white-collar workers, because their work often requires physical skills that peak in early adulthood. In contrast, other studies show that executives see themselves as maturing slowly and believe that old age comes later for them. Clearly, the meaning of achievement varies with environment, age, gender, and culture (Saili, 1995).

Even after retirement, many elders work part-time or volunteer their skills in the community.

COPING WITH STRESS AND ILLNESS

People who are chronologically young can be "old before their time" if they exhibit the physical and mental traits characteristic of more advanced age. An approach to studying the link between stress, illness, and physiological aging began with an attempt to estimate the amount of stress experienced by various life events (Schaie & Willis, 1996). Thirty years ago Holmes and Rahe (1967) developed a rating scale to measure stress over a year's time using 43 "life events." The scale is commonly known as the Stressful Life Events Scale. It is typically used by tabulating all the events an individual has experienced over a specific period of time (six months, or one year, generally) and tallied to predict illness in the people with higher scores. The events are weighted by stress-load: for example, in the 1967 scale, death of a spouse was rated at 100 life change units, and change in financial status was 38 LCUs. We have understood for about 20 years now that psychosocial and environmental stress ages people, and stress is a well-documented cause of anxiety, depression, migraine headaches, and peptic ulcers (Rahe & Arthur, 1978). Research has also clearly documented that stress is an associated precurser of coronary heart disease and stroke (Rahe, 1995).

The Stressful Life Events Scale was adjusted in 1977 and again in 1995 to reflect cultural changes in perceptions of stress. Modern day raters saw marriage, for example, as a less-meaningful event than did persons 18 and 30 years earlier (Rahe, 1995). "Death of a close family member," adjusted significantly upward in LCUs in the 1995 sample, compared with the 1965 and 1977 samples. Longevity is an important part of this adjustment: A greater proportion of adults have older parents and grandparents living—and dying—in their lives than did the 1965 sample. Similarly, economic and work-related events are more highly loaded among women in the 1990s than for women in the 1960s and 70s. One consistent finding in the measurement of stressful life events over the past 30 years stands out, however. Many of the most stressful life events occur most frequently in one's later years, including death of a spouse, death of a close family member, death of a friend, change in health or behavior of a family member, and major personal injury or illness (Rahe, 1995).

How does stress affect the individual? The individual's *response* to stress is the key, including the perception of ill health itself. The mechanism connecting stress and illness is still not completely understood; however, individuals who are highly stressed, who feel they have little control over their lives, and who have limited social support systems appear to be most vulnerable to disease (Krause, 1988, 1991).

To summarize, aging often brings multiple life events. If the individual lacks the resources to cope with the consequent stress, illness may result or the aging process may speed up. An individual's "age," then, may depend on the number of severely stressful events he or she experiences and the ability to cope with them. Throughout life, adjustment requires adapting to change. Some people resist change, and stress hits them particularly hard. Others, who are more flexible, compromise and adapt to whatever life brings. Psychologically, the ability to address stress by adapting to change—one's coping and adaptation resources—reflects how one will age.

Summary Statement of Who Is Old

If people were more aware of the tremendous diversity in the older population, they would know it is not easy to say who is old and who isn't. And there would be fewer constricting labels and stereotypes.

STUDIES OF CHILDREN'S ATTITUDES

Since the mid-1960s, interest has grown in studying attitudes young children and adolescents have toward the aged. The body of research developed since that time has produced varied and contradictory results, but uniformly shows that children do tend to stereotype older adults. However, those stereotypes have become incrementally less overtly negative in the past 30 years.

Children formulate attitudes about elders and the aging process at an early age. These attitudes are shaped by various outside forces: families, social interactions with peers, school influences, and media influence (Aday et al., 1991). Children as young as three exhibit ageist language (Burke, 1981), and by age five begin to have clear attitudes about aging and being old (Fullmer, 1984). In adolescence, children appear to stereotype and adopt values in a way similar to adults (Carstensen et al., 1982)

The media are a primary source of ageist messages for children. Studies show that even fairy tales instill ageist feelings in the very young. The evil, ugly, old witches or the old stepmothers endanger the children in the stories. Some contemporary books are changing this theme, emphasizing, for example, the grandparent-grandchild connection (Steinberg, 1993). In a study of children in four countries (Australia, England, North America, and Sweden), Goldman and Goldman (1981) found that children believe that physical, psychological, socioeconomic, and sexual powers of old people decline, and that old people's skills become less useful with age. These views reflect a negative stereotype based on a biological model of decline—a decline, of course, that children can observe by watching their grandparents age and die, for example. It is particularly important that children be provided greater opportunities to develop positive interactions with older people, in part because their internalized attitudes about old age will have a significant influence on their own lives and the ways in which they see themselves as they age.

The ways in which attitudes can be changed has been extensively examined in the past 30 years (Amir, 1969; Corbin et al., 1989; Sanders et al., 1984; Bengtson & Achenbaum, 1993). Three primary ways to impact attitudes were identified in 1982 by Class and Knott as being (1) through discussions with peers, (2) through direct experience with attitude objects, and (3) through increased information or knowledge. This model has been used in several projects for school-based programs to change children's attitudes toward the elderly. In one very well designed classroom experiment (Aday et al., 1996), older volunteers were paired with children to assist with a school-based task. The interactions also included structured and informal discussions designed to foster more intimate relationships between the pairs, and it tested attitude changes in one-year and five-year follow-ups. They found, as a result of the interactions, the children and youth developed more positive attitudes about the aged and about aging, and those attitudes remained part of the children's perceptual schema five years later. Responses by the children to the question "What have you learned from the intergenerational project?" included:

> *I never knew some older people were so active. . . . That not all older people are mean and stingy. . . . I learned that older people were once a young person just like me. I never thought about it before (Aday et al., 1996, p. 150)*

In response to the question "How has this project changed you?" some responses were:

> *I learned that everyone on this earth is equal, no matter what their age. . . . I'm not so afraid of older people. . . . It has changed my outlook on older people to a more positive one. . . . I'm not as scared of growing old as I used to be. . . . I'm more apt to smile and speak to older people . . . (Aday et al., 1996, p. 150)*

Teachers can improve children's attitudes toward old age by telling about the physical and mental capabilities of old people. They can present accurate information about old age, and they can bring active, creative elders into the classroom. Teachers can also help children explore attitudes toward older people as they explore cultural and ethnic differences among classmates' backgrounds. Children generally follow the traditional values of their families' cultures, whatever that cultural heritage might be. Discussing different ways parents and grandchildren interact with grandparents is a wonderful way to honor cultural differences and to identify and explore different attitudes about aging.

STUDIES OF COLLEGE STUDENTS' ATTITUDES

Understanding the nature of how younger adults view older adults is important because those attitudes will impact intergenerational relationships, the level of concern for social programs that benefit older adults, and the self-concept of that younger adult as he or she matures into middle age and later life.

Studies of college student attitudes toward aging, like those of the population in general, show very mixed results. Some of this lack of consistency is methodological—different researchers ask different questions, and they often are not actually measuring the same thing. Attitude is a multidimensional mental schema, influenced by many factors, including exposure to older people, gender, culture, and individual differences of personality. "The elderly," too, do not comprise a single category: vast individual differences exist among elders. A second reason for mixed findings on young adults' attitudes toward their elders is that older adults may be seen to some extent as multidimensional people, with both positive and negative attributes (Slotterback & Saarnio, 1996). The most generalized stereotype among college students is based on a biological model of decrement and excludes personality, skill, and interactional factors. This can be a particularly problematic perspective among students training for the health and healing professions.

Researchers have studied attitudes of pharmacy students (Shepherd & Erwin, 1983), medical students (Intrieri et al., 1993), nursing students (Downe-Wamboldt & Melanson, 1990; Rowland & Shoemake, 1995), and college students (Shoemake & Rowland, 1993; Barrow, 1994a). A conclusion drawn in one study of nursing students (Rowland & Shoemake, 1995) also summarizes the findings of other studies:

> *Change comes in small increments, but changes in attitudes come only after learning has occurred. Providing students opportunities to test their professional skills and meet challenges to their preconceptions of the elderly can increase the rate of change (p. 747).*

Barrow (1994a) conducted a study of college students in which they developed their own descriptions of older people. In this methodology, stereotypes emerged directly from students' minds, not from potentially suggestive wording in preformulated phrases. A salient finding in her study was that students paid the most attention to the changing physical appearance and capabilities of older people. Many students responded to the word *aged* with a description of physical decline. Thus college students biggest focus is on sagging, bagging, wrinkles, canes, walkers, and more serious health problems that lead to physical dependence. A fewer number responded to the word *aged* with a social position or role description, such as "bad driver," "interesting life stories," "bingo," "grandparent," or "calm life." Others included psychological qualities such as "wise," "lonely," "fear of death," or "experienced." But the most attention was paid to physical appearance and declining physical capacity.

Explaining Stereotypes

We can explain the existence of stereotypes on a number of levels. On one level, the historical/cultural explanation requires the gerontologist to look at the roots and cultural context of our concepts about old age. On another level, current social explanations look at elements such as social class and the influence of the media. On yet another level, psychologists ask why some individuals, either young or old, accept the negative stereotypes of old age whereas others accept the positive ones.

> *Whatever new object we see, we perceive to be only a new version of our familiar experience, and we set about translating it at once into our parallel facts. We have thereby our vocabulary.*
>
> RALPH WALDO EMERSON, "ART AND CRITICISM"

HISTORICAL AND CULTURAL EXPLANATIONS

Understanding the relationships between generations and exploring views about growing old in a previous era are the jobs of a historian. For example, a historian in Chapter 1 described how, throughout American history, society's view of elders shifted from one of veneration and favor to one of scorn. Reasons for the change are extraordinarily complex, related to larger philosophical issues, influences of multiple cultures brought about by immigration, advancements in science and medicine, longevity, global and local economic structures, and the shift of cultural values as a result of all those factors.

Becca Levy and Ellen Langer (1994) identified a dramatic relationship between cultural beliefs and the degree of memory loss people experience in old age. They conducted memory tests with (1) old and young mainland Chinese, (2) old and young from the American Deaf culture, and (3) old and young hearing Americans They expected that the Chinese and Deaf cultural groups would be less likely than the hearing Americans to be exposed to and accept negative stereotypes about aging. They found that younger subjects, regardless of culture, perform similarly on memory tests. Older Chinese and older Deaf participants, however, outperformed the older American hearing group. They described their findings:

> *A social psychological mechanism contributes to the often-reported memory decline that accompanies aging. . . . The negative stereotypes about how old people cognitively age, to which individuals starting at a young age are exposed, become self-fulfilling prophecies (p. 996).*

An unexpected finding of the research was that the old Chinese sample performed similarly to the young Chinese sample. The scores for the two groups did not differ significantly, even though the memory tasks being used typically reflect memory loss with age in the United States. The results were even more surprising because the older Chinese group had completed fewer years of education than the young Chinese and the old and young American samples. Of the three groups studied (old and young hearing Americans, old and young Chinese, and members of the American Deaf culture), the Chinese reported the most positive, active, and internal image of aging. Because of this, the authors conclude that " . . . the social psychological component of memory retention in old age may be even stronger than we believed" (p. 966).

Rude, insulting, or negative labels directed to anyone whom we consider "other" is not new, however, and seems to endure throughout history. The words we use to describe people provide a basis for the formation of stereotypes, and people often internalize those labels, incorporating them into their own self-concepts. Language is powerful; it shapes consciousness, and our consciousness affects our health and well-being as well as our interpersonal relationships.

Use of ageist language is hardly unique to the 20th century. Herbert Covey (1991) beautifully illustrated the extent to which a culture's religious and philosophical values play out in stereotypes and/or expectations in his history of the term *miser*. Covey associates the miser, a social role meaning a mean or grasping person, with "avarice," one of the seven deadly sins and thought for centuries to be the chief sin of old age (Chew, 1962). He traced the image of the miser from classic literature and religious thought through to modern times, exploring both literature and art. He concludes:

> *There are justifiable reasons why older people have been associated with miserly behavior, such as the need to be frugal to ensure their future survival. Other reasons accounting for this association have been proposed, such as the reluctance of older parents to surrender family wealth to their demanding offspring. In addition, social support programs for older people were not readily available and stigma was sometimes attached to those receiving benefits. The depictions of older people dying while surrounded by their worldly possessions also fueled the image of the miser. Older people were expected to surrender their worldly concerns and possessions in order to enter heaven. Those who were reluctant were viewed as misers and avaricious (p. 677).*

In a previous study of the **language of aging** used in the 1800s and earlier, Covey (1988) identified widely used terminology that augmented negative stereotypes about elders (see Table 2.1).

Present-day researchers observe few age-specific terms that refer positively to older people. Several of the rare examples are *mature, sage, venerable,* and *veteran.* A study of the language of aging found that even the terms *aged person* and *elderly* were considered less than positive (Barbato & Freezel, 1987). For example, presidents of companies or anyone in a position of power typically do not want to be called "aged" or "elderly." The core of the problem is that as long as there are negative attitudes about aging, even initially positive terms may develop into negative stereotypes.

Historians examine magazines, newspapers, poetry, sermons, and other written materials for information about aging in prior times. For example, sheet music of the 1800s and 1900s reflects the then popular sentiments about age

TABLE 2.1

Historical Terminology Used to Describe Older People

Terms for Old Women	Terms for Old Men	Either Sex
Old bird	Old buzzard	Old bean
Old trout	Old goat	Mouldy
Old crow	Old coot	Crone
Old hag	Old crock	Gummer
Little old lady	Old fogey	Has-been
Witch	Dirty old man	Fossil
Tabby or cat		Dodo
Old hen		Fuddy duddy
Old bag		Gink
Old biddy		
Quail		

Source: Adapted from Herbert Covey, "Historical Terminology Used to Represent Older People," *Gerontologist* 28 (May 1988): 291–297.

(Cohen & Kruschwitz, 1990). With few exceptions, writers of tunes popular in the late 19th and early 20th centuries saw old age as a time of failing capacities, clearly preferring youth and dreading growing old. In these songs, elders fear that their children will abandon them; they worry about spousal death, loneliness, disability, and their own deaths. "Silver Threads Among the Gold" (1873), a classic of the period, is a touching song that emphasizes the declines in old age. Another example is the song "Old Joe Has Had His Day" (1912).

A whole series of songs, such as "Will You Love Me When My Face Is Worn and Old?" (1914), echoes the fear of loss of attractiveness. Perhaps the most poignant of all is "Over the Hill to the Poor House" (1874). It ends with the following lines:

For I'm old and helpless and feeble
The days of my youth have gone by
Then over the hill to the poor house
I wander alone there to die.

In contrast, only a few songs during this time period celebrated positive aging—growing old together and being young at heart, for example.

Songs of recent decades continue the themes of the past. A well-known song, the Beatles' "When I'm 64," carries ambiguities about aging. Although anticipating the joys of growing old together with his wife, the singer has doubts: "Will you still need me, will you still feed me, when I'm 64?" The Alan Parsons Project sees aging as a time to simply bid life farewell in "Old and Wise" (1982): "As far as my eyes can see/There are shadows approaching me." Bette Midler's "Hello in There" evokes the compassionate stereotypes with ". . . but old people they just grow lonely, waiting for someone to say 'Hello in there; hello.'" One of the biggest country songs of 1990, "Where've You Been?" by Kathy Mattea, finds an older woman lying helplessly in a hospital, waiting for death and a last visit from her husband. We do not see the full range of the status of elders in popular music, but we do see some historical roots of both acceptance and fear. We also see various stereotypes, many of which are negative.

The fears of aging expressed in the songs at the turn of the century, such as going to the poor house to die, were more valid then than now. Life expectancy was lower and so was overall health status. Resignation and sadness were more appropriate to them. Older people are now leading healthier, more active lives. The negative stereotypes still present in popular songs are an example of the **cultural lag** that makes our attitudes slower to change than the technology that has improved our longevity.

SOCIAL FORCES: THE MEDIA

Sociologists study present-day situations to find explanations for negative stereotyping. The media, which can both reflect and create society's views, have a strong impact on our views of life. *Redbook* magazine (April 1994) had a boldface title on its cover that read, "When It's Smart to Lie about Your Age." The article inside cited sexual attractiveness and career pressures as reasons to lie. The author said, "We all want to be young. Despite feminist assertions, 20 implies desirable, attractive, sexy, and 40 doesn't" (Peters, 1994). This article creates a fear of aging in its readers. The obvious message is that by the age of 40, aging has taken an insurmountable toll on women.

Television and Movies

In 1972, Lydia Bragger, the articulate former public relations director for the Rhode Island State Council of Churches, met Maggie Kuhn, founder of The Gray Panthers, a group organized to fight for the rights and interests of older persons. Following their meeting, Bragger organized the **Media Watch Task Force**, supported by the Gray Panthers, to identify and protest television programs that present stereotypical and unrealistic portrayals of older people. In an interview in 1975, Bragger expressed her outrage at television's portrayal of older people. "Look at how rarely we see older couples on TV sharing affection or, heaven forbid, making love," (Hickey, 1990). Two decades later, discussing her role with Media Watch, Bragger discussed television's negative portrayal of elders. "People would watch old people in the commercials who did nothing but take laxatives and use denture cream. . . . On TV, they were shown as helpless, toothless, sexless, and ridiculous. They were walking in a certain way, dropping things, forgetting things (Tanenbaum, 1997)."

Television *is* better than it used to be. We see the faces and hear the voices of older actors more now than 10, 15, and certainly 20 years ago. Judd Hirsh and Bob Newhart are two examples. Through her best-selling exercise books, audiotapes, and videocassettes, Jane Fonda, now in her fifties, offers women of all ages a role model with whom to stay in shape. Television has offered more programming with older male stars.

Industrial standards have improved the representation of older people, based on greater understanding of the shifting market potential. The Nielsen Television Index did not even regularly identify individuals over 55 years of age until 1977, but now that population is carefully examined (Greco & Swayne, 1992). There is a great distance to go, yet, before ageist stereotypes are eliminated from advertising and programming. A review of the literature shows that much of the information about aging that informs advertising decisions is based on research conducted in the early 1970s and 1980s, emphasizing the biological model of cognitive decline. This is another example of a cultural lag between current research in aging and the incorporation of that information culturally.

Studies concur that television consistently underrepresents older women (Mundorf & Brownell, 1990). Older female news anchors are a rare species, in contrast with their male coun-

Older people are not as ill, as lonely, or as isolated as the stereotypes would lead us to believe.

terparts. In a widely publicized, successful lawsuit in the 1990s, Christine Craft sued a Kansas City broadcasting station for sex discrimination, claiming she was demoted for being "too old, unattractive, and not deferential enough to men." The "elderly" Ms. Craft was 38. Barbara Walters remains a star news reporter in a field dominated by youth and men. Older men such as Hugh Downs, Mike Wallace, Morley Safer, and Larry King are more common.

Television typically pairs older women romantically with men who are older, thereby avoiding role models for same-age, or older woman/younger man relationships. Singer/actress Cher said she worries about her looks as she gets older. "The roughest thing in the world," she said, "is to be an older woman." She was referring both to the entertainment world and to her personal life (DeVries, 1991). Sally Field reported that only 8 percent of all theatrical roles go to women over 40, and in television, 9 percent. According to Field, the Hollywood stigma attached to aging actresses has been around "since the beginning of time" (Bash, 1995). And in *Modern Maturity*'s list of the 50 most powerful stars over 50, most are men. See Table 2.2. Further, men over 50 are much more likely to get a romantic lead role than are 50-plus women, who tend to get supporting character acting roles.

Despite the increased exposure older performers now enjoy, including older women, television still has problems with its portrayal of older Americans. Television programming commonly and unfortunately uses a comedy gimmick—a **reversed stereotype of aging**. A reversed stereotype refers to older characters driving race cars, break-dancing with great abandon, or referring to their amazing sex life. Such images are, of course, intended to be comical, because they are in stark contrast with the held stereotypes of a low-energy, sedentary lifestyle.

Reversed stereotypes used for comedy do more harm than good. The public tends to believe what stereotypes, reversed or not, present. Laughing at a reversed stereotype is showing unconscious, uncritical acceptance of the underlying negative image. Older respondents are even less critical than the young. In other words, older people as a general segment of the viewing public do not complain about their television image.

Aging experts believe that the television industry needs to revise its unrealistic portrayal of older Americans to become a medium that reflects the aging experience of the 1990s (Deets, 1993). The challenge of television is to offer a true portrait of aging. A sensitive, realistic portrayal is the goal. On the one hand, older adults must not be demeaned; yet on the other hand, television must not gloss over the real problems of aging. Portrayals should attempt to balance strengths and satisfactions with the real problems of aging.

Television viewing time increases with age. Nielsen Media Research estimates that women over age 55 watch more television (40 hours per week) than any other age group (Hickey, 1990; Mundorf & Brownell, 1990). Other sources list the 55-plus female viewing time as close to 30 hours per week. To isolated persons, television commonly acts as a companion. The widowed and lonely often prefer programs that emphasize family solidarity and a sense of belonging.

Movies

For most makers of feature-length commercial films, a major aim is to reach young people, particularly males of ages 16 to 24. Consumer studies conclude that most moviegoers are teenagers and young adults; studios market their products accordingly. Many commercially successfully movies seem to be rather mindless entertainment with a focus on high-speed chases and violence. Exceptions to the standard movie formula are rare. In the typical movie, youth holds much more promise than age. It is the exceptional movie that stars older persons and promotes understanding of the challenges and joys of aging.

A Chicago philanthropic group that gives annual "Owl" awards for film and television shows that treat older people with respect. Recent movies that have also been recommended by experts on aging are:

TABLE 2.2

The 50 Most Powerful Stars Over 50

	Star	Age		Star	Age
1.	Clint Eastwood	67	26.	Robert Duvall	67
2.	Harrison Ford	55	27.	Sylvester Stallone	51
3.	Michael Douglas	53	28.	Paul Newman	73
4.	Robert Redford	60	29.	Nick Nolte	58
5.	Arnold Schwarzenegger	50	*30.	Bette Midler	52
6.	Sean Connery	67	31.	James Woods	51
7.	Morgan Freeman	60	32.	Jon Voight	59
8.	Jack Nicholson	61	33.	Billy Crystal	51
*9.	Barbra Streisand	56	34.	Danny Glover	50
10.	Jack Lemmon	73	*35.	Lauren Bacall	73
11.	Danny DeVito	53	36.	Steve Martin	52
12.	Al Pacino	58	*37.	Vanessa Redgrave	61
13.	Anthony Hopkins	60	38.	Richard Dreyfus	50
14.	Woody Allen	62	39.	Marlon Brando	74
15.	Warren Beatty	61	40.	Donald Sutherland	63
16.	Robert De Niro	54	*41.	Shirley MacLaine	64
17.	Dustin Hoffman	60	42.	Harvey Keitel	58
*18.	Susan Sarandon	51	43.	Christopher Walken	55
*19.	Glenn Close	51	*44.	Anne Bancroft	66
*20.	Goldie Hawn	52	45.	Patrick Stewart	57
*21.	Diane Keaton	52	46.	Dennis Hopper	61
22.	Gene Hackman	68	*47.	Sophia Loren	63
23.	Kevin Kline	50	48.	Sidney Poitier	71
24.	Tommy Lee Jones	51	49.	Tom Selleck	53
25.	Leslie Nielson	72	50.	Ian Holm	66

*women

Adapted from *Modern Maturity* Magazine, March-April 1998, pp. 32-40. A bimonthly publication of AARP Washington D.C.

- *Marvin's Room* (1996): Two middle-aged sisters react to their dying father
- *Complaints of a Dutiful Daughter* (1994): Oscar-nominated documentary about a daughter caring for her mother with Alzheimer's disease.
- *The Cemetery Club* (1993): Three widowed women who are best friends adjust to their new status in conflicting ways.
- *Enchanted April* (1992, British): A snippy aristocratic widow joins three younger women in renting a vacation home on the Italian coast.
- *Strangers in Good Company* (1991): Seven

elderly women, stranded when their bus breaks down, share their stories, fears, and dreams.

- *Thank You and Goodnight!* (1990): A documentary of a grandmother dying of cancer—her fear, pain, and humor.
- *Age Old Friends* (1990): Two buddies living in a retirement home cope with frailty. Their minds remain sharp as their bodies decline.

Movies are good that realistically describe aging, care of the ill, spousal relationships, friendships over the years, and intergenerational relationships. They should attempt to portray older people as complex characters, not caricatures. The 1997 movie *Mother* starring Debbie Reynolds and Albert Brooks has some interesting mother-son dynamics. Paul Newman, at age 70, brought insights into healing family relationships in his role as Sully in the 1994 movie *Nobody's Fool.* The *Entertainment Tonight* documentary "Power and Fear" (July 26, 1990) showed that ageism remains a powerful force in the movie industry, which clearly still favors youth over age. Film and other popular media continue to glorify youth and play on fears of aging, thus enhancing negative stereotypes of age.

THE PSYCHOLOGY OF PREJUDICE

Those who hold negative stereotypes of aging are prejudiced against older persons. The two variables go hand in hand. To explain why an individual would subscribe to negative stereotyping is to explain why a person is prejudiced. The **psychology of prejudice** draws attention to the psychological causes of prejudice, as opposed to social causes previously discussed, such as TV and magazine advertising. One psychological explanation is self-concept. Someone having a positive self-concept may be less prone to believe the negative stereotypes of other groups. And when that person ages, he or she may well choose to accept only positive stereotypes of age. Psychologists use the term *projection* here. If we feel negative about ourselves, we project it on to others. This might explain why prejudice against elders correlates with one's personal degree of anxiety about death (Palmore, 1988).

Three well-known theories that explain racism may also be used to explain ageism (Palmore, 1990): (1) the **authoritarian personality,** in which less-educated, rigid, untrusting, insecure persons are the ones who hold prejudices; (2) the **frustration-aggression hypothesis,** in which those who are frustrated, perhaps by poverty and low status, take it out in aggression toward others; and (3) **selective perception,** in which we see what we expect to see and selectively ignore what we do not expect to see. Our perceptions then confirm our stereotypes. For example, we "see" only old drivers driving badly. We do not "see" young drivers mishandling a vehicle. Nor do we "see" all the old drivers who do well. In fact, we may perceive as "old" only those who are stooped, feeble, or ill. For example, viewers perceive Angela Lansbury, heroine of "Murder She Wrote," as middle-aged, because she is so healthy, vigorous, and clever. Actually, she celebrated her 70th birthday in 1995. If viewers understood this, perhaps some of the negative stereotypes of old age would disappear.

Breaking Negative Stereotypes

The negative stereotypes of age must be disproved if we are to have a true picture of older people. One way to do this is to draw attention to people who have made significant contributions in their old age. Michelangelo, Leo Tolstoy, Sigmund Freud, Georgia O'Keefe, Pablo Picasso, and Bertrand Russell, for example, continued to produce recognized classics until the ends of long lives. Other prominent men and women are still working productively at relatively advanced ages: writer Norman Mailer, the nation's first female poet laureate, Mona Van

Duyn, pianist Alicia de Larrocha, stage actress Julie Harris, vocalist Lena Horne, jazz musician B. B. King, Dr. Jonas Salk, and scientist/lecturer Jane Goodall. Numerous Nobel prize winners in the sciences every year are 65 or over.

EMPHASIZING THE POSITIVE

Negative stereotypes must be countered with accurate information. For example, the myth that elders as a group suffer mental impairment still persists. More specifically, commonly held beliefs are (1) that the mental faculties of older people decline, and (2) that most old people are senile. However, longitudinal studies of the same persons over many years have found little overall decline in intelligence scores. Studies show that older individuals are just as capable of learning as younger people—although the learning process may take a little more time. One longitudinal study of intelligence in subjects ranging in age from 21 to 70 shows that on two out of four measures, intelligence *increases* with age and concludes that "general intellectual decline in old age is largely a myth" (Baltes & Horgas, 1996).

The stereotype that most old people are senile simply is not true. Proportionately few ever show overt signs of senility. Those who do can often be helped by treatment. Although mental health is a problem for some, only a small percentage of the elderly have Alzheimer's disease or any other severe mental disorder. This will be addressed more fully in a later chapter of the text.

Physical stereotypes are as common as mental ones and are just as false. More positive images are replacing the "rocking chair" stereotype of old age, as older Americans stay more physically active and fit. The physical fitness craze has not been lost on the over-65 generation. Aerobics classes, jogging, walking, and bicycling have become very popular among this group.

Many sports now have competition in senior divisions. Tennis is one example. It's never too late for a shot at Wimbleton—"Senior Wimbleton West" is held annually in the western part of the United States. Divisions of this tournament, for both men and women, exist for those in their fifties, sixties, seventies, and eighties. Golf, swimming, cycling, bowling, softball, competitive weight-lifting, and basketball have senior events. Sports and physical fitness can extend throughout one's life.

The key ingredient to a long, full life, according to psychologist Lee Hurwich, who happens to be in her seventies, is not physical health, but attitude (Opatrny, 1991). With the right attitude—one of passion about life, whether this passion is found in career, friendships, or interests—a person can enjoy some of the best and most rewarding years in later life. Hurwich, who interviewed active, socially committed women, discovered that her subjects live in the present, squeezing from daily life all its enjoyment. They had relationships with people of all ages. Many had suffered physical afflictions that would send most people into despair, but they had optimistic attitudes and a trust in people. One woman was studying Spanish at age 87. Why? "I want to keep the cobwebs out of my head," she told Hurwich. As they reached their eighties and nineties, Hurwich's subjects still felt life has meaning, and they were satisfied with their lives. Four well-known women she studied in 1991 who were still vital at 70 and beyond are Elizabeth Terwilliger, naturalist; Betty Friedan, feminist leader; Julia Child, chef; and Jessica Mitford, author (Opatrny, 1991).

CONSEQUENCES AND IMPLICATIONS OF STEREOTYPING

Negative stereotyping of old people has detrimental effects on both society in general and old people in particular. First, negative stereotyping perpetuates ageism in our society. Ageism increases when society views all old people as senile, decrepit, and rigid. These and other negative stereotypes, which do not apply to the majority of elders, reinforce prejudice and lead to discrimination. Perpetuating ageism often results in polarization (a feeling of "us" against "them") and segregation. One student in an unpublished study (Barrow, 1994a) had this to say:

I can't stand old people and I don't get along with them at all. To me they seem useless and without a purpose. I try to avoid the aged.

This opinion serves as a good example of the negative stereotyping and ageist attitudes that result in the avoidance of old people. When we avoid old people, society becomes age segregated. Real communication cannot take place in a segregated society, and the cycle of stereotyping, ageism, and polarization continues.

Ageism even affects professional objectivity. In a study of psychologists, ageism was evident. When presented with clinical vignettes in which the ages of the clients varied, clinical psychologists considered older, depressed clients to be significantly less ideal than younger clients with identical symptoms and histories; and older clients were given poorer prognoses than younger ones. However, older psychologists were more favorable toward older clients than were young psychologists (Ray, 1987). An experimental program was introduced in a medical school to improve the medical students' attitudes and skills in working with elders. In another study, an experimental group participated in four 10-minute group sessions that emphasized psychological and biological knowledge as well as communication skills. The experimental group developed more positive attitudes and more socially skilled behavior in their work with older adults than did members of a control group (Intrieri et al., 1993).

Employees could relate better to older clients if they rid themselves of negative stereotypes, especially the stereotype that older people are in their second childhood, which is a very poor way to elicit the highest potential from a person. Even if the older person has a mental disorder and is physically dependent, the "second childhood" stereotype glosses over the ways in which he or she is not childlike.

Negative stereotyping fosters fear of aging in both old and young. Who wants to be "hunched over," "grouchy," "useless," "rejected," and "alone"? One study, which used agree-disagree statements to measure fear of aging, showed a clear and strong relationship between low fear of aging and subjective well-being (Klemmack & Roff, 1984). The study measured fear of aging with statements such as these:

I feel that people will ignore me when I'm old.

I am afraid that I will be lonely when I'm old.

I am afraid that I will be poor when I'm old.

Subjective well-being was measured by agree-disagree statements such as these:

I have made plans for things I'll be doing a month or year from now.

Compared to other people I get down in the dumps less often.

The things I do now are as interesting to me as they were when I was younger.

Those who did not fear aging felt good about themselves and their lives. On the other hand, those who feared aging did not have a good personal sense of well-being.

A question asked of the aged participants in the Berkeley Older Generation Study was "Looking back, what period of your life brought you the most satisfaction?" This question was asked when the respondents were, on the average, 69 years old, and 14 years later when the average age was 83. The findings remained consistent over time. Adolescence was considered the most unsatisfactory time. The decade of the thirties was named as most satisfying time period by 16 percent of the sample. The period of the fifties was second most popular, named by 15 percent of the sample. Old age was seen as more satisfying than childhood. Twelve percent said their sixties brought them the most satisfaction; 13 percent named their seventies and 5 percent described their eighties as the most satisfying period of their lives. The common stereotypes that old persons are fixated on childhood memories, that youth is best, and that old age contains few satisfactions were thus dispelled (Field, 1993).

Negative stereotyping stifles the potential of older people and draws attention away from the happy, sociable, successful, active oldsters. A self-fulfilling prophecy is created: older people do not do anything because they assume they are not able. Their lives, therefore, are neither as satisfying nor as fulfilling as they might be.

We have hardly begun to explore the potential of elders in this society. Too often, larger companies try to remove older persons from the labor market to make room for the young. Too often, we provide no alternative ways for them to make contributions. Too often, society works against elders instead of for them. We need to put more thought and effort into conserving a valuable natural resource: older Americans.

Chapter Summary

Many stereotypes of old age exist, and a large portion are negative. Sources of negative stereotyping are the language we use to describe elders, songs, speeches, television, advertising, movies, and a complex sociohistorical heritage. The psychology of prejudice examines ageism to understand the roots of this prejudice.

Far greater public education and interaction with older people needs to take place if we are to develop a full understanding of the potential of elders in our culture. Action directed to diminish our cultural belief in stereotypes about aging can and must take place on a personal level, as well as the level of social policy. Emphasizing the accomplishments of older scholars, scientists, and artists is helpful. Senior sports events draw attention to the physical fitness potential of elders and their ability to enjoy competition. The entire society is benefited when we have a more holistic understanding of what the nation's elderly look and act like in the present, and who they will be in the future.

Key Terms

authoritarian personality
biomedicalization of aging
compassionate stereotypes
cultural lag
frustration-aggression hypothesis
heterogeneity
language of aging
Media Watch Task Force
negative stereotypes
phenomenology
positive stereotypes
pragmatic knowledge
psychology of prejudice
reversed stereotype of aging
selective perception
self-concept
social construction of self
stereotypes

Questions for Discussion

1. Everyone bring one birthday card to class with an "age message." Is the message about aging positive or negative? Discuss both the explicit messages and the implicit messages of the cards. Categorize them by style and type.
2. Bring an advertisement with an "age message" to class. Write an advertisement in which you use implicit ageism. Write one in which you use *explicit* ageism.
3. Try to recall some children's literature that contains stories about or references to old people. What are the images portrayed? Who were your aging "models" as a child? Have these models affected you in a positive or negative way?
4. Describe yourself at age 85: what you will look like, what you will be doing, where you will live, who your friends will be.

Fieldwork Suggestions

1. List the first 10 words that come into your mind upon seeing the words *aged, middle-*

aged, adult, adolescent. Analyze your words. Do they reveal your personal biases and judgments about these age groups? Ask three people—preferably representing different age cohorts—to list the first 10 words that come into their minds when they see the words *aged, middle-aged, adult, adolescent.* Compare your lists in a discussion group in class. What are the common patterns and language can you identify? What differences do you see? Can you draw any conclusions from your comparisons?

2. Design a study to identify stereotypes of aging. Identify your focus of inquiry—popular music? Preschool children? Advertisements in public places? Determine a systematic way in which you will record your observations; draw your conclusions.
3. Watch a couple of hours of prime-time television, including advertising. How is the topic of aging handled? Are old people visible? How are they characterized? To what age group is the advertising targeted? Watch the news, both local and national and including Public Broadcasting. In your estimation, what age group is the "target" audience? Why?
4. Study magazine ads of the 1960s, 1970s, 1980s, and 1990s in regard to aging. Do you observe any changes? Write a "good" ad for an antiaging skin cream.

Online Activities

1. Identify the target audience for the advertisements on any search engine on the Internet. What are your criteria for determining what that audience is?
2. Use the key word *elderly* and make a list of the *range* of references—that is, the various information networks that are linked to this word.
3. Repeat this exercise, using the word *ageism* and *ageist literature*. What are you finding? What are you *not* finding?
4. Look up the name of a recording artist with whom you are familiar, and see if you can locate words to a song of his/hers that addresses ageism, or that speaks to the topic of aging.

3

Theories in Adult Development

The Stones Age

Richard Harrington

Venerable archetypes in rock's longest-running soap opera, Keith Richards, Mick Jagger, Charlie Watts and Ron Wood (no longer the new boy after 19 years) have finished dinner and are waiting for their just desserts.

Just as Jagger mumbles to his wife that this last rehearsal seems to be ending with no nod to his birthday—surprise!—a gigantic and calorically daunting chocolate cake (sporting the "Voodoo Lounge" cover, of course) is wheeled out from the kitchen, adorned with a single candle. Jagger's birthday, his 51st, is actually a few days away, but it's the last time this whole group will be together until opening night.

This private moment is a decided contrast to last year, when Jagger's 50th birthday provoked ridiculous media coverage. After dinner, Jagger expresses relief not just at the single candle, but the absent fuss.

"God, yes!" he sighs.

Jagger's never been particularly fond of looking backward, which becomes a problem as the Stones mythology stretches into each new decade. Experimentally, the distance between "It's All Over Now" and the new "Voodoo Lounge" album seems greater than 30 years. After all, rock-and-roll is central to a pop culture, and the music industry within it, where planned obsolescence is the norm and where longevity is traditionally suspect.

"The Stones gave it everything they had; these old pros, crippled by age and dissipation, but still holding the flag high . . . "

—Chet Flippo writing in *Rolling Stone*—back in 1978.

"The Famous heads are going gray now, the faces beginning to age like trail-weathered saddlebags . . . "

—Same band, same magazine, Kurt Loder—in 1981.

"The Stones are not anachronisms. They are still able, at will, to tap the unruly, anarchic essense of what their music has always been about . . . "

—Ditto, ditto, Anthony DeCurtis—in 1989.

In the process of transforming themselves from rock's original menace to society into music industry figureheads, the group that once sang "what a drag it is getting old" is finding what an interesting thing it is getting older.

"It is," insists Keith Richards, 50. "It's fresh because no one as taken a band this far down the road before. For that very reason you expect the 'Ah, they're still hackin' it out,' but that stuff is a really peripheral thing for us. Hey, you come up with something better, we'll get out of the way."

When the Stones were indicted—er, inducted—into the Rock and Roll Hall of Fame five years ago, The Who's Pete Townsend counseled: "Don't try to grow old gracefully, it wouldn't suit you!" That same year, the group released "Steel Wheels" and won both the readers and critics polls in *Rolling Stone* for artist of the year and tour of the year.

At times, a Rolling Stones group photo can look like a classic tintype. It would be easy to mistake them for a band of outlaws in a West still wild, or for Welsh miners not long out of the mines. They may sport elegant tailored clothes (the perennial prole Richards expected) but the faces are all weathered (okay, Richard's is weather-beaten). The wear and tear of 30 years in the trenches is not absent even in the perpetually vigorous Jagger, whose impossibly thin waist and taut physique seem as time-defiant as his rooster strut . . . .

"We can maybe shed an old lady here and there, if necessary, but Mick and I, we cannot divorce each other," says Richards. "Even if we never wanted to see each other again, we'd have to! Even if it was just to deal with what we'd done already and never learn anything else.

"I suppose it's something to be pleased about, that a band can last that long," says Jagger, he of the perpetually mixed emotions. "Of course it has its down and up moments and there's bound to be periods where it's not much fun, and it doesn't have a lot of definition after a while. I think the beginning was all right but then you're just redoing it . . . . It's kind of hard to keep it all together, hard to make long-term plans because that monster looms on the horizon."

Author's Note: In 1997 The Rolling Stones kicked off their Bridges to Babylon tour in Chicago's Soldier Field. Jagger, who owns a New York apartment, a retreat on a Caribbean island, and a chateau in the Loire Valley of France, has every intention of continuing to perform his music. In the Voodoo album the subject of aging is touched on in a wistful way "I can still paint the town/All the colors of your evening gown/While I'm waiting/For your blond hair to turn gray." The band's 39th album released on the virgin label contains rap and hip hop along with their traditional emphasis on blues.

Jagger has 3 children with Texas model Jerry Hall, a daughter Jade by ex-wife Bianca Jagger and daughter Karis (both girls in their early '20s) by Marsha Hunt. He became a grandfather in 1992 with the birth of Jade's daughter.

This chapter considers the human life cycle from the psychological perspective of adult development. In it, we see how developmental perspectives are useful in understanding the fear of aging and age transitions. The personality variables are studied that affect aging and are in turn affected in the aging process.

Theories help to understand and organize what we see—the empirical observations we make. Some areas of study, biology for example, have highly developed theoretical structures that allow questions, or hypotheses, to be studied with scientific precision. Mendel's theory of plant genetics integrated a series of observations and allowed for the prediction of what size or color a plant's flower would be, or how many ears a cornstalk would produce. A theory of human development would need to have a similar capacity for outcome prediction; however, many competing forces affect the growth and development of an individual. For this reason, there are many different theoretical approaches to human development.

Imagine for a moment six people watching a tennis match. The eye of a ballet dancer would probably be skilled at observing the movement of body in relation to the space of the court and the ball. The artist might see color, shape, proportion, and intensity. The corporate sponsor's perspective, on the other hand, would include assessing the apparent popularity of the players by the crowd, perhaps calculating the value of corporate exposure to a given size audience. There are many different lenses from which to view an event, and different theoretical approaches describe that phenomenon from a slightly—or not so slightly—different lens.

Data is the information being gathered by each of the viewers above, as a means for testing or developing their perspective, whether it be economic or physical. Data might be summary scores on objective tests, used to elaborate **quantitative development**. This methodology emphasizes the changes in the number or amount of something. Data might also be the telling of a story, of the kinds of things that people do, or how they do them. This approach emphasizes **qualitative development**.

The different perspectives, or theories, used to describe an event or process shape what is observed, and they can be described by different metaphors. A **metaphor** is a figure of speech that implies a comparison: being in "the autumn of life," for example. Metaphors can describe theories, too. The primary metaphors in personality or ego psychology are outlined in Table 3.1 and described at length in Susan Cloninger's book *Theories of Personality* (1996).

Early Developmental Models

According to early human developmentalists, distinct stages or phases form the **life cycle** through which humans pass. We proceed from infancy to childhood, through adolescence to adulthood, and then into parenthood and grandparenthood, and the cycle begins anew for each newborn baby. The life cycle is the course of aging: individuals adapt throughout their lives to their own biological, psychological, and social role changes.

The experiences common to all people in their passage through the life cycle give life some consistency. On the other hand, individual variations supply a measure of uniqueness to each person. We are all different, but we are not different in all ways, nor are we necessarily different in the *same* ways. Yet we are like *all* others in that we are conceived and born in a given time period, we age, and we die.

FREUD, 1856–1939

The influence of Sigmund Freud, father of the psychoanalytic perspective, on the field of psychology is profound and indisputable. Freud believed that it is not human reason, but unconscious psychological forces, that most profoundly affect our thought and behavior. These forces originate in the emotions of early childhood, and continue their influence throughout our lives

Psychoanalytic theory established the impact of early life experiences on the psychology, and therefore the life choices, of the individual. The focus on the unconscious, including our understanding of sex and aggression, has transformed

TABLE 3.1

Theories as metaphors

Metaphor	Description	Exemplary theorist
Information processing	Personality reflected by cognition of subjective experience, which differs among people; recognizes multiple potentials; is causal	Sperry (1980, 1990) Kelly Bandura Mischel
Mechanistic	Personality determined by external determinism; adopted from the physical sciences; biological in nature; empirically testable	Freud through behaviorists
Organic	Personality compared with growth of plants and animals; potential is within the person, not the environment	Erikson Levinson
Narrative	Personality as the story of a person's life; when personality changes, we rewrite our life stories; narrative has plot, characters, time progression, and episodes	Saarbin Kelly
Emergent self	Self-directed, willful personality from internal determinism; emphasis on choice and striving; free will, and individual behavior; future oriented, not past oriented	Adler Sappington Ziller Sperry Rychlak
Transcendent self	Individual personality is not separate and self-contained but connected with others on a plane of shared experience; experience beyond individual ego	Jung Maslow Rogers

Source: Cloninger, Susan (1996). *Theories of personality: Understanding persons*. New York: Prentice Hall.

the way in which people in modern times understand their conscious experience.

JUNG, 1875–1961

A younger contemporary of Freud's, Carl Gustav Jung initially had strong professional ties with Freud. Over time, however, Jung developed a strong intellectual disagreement with Freud based primarily on Freud's emphasis of the role of sexuality and his relative failure to address the potential of the unconscious to contribute positively to psychological growth. The two men, by this time both preeminent theorists in the field of psychology, developed a powerful personal conflict from which two separate schools of psychological orientation emerged. The Freudian school continued to focus on the shaping power of past events, whereas Jungians began to focus attention to the future direction of personality development.

> *We cannot live the afternoon of life according to the program of life's morning, for what was great in morning will be little at evening, and what in the morning was true will at evening have become a lie.*
>
> CARL JUNG, 1933

Jung was perhaps the first modern voice to focus on the possibility of adult personality development. After 40, Jung believed, the individual begins to develop an internal self-potential. An important aspect of this development is the identification and balance of opposite characteristics, which he called **archetypes**. Through the balance of these competing opposites, the personality can reach maturity; otherwise, the personality remains in struggle, incomplete. For example, all people have both a feminine and a masculine side, produced by biological and social conditioning factors (Dolliver, 1994).

Over the life course, individuals move from self-in-society—a focus on social interactions and institutions—to a more internal focus, referred to by Bernice Neugarten in 1964 as **interiority**. This process of self-reflection begins taking place around midlife and becomes a central way in which the individual is able to prepare for life's final state, which is death. The idea initiated for us by Jung that individuals become more introverted with age, has become one of the most studied issues in personality research on aging (Cavanaugh, 1993).

ERIKSON, 1902–1994

Erikson's lifespan model of the **stages of human development** extend beyond childhood and adolescence to include middle and old age, although the adult years, from roughly 20 through 60, were described by only two ego stages (Erikson, 1963). He recognized that personality continues to develop throughout the life cycle, and he believed the individual progresses through eight psychosocial stages in order to establish new orientations to self and the social world over time (see Table 3.2). Each of Erikson's stages is identified with a developmental task, or challenge, to be accomplished. There may be either a positive or a negative resolution of the challenge, and the ego resources we gain (or do not gain) on completion of one stage are brought with us to the next stage of development (Richman, 1995). The first five stages are similar to Freud's stages of psychosexual development.

Erikson's last three stages deal with early, middle, and later adulthood. In early adulthood, intimacy versus isolation is the focus of psychosocial development. Relationships in friendship, sex, competition, and cooperation are emphasized. Mature, stable relationships tend to form in the late teens and twenties. According to this model, one's task in early adulthood is to first lose and then find oneself in another, so that affiliation and love behaviors may be learned and expressed.

In middle adulthood the developmental task is generativity versus stagnation. **Generativity** involves a concern for the welfare of society rather than contentment with self-absorption. The positive outcomes of balance in middle adulthood are to be able to create, to care for, and to share. Parenting and grandparenting are manifestations of generativity, but examples might also include mentoring relationships, and circumstances of "husbandry" in terms of tending to growing plants, or concern with the environment.

In later adulthood, Erikson's psychosocial emphasis shifts to the considerations of being nearly finished with life and facing the reality of not being. The crisis of later adulthood is **integrity versus despair**. Erikson (1966, p. 230) writes:

> *[Integrity] is acceptance of one's one and only life cycle as something that had to be and that, by necessity, permitted no substitutions. The lack or loss of this (accumulated) ego integration is signified by fear of death: the one and only life cycle is not accepted as the ultimate of life. Despair expresses the feeling that the time is now short, too short for the attempt to start another life and to try out alternate roads to integrity. Disgust hides this despair. Healthy children will not fear life if their elders have the integrity not to fear death.*

We are fortunate if, in old age, our passage through the first seven stages has provided us with a balance of ego resources adequate to take on the final task of preparing ourselves for death. The primary and profound task of Erikson's final stage is to integrate all the experiences of our life in a way that provides meaning to the

TABLE 3.2

Erikson's eight stages of human development

Psychosocial crisis	Age	Goal
Basic trust vs. mistrust	0–1	Establish trust in parent/caretaker to meet basic needs vs. mistrust
Autonomy vs. shame and doubt	1–2	Develop will, independence, and self-control vs. shame and doubt
Initiative vs. guilt	3–5	Learn to initiate interaction within family, develop language and conscience, gain sense of direction and purpose vs. guilt for being independent
Industry vs. inferiority	6–puberty	Develop interaction with teachers and peers, learn to accomplish tasks vs. feeling inferior and not trying to learn
Ego identity vs. role confusion	Adolescence	Interact primarily with peers. Develop heterosexual friendships. Integrate previous stages into unique sense of self vs. unresolved identity crisis
Generativity vs. stagnation	Middle adulthood	Have and care for children. Guide the future generation. Be productive and creative. Contribute to the world vs. being self-centered and unproductive
Ego integrity vs. despair	Late adulthood	Reflect on one's place in the life cycle. Become assured that one's life had meaning. Face death with dignity and without fear vs. despair that life is useless

life as lived. It is the time during which an individual determines, in the process of reviewing her life, whether that life has been "successful" in a social and spiritual way. In essence, the final stage is a time when an individual asks and seeks the answer to the question, What is the meaning of my life? What difference has my life made? The process involves the remembering and the telling of stories; sorting through and adjusting or arranging remembered events until a cohesive life "story" can be made from all the events of life. In having a witness to that story, it becomes tangible—real—and the telling of it helps to clarify it for ourselves. The process has been called **life review**, or **reminiscence**, and will be addressed more fully later in the text.

Positive resolution of Erikson's eighth and final stage allows the individual to interpret his/her life as having purpose. Meaning is ascribed to those many lived experiences, and the outcome of that meaning is a sense of life satisfaction. The negative resolution of this stage is one of meaninglessness and despair, the feeling that one's life has been useless. The final stage is one of reflection on major life efforts that are nearly complete. The reason for this process is to prepare the person to leave life—to die—with a sense of peace and completion. Life has had a purpose, and I have fulfilled my small part of a larger whole in a meaningful and fulfilling way. This accomplished, I can now leave.

Erikson's model is difficult to test. In one of the few empirical studies of Erikson's model, McAdams and de St. Aubin (1992) and McAdams et al. (1992) developed an elegant measure of generativity. Their findings support

People change *and* remain the same as they age. This woman's story is reflected in her remarkable eyes, from her youth to her old age.

that generativity peaks in middle life, consistent with Erikson's expectations. Another study on generativity, of Mills College and Radcliffe College graduates, looked at which personality, attitudes, and life outcome factors were related to generativity at midlife (Peterson & Klohnen, 1995). This study concluded that generative women have pro-social personality characteristics, express generative attitudes through their work, are invested in the parenting process, and exhibit an expanded radius of care.

In general however, Jung's and Erikson's formulations give rise to more hypotheses than conclusions concerning development of the basic personality orientations in childhood, middle, and old age. Perhaps Erikson's most lasting gift to the field of adult development was his emphasis on the process of living, the idea of life history rather than case history, and the use of biography rather than therapy as the chief research method (Levinson, 1996).

LEVINSON, 1923–1994

Daniel Levinson's interest was development in adulthood; he published an extraordinary longitudinal study of men's lives in 1978. In it, he conceived of the life cycle as a sequence of eras, each of which has its own biopsychosocial character. Major changes occur in our lives from one era to the next, and lesser (although equally crucial) changes occur within each era. The eras partially overlap, with one era ending as another begins. These are referred to as a **cross-era transitions**, and they generally last about five years.

The eras and transitions described by Levinson form a broader **life structure**—the underlying pattern or design of a person's life at a given time. The primary components of a life structure are the person's *relationships* with others in the external world, identified as *central components* and *peripheral components*, depending on their significance for the self and the life.

Levinson's theoretical model was developed using only the life experiences of men, and as such has been criticized as being sexist. Levinson himself, however, addressed the need to study male and female development separately, and he chose to study men's lives first, primarily because he is male.

In 1996 Levinson's second major longitudinal study was published: *The Seasons of a Woman's Life*. In this study, he attempted to develop a model of the structure of women's lives, including the significance of gender. In this study, he made the "surprising discovery" (p. 6) that women and men go through the same sequence of periods at roughly the same ages, although he identified wide variations in the ways in which the genders traverse each period.

An important concept emerging from the second longitudinal study is what Levinson called **gender splitting**—a sharp division between feminine and masculine that permeates all aspects of life. It is through this cultural and psychological process of gender splitting, Levinson postulated, that the seasons of a woman's life are primarily distinguished from seasons of the life of a man.

Transitions in Adult Life: Developmental Patterns

Psychologists have drawn attention to the need for a psychology explaining changes throughout the life span. A subdiscipline called developmental psychology has responded. This area of study is concerned with continuity and discontinuity over time. In other words, stability versus change in personality and the ways stability and change play out in the context of life are concerns of the developmental perspective. Developmentalists also incorporate human biology and the impact biology has on our progression through the human life course in explaining human psychological growth.

Up until about 20 years ago, "human development" in psychology actually meant "child development." The field of psychology at that time reflected the profound influence of Freud's model of development, which did not recognize growth and development in adulthood and later life. A new focus on early, middle, and later adulthood now characterizes the field of human development. Considering that we will live approximately two-thirds of our life as adults, it is reasonable that adulthood and later life are now major foci in developmental psychology.

The study of personality in middle and later life is sometimes referred to as *adult development*. The word ***transitions*** is used to describe points at which the person's development is moving, or transitioning, between one phase or stage and the next. During different periods of adulthood, we appear to have different levels of awareness of our own aging. Immediate concerns—careers, personal relationships, and leisure pursuits—tend to take up more of our time when we are younger. As we grow older, we may experience an undercurrent of fear at the thought of aging. We might just as likely, however, experience awe, excitement, satisfaction, and anticipation. Among most people, change can foster fear and dread as well as excitement.

The following section provides summary descriptions of the global categories identifying the life course: young adulthood, middle age, and old age.

Young Adulthood

Young adulthood comprises the years between 18 and 35 or so. A variety of challenging tasks present themselves at this time. Late adolescence in America often involves physical separation from one's family. College or military service can be the separating factor, or the young person may leave home to share an apartment or house with friends. Young people tend to have more friends than any other age group. This is perhaps to help them with the real task, which is one of psychological separation—of becoming an independent, autonomous person. Many adolescents find the passage stormy; identities are difficult to create when many options exist. "Who am I?" can bring much inner turmoil before an answer is formed.

Family and society place many "shoulds" on young adults. After establishing an identity and an occupational goal, the young man or woman may be expected to finish his or her education, begin a job or career, get married, set up housekeeping, and have children.

Now, at the beginning of the 21st century, the "shoulds" for getting married are not as clear as they once were. Parents are anxious for their children to become established in the economic structure; they are concerned about jobs and their children's future economic prospects. In response to this parental "should," young people increasingly delay marriage per se, opting instead to set up shared living with their significant other mate while they pursue education and/or concentrate on performing in their first jobs. In effect, marriage is postponed but the development of intimacy and affiliation, identified by Erikson as the task of young adulthood, is not postponed.

This pattern, it must be noted, is evident among some people in the United States but does not speak for all cultural groups in the country. This caution must be kept foremost in mind as we study human development, because in the search for similarities to describe a human process, it can become easy to overlook the differences. As we look through our particular lens, we must not forget to watch also for the individuating patterns of culture that have profound impact on our lives.

The centrality of major culture values creates a particularly intense pull for minorities. Internal and family expectations, as well as the social rules in which people are embedded, are culturally mediated. Minority culture young adults have been asked through public education in the United States to give up their cultural roots and embrace a culture that is different than their own. This is known as **acculturation**, and it serves the purpose of helping to assimilate nonmainstream cultures into the American economic reward system (Calabrese & Barton, 1995).

The difficulty of maturing and finding a place in the world for young adults depends on a range of sociocultural factors, including their ethnicity, family resources, place of birth, and so forth. Most people are so busy coming to terms with life that they do not consciously think about growing old. But when asked, they do express attitudes and opinions about aging.

Some responses from young people show a degree of acceptance and anticipation of aging, while others show fear (Fleeson & Heckhausen, 1997). How and why do people come to fear aging? We can assume that fear and worry about aging does not make the coming stages of the life course easier. Women seem to have the most fears, because their aging is judged more harshly by society. In other words, they, indeed, have more to fear.

THE MIDLIFE CRISIS?

Is midlife a point of transition, or is it a crisis? In 1965, psychoanalyst Elliot Jaques coined the term *midlife crisis* in his essay, "Death and the Mid-Life Crisis." This change was generally precipitated by the individual's recognition of his or her own mortality—often generated by the death of a parent or a long term friend.

> *When I had journeyed half of our life's way, I found myself within a shadowed forest, for I had lost the path that does not stray. Ah, it is hard to speak of what it was, that savage forest, dense and difficult, which even in recall renews my fear: So bitter—death is hardly more severe!*
>
> DANTE, 1308

The phrase "midlife crisis" apparently spoke to the experiences of enough people that it took hold in the language. In addition to being intuitively compelling, it is consistent with the theoretical underpinnings of adulthood developed in the early part of the century by Jung, van Gennep, Ortega y Gasset, and Erikson (see Table 3. 3). Numerous psychologists took up the popular concept, and developed a more popularized literature that assumed or further developed the idea of a crisis at midlife. Three primary writers in this vein were Levinson, in his *Seasons of a Man's Life* (1977) and *Seasons of a Woman's Life* (1996), Gould (*Transformations: Growth and Change in Adult Life*, 1978); and, just before Levinson or Gould, Gail Sheehy—whose book *Passages* (1976) launched the term *midlife crisis* into the popular media.

> *I suggest that the midlife crisis is a chimera, that is, . . . "an unreal creature of the imagination, a mere wild fancy; an unfounded conception . . . a phantasm, a body."*
>
> KRUGER, 1994

Despite all the attention paid to midlife in the past 20 years, the time period is variously referred to as "the prime of life," or as a "crisis." Most studies have found that midlife is both, depending on what life sends a person's way, and the coping skills and resources the person has to deal with life. Among those who clearly identify having had a crisis at midlife, it could have taken place not just between ages 35 and 45 but anytime between about 30 and 60. Even before 30, some individuals refer to an "early midlife crisis," and others after 60 to a "late midlife crisis," therefore midlife as a factor to predict an age crisis is virtually meaningless.

There's some kind of profound something going on—a reassessment, a rethinking, a big gulp, whatever. It's not biological. It has to do with self-image and the work-place. And I find this astonishing.

A. CLURMAN, A PARTNER AT YANKELOVICH SURVEY PARTNERS, 1995

As a self-fulfilling prophecy, many people anticipate a midlife crisis because its existence is generally accepted (Fleeson & Heckhausen, 1997). Cultural norms create psychological and interpersonal pressures on individuals to conform to those behaviors and attitudes that express "human nature" as it should (Dannefer, 1996). A new wrinkle; not knowing any Top Forty tunes; having a doctor who looks too young to have graduated from medical school; or being the age of coworkers' parents can precipitate feelings of being out of control, of being dated. The death of a close friend or of a parent can precipitate a profound process of self-reflection: how much time do I have? What have I really accomplished? Am I clear about what happens after death?

Those are the very questions predicted by developmental theorists including Jung and Levinson (Table 3.3), who postulate that midlife is a special time for reflection—a time when one's focus begins to become more interior as the full meaning of mortality begins to emerge and take shape in an individual's consciousness. The jury on the presence or absence of a midlife crisis is still out; however, it is clear that midlife is a uniquely identifiable period in the life course.

MIDDLE AGE

Middle age is an interesting period: the *transition* between young adulthood and old age. It is often stereotyped as being either dull, boring, and routine, or consumed by a life and lifestyle-threatening crisis. However this time of life plays out, an individual's reactions and adjustments to changes in middle age surely affect his or her reactions and adjustments to old age, just as one's response to aging at any point surely affects the points that follow.

Those in their middle years frequently accomplish or conclude certain developmental tasks. The normative expectation is that most people typically spend their twenties settling down and become further established in their thirties, forties, and fifties. This frequently becomes a time to buy a house and establish an economic base. In middle age, those who are married may feel satisfaction or discontent, but those who have not married and settled may feel a stronger push to do so. Age norms constrain those who do not fill the appropriate social role at the appropriate time. Middle age can become a time to sort through which roles one might still fill and which roles to abandon, and to deal with the feelings of loss for those roles that never will be (Foner, 1996).

Major role changes and events occur in the forties and fifties. Our parents are likely to be in their old age, and this is our time to cope with their old age and eventual death. The older generation, in turn, must confront the reality of their children's middle age (Tillman, 1997). Many popular books are on the market to provide guidance for middle-aged children who are helping and coping with older parents.

Grown children launch out on their own during one's middle years. This event can be sad and

TABLE 3.3

Models of adult development: Intellectual generation of basic concepts

Theorist	Historical/cultural location	Theoretical concept
Sigmund Freud	1880s through 1930s; Austrian; father of psychoanalysis	Personality is based on the first 5 years of life. It is divided into id, ego, and superego, representing impulsive, realistic, and moralistic tendencies. Individuals attend to conscious awareness, yet are driven and motivated by the unconscious
Carl Jung	1900s through 1950s; Swiss; first modern voice in psychiatry-psychology in adult development	Inner struggles of the 20s–30s deal with the "shadow" (repressed childhood attributes); 40s deal with potentials within the self, archetypes, that are primitive until midlife
Arnold van Gennep	Early 1900s; Dutch anthropologist; *Rites of Passage*, 1908	Life cycle is a series of transitions incorporating major life events such as birth, death, marriage, divorce. People in transition are a threat to society because they are not well integrated in the group they leave or the group they are entering. . . it is a psychologically unstable time. Ritual provides a collective vehicle for gaining personal control over anxieties generated by transitions.
Jose Ortega y Gasset	Spanish historian/ Philosopher; *Man and Crisis*, 1933;	Generational divisions (childhood, 0–15; youth, 15–30; initiation, 30–45; dominant, 45–60; old age) contribute to the shape of life. Potentials in the cycle affect how generational boundaries are drawn.
Erik Erikson	German and U.S. stages of psychosocial development; *Childhood and Society*, 1950	Human development comprised of 8 linear, age-based stages of human development from which specific ego strengths emerge. First theorist to focus on ego development in late life, e.g., *integrity* vs. *despair*.
Daniel Levinson	1970s; American psychologist; *Seasons of a Man's Life*, 1978; *Seasons of a Woman's Life*, 1996. adult development.	*Life structure* is the design of a life based on what a person finds most important. *Phases*, or loose stages, are identified by approximate age; *transitions* of about 5-years' duration connect the overlapping phases.

Source: Levinson, Daniel (1996). *The seasons of a woman's life*. New York: Knopf.

depressing, a relief, or a mixture of both. Though the postparental period has often been described negatively, for many, this new freedom is cause for a celebration rather than a crisis, depending on their outlook and perhaps on the ability to redefine one's goals and purpose in life.

The concept of "empty-nest syndrome" has been used to describe a midlife depression experienced by some women whose energies have been focused on child rearing (fathers' experience of children leaving home has unfortunately not been well studied). However, the consequences of the "empty-nest" phenomenon, research tells us, is as varied as the individuals experiencing it. Some people perceive their lives as having little purpose once their children have left home. Others identify a new sense of life satisfaction—a time to renew the marriage relationship, to attend to personal interests that were pushed aside by the necessity of addressing the needs of children.

A relatively new social phenomenon is the return home ("empty nest refilled") by either unmarried or married adult children. This is most likely to happen in an uncertain economic environment when the adult child has lost a job or accepted a very low paying job (Kausler & Kausler, 1996), or if the adult child has had a divorce. A survey in 1990 revealed that 16 percent of young adults ages 25 to 29 were living with their parents. This proportion is probably even higher today (Kausler & Kausler, 1996). The return of adult children to the parental home is not in and of itself negative, however. For many cultural groups in the United States, adult children once again living in the home might seem to be "traditional," as opposed to being aberrant. It is, however, contrary to larger cultural expectations of the progression of the life course.

Nowadays the majority of middle-aged people have more parents than they have children.

ELDON WEISHEIT, 1994

In some families, the needs of aging parents for caregiving are synchronous with the return of adult children—indeed, those needs become determinants in the decision to "move home." In other families, the older parent moves in with their middle-aged child because of the parent's frail health or for economic reasons. The impact of increased longevity substantially increases the likelihood of intergenerational responsibilities for elderly parents by middle-aged people (Uhlenberg, 1996). For example, in 1900, a 50-year-old had a 4 percent chance of both parents still living. Today, the midlife grandchild of that person will have a 31 percent chance of both parents being alive in 2000, and an 80 percent chance of having one parent still living (Cutler, 1997).

For those in midlife who have jobs or careers, the forties and fifties are generally also a time of experiencing peaks, or at least of evaluating a present occupation's potential for status, money, or power. Midlife is a time to come to terms with what is not possible. We may acknowledge, at this point, the impossibility of becoming president of the company or of fulfilling any of a host of goals.

Midlife is likewise a time of peak competence, professional respect, and earnings. People in midlife who have been working can look toward retirement in the first two decades of the 21st century with optimism. It is very possible that their needs for wealth will exceed those of their parents, however, they are better positioned for retirement than their parents were. They will have higher preretirement earnings than their parents did, and this earnings growth will increase pension benefits and allow greater savings for retirements (Manchester, 1997). Additionally, more women will be eligible for their own Social Security and pension benefits than were their mothers. This optimistic vision of a future old age might follow the pattern of the self-fulfilling prophecy and help to psychologically position midlifers for their later life.

Those who are unemployed or in low-paying jobs, however, may have more trouble squaring their dreams with reality. Aligning dreams with the facts can be a daunting task or none at all, depending on the dreams and the degree of success we expect. Some individuals have both the inner strengths (self-confidence and motivation) and outer resources (monetary savings and cultural support) to find new jobs or careers in their forties and fifties. However, those seeking new lines of work sometimes must forfeit seniority and retirement benefits from their original-career companies. Changing jobs may require risk taking and sacrifice and, for many, can literally be a time for starting over.

Middle age brings biological changes as well as changes in career and family. For women, menopause—the ending of menstruation—is a major physiological change: the childbearing years have ended. The decrease in estrogen in menopausal and postmenopausal women can create numerous physical changes and symptoms, such as hot flashes, genital atrophy, urinary tract changes, and loss of bone density. Hormone replacement therapy (HRT) is chosen by many women to alleviate symptoms, but there are risks associated with it. A slight increase in risk of endometrial or uterine cancer exists for women receiving estrogen over a long period of time, although this risk is reduced when estrogen is combined with progesterone. On the other hand, there is evidence of reduced stroke and hypertension, as well as strong evidence for the reduction of osteoporosis when estrogen supplements are taken. The negative findings are frightening, however, and for all women, particularly for those with family histories of breast or uterine cancer, taking hormone supplements must be carefully thought through.

Making the decision to take or not to take hormones for the remainder of one's life is not an easy one to make. Done well, it takes a thoughtful, self-reflective approach, and therefore creates an opportunity that many women take to reflect on who they see themselves as being as they come to terms with the ending of one stage of life and the beginning of another. In this way, a biologically-determined experience can become a time of self-reflection and examination. Women in their forties and fifties may mourn the loss of their fertility, but at the same time be relieved. It is a profound change in the rhythm of a woman's life, and sometimes women and their partners need reassurance that menopause does not, in itself, diminish sexuality. Rather, it can free partners from concern about pregnancy; many couples report improved pleasure and joy in their sexual relationship after menopause.

Karp (1988) provides a symbolic interactionist perspective from which to view the middle-aged years from age 50 to 60. He describes these years as a decade of reminders that bring age consciousness to new heights. These reminders come from the reflections of self that come from the appraisals of other people, a **looking-glass self,** which gives rise to self-appraisals about aging. Those in their fifties who were studied by Karp were surprised by their own aging. In their minds, they were young; but either their bodies or people around them were giving them different messages. A man who played on a basketball team was referred to as "sir" by a younger team member.

> *Each to each a looking glass*
> *Reflects the other that doth pass.*
>
> Cooley, 1902

Self-concept is socially constructed, at least in part. "Our self-identity is the product which springs from the responses of many others and it is their collective reactions which form the underpinning of our self-concepts" (Hensley, 1996). Who we are and how we respond is affected by the way we are treated by others, and how we believe we *ought* to be in the world. We have, according to sociologist Cooley in 1902, a tendency to become the person others say we are.

One category of reminders is generational—fiftieth birthday bashes focus on the fact that the birthday "boy" or "girl" has made it to the "big 5-0." Children grow up and become independent; they have children of their own. Parents die, long term friends die, and the reality of being at or near the Alpha generation is ever-present. The person in midlife is surrounded by social reminders of age: being the oldest member of a group or club; self-consciousness about going to places such as singles dances or bars where most people are young; or being old enough to be the parent or even grandparent of students, clients, or patients.

The age consciousness in Karp's study was not necessarily a negative commentary on aging. Research on the perception of self over time suggests that many people expect a peak in integrity in late life and a peak in generativity in midlife. They anticipate high levels of well-being in midlife and later (Fleeson & Heckhausen, 1997). The way in which people anticipate their future self can profoundly affect the choices they make in the process of becoming old. A projected self-concept of well-being in later life is, perhaps, half the battle.

LATE LIFE

In the mid-20th century, when psychological models of human development began to expand inquiry from child development to the adult experience, late life remained the least examined part of life. It has been characterized by decline and loss: loss of physical health; loss of lifelong partners and friends; loss of mental capacity; loss of creativity; loss of social roles—in short, depressing, discouraging, and barely worth spending much time on.

Late adulthood is still the least studied portion of the life course; however, the interest in social gerontology brought about by longevity and demographics in the past 20 years has created a parallel interest in the psychological development of later life. Today, many people will spend about one-third of their entire life span in their "old age"—a fact that the French address by calling old age **le troisiéme age,** "the third age" (Schaie & Willis, 1996). Although the student of gerontology is still likely to be met with the incredulous question, Why are you studying *that?*, the exploration of growth and development in later life is now seen as an exciting field of inquiry attracting increased numbers of scholars.

Loss does occur in late life, but it is important to distinguish between normal, pathological, and optimal late life experience. Although physical changes do occur with advancing age, physical and mental decline are not necessarily part of normal aging. Just as wearing prescription lenses to maintain 20/20 vision is considered to be an adaptive compensation, so too are the compensations an individual develops for minor dysfunctions that accompany the normal aging process (Schaie & Willis, 1996). Walking more slowly on a hike to compensate for a reduced energy level might be an example. Being unable to take a walk at all, however, is not a consequence of normal aging, but an indication of pathological aging—a physical state based on disease or injury rather than as an outcome of the aging process.

"The aged" are a very diverse population: well-being in old age is largely a function of the physical and psychological processes that preceded it. Losses tend to be counterbalanced with gains: the death of spouse, for example, can lead to remarriage and a regeneration of a loving relationship. Retirement from a full-time career may lead to part-time work at the same place or another job elsewhere or to the expansion of a creative hobby.

Developmentalists generally divide *le troisieme age* into categories of the young-old (around 65 to 75 or 80), the old-old (75 or so to about 90), and the very-old (around 90 and older). This distinction is very important when we talk about "old age," because if we are talking about a 95-year-old and a 68-year-old, we are speaking of people in profoundly different developmental places. Clearly, 40 years ago this was almost a moot point, because so few people lived past what we now call the young-old group. Today, the young-old are more like the middle-aged than they are like the old-old.

Erikson (1982) defined old age as a time when one is seeking balance between the search for ego integrity and feelings of despair. Other scholars have elaborated on Erikson's theme. Havighurst (1972) developed six tasks of late life as

1. Adjusting to decreasing physical strength and health
2. Adjusting to retirement and reduced income
3. Adjusting to the death of a spouse
4. Establishing an explicit association with one's age group
5. Adopting and adapting societal roles in a flexible way
6. Establishing satisfactory physical arrangements

The function of these tasks is to promote well-being in later life—optimal aging. Note the extent of adaptation required of older people in Havighurst's model.

Extreme old age is a very special time. In his nineties, Erikson wrote from personal experience about the final stage of the life cycle model that he presented with the help of his wife, Joan, 40 years earlier. He expanded on his late life stage, "integrity versus despair," by describing the wisdom that comes with age if one completes the developmental tasks that began earlier in the life cycle. For example, the basic trust learned in infancy evolves into the knowledge in old age of how interdependent we are—of how much we need each other. In early childhood, the life cycle's second phase, learning physical autonomy and control of one's bodily functions, versus shame and doubt in not learning them, paves the way for coping with deterioration of the body in old age. Old age is basically the second phase in reverse. One must "grow" in order to avoid the shame and doubt that can accompany decline, just as one "learned" bodily development without having shame and doubt. Every stage offers lessons that can apply in old age.

TRANSITIONS IN LATE LIFE

As a result of the longer life expectancy in the late 20th century, most Americans can expect to pass through these age-linked events: long term survival, empty nest, retirement, and for women an extended term of widowhood characterized by solitary living. Actually, a transition can be movement either from one age to another or from one age-linked event to another (e.g., children leave home or a spouse dies).

Every decade has its share of tasks and challenges. In later life, illness, death of a spouse, or increased frailty may take its toll; but personal growth and joy in living is still possible and probable. While Socrates awaited death in prison, at the age of 71, he was learning to play the lyre. Transitions do not end at age 65; we continue making them until the final transition. We can begin early in life to teach ourselves and our children that growing older is a natural event, one not to be feared, but rather one to be anticipated for new roles, new avenues of expressions, and new opportunities.

Continuity Theory: "You Haven't Changed One Bit"

Continuity theory is broad enough to be considered a sociological theory as well as a psychological one. Continuity theorists propose that a person's adaptations to young adulthood and middle age predict that person's general pattern of adaptation to old age. According to continuity theory, the personality formed early in life continues throughout the life span with no basic changes. This theory implies that neither activity nor disengagement theory explains adjustment to aging: adjustment depends on personality patterns of one's former years. This approach is consistent with the core of personality theory. Some therapists believe that significant personality change after about the age of 30 is unlikely. Although some researchers continue to debate the degree to which the personality remains stable throughout the life course, continuity theory maintains that the individual achieves a core personality by adulthood. By adulthood, people have adopted coping mechanisms, established stress and frustration tolerance levels, and defined ego defenses.

> *Surely enduring personality traits . . . form the core of our identity. For better or worse, we are what we are, and the recognition of that fact is a crucial step in successful aging.*
>
> COSTA, METTER, & MCCRAE, 1994.

Trait theorists look for consistency in the personality: **traits** are the enduring response patterns that are exhibited by a person in many different contexts. A **state**, on the other hand, more accurately describes something that is transient in the personality. Not unexpectedly, trait theorists find consistency in personality development over a lifetime. They define personality in terms of the basic tendencies that are the core potential of the person.

Two of the primary trait theorists, Paul Costa and Robert McCrae, feel that personality stability is crucial for successful aging. Personality traits are central to an individual's self-concept. They form the core of how people see themselves, and the continued sense that we are the "same" person provides the basis by which we can move on to make meaning of that life as lived. Enduring dispositions provide a dependable and necessary basis for adaptation to a changing world (Costa et al., 1994).

Trait theorists say that lives change, but personality does not. One study found, for example, that *states* were associated with different feelings of well-being among older people, but that *traits* (those more enduring personality characteristics) did not predict shifts in affect (Adkins et al., 1996). It is those more enduring traits that provide solidity for the ongoing sense of self, even in the midst of change.

Personality shortcomings can be addressed and, to some extent, overcome. With effort, tempers can be controlled, fears lessened, organization learned, and social skills practiced; thus, personalities can improve with age.

Analysis of longitudinal data suggests that personality stability might be associated with generations, that is to say, that stability in personality might be the result of early socialization. Schaie and Willis (1996) report that "substantial positive development toward more flexible personality styles, behaviors, and attitudes [are seen] in successive generations" (p. 213).

Most people, however, believe they remain "themselves" over time, and that belief seems to be reinforced in research studies (Troll & Skaff, 1997; Gold et al., 1995; Onega & Tripp-Reimer, 1997; Parker, 1995). By feeling a sense of continuity in their personalities, people are enabled to view change as connected to their past and linked to their present and future. This sense of the ongoing self is consistent with Kaufman's findings (previously reported) of the ageless self.

Two theorists in the 1980s studied adaptation skills among people who were moving from their homes into long term care facilities (Lieberman & Tobin, 1983). They found that their respondents maintained stable self-concepts primarily by drawing on their pasts. When possible, they altered their daily activities in ways that were similar with past interests. Self-concept in very old age was described by Tobin (1991) as being "not so much a current self-picture as a view of an entire life."

These findings can help to shatter the stereotypes that older people become less flexible, more cranky, more conservative, and less satisfied with their lives. Continuity theory suggests, as do other developmental psychologists, that growing old is a process of *becoming*; who we are in late life is a culmination of who we have been throughout our lives.

Aging Research

LONGITUDINAL STUDIES

The Maas-Kuypers Study

The Maas-Kuypers study, which observed personality change in women and men over a 40-year period, found personality to be stable throughout adulthood. Evidence in the research suggested that "qualities of life in old age are, indeed, highly associated, in complex ways, to qualities of life 40 years earlier" (Maas & Kuypers, 1977; Field, 1991). Those who had negative attributes in young adulthood had various negative personality characteristics in old age; fearful oldsters were rigid, apathetic, and melancholy as young mothers; anxious mothers were restless and dissatisfied in old age; the defensive elderly were withdrawn in early adulthood. The personality types that seemed most firmly connected to early adult-life behaviors were those with the most "negative" features. On the positive side, cheerfulness, lack of worries, and self-assurance in young adulthood seemed to match high self-esteem and self-satisfaction in old age.

Love, courtship, marriage, and widowhood are part of the life course for many people. Each experience remains a part of a person's identity throughout his or her life.

The Elder-Liker Study

Another 40-year longitudinal study assessed the **coping** mechanisms and consequences for women who lived through the Great Depression of the 1930s (Elder & Liker, 1982). During the depression, financial losses were more severe for working-class women than for middle-class women; and many working-class women, lacking the educational, financial, or emotional resources to master their circumstances, were too hard hit to make a comeback. The researchers suggest that the hardship of the depression offered these women a trial run through the inevitable losses of old age. Economic hardships meant new challenges for women— coping with unemployed husbands, taking in boarders for pay, looking for work, borrowing money from relatives, and getting along on less by reducing purchases to a bare minimum. In short, women had to become more self-reliant.

The conclusion was that a life history of mastery enables women to manage traumatic experiences throughout their lives. Women like the middle-class women in the study are lucky if they have the resources for such mastery—economic resources do matter significantly. Coping skills are acquired in hard times, not in tranquil ones. One who experiences no hard times until old age may not have developed coping skills. "Neither a privileged life nor one of unrelenting deprivation assures the inner resources for successful aging" (Elder & Liker, 1982).

The Baltimore Study

The Baltimore Longitudinal Study of Aging, spanning 30 years, confirmed that personality remains remarkably stable with aging. A cheerful, optimistic young person usually remains so throughout life. Conversely, a negative person maintains pessimism (Shock et al., 1989). Personality, in fact, was found to be more stable than gender roles when changes in activities over the life course were examined (Verbrugge et al., 1996).

Stress appears to be a key modifier in the extent to which personality continuity takes place. One recent study developed a clear relationship between self-criticism and stress-induced changes in biochemistry, which in turn make the individual more vulnerable to ill health and depression (Gruen et al., 1997). In a 12-year study of 216 lower-middle-class people, continuity was the norm in personal functioning. Stress altered the pattern; with high exposure to stress, morale and self-concept deteriorated (Fiske & Chiriboga, 1990). Low morale, negative self-concept, and self-criticism have been found to be highly associated (Troll & Skaff, 1996; Lieberman & Tobin, 1983).

ADAPTING TO LOSS

A study monitoring the stress patterns experienced when relocated to different nursing homes found the very old to be unique. Continuity theory did not apply. Their roles had changed, their bodies had declined, important people in their lives had died. Emotional problems are not physical in origin, but they may be related to physical losses. The older one is, the more likely one is to face physical disability and imminent death. Loss of hearing, loss of vision, and loss of the use of limbs have a strong psychological impact at any age. So does being told you have only five years, six months, or two weeks to live. Denial, depression, anger—even rage—are common responses.

Other age-related losses are the death of a spouse, the deaths of siblings, and the deaths of friends. Retirement, the loss of one's driver's license, the sale of the home, or a move to an institution are the types of losses that frighten people about aging. They do not happen to every older person, but the longer a person lives, the more likely they are to happen. There is a considerable difference between the young-old (65 to 74) and the old-old (75 and over) as to the losses they can expect. In fact, by comparison, the young-old experience very few losses.

Older people, on the whole, adapt relatively well to loss. Most elderly persons adapt to the loss of their spouse without severe, enduring psychiatric repercussions. However, the initial period of widowhood can be especially difficult. During the first year of widowhood, there are high incidences of psychological and physical symptoms, an increase in the use of psychiatric services, and an increased risk of suicide. Loss is always difficult, but older people adjust—come to grips with their losses—just as do younger people.

PERSONALITY THEORY

Personality strongly influences learning. Interest, motivation, self-esteem, rigidity, flexibility, cautiousness, fearfulness, and anxiety all affect one's ability to learn. Old people vary in personality characteristics just as young people do.

Personality theory focuses on the many traits of individual personality, such as friendliness, shyness, humor, and aggressiveness. The study of personality has been a major focus of developmentalists who analyze personality and its change over the life course. Theorists have used personality variables to explain why some older individuals withdraw from society whereas others do not, and why some individuals are satisfied with an active lifestyle whereas others prefer noninvolvement. Personality theorists generally use personality characteristics to explain why some people readily adapt to and cope with aging and why others have problems.

Personality studies show that many older individuals are mature, focused types, happy and satisfied with life. But others are striving, defensive about aging, and discontent. Some are very passive types who depend on others. They may be apathetic and bored much of the time. They

may see the world as collapsing and become preoccupied with holding on to what they have. The most disorganized personalities suffer major impairments to their mental health and cannot function outside a mental hospital.

A constricted or rigid personality type has a difficult time dealing with change. In contrast, a flexible personality type adapts to change, whether it be positive or negative (such as widowhood, ailing health, or shrinking finances). One extensive longitudinal study grouped personalities into five categories:

1. Neurotic—characterized by feelings of anxiety, worry, hostility, and depression.
2. Extroverted—characterized by tendencies to be outgoing, active, and assertive.
3. Open—characterized by receptiveness to new experiences, new ideas, and change.
4. Agreeable–Antagonistic—Antagonistic types tend to set themselves against the grain and be opposed to others, whereas agreeable types are pleasers. Antagonists may be skeptical, mistrustful, stubborn, and rude.
5. Conscientious–Undirected—The conscientious are hardworking and responsible. They have a drive to achieve. The undirected have no focus and tend to be lackadaisical and aimless (Costa & McCrae, 1987).

The personality traits in the many studies reviewed by Costa and McCrae show astonishing stability. The traits remained consistent over time, and individuals who were extroverted and open experienced less stress as they aged.

GENDER DEVELOPMENT

The developmental model emphasizes the psychology of the individual. Developmental psychologists who look at how individuals change over the life course focus on the individual by studying variables such as personality, motivation, cognition, and morale. Social and cultural factors are examined for their role in personality changes. Maturation, or some inherent biological mechanism, may also be a strong force in creating change in persons as they progress through life. As theoretical models of aging are set forth, empirical studies test and refine them. The question of which attitudes, behaviors, and individual characteristics are **intrinsic** (biologically mandated) and which are **extrinsic** (formed by changes in social structure and roles) is still an issue for study and discussion.

One example of the question of intrinsic or extrinsic causality is that of gender differences. Carl Jung postulated the existence of opposites in our personalities, with young adults generally expressing only one sexual aspect as they developed into adulthood. The expression of that sexual self is usually defined by sex-role stereotypes.

As a person ages, he or she may become more self-accepting and more comfortable exploring all sides to one's personality. Both sexes, according to Jung, move psychologically closer to middle ground

Psychologist David Gutmann (1987) believes that this path toward the opposite characteristic is intrinsic. Regardless of the cause of the initial gender behavior, he says, at around midlife, generally all males begin to grow more nurturing, and all women become gradually more "executive." This finding is cross-cultural, according to Gutmann's research (1997; 1987). In effect, there is a "crossover effect" from one gender-defined set of behaviors closer to the other, which he names the **post-parental transition** (1992). Older men become more free in expressing behaviors that would be considered feminine, and women show more "masculine" behaviors.

Gutmann proposed that the initial reason for gender role differentiation (and the subsequent cultural norms for male/female behavior) is the "parental emergency." The arrival of children requires an extensive period of "parental service" in which clearly differentiated gender roles are necessary. Therefore, for the good of society, women become the nurturers and fathers, the providers. When this period of time is over, men and women can expect the release of previously unused potential (James et al., 1995).

We have all seen the old person who is bitter, depressed, and very anxious about life and

Rather than internalizing negative messages about old age, some people defy the belief that they cannot learn or cannot be active and effective citizens and become community leaders in their elderhood.

living. We have also all seen the old person who has a clarity and grace, with a special understanding of the meaning of their existence, and the willingness to share the story of their understandings. Clearly, we want to be like the latter person when *we* are 70 or 80 or 90. Psychologists are only beginning to ask some of the questions that are central to a better understanding of the development of well-being in later life. They are not in agreement with which theoretical perspectives most accurately describe the growth and development taking place in later life, possibly because there is no single unifying theory to be found. The human life and human psyche is dynamic and infinitely resilient. We return, after crushing life events, after multiple experiences and cultural ways of interpreting those experiences, to a central human core. It is the task of gerontological psychology to better understand and describe that core, as well as the process for getting there.

Chapter Summary

This chapter considers the progression to late life from the perspective of developmental psychology. From this view, individuals move through stages, or identifiable eras, in their development. A complex interaction of internal (biological) and external (social) factors combine to shape the person as we age. Expected behavior patterns exist at every level of adulthood, whether young adulthood or advanced middle age. Ageism in a society can be internalized to fear of aging within the individual. Some individuals experience a traumatic transitional crisis at midlife, but it is unclear whether *or if* this crisis affects all people, whether it affects every person in the same way, or whether it affects every person in every culture. Psychologists coming from a biological perspective say it is universal to our human condition; psychologists coming from a social perspective say it is cultural; increasingly more psychologists say it is both.

Personality theory draws attention to how personality changes as a function of age and how individual variations in personality may affect one's own aging process. Continuity theory suggests that personality remains stable throughout life. Personality and the struggle to cope with the world interact to shape the aging process.

Perhaps most importantly, psychologists believe there is a profoundly important human task to be dealt with in later life, and that is the hard work of making coherent meaning of all of life's experiences. It is the task of pulling together a meaningful life story, ending with a sense of *integrity*.

Key Words

acculturation
archetypes
coping
cross-era transitions
data
emergent self
epigenetic principle
Erikson's stages of human development
extrinsic characteristics
extroversion
gender splitting
generativity
information processing
integrity versus despair
interiority
intrinsic characteristics
introversion
le troisiéme age
life cycle
life review
life structure
looking-glass self
mechanistic metaphor
metaphor
narrative
organic metaphor
personality theory
post-parental transition
qualitative development
quantitative development
reminiscence
shadow side
state
Theories
traits
transcendent self
transitions

Questions for Discussion

1. Is there a midlife crisis? In small groups, take a position either in support of a midlife crisis, or in nonsupport, and argue it. Substantiate your position with evidence, both empirical (your observations) and from the studies presented in the chapter.
2. Why do some individuals have difficulty making the transition from early adulthood to middle age? From middle age to old age?
3. Discuss Erikson's final two stages, adding Havighurst's elaboration of the stage of generativity vs. stagnation. Do these stages describe your observations? Do you think they represent experiences of people from a culture different than your own? Why or why not?
4. What personality variables would you choose to examine in a longitudinal study of students throughout their lives? Why?

Fieldwork Suggestions

1. Interview someone who is age 65 or older. Ask that person if they believe they have changed, and if so to what extent, in the past 30 years. In the past 40 years?
2. Interview a young woman about her expectations about menopause. Does she have expectations about her physical appearance? Symptoms? Self-concept?
3. Ask six middle-aged or older women their ages. Did you violate a norm? Did they answer you? What was their reaction? Ask six middle-aged men their ages. Are responses the same? What did you expect?

Online Activities

1. Beginning with the key search words "narrative therapy," search the Internet for information about this emerging therapeutic field. Repeat, using key words "Jung" or "Jungian psychology," and see what comes up.
2. Locate the Internet site of a university that is not in your state. Find a psychology department that has a faculty member doing research in human aging. What are the research interests of this professor? What classes does the department have that would provide more specific information about some of the topics touched on in this chapter?

4

Theories in Social Gerontology

I Remember Back When . . .

Susan L. Crowley

"Let your memory tell the story," Lou Willett Stanek says, her voice rising above the clanking of the ventilator fan in the ceiling. "Writing is not a competitive sport, you have your own voice." Her students at the New School for Social Research in New York City nod appreciatively as Stanek gently critiques a classmate's writing. Seated at tables pushed into a square, they scribble notes and listen intently.

Like thousands of other Americans signing up for classes at colleges and community centers, Stanek's students are here not just to learn to write but to write their memoirs, a pastime that has taken the country by storm.

No longer is penning one's personal history the domain of presidents, movie stars and other public figures. Americans of all stripes are digging up their pasts and putting down their recollections on paper (or tape). They are war veterans, housewives, retirees, blue-collar workers and professionals—and of all ages. In Stanek's class, students range from their late 20s to their mid-80s.

No one is exactly sure what's behind the outbreak of memoir fever, but some speculate that people may feel compelled to tell their unique histories as an antidote to the anonymity and lack of connectedness in a crowded, bureaucratic world.

"The individual in many cases has been severely depreciated," says James E. Birren, M.D., associate director of the UCLA Center on Aging who for more than 20 years has taught courses on "guided" autobiography as a means of taking stock of one's life. "By looking back at the way you grew up and grew old," he says, "you come to realize that you've survived a good deal, that there's some substance there."

The national penchant for publicly airing private stories on TV talk shows may also stoke the trend, says Stanek.

So might the financial success and/or overnight fame of memoirists like Frank McCourt ("Angela's Ashes"), Mary Karr ("The Liar's Club") and Elizabeth and Sarah Delany ("Having Our Say: The Delany Sisters' First 100 Years").

Or like the 98-year-old great-great-grandmother from Kansas whose raw, unadorned memoirs, "Any Given Day: The Life and Times of Jessie Lee Brown Forveaux" (Simon & Schuster), comes out this month. Forveaux chronicled her life for a class at a senior center in 1979. Last spring her teacher sent her stories to a *Wall Street Journal* reporter, who wrote a page-one story about her. Within days, the frugal, plain-living Forveaux had scores of lucrative publishing, film and TV offers.

What happens to people as they grow old? What methods can we use to study old people—their bodies, their perceptions, their motivations, their relationship to society? These topics are the subject matter of gerontology. By omitting the physiology and biology of aging, we narrow the field to social aspects of aging. **Social gerontology,** the study of aging from a social science perspective, has been recognized as a distinct area of study for less than 60 years. Aging and related subjects have received limited attention since the mid-1940s, but now the sharp rise in the number of older persons, along with their increased visibility, has increased interest in the development of theory and in research. Social gerontology will continue to grow in importance as it becomes increasingly able to explain the phenomenon of aging.

In an effort to explain aging, social gerontologists have developed numerous theories to examine how people respond to the aging process. Bengtson et al. (1997) reviewed the literature to determine which theoretical models were most commonly used to explain social gerontology in the 1990s. They found seven theoretical perspectives most frequently referenced in recent journals: (1) social constructionist, (2) social exchange, (3) life course, (4) feminist, (5) age stratification (age and society), (6) political economy of aging, and (7) critical theory. These theories are summarized in Table 4.1.

Scientists never entirely prove or disprove a theory. They merely develop greater confidence in the theory or move closer to rejecting it by proving that parts of it are untrue. Traditionally a theory does not rest on a single proposition but on a series of propositions, any one of which may be partially in error. Any single proposition contained in a theory, a hypothesis, can be subjected to testing by empirical research, which collects evidence that may or may not support the hypothesis. Through this testing, scientists formulate new questions that require further research. Also, social theories can be used to predict what will happen if society maintains its present course and to suggest ways the social world could be altered to achieve specific results. The **theoretical frameworks** we examine in this chapter attempt to identify the important factors in aging and to offer guidelines for further inquiry.

Historical Foundations: Activity versus Disengagement

Controversy over two contradictory theories of aging shaped the field of social gerontology in the 1960s. Both activity theory and disengagement theory attempt to predict how a person might respond to old age. Activity theory was the first social theory of aging, but only after the development of disengagement theory did it receive both its name and recognition as a distinct theory. These two somewhat opposing theoretical models remain central in social gerontology in part because they are intuitively compelling—that is, they appeal to our common sense about people, and they are easily understood and observed in our daily lives.

ACTIVITY THEORY

Because it continues to be widely accepted by social scientists, as well as by many people working with the elderly, we can say that activity theory is still a dominant theoretical perspective. **Activity theory** implies that social activity is the essence of life for all people of all ages. Early studies found that positive personal adjustment correlates highly with activity. The more active people are—mentally, physically, socially—the better adjusted they are. Early proponents of this theory believed that normal aging involves maintaining the activities and attitudes of middle age as long as possible. Any activities and roles that the individual has been forced to give up should be replaced with new activities. Activity theory predicts that those who are able to remain socially active will be

TABLE 4.1

Theoretical models in social gerontology

Theory	Description	Key Concepts
Social constructionist	Focuses on individual agency and social behavior within larger structures of society; interest in understanding individual processes of aging as influenced by social definitions and structures	Labeling; social breakdown theory; situational features of aging
Social exchange theories	Examines exchange behavior between people of different ages as a result of the shift in roles, skills, resources that accompanies aging	Social costs and benefits; social resources; interaction; reciprocity; social power
Life course perspective	Explains the dynamic, context, and process nature of aging; age-related transitions; social meaning of aging as a process; focus on individuals, cohorts, and groups	Developmental tasks; social time clocks; social ecology; life trajectories and transitions, age roles and norms
Feminist theories	As a primary organizing principle for social life across the life course, gender is a primary consideration in understanding aging and the aged	Gender stratification; power structures; macrolevel analysis of social institutions; social networks and caregiving; family work
Age stratification	Focuses on role of social structures in the process of aging, looking at age cohort movement across time; asychrony between structural and individual change over time; interdependence of age cohorts and social structures	Age cohorts; social structures; structural lag; cohort flow
Political economy of aging	Explains how interaction of economic and political forces determines how social resources are allocated; how variations in treatment and status of elderly are reflected in policy, economic trends	Structural constraints, control of social resources, marginalization, social class
Critical theory	Focuses on humanistic dimensions of aging; structural components of aging; interested in understanding subjective and interpretive dimensions of aging, processes creating practical change, and knowledge that helps people change	Positive models of aging; power, social action, and social meaning in aging

Source: Bengtson, Vern L., Burgess, Elisabeth O., & Parrott, Tonya M. (1997). Theory, explanation, and a third generation of theoretical development in social gerontology. *Journal of Gerontology, Social Sciences, 52B* (2), S72–S88.

more likely to achieve a positive self-image, social integration, and satisfaction with life, and , therefore, that they will probably age successfully.

Generally speaking, the last 50 years of research have found a positive correlation between being active and aging successfully. In many of these studies, "successful aging" was defined in relationship to life satisfaction: people with strong reports or measures of life satisfaction were considered to be aging "successfully." As the complexity of human aging has become more clear, however, questions have arisen about those life satisfaction studies. What is the relationship of other important factors to life satisfaction, such as health, gender, culture, socioeconomic status, desire to remain active? Might not one person's internal experience of "activity" be different than another's, based on their histories and interests? What about different cultural expectations, and gender differences? Indeed, Jacob and Guarnaccia (1997), in a study of life satisfaction and social engagement, suggested that *life satisfaction* is probably a misnomer that might better be termed *momentary contentment* (p. 816). They concluded that the culture reinforces disengagement among elders, therefore commitment to new goals and relationships is less necessary to psychological health in old age than it is in early life.

Some studies conclude that it is unnecessary for elders to maintain the same high degree of activity they had in middle age in order to have a high degree of self-esteem and life satisfaction in old age. The concept of **planned behavior**, or the extent to which an individual *intends* to perform a behavior, has been developed recently in understanding *readiness for activity* (Courneya, 1995; Chodzko-Zajko, 1997). This deals with the internal meaning and motivation structure of the individual: I am committed to walking one mile a day again, after I feel stronger. Many older people seek a more relaxed lifestyle and are quite happy when they achieve it. For example, a 65-year-old woman may long for the time when she can work half-time instead of full-time, sleep in, and devote more time to her aerobics classes and to reading the newspaper at a local coffeehouse.

DISENGAGEMENT THEORY

Disengagement theory is an explicit theory developed through research and explained in the book *Growing Old* (1961) by Elaine Cumming and William E. Henry. This book, one of the best known in the history of social gerontology, contends that it is both normal and inevitable for people to decrease their activity and seek more passive roles as they age. Disengagement is a mutual withdrawal of the elderly from society and society from the elderly in order to insure the optimal functioning of both the individual and of society. Aging individuals, wishing to escape the stress of recognizing their own diminishing capacity, collaborate in the withdrawal.

The disengagement theory has generated a great deal of criticism. Some say the theory is ethnocentric, in that it reflects the bias of a male-dominant industrial society. Others have suggested that it discourages interventions to help old people. Still others have questioned why some elderly choose to disengage and others do not, contending that society pressures people into disengagement against their will. However, it must be remembered that the theory emerged from a particular context of social thought—one in which biology-as-destiny prevailed, and the extent of interacting variables (such as gender, socioeconomic and cultural factors) with the process of aging was not yet clearly understood (Achenbaum & Bengtson, 1994).

> *The relation between biological and social factors is recognized in that physiological and psychological measures of capacity are...used [to study] the relation of declining capacity to problems of individual adjustment in old age.*
>
> POLLAK, 1948

Do relationships and our need to be connected in order to maintain psychological well-being alter with time? Particularly in most recent research, support is emerging for a more complex form of disengagement. In 1994, Tornstam used the term **gero-transcencence** to refer to the elderly as selectively investing in some relationships over others, rather than comprehensively withdrawing. In his model, elders do seem to disengage, but do so more *at will*, choosing where their priorities lie and divesting themselves of superfluous relationships to focus on a more transcendent view of experience. According to Quinnan (1997), in his study of elderly religious men:

> *Thus the elderly demonstrate a higher degree of autonomy by dispensing with forms of social intercourse which have little value for them. This exercise of autonomy, rather than breaking connectedness, selectively enhances those relationships which the gero-transcendent find filled with meaning (p. 118).*

Gero-transcendence is rooted in stage theories such as Erikson's (Chapter 3), which postulates a movement from dependence to greater autonomy with maturity. From this perspective, growth in autonomy takes place through a shift in connections—for example, reducing connection (the process of individuating) from the family occurs among adolescents in conjunction with a growing connection with peers and people outside the family (Quinnan, 1997).

In another line of inquiry, comfort in being alone was found to be related to lower depression, fewer physical symptoms, and greater life satisfaction in a survey of 500 U.S. adults in 1995 (Larson & Lee, 1995). This finding is also consistent with our intuitive observations: some people deal with stress by secluding themselves from social contact—spending time reflecting and engaging in self-care activities. Clearly this does not imply that it is healthy to be involuntarily isolated from others. However, consistent reports continue that people do spend less time with others as they age, and those who are able to enjoy this segment of their lives are better adjusted and have a greater sense of well-being.

> *The habit of retiring into myself eventually made me immune to the ills that beset me.*
>
> ROUSESEAU, 1778.

Despite these more positive findings, the controversy over disengagement theory continues. Unanswered questions remain about each of the major aspects of disengagement: the role of the individual, the role of society, and satisfaction versus dissatisfaction with disengagement.

THE ROLE OF THE INDIVIDUAL

It appears that disengagement is not inevitable with old age. Some elders disengage; others do not. Yet, according to the theory, the individual's inner processes lead to a loosening of social ties, which is a relatively natural process. This process is "primarily intrinsic, and secondarily responsive" (Cumming & Henry, 1961). Research should perhaps concentrate on the very old. If disengagement is a process preparing both the individual and society for the ultimate release of the elderly member, why would it begin at the relatively early age of 65? If disengagement is in fact a developmental task of old age, perhaps it actually begins in the eighties or nineties, when one is nearer the end of the life span. We do not universally enter stages of life at a given age.

THE ROLE OF SOCIETY

According to disengagement theory, society must withdraw from its older members to insure the smooth operation and survival of the social system. Yet one can question this assumption. That disengaging older people from employment or other active roles is in society's best interest remains to be demonstrated. One might easily argue that the disengagement of older people is wasteful or dysfunctional because it removes many experienced, knowledgeable, and capable members. One might just as well speak of society excluding its older members as disengaging them; perhaps the older people who withdraw are merely reacting to a society that would exclude them anyway.

Neither activity theory nor disengagement theory fully explains successful or well-adjusted aging. More variables must be examined to explain why some people are happy in an active old age whereas others are content to narrow their activities and involvement in life. Getting rid of negative or unrewarding activities and events alone does not seem to be adequate to promote well-being—it seems to also take specifically positive interactions to promote a healthy existence (Stallings et al., 1997). This implies that eliminating (disengaging from) interactions that are not satisfying in order to pursue satisfying activities is an indicator of appropriate and positive aging, as long as something satisfying is added. Those newer activities being engaged in, however, might very well include exploring solitude (Larson, 1997).

Psychological Well-being

Well-being itself is a complex concept. It is one of the most popular, most persistently investigated issues in the social scientific study of aging. A major focus in gerontology over the last 50 years has been to define and measure well-being and to identify factors that will increase it in the older population. Generally speaking, well-being means feeling good, or having good mental health. Oftentimes, researchers use the phrase *subjective well-being*. The word *subjective* indicates a personal evaluation based on how the respondent feels, not an evaluation based on external criteria, such as visits to mental hospitals or psychologists' evaluations.

Psychological well-being is a broad term that has different meanings for different social scientists. Linda George (1981) offered a definition that differentiated among three concepts that measure well-being—morale (courage, discipline, confidence, enthusiasm, etc.), happiness (mood of gaiety or euphoria), and **life satisfaction** (an assessment of overall conditions of existence or progress toward desired goals). One critical reason to develop a clear definition of well-being is to develop assessment tools to help elders and people working with elders to make the best decisions (George, 1997). An assessment describes the individual in terms of characteristics relevant to the service being offered and gathers the information needed to tailor programs specifically to the needs of that person. Cummins (1996) further defined life satisfaction as "subjective life quality" and identified seven domains: material well-being; health; productivity; intimacy; safety; community; and emotional well-being. This definition includes psychological security as well as physical and environmental security and well-being. In the helping professions, merely knowing how a person interprets his or her life situation is not adequate. Understanding the different domains of that sense of quality of life can help the individual and the helper to better focus on strengths and needs.

The Life Satisfaction Index A (LSIA), the most frequently used scale in social gerontology, offers another method of defining well-being. The LSIA is one of the best-known instruments for measuring well-being. As originally developed by Neugarten, Havighurst, and Tobin (1961), it consisted of 20 items representing five components: zest for life versus apathy; resolution and fortitude versus merely accepting that which life has given; congruence between desired and achieved goals; self-concept; and mood tone of optimism versus pessimism.

Researchers continue to refine the LSIA. They still debate whether the scale is **valid** (whether it measures what it is supposed to measure) and **reliable** (whether its results are consistent). They also continue to question whether the scale is unidimensional (measuring only the concept of life satisfaction) or is multidimensional (measuring more than one concept). Table 4.2 shows the model developed from the LSIA measure by Liang (1984) to identify the three domains of mood tone, zest for life, congruence, and a generalized "other" category. Note that this measure deals less with the context and more with the internal meaning the individual makes of their life.

Some studies, combining personal narrative with the psychometric measure LSIA, report that life satisfaction appears to be the construct being measured (Hawkins et al., 1995; Sherrard, 1997; Rosen et al., 1995). Other researchers believe that the measure taps a multidimensional concept, which *contains* life satisfaction, but does not measure that alone (Kahana et al., 1995).

The items in the LSIA, however, do seem to provide us with a general overview of a person's

TABLE 4.2

A proposed use of the 20 LSIA items

Agree or disagree with each item
Mood tone
This is the dreariest time of my life.
I am just as happy now as when I was younger.
My life could be happier than it is now.
These are the best years of my life.
Compared to other people, I get down in the dumps too often.
Zest for life
As I look back on my life, I am fairly well satisfied.
I would not change my past life even if I could.
I have gotten pretty much what I expected out of my life.
I have gotten more breaks in life than most of the people I know.
When I think back over my life, I didn't get most of the important things I wanted.
Other items (Originated by Neugarten)
In spite of what people say, the lot of the average person is getting worse.
I feel my age but it does not bother me.
Compared to other people my age, I've made a lot of foolish decisions in my life.

Most elders choose to remain actively engaged with friends and in the community. Shared lifetime experiences form the basis for meaningful relationships in later life.

psychological well-being. Increasingly, current research in the United States seems to converge on the domains of positive interactions, negative interactions, and stress management as primary factors in life satisfaction and well-being (Kahana et al., 1995; Krause, 1995; Glass & Jolly, 1997; Lawton, 1997). This research is consistent with findings from other industrialized countries, as well (Liang, 1992; Shmotkin, 1996; Allain et al., 1997). This group of researchers has concluded that the presence of negative interactions is separate from positive self-assessment. Eliminating negative conditions in life does not in and of itself promote well-being. It reduces depression, low self-esteem, and general negative mood tone. But it takes positive interactions and conditions to have high life satisfaction and to experience well-being. Clearly much work needs to be done on the concept of happiness in life; if we had the key to well-being, we could use it to create more happiness for everyone.

Morale and well-being in later life have been extensively studied. Studies by Neal Krause (1991, 1995) have tested the relationship between general evaluations of life satisfaction and evaluations of specific domains. Krause presented two hypotheses. The "top-down" hypothesis suggested that a person's ongoing sense of satisfaction with life as a whole predisposes him or her to develop similar feelings about specific domains, such as health and employment. The "bottom-up" hypothesis maintained that satisfaction with the specific areas of one's life synthesized to form an overall sense of satisfaction with life as a whole. Krause, whose findings supported this latter theory, expresses concern that survey self-assessment scales are the only major tools used to study subjective well-being.

Current life satisfaction research includes a broad range of predictors of high morale and life satisfaction indicators, reflecting the perspective of the investigator. These include: activities, relationships, health, and income (Kahana et al., 1995); subjective health and health self-image (Sherrard, 1997); reduced barriers to participation (Hawkins et al., 1995); having a spouse; participating in community activities and interacting with friends; and interacting with one's children (Hong & Duff, 1997). Ardelt (1997), summarizing research on wisdom (Orwoll & Achenbaum, 1993; Pascual-Leone, 1990), made a particularly strong argument for including the construct of wisdom in studies of life satisfaction. "I [propose] that people experience satisfaction and a sense of fulfillment in old age as a consequence of achieving greater wisdom over the life course and that wisdom, rather than objective life conditions, explains most of the variation in life satisfaction during old age" (p. P16). In her argument, happiness in later life is strongly related to the life we have lived and the way we integrate it with our present sense of self.

Life satisfaction research also contains predictors of low morale and life satisfaction, including limited choice, limited responsibility, social resources, physical health, personal meaning, and optimism (Reker, 1997); and envy, need to control, complaining and critical thought, sense of entitlement, regret, perfectionism, and unrealistically high expectations (Hosen, 1996). Eliminating predictors of low morale does not create high life satisfaction, but it does seem to be strongly associated with health.

Clinical observations and qualitative data derived from narrative methodologies will add an important and perhaps clarifying perspective to the burgeoning body of knowledge about morale and life satisfaction. It is one thing to measure someone's attitudes and feelings; it is quite another to systematically record that person's perception of him or herself. The field is poised to take on the latter charge.

Sociological Well-being

STRUCTURAL-FUNCTIONAL FRAMEWORKS

Sociologists study society—social factors such as values, norms, roles, social structures, institutions, stratification, and subcultures. Social gerontologists study these social factors as they affect elders. The studies that fall under this broad category delve into every social group in an older person's life. Studies have included economic structure, the family, race, and demography. Studies on the historical context of aging, the media, work, friendship, and communication networks provide data on the social context of aging.

Sociological theories of aging use the same concepts as those used in contemporary general sociological theory. One dominant framework in sociological theory is the **structural-functional framework,** which views societies as systems and subsystems of social rules and roles. Members become socialized by internalizing the social system's norms and values, and the entire system functions in a reasonably orderly fashion if its structures are organized and intact. The activity theory of aging and the disengagement theory are structural-functional in that they deal with systems of rules and roles for the aged in society. Three more structural-functional concepts for understanding aging are considered here: age stratification, role theory, and age grading.

AGE STRATIFICATION

The **age stratification** theory studies older persons in relation to all other age groups, or age strata, in a society. It examines the differences between the age strata and studies the way in which society allocates opportunities, social roles, rights, privileges, status, power, and entitlements on the basis of age. The persons in an age strata have similar characteristics because they are at

Being alone does not necessarily mean being lonely. Here a businessman reads while enjoying a quiet lunch.

the same stage in the life course and share a common history. Changing social environments produce different patterns of adaptation in successive age groups, and cultures vary in the extent to and manner in which they are stratified by age (Liu et al., 1995; Bowling, 1995). Age stratification theory has been used to explain power and status inequities between young and old in given societies. For example, sociologists have used the theory to analyze the power—and lack of power—in younger generations in China.

ROLES, GENDER, AND ETHNICITY

Role is one of the most basic concepts in all of sociology, one that you will find used in almost every sociological framework. Sociologists are quick to point out that the word *role* is a concept, not a theory. A role is a status or position, which carries known attributes, accorded to an individual in a given social system. "Doctor," "mommy," "sports fan," and "church-goer" are all roles.

In studies of aging we find analyses of age roles, role transitions, role acquisitions, role relinquishment, and socialization to and from roles. Roles are modified, redefined, and transformed as people age. Roles in marriage, families, careers, and in community change throughout the life course. People have informal roles in friendship and neighboring. They have formal roles in institutional settings, such as schools and hospitals, and more informal roles in less structured settings. Role exit was once a major focus of aging studies, but *role transition*, or moving from one role to another, now seems a more appropriate term.

Gender roles have to do with the cultural aspects of being male or female. Being male and female in every culture is linked to specific roles, attitudes, and behaviors. Because aging men and women are looked upon differently in our society and in other cultures around the world, the study of gender is very important. Being old is a different experience for men than for women.

Ethnic diversity has become a major focus of gerontology. Ethnicity refers to one's identification with a subgroup in society having a unique set of values, traditions, or language, often originating in another country. The role of ethnicity as it affects aging and the aged is often overlooked in the studies of gerontology and yet it is an incredibly important aspect of who we are. Particularly in earlier studies, generalizations were made on the basis of white, middle-class, mostly male, respondents. Clearly these generalizations did not apply to all racial and ethnic groups. Numerous international studies now add richness to our understanding of aging (Shmotkin & Hadari, 1996; Allain et al., 1997; Liu et al., 1995; Bowling et al., 1997). Newer studies of cultural groups within the United States (Liang et al., 1992; Uehara, 1995; Guyotte, 1997) can further develop a true understanding of the experience of all U.S. elders.

Looking at older people in diverse groups has added to the richness and complexity of the research of aging.

AGE GRADING AND AGE NORMS

We live in an age-graded society. **Age grading** means that age is a prime criterion in determining the opportunities people may enjoy. Our age partially establishes the roles we may play. Both children and old people are welcomed to or barred from various opportunities because of the often-stereotyped images society forms for the young and the old. Such beliefs often prevent the young and the old from expressing individual differences and, thereby, lead to injustices. In other words, older people may be less active not because of their biology or the aging process, but because they are expected to present an image of idleness. Indeed, social roles sometimes do not permit elders to be active and involved. Role expectations at various age levels are called **age norms**. Society pressures individuals to engage in activities such as marriage, schooling, and child rearing at a socially approved age. One way to determine the presence of age norms would be to ask questions such as, Would you approve of a woman who decided to have a child at age 42? Age 60? Would you approve of a couple who moved across the country to live near their married children when the couple was 50? 65? What about at 80?

Answers to these and similar questions would reveal age norms for child rearing and other activities. Age norms affecting the older population can be studied by asking a sample group whether situations such as the following are appropriate or inappropriate:

- A very old man buys and drives a flashy new sports car.
- An older woman dresses in "new age" fashion, including a nose ring.
- A retired couple frequents heavy metal rock concerts and festivals.

We can view age norms as a form of social control. If one follows the age norms, one receives approval; if not, disapproval and possibly negative sanctions result.

A continuing shift is occurring toward a loosening of age grading and age norms in the United States. Lives are becoming more fluid. There is no longer a definite age at which one marries, enters the labor market, goes to school, or has children. It no longer surprises us to hear of a 23-year-old computer company owner, a 34-year-old governor, a 36-year-old grandmother, or a retiree of 52. No one is shocked at a 60-year-old college student, a 50-year-old man who becomes a father for the first time, or an 80-year-old who launches a new business. Our ever-advancing technologies continue to test and stretch the limits of what people find acceptable, from transplanted hearts to childbirth by postmenopausal women.

Age Groupings

STUDYING COHORTS AND GENERATIONS

Studies of cohorts and generations are conducted by demographers, sociologists who study social change, and psychologists studying the life course. A major problem in understanding age differences is to determine whether change is due to "age" or "period" effects. A change due to an age effect is caused by maturation, that is, biological change from the physical aging process. Period effects are changes in different age groups resulting from historical events that have affected one age group differently than another.

AGE COHORT

For our purposes, an **age cohort** is a group of individuals exposed to a similar set of life experiences and historical events. Demographers often use cohort analysis to compare groups of people born during specific time periods, usually separated by 5- or 10-year intervals. We expect that age cohorts will show similarities to one another. Cohort analysis permits the sociologist to study the effects that events or demographics may have on a broad group of individuals, all of whom have experienced the same events at a similar state of biological and physical development.

With the tendency of the media to homogenize social groups, a cultural image has evolved of Baby Boomers as the free-loving hippie generation who dodged the draft, protested against the Vietnam War, attended Woodstock, and enjoyed economic prosperity (Williams, 1997). Likewise, young adult cohorts in their twenties have been referred to by the media as Generation X (Keil, 1998). The "twenty somethings" who represent **Generation X** are stereotyped as whiners and slackers, complaining about the national debt they have inherited and totally unappreciative of "how good they have it." This cohort has watched more television and as a result has probably witnessed more violence and murder than any generation in history. It has had more time alone as young children and is the first generation to spend considerable time in day care (Losyk, 1997). Many of them grew up with stepparents and stepsiblings, and with both parents in full-time employment.

Generation X is the smallest cohort since the early 1950s and is thus labeled a "baby bust" generation as opposed to their Boomers parents. They are the first generation in the United States to be smaller than the generation that precedes them (Williams et al., 1997). For this reason, their chances in the job market are increased. If the higher productivity of American business continues into the new century, and if homes stay affordable, Generation X should do well compared with the cohorts before them (Miniter, 1997).

Another important first with the Generation X cohort: the media is profoundly powerful in their lives. All of the characterizations outlined above are media created and media reinforced. Social scientists have been woefully silent as characterizations have been reinforced into stereotypes of all the generational cohorts.

Despite the many similarities in individuals as members of cohorts as a result of growing into maturity within a specific cultural and economic moment in history, the differences among people remain greater than their similarities, and the reminder to avoid overgeneralization must be restated. Subgroups within a cohort experience the world in different ways based on such variables as class, gender, ethnic background, or region of residence

GENERATIONS AND EVENTS

The concept of *generation* is more complex than the concept of a cohort. The journalistic and electronic media have used the term widely (and loosely) to indicate the differences in values between parents and children (the so-called generation gap). Others have used the term to identify the values of those who are older or younger than some arbitrary age—the "over-thirty generation" or the "under-thirty generation," for instance. Historians and sociologists have applied the term in additional ways. For them, *generation* may mean distinctive life patterns and values as they emerge by age; or it may connote not only distinctive life patterns but also a collective mentality that sets one age group apart from another.

Karl Mannheim (1952, 1992) formulated the latter definition of **generation** and described the process by which group consciousness of generations develops. According to Mannheim, generations are not an arbitrarily defined number of years imposed by researchers; instead, they represent a reflection of historical events and social change. For example, the invention of the automobile may have led to the formation of two generations—those who grew up with access to cars and those who did not. And children's use of computers may lead nonusing parents to feel a generation apart from their kids.

An age group that has lived through a major social event, such as the Great Depression, may exhibit characteristics that are not due to internal or biological aging and that are not found in other age groups. The impact of widespread social events on their survivors has not received enough systematic investigation; indeed, events that your parents or you have experienced may well continue to influence your lives. What, for example, are the effects of having lived through the Vietnam or Watergate eras? The war in the Persian Gulf? If you were a young adult during the Iran-Contra affair or the Savings and Loan Crisis, will you be more skeptical of politicians than your children, assuming no comparable incidents occur in their early adulthood? Would a young adult of the Vietnam era be less patriotic than you were, if you were a young adult during the 1990 war in Iraq? If so, one might conclude that events, rather than the aging process, made you more skeptical or more patriotic. Events of our younger years play an especially important role in shaping feelings and attitudes that persist throughout our lives.

According to Mannheim, broad social movements, including somewhat trivial changes in fads and fashions, are concrete manifestations of a generation's social reality. Consequently, if social change is rapid, then different generations could theoretically appear every few years. Conversely, if social change is slow, then the same generation might exist for several decades. Mannheim's definition of *generation* is quite specific; birth cohorts do not form "true generations" unless they develop not only a distinctive life pattern but also a collective identity and a political consciousness of themselves as a unique group.

Some social scientists speak of the "post–World War II generation," as opposed to the "World War II generation," in the sense Mannheim describes. Those who remember the patriotism that World War II generated are not the same as those who were born too late to have experienced it. The post–World War II generation is described as being less patriotic, less traditional, more alienated, and more skeptical of war than their generational predecessors. Collectively, in contrast, those who experienced World War II are more optimistic about the U.S. role in world politics and political leadership and show more support and respect for the president. During the 1991 war in the Persian Gulf, this patriotic mentality seemed to assert itself once again; perhaps a new "generation" has been born. Social commentators also define as a "new" generation those who use high-tech equipment—computers, video games, and VCRs—with ease. New technologies can indeed make one feel a generation removed, hopelessly dated and at odds with changing times. With motivation and training, however, one can join the new generation.

What gives meaning in life depends on the individual. For many people grandchildren are a profound source of meaning.

LINEAGE

Sociologists use the concept of **lineage** to discuss generations within families. Parents transmit values to children, and continuity or discontinuity may distinguish the transmission of specific values within a particular family or families. Social, political, or technological events may intervene in this transmission and thereby alter roles and values within the family context. Consequently, the authority of older family members may be strengthened, weakened, or changed in a way that also alters parent-child relationships.

Given the increase in life expectancy in the United States today, four- and even five-generation families are quite common. Although this interaction of family members can be a source of great personal enrichment, differences in values can produce tension and conflict among the family's generations. These value differences may be a source of age prejudice, or ageism, within the family. We may reduce these age prejudices in our own families by understanding the social and historical development of another family member's generation.

Generational Changes

A **generation gap** refers to profound differences in perspective between cohorts whose historical, social, educational, and/or personal experiences are shaped differently because of the historical context of their lives.

BIOLOGY

For example, a woman in her twenties may be extremely lively and active, wanting to constantly experience new adventures and excitement. But with age, she becomes more and more settled and more content to be relaxed and mellow. Her mother, who followed the same pattern, may have little tolerance for her lively lifestyle, constantly nagging her to settle down, even though she had a similar life experience as her daughter.

HISTORICAL/SOCIAL EVENTS

Suppose a mother grew up in a conservative time period when, say, early marriage was expected for women. We would probably label her values as traditional. We would consider her child, who grew up in a later time period that might be called more liberal, as having modern values, when she and her boyfriend decided to move in together. In this case, history or social events cause the generation gap. Sociologists are interested in knowing how changing cultural values affect relationships between generations.

Social change may be a major cause of age prejudice, principally because the more rapid the social change, the greater the possibility of value clashes. Social observers may sometimes overestimate the rapidity of social change. Studies have shown that *basic* value orientations remain fairly constant across several generations. For example, analysis of the generation gap in the late 1960s, a time of considerable social unrest, showed that politically liberal students tended to have politically liberal parents. Thus, measured in terms of differences between a specific parent and child, the generation gap of the 1960s was not as extreme as it appeared overall. The generation gap in such countries as Israel, Russia, and Korea is greater than the gap in the United States, because value systems for the young and the old show greater extremes in these countries and because many of these countries are undergoing rapid social change.

PERSONAL CHANGE

A generation gap caused by personal change is an individual matter that does not necessarily reflect widespread cultural changes. One child, for example, may move from a cattle ranch to the city to get an education and, upon returning to visit her parents, announce that she is now a vegetarian and that killing animals is morally wrong. The cattle-growing father may comment with exasperation about the "generation gap" between himself and his daughter. This single occurrence, however, is an example of shifting values within a family. It does not necessarily reflect a larger social pattern indicating that young people are becoming vegetarians. It is therefore not consistent with Mannheim's use of the term *generation*.

Although a number of studies have examined generational differences, most have focused on middle-aged parents and children. Few have focused on the very old. A generation gap can exist between middle-aged offspring and their parents, or between elders and their grandchildren or great-grandchildren. We generally think of young people when we hear the term "generation gap." But differences between the beliefs and values of the middle-aged and oldsters can be as real as the differences between the beliefs and values of the old and the young.

CROSS-SECTIONAL VERSUS LONGITUDINAL STUDIES

Two helpful methods of studying different cohorts or generations have been cross-sectional and longitudinal studies. A **cross-sectional study** samples, at one point in time, persons belonging to different cohorts or generations and observes the differences. It is like a snapshot, recording who people are at the time the study happens. **Longitudinal studies,** in contrast, sample individuals or cohorts and follow them over a long period of time. In general, longitudinal studies have been more fruitful than cross-sectional studies in analyzing change over the life course, and cross-sectional studies have provided more richly descriptive profiles of different age groups at a particular point.

Although cross-sectional research offers the social scientist the unique opportunity of simultaneously studying the young, the middle-aged, and the old, it cannot account for the *process* of change. Differences in attitude or behavior may be due to the aging process or to other factors, but cause and effect are quite difficult to determine in a cross-sectional study. For example, if old persons attend church more often than younger people, can we assume that individuals become more religious with age? Not really. Perhaps the older people have always been faithful in attending church, even as youngsters; and the young who do not now attend church may not do so in old age.

Generalizing about cause and effect may become more reliable with longitudinal study. Several years ago, an assumption that IQ decreased with age was based on cross-sectional studies that showed older people to have lower IQs than younger adults. On closer examination it became clear that the older individuals had left school earlier at a time when many children did not have an opportunity to attend high school, such as people usually have today. Differences in education (a cohort effect) explained much of the presumed decline found in the cross-sectional studies. In fact, clear evidence now exists that IQ does not decrease with age, but remains stable into the seventies. Many of these misconceptions about aging may be blamed on cross-sectional research.

Separating the effects of age (maturation that comes with the aging process), period (history and events), and cohort (differences in social class, education, and occupation) can be difficult. To separate these effects, one must first consider cross-sectional differences. Second, one must consider longitudinal differences. Let us use Figure 4.1 as an example. The top row of 20-year-olds, 40-year-olds, and 60-year-olds represents one cross-sectional study, which could compare all three age groups at once in 2000. Reading down, in columns, represents longitudinal studies. A study using the model in Figure 4.1 would provide a basis for many interesting comparisons and could produce findings about the effects of the aging process, "the times" (external social forces), and cohort differences. If such a model were used to study voting behavior, fear of aging, personal contentment with life, or political alienation, what do you think the results would show? In the final analysis, one would have (1) one cohort of 20-year-olds, (2) two cohorts of 40-year-olds, (3) two cohorts of 60-year-olds, and (4) one cohort of 80-year-olds.

Comparisons could be made within and between all these groups. If, for example, the two groups of 40-year-olds scored dramatically differently on a political alienation scale, one could assume that the time period during which they were raised, not biological aging, was a key factor. These massive studies incorporating both

FIGURE 4.1

Longitudinal study method

Three cohorts are studied in the year 2000. Those same cohorts are studied 20 years later.

Year of study: 2000	Cohort 1: 20-year-olds	Cohort 2: 40-year-olds	Cohort 3: 60-year-olds
Year of study: 2020	Cohort 1: 40-year-olds	Cohort 2: 60-year-olds	Cohort 3: 80-year-olds

cross-sectional and longitudinal approaches may allow us to unravel the complicated effects of age, period, and cohort differences.

Exchange Theory

Exchange theory is based on the premises that individuals and groups act to maximize rewards and minimize costs. Interaction will be maintained if it continues to be more rewarding than costly; when one person is dependent on another, that person loses power. This model explained decreased interaction between the old and the young in terms of the older generation having fewer resources to offer in the social exchanges, and thus less to bring to the encounter (Dowd, 1975; Bengtson & Dowd, 1981).

Power is thus derived from imbalances in social exchange. Social exchanges are more than economic transactions. They involve psychological satisfaction and need gratification. Though this perspective sounds rather cold and calculating, social life according to exchange theory, is a series of exchanges that add to or subtract from one's store of power and prestige. The concept has become particularly useful recently in studies of leadership (Gerstner & Day, 1997; Williams et al., 1996) and of friendship (Burger et al., 1997; Roberto, 1997).

The first gerontologist to apply exchange theory was J. David Martin (1971), who used the theory to aid in understanding visiting patterns among family members. Some older individuals have little power. Families feel an obligation to visit but may not really want to. The older person's persistent complaints that relatives do not visit may motivate some visiting behavior, but the complaints may also decrease any pleasure and satisfaction felt by those who visit. Those elders who have other sources of power, such as financial resources or having interesting stories to tell, are in a better position. In fact, they could hold "power" positions over "dependent" relatives. Similar equity considerations have been applied to the study of shifts in roles, skills, and resources that accompany advancing age (Hendricks, 1995).

RECIPROCITY

Another way of discussing change is to use a concept popular among anthropologists: reciprocity. The **norm of reciprocity** involves maintaining balance in relationships by paying for goods or deeds with equivalent goods or deeds. It is a social rule that requires us to return favors to those who do something nice for us. It does not imply an open-ended obligation to return a favor. Rather, it requires only that acts of kindness be returned within a reasonable period of time (Burger et al., 1997). It can be applied in business or in relationships with family and friends. For example, I'll trade you this radio and five cassettes for that stereo. The goods' values are equal, so we are "balanced." The "goods" might be less tangible, such as, I will come to

People from several generations combine forces in a Walk to End Hunger. Here participants stop for lunch during a daylong walk.

stay with your frail mother while you go shopping, because you were there for me when my husband was ill. A kindness is exchanged for a kindness. One study used exchange theory to interpret differences over time in a group of older women's close friendships (Roberto, 1997). They found that the essential elements of the women's friendships (understanding, affection, trust, and acceptance) endured over time, although the balance of the exchanges of those elements shifted: I can be trusted to keep your confidence because, in the past, I have been able to trust you.

Some groups in society are unable to repay what they receive—children and mentally disabled people are two examples. In these cases, beneficence becomes the norm. The person giving does not expect a material reward, but does expect love or gratitude. The **norm of beneficence** calls into play such nonrational sentiments as loyalty, gratitude, and faithfulness. The norm is particularly relevant for care providers of frail and vulnerable people. One study comparing the use of restraints in chronic and acute patient care found that fewer restraints and a greater range of alternatives were used by chronic care nurses than by acute care nurses (Bryant & Fernald, 1997). The authors concluded that the differences were due in part to the norm of beneficence that chronic care nurses must honor to be effective in their professions.

Dowd (1984) asserts that the very old—but not the young-old—in our society benefit from the norm of beneficence. He directs his attention not to personal relationships but to social ones, noting that benefits from the government, such as Medicaid, Meals on Wheels, and other social services, are being less strongly supported and becoming increasingly unavailable to the young-old. In a classic analysis of interactions made nearly four decades ago, Gouldner (1960) distinguished between reciprocity as a pattern of social exchange and reciprocity as a general moral belief. The **reciprocity norm** dictates that one does not gain at the expense of another's beneficial acts (a moral belief). **Equity theory** suggests that people react equally negatively to under- and to overbenefiting. Balanced benefit is the moral standard, but this might depend on larger cultural values. Studies on African American women, midwestern rural elderly, and the very old in Appalachia conclude that people have far greater concern about over-benefiting, or being on the receiving end of the balance (Uehara, 1995; McCulloch & Kivet, 1995). This finding has implications both for service providers and for those who receive senior services.

Exchange theory and the norms of reciprocity and beneficence remain valuable concepts with which to view the position of elders. We can apply exchange theory at a small-group level, between one older individual and another person, or at a societal level.

Meaning in Everyday Life

Studies of the *meaning in everyday life* come to us from philosophy, phenomenology, symbolic interaction, and social psychology. The studies forming this body of information are diverse, but they intersect at the point of seeking to understand, from person to person, the meaning we attach to living our lives and the communications we have with others. **Symbolic interaction,** for example, examines the way in which people attach meaning to their own behavior. This meaning is based partly on their perceptions of others with whom they interact.

Gerontologists concerned with psychological well-being are becoming increasingly concerned with what aging means to the individual experiencing it. One scholar describes the findings of old age as a paradox: although old age is often negatively described as a marginal status, this seems to have little effect on the everyday lives and feelings of older people (Ward, 1984). Old age may be derogated, yet old people are often happy with themselves and their circumstances. Ward explains this paradox with the term **salience**—the degree to which something is central, important, or meaningful. If age is not salient to older people, they may not think about their age or feel the marginal status they supposedly hold. Older individuals may not feel that their age is a prominent trait, even though gerontologists and others think it is.

Learning what is salient to individuals requires listening to what they say. What elders have to say frequently emerges in the telling of stories—of sorting through memories, making sense of the present in terms of the past. This is the artful skill of drawing from the community and from past experience to help construct a positive self-image in the present (Encandela, 1997). The meanings represented in life stories might be work in process, might already be a clear part of the individual's meaning structure, or might represent a dilemma on which the individual is working—aspects of the self that are not yet coherent or well integrated (Luborsky, 1993).

> *In life stories, the narrator shows how [an] event takes on new meaning as the self is realigned in relation to some larger collective body and ideology.*
>
> GINSBURG, 1989

In a recent study designed to test psychometric measures, an interesting finding emerged that is remarkably consistent with phenomenological research that pulls its conclusions from people's own voices. Van Ranst and Marcoen (1997) began their research with the premise that one's need for personal meaning should increase with age. Their findings, based on statistical analysis of the Life Regard Index, concluded that there were age differences in the experienced meaning in life. The older the individual, the greater was the ability to see life within some perspective, and the more that person considered him or herself as having fulfilled or as being in the process of fulfilling life goals. Young adults, on the other hand, seemed to experience less meaning in life than did the elderly. Perhaps the *work of making meaning* was less salient for the young adults than it was for the older adults. Examples of the 30 items in the measure are purpose in living, clear direction, philosophy of life, accomplishment, attainment of goals, and the value of potential (Debats et al., 1993).

Older people may not feel that their age changes their circumstances or their personal "worlds." Age is, in essence, irrelevant to who they are. To better understand aging *as experienced by those who are aged*, gerontologists work to understand more clearly when age is relevant to individuals, what the consequences of that relevance is, and what is the function of friendship networks to aging.

Many studies of meaning in everyday life derive their basic approach from the school of sociological theory known as phenomenology. The **phenomenological theory** of aging is primarily concerned with the meaning that life and growing old have for aging people. Rather than constructing a theory about aging, phenomenologists attempt to define growing old through close association with those who are actively participating in the process. A major methodology of the phenomenological approach is to observe older people. Rather than, say, give the elders statements with which to agree or disagree, this approach would let their words or actions speak for themselves.

Phenomenologists often live in the settings they studied. Early in the history of social gerontology, Gubrium (1975) constructed the meaning of living in the nursing home by documenting the lives of the participants, who included patients, residents, staff, administrators, and visitors. Jacobs (1975) followed a similar strategy in studying two other housing arrangements for elders—a middle-class retirement community and a high-rise apartment building in an urban environment. His more recent studies have focused on aspects of everyday life of which people have little conscious awareness—the small, routine aspects of life. His studies direct attention to the "nontrivial nature of trivia"—the everyday, taken-for-granted knowledge, skills, and interactions of which most social life is composed (Jacobs, 1994).

Whether the study takes a phenomenological approach or not, researchers who study meaning in everyday life typically try to use techniques that do not allow the researcher's perspective or presence to influence the subjects' words and actions. The goal is to encourage respondents to articulate a life perspective free of any bias the researcher's theoretical framework might cause.

A significant study using phenomenological methods was published in 1987 by Sharon Kaufman, entitled *The Ageless Self: Sources of Meaning in Late Life*. Kaufman used open-ended questions as she conducted lengthy interviews with 60 aged people in their own homes. In studying the 60 people, Kaufman looked for themes that arose from *their* voices—not her theory—to discover what gave them a sense of life meaning. What Kaufman discovered was what she called an "ageless self."

For 80-year-old Millie, life gained its meaning from close, emotional ties:

> *My mother cherished me ... I adored my father and he clung to me ... I adored my principal ... I was attached to the other children in the neighborhood. I took care of all of them ... I loved my piano teacher ... (Kaufman, 1986, p. 34).*

Millie's meaning in life came from the positive feelings she got from relationships with others.

For others, meaning in life came from a variety of sources: making money, overcoming alcoholism, or achieving status. Dorfman's study (1994) of Franklin Village is, in her words,

> *...a personal odyssey into the inner experience of aging. The journey began with my immersion into a community of elders and the honing of my observational skills. It ends with a clearer understanding of the phenomenology of aging—one that is divested of ageist myths and stereotypes and that high-*

lights the significance of aspirations and values in late life (p. xiii).

Franklin Village is a continuing-care retirement community in which the researcher lived and took part in the daily life of the community. What resulted is an ethnography (field research study) encompassing in-depth interviews, case studies, and participant observation. Eighty-one residents shared their aspirations with her in both prearranged interviews and informal chats. When she left, she had spent 1,000 hours talking to people who ultimately became her friends in addition to providing her with a look into the inner experience of aging. Examples of residents' aspirations were to be independent, to have new experiences, to have intimate contact, to recreate past experiences, and to have a quick, easy death when the time came (Dorfman, 1994).

Symbolic interaction, another theoretical framework, also studies meaning in everyday life. **Symbolic interaction** examines interactions that individuals have with each other; that is, ways that verbal and nonverbal messages are communicated by one party to another, and how these messages are understood by another party. Such interaction modifies one's self-concept and one's view of the other interactant, and on a larger scale, of the social order. Symbolic interaction offers a dynamic rather than a static view of social life. Individuals continually change their self-concepts and their views of others based on continuing interactions.

Life is a vapor. It passes in a blink of an eye.

SARAH DELANY, AGE 107.

Meaning in life can also be gleaned from poems, diaries, journals, and other sources of life history narratives. Older people who are not able to write may give their life history orally. Two sisters, Sarah and Elizabeth (Bessie) Delany, when they were over 100 years old, told their life history of being born into slavery and eventually being freed, getting their education, and becoming educators themselves. On September 25, 1995, Bessie Delany died at home, in her sleep. Life's meaning is beautifully and poignantly reflected by her sister, Sarah, in her subsequent book, *On my own at 107: Reflections on life without Bessie* (Delany & Hearth, 1997). In it, she speaks to her sister:

> *I'm very conscious of being alone....The winter after you left us was the longest, coldest, snowiest one that anyone had ever see in these parts. It seemed fitting, somehow. But once the spring came I began to feel better. How can you not feel optimistic when the days are longer and warmer? And the birds are singing? The spring reminded me,* Life goes on *(p. 32).*

Life narratives have wide appeal, because they promote the ideal of freeing people to reflect on their lives and share personal meanings. Constructing a life story is thought to be therapeutic for older people, but gerontologists caution that the telling of life stories does not always enhance well-being for the aged person. It can bring distress if the memories are negative or painful. Another problem in this area of research is that very rarely is the entire text of the tale printed. Instead it is glimpsed in fragments selected by authors, despite its being upheld as a means to empower individual voices (Luborsky, 1993). Qualitative research raises new issues about context, process, and meaning (Abel & Sankar, 1995). According to another expert on qualitative research, experience and voice should be represented from those studied—whether it be caregivers, care receivers, family members, or significant others. This requires that researchers keep subjects and their worlds on center stage, never in the background (Gubrium & Holstein, 1995).

The use of qualitative research is particularly cogent for studies on aging. Bernice Neugarten (1985) summarizes:

> *If ever there was an area of inquiry that should be approached from the perspective of interpretive social science, this is one. It is apparent even to the most casual observer*

that aging has multiple biological, psychological, and sociological components; that neither the behavior of older people nor the status of older people can be understood otherwise; and that the primary need is for explication of contexts and for multiplicity of methods (p. 294).

Qualitative research is a means for *connecting* lives—of understanding more fully how individual experience shapes a life. This understanding provides the perspective necessary to design programs and policy interventions that have the capacity to respond to particular, as well as to general, needs (Holstein, 1995).

The particulars of any story in a narrative may not have ever occurred, or may have occurred quite differently to another participant than to the person remembering it. This does not mean that the storyteller is lying. Understanding another's story is the true test of the statement, "The truth is relative." One person's truth, or interpretation of an event, might be very different than another's interpretation. It is our *interpretation* that is remembered, not necessarily the cold, hard facts. The storyteller may believe the story, but memory and circumstances may have altered the actual facts. However, if the teller and listener of the story believe it is true, they act toward each other as if it were true. Whether exact in terms of the cold, hard facts or not, the truth as spoken has symbolic meaning to the speaker, and also, therefore, to the receptive listener.

Things perceived as real are real in their consequences.

W. I. THOMAS, 1927

Critical Gerontology

Critical gerontology evolved from critical sociology, which uses a neo-Marxian theory to critique the social fabric. Marxian theory looks to economic structures as the root cause of social manifestations. Members of society can form an individual or group consciousness of their struggle against powerful economic forces. Only then can they unite to fight against these forces. The focus in this perspective on individual and group consciousness borrows from symbolic interaction theory. The main goal of the critical gerontology perspective is to identify wider social influences on issues that affect individuals' lives. In 1989, for example, Cohen and Sokolovsky used a critical gerontology perspective in their report describing how the living conditions of men in the Bowery became defined in individual terms, not in terms of the larger social and political context. The critical perspective says that as long as social problems are defined in individual terms, change cannot happen. The analysis moves issues from "feed a man a fish" and "teach a man to fish" to "examine the environment in which fish might thrive, so a man can both fish and eat."

...current and future generations of the elderly are part of a quiet revolution...of older individuals representing the broadest range of ethnic, racial...and [regional and class] diversity ever witnessed... This diversity challenges us to evaluate the applicability of existing research, policy and programs to emerging elderly populations.

LINDA BURTON, 1992

The "**political economy of aging**" draws attention to the political side of economics with regard to the aged—how political power affects the amount of money given to fund social services for elders. For example, critical theorists find that capitalism and the profit motive shortchange elders. It criticizes the class structure for perpetuating poverty among older women and minorities. Programs addressing individuals fail to address the larger issue of social inequity (Estes, 1991). The causes are rooted in market and class structures—in other words, American capitalist institutions.

Minkler and Estes (1991) described the American values that undermine true reform as the ethic of individual responsibility, the negative view of centralized government by so many citizens, and the individualistic view of social problems. These perceptions "obscure an understanding of aging as a socially generated problem and status" (Estes, 1983, p. 171). Laws (1995) argues that ageism is rooted in values that devalue the aged body. She wants to use critical theory to understand the way morality and values place their stamp on our conceptions of the aging body.

The critical approach focuses on the negative experiences of aging, with the premise that the problems of aging are social and thus can be corrected with political and social action. A structural explanation is, therefore, tied to activism. Other branches of critical gerontology are working to identify wide social influences that shape what gets defined as a problem, how the problem gets looked at, and the consequences of different patterns of research. The worldviews of gerontologists should come under study as well as the people they are studying (Luborsky & Sankar, 1993.) These studies can overlap with philosophy. They are important in directing our attention to biases that affect our choice of what to study, how to study, and even our choice of concepts and the wording of hypotheses.

Minkler (1996) concludes, "For gerontology to reach its full potential, ...the important work that continues to take place in the biological and psychological aspects of ageing must be complemented by critical perspectives from political economy, feminist scholarship, and the humanities, coupled with newer, culturally relevant ways of thinking about ageing in multicultural societies."

PURE VERSUS APPLIED RESEARCH

Pure research is the search for knowledge in the most unbiased fashion possible. The natural, physical, and social sciences use the scientific method to test hypotheses objectively and to accept or reject hypotheses using clearly defined criteria. The pure researcher first formulates a theory; then he or she generates hypotheses and devises a plan for testing them. The researcher must find ways of empirically measuring theoretical concepts or variables.

Let us consider an example from the activity/disengagement controversy. A researcher might want to test the following hypothesis: The morale of the older person increases with the number of activities in which he or she is involved. To test this hypothesis, at least two variables must be measured—morale and number of activities. This task may seem easy, but it is not. Morale is a complex variable, hard to define and hard to scale in a meaningful way. The number-of-activities variable is somewhat easier to deal with, but it *too* can present problems. The researcher must decide, for example, if watching television or reading should be regarded as activities. Once variables are defined and scaled, the pure researcher must then identify the sample group.

A study of all elderly persons is impossible, so some smaller group, or sample, must be identified and selected. Next, methods of collecting the data from this sample must be devised. Typical methods for collecting data are the interview and the questionnaire. After the social scientist has collected all the data, he or she uses methods of analysis, which often involve statistical techniques, to tabulate the results of the study.

The objective of all this work is to produce a study that is valid (accurate) and replicable (capable of yielding the same results when repeated). The data analysis will usually determine whether the initial hypothesis should be accepted or rejected, but the study's validity and replicability are just as important in determining the authority and persuasiveness of the conclusions about the hypothesis made in the study.

Using scales and tabulating totals is known as **quantitative research.** Survey research is typically quantitative. Another kind of research widely used in the study of people is called **qualitative research.** Making observations in a retirement setting or nursing home, conducting lengthy oral interviews to get oral histories, or asking open-ended questions that explore the meaning of life may not yield results that can be scaled or analyzed statistically, yet these observations and interviews are scientific studies. They represent qualitative studies rather than quantitative ones. One qualitative study consisted of taped interviews, an approach the researcher called "retrospective life span analysis" (Job, 1983). Very old persons answered open-ended questions and told of important and meaningful life events. This model incorporates ethnographic methods developed by anthropologists in which narrative data, or people's stories about their lives, are the units of analysis (Gubrium & Holstein, 1995).

Gerontologists do not agree on the best approach to study, or even that there is a best approach. In a sense, each one has a camera standing in a different position, getting a different angle on the subject.

The applied branch of any science is concerned with using the findings of pure research to improve the quality of life. **Applied research,** to state it simply, yields practical solutions to a particular problem and is not concerned with theoretical speculation as to why the problem exists. Are most elderly poorly nourished, poorly housed, victims of high crime rates, and living below the poverty line? If they are, what is the best way to solve these problems? Just as physicians apply findings from biological science to help people get well and engineers apply findings from the physical and natural sciences to build better dams, bridges, and buildings, the applied social scientist might analyze the delivery of services or devise ways to improve the social environment in which people live. Of course, individuals may have differing ideas of what constitutes an improvement. Applied gerontology is most effective, for example, to evaluate housing, transportation, pensions, employment programs, and Older Americans Act services. Applied research can also be used to explore the ways in which government regulations affect older people (Kane, 1992; Minkler, 1996).

One might think that pure and applied research approaches are separate and distinct, yet in gerontological study, the pure and applied are often used together. Some research clearly represents value judgments that proscribe how the research can be applied. The "everyday life" approach, however, may or may not imply intervention. It can be pure research in the sense of its goal: to study the meaning that life has for old people. Some of the findings from this theoretical approach also imply ways for improving the lot of older people. Thus, the distinction between pure and applied research is often arbitrary. Applied research can identify and suggest ways to solve existing problems. Pure research can question why the problems exist. If solutions are implemented, applied research can then investigate the effectiveness of the solutions. All in all, pure and applied research stimulate each other.

The Future of Social Gerontology

Social theories of aging come from two principal viewpoints—the psychological and the sociological—or from some combination of the two. Gerontology is far more interdisciplinary than many fields of study. Subjective well-being adds a psychological dimension to studies of aging, for example, whereas age stratification emphasizes the sociological dimension.

Sometimes the distinction between the psychological and sociological can be quite arbitrary, and this can be confusing to students just beginning their study of gerontology. If one can imagine gerontologists as photographers taking pictures of aging from many different angles, one can go on to conceptualize theorists looking at the lives of older people from many different angles. The pictures have a great deal in common, but the angles offer shades of difference and meaning. Theories overlap, but each has its unique emphasis.

Because older people face so many practical problems that demand immediate solutions, research in the field of gerontology has often been applied rather than purely theoretical. Researchers have invested much of their time in seeking effective social solutions, often ignoring the broader theoretical questions.

The 1960s brought forth a flurry of research instigated by the activity/disengagement controversy, whereas the 1970s and 1980s saw a greater diversity of theoretical frameworks. The 1990s fostered an even wider and richer array of theories and concepts to the study of gerontology, with special emphasis on issues relevant to our extraordinary diversity of culture. As the 20th century comes to an end, the voices of scholars are beginning to call for acknowledgement that societies and cultures are woven together in complex strands, thus highlighting the need to study and understand that interdependence.

Likewise, as the percentage of older persons continues to climb, society needs more workers in fields such as education, outreach, and long term care. We have many more research questions to answer before our society can fulfill the physical, psychological, and social needs of our older population.

Chapter Summary

Social gerontology studies social aspects of aging. Various theoretical frameworks have been used to study aging from a social science perspective. Controversy over the activity versus disengagement theory of aging shaped the field of social gerontology in the 1960s. The controversy has never been resolved, though the activity theory seems to be favored. The most often studied variable in all of gerontology is psychological well-being. The implications of this concept are deep and numerous. Sociologists study how societies are stratified by age and how roles are differentiated by age. Society imposes age norms or age constraints, which also shape the way we behave at any given age. Every level of adulthood, whether young adulthood or advanced middle age, has expected behavior patterns. Exchange theory has been developed by sociologists and social psychologists and has been used to show that elders in society suffer from an imbalance of power. Balancing operations could bring more power and, thus, equality to the aged in the United States. A phenomenological perspective studies the meaning that elders find in life—in everyday events and in their relationships with others. Finally, from critical anthropology and sociology comes critical gerontology—the perspective that basic capitalist institutions interfere with the status and power of elders.

Key Terms

activity theory
age cohort
age grading
age norms
age stratification
applied research
critical gerontology
cross-sectional study
disengagement theory
equity theory
ethnicity
exchange theory
gender roles
Generation X
gero-transcendence
life satisfaction
lineage
longitudinal studies
Mannheim's 'generation'
norm of beneficence
norm of reciprocity
phenomenological theory
planned behavior
political economy of aging
pure research
qualitative research
quantitative research
reliable
role
salience
social gerontology
structural-functional framework
symbolic interaction
theoretical frameworks
valid

Questions for Discussion

1. If you were to study aging from a sociological perspective, which theoretical framework would you choose and why?

2. How do our value systems affect the theoretical frameworks we design?
3. Do you personally expect to remain active or to disengage at age 65? At age 95? Explain.
4. Would you prefer to work in pure or applied social gerontology? Why?

Fieldwork Suggestions

1. Develop a measure of life satisfaction, beginning with your definition of the term. Interview three older adults to determine their degree of life satisfaction. What are some of their sources of satisfaction or dissatisfaction? Ask them what they thought about your measure, and how they might have changed the way you went about getting your information.
2. Following a "meaning in everyday life" framework, make a visit to a nursing home. How would you describe the feelings and reactions of the elderly people there? Are they finding meaning in life? If so, how? In what way is your own perspective—your lens—shaping what it is that you see?

Online Activities

1. Look up the American Anthropological Association home page and see what you might find about critical anthropology. Does this give you any information about the use of life story and narrative to study aging?
2. Look up the home page for the Gerontological Society of America. How much information can you glean about methodology from this site and its links?
3. Using one of the key words, conduct an information search. See if you can categorize the sources you find by "scholarly," "popular," and other appropriate groupings. Do some levels of information seem more solid, or believable, than others? How do you distinguish between off-the-cuff opinion and thoughtful, informed discourse?

5

Friends, Family, and Community

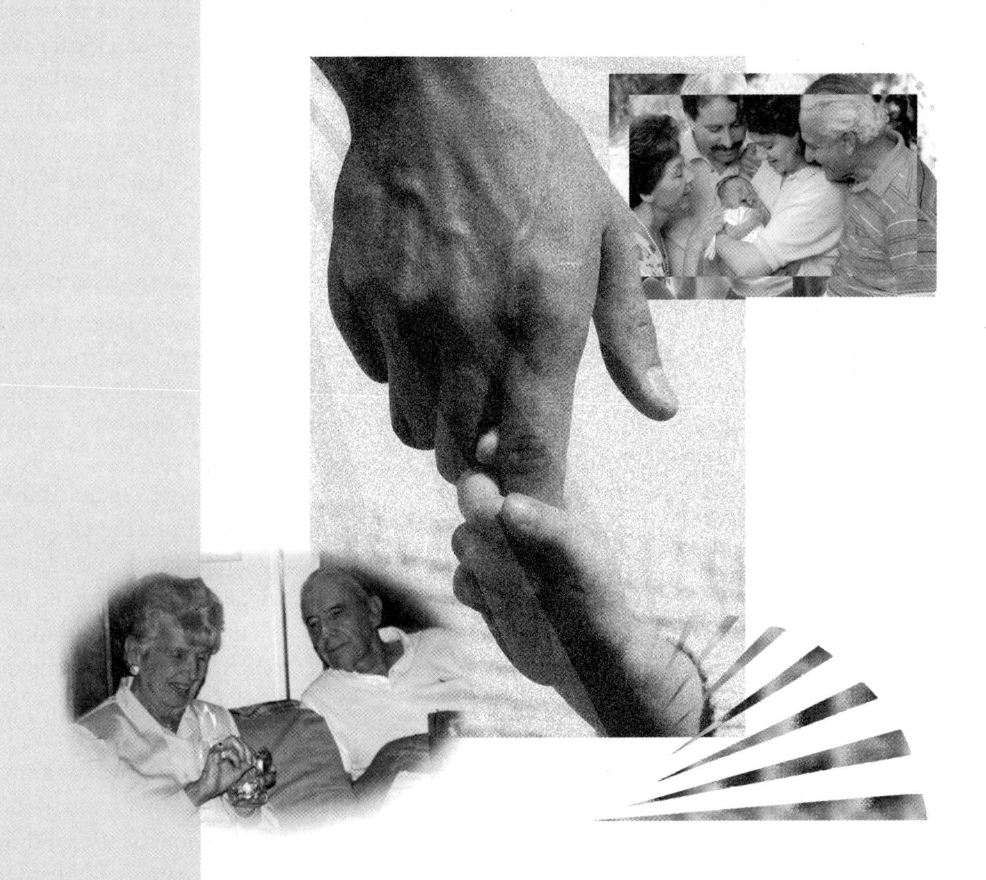

Tough Act to Follow

John M. Glionna

At long last, the folks in Culver City are saying goodbye to the old man they call Uncle Syd. Next Tuesday, as the fiscal year ends, the ageless Sydney Kronenthal will slowly don his blue blazer and walk for the last time from his office in the parks and recreation complex, leaving behind his post as city director of human services.

Funny thing, city officials quip, they didn't even have to use those sticks of dynamite to get the old boy out—he left of his own accord. After 52 years in the same city department, all that time doing essentially the same job, Kronenthal is finally stepping down.

Since 1946, he has spent his life developing a growing parks and recreation system in a tenure that spanned the administrations of 10 U.S. presidents. He has attended more than 10,000 city meetings and lain awake too many nights thinking about how to run his little corner of the world more efficiently.

But not to worry, Uncle Syd says, he's still got things well under control, including the appointment of a successor—a young whippersnapper with a mere 25 years of municipal service. Kronenthal's story is a testament to a lost ethic of permanence that seems alien in an era of diminished employment security and frenetic job-hopping. How on earth, you want to ask him, does somebody stay at the same job for 52 years?

"I just never wanted to leave," says Uncle Syd, a self-professed workaholic. "Every morning, I just couldn't wait to get to the office, to see what I could get accomplished that day."

Many mornings he was at work by 7 a.m. and didn't leave until after midnight.

"Syd's always in his office; you call him up, he's there," says Steve Gourley, a former Culver City mayor. "One night some of us were locked out of a candidates forum at a local park hall. It was after 8 p.m. when I called his office. But Syd was still there. He said 'Ok, kid, I'll have somebody there in five minutes.' And he did."

Some officials say Uncle Syd hasn't taken a vacation in 25 years. Kronenthal calls that a bunch of hooey.

"It's only been 10 years," he says.

Along the way he forgot a few important steps. For one, he never got married. Nor did he ever buy a house. For the last 48 years, he's rented the same bungalow out behind the old widow's place on Harter Street.

"I've just never been able for figure out how to divorce my life from the city's life," he says. "The city is my family. Really, it's something I'd die for. When I finally retire, I'm going to have to find out who I am and who I really belong to."

Who Syd Kronenthal is, friends and co-workers say, is a relentless go-getter whose obsessiveness helped establish some 14 parks, including one that bears his name. Not bad for a small suburban city of just five square miles and 42,000 residents.

Syd fought for the establishment of the city's youth and senior centers, for soccer and baseball fields and better after-school care and youth job programs.

It wasn't the life he had planned. He wanted to be a doctor. Born in Chicago, he started medical school and stopped during World War II to serve in the Army Air Corps. He was ready to return to school when he took a job as an assistant parks director in Culver City. After a brief hiatus with the Veterans Administration, working to rehabilitate wounded servicemen, he came back to City Hall.

His pet project away from the office has been his work at the Therapeutic Living Center for the Blind, a Los Angeles residence center and group home for blind people with other disabilities, where he donates time. His daily schedule also includes a walk through the senior center adjacent to his office, where he tells his stories and spreads his cheer.

On one of his recent tours, a woman who has just left the center pulls curbside in her car. "Don't believe a word he tells you," she warns a visitor jocularly after giving Uncle Syd a peck on the cheek.

For several years, friends say, Kronenthal has silently donated money to provide full college scholarships to needy students who otherwise might not have had the chance to go to school. "Yeah," he acknowledges wryly. "and my accountant just keeps shaking his head."

He keeps his age a mystery. Rumors place him between 70 and 80.

"He's really a very private man in his own life," says longtime friend Fred Cunningham, retired Beverly Hills city public affairs director. "But his giving money to the scholarships makes sense with Syd. With his not having a family, being a bachelor all his life, he just decided to go behind the scenes and do this for his city what any good parent would do. He's a remarkable young man. He'll always be young."

When Kronenthal looks back, he wonders if he listened too much to the doubters, "the ones who said, 'Kronenthal's gonna bankrupt the city, we've already got too many parks.'"

"I should have fought harder for park space. And that includes punching out some of the city councilmen who wanted to stand in my way."

Walking around the city's parks and recreation complex, with its Olympic-sized public pool, he says: "This was all an empty lot when I came here. They all criticized me for pushing to build this place for $650,000. Now you couldn't paint it for that price."

Last week, Kronenthal attended his last City Council meeting, where officials threw him a party, and gave him a gold ring and letters from the surviving U.S. presidents.

"I'm pretty stoic, but I've got to tell you, it was hard not to cry," he says.

He plans to devote his energies to charity, maybe take on another class at USC, where he has taught public administration for 35 years. The city's historical society wants to get its hands on the mementos he's collected in half a century of public service.

Regrets? "Oh sure," he says. "Sometimes I wonder what it would have been like to have taken on a wife and have raised 10 kids.

"I guess it's too late to find out though, huh?"

Family and friendship connections take on a special significance when it becomes clear that they might not be in our life throughout *all* our life. Those significant connections include romantic and sexual relationships. Maintaining relationships can be a challenge when people become ill or frail, when friends die or move, or when family pressures for traditional grandparenthood take precedence over developing an independent lifestyle in later life.

Family Development in Later Life

Later life is not a static, stagnant time for the older family member. Transition events such as widowhood, retirement, remarriage, or a child's departure punctuate the life course. Transitions lead to changed perceptions, ways of behaving, and interdependence with kin and community. The older person's life is also influenced by family development events in the past, such as whether he or she was childless or a parent; the person's culture; and certainly, the gender of the older person.

All of these events add to the ever-changing character of the older person's role as a family member. Older persons may face adjustments equal to or more difficult than those younger family members face. For the newly married couple, the birth of a first child may require a difficult adjustment; but for the middle-aged or elderly couple, learning to relate to an independent adult offspring who was once "my baby" might be equally traumatic. Adjusting to the death of a spouse can be the most challenging of all changes in the life cycle. Each event in the life cycle calls for relating to others in new ways and facing the problems inherent in every transition.

Because of increased survival through childhood, adulthood, and into old age, Americans have experienced predictably longer lives in this century. Marriages are more likely to last 50 or 60 years, and parents are more likely to survive to see their children become adults and to see their grandchildren grow up. Whole stages of life that were brief and rare in the past, such as the postparental stage, are now long-lasting. Many kin relationships last much longer now than they did in past generations.

ELDERS IN THE KIN STRUCTURE

The family is a vital part of the older person's life. Elderly people give a great deal to their families, and they receive a great deal in return. Family members tend to exchange emotional and financial support throughout their lives. A person's confidant in life is typically a close family member—a spouse or a child. Only when a closely related family member is unavailable does a friend rather than a relative act as confidant (Kendig et al., 1988). In this section, we will discuss siblings and grandparenthood. Parent-child ties are discussed in the next chapter.

Blood is thicker than water.

SHAKESPEARE, 1581

ELDER SIBLINGS

Brothers and sisters are brothers and sisters for life, no matter how intimate or how estranged they might be. The relationship with siblings, solid or shaky, is likely to be the longest relationship in an individual's life. If we have a brother or sister, it is likely that we will be a sibling and have a sibling from the time we are very young through to the time either we or they die. In later life, because of the duration and the shared experiences of childhood, the sibling relationship can be emotionally very intense, and that intensity can be either positive and life confirming, or bitter. There are as many different types of sibling relationships as there are types of families, but the fact remains that a sibling is a close kin connection over which we have no choice, and from which we can gain pleasure, irritation, or rage.

Family systems in particular, because of their culturally ascribed and socially recognized status, implicate *or entangle their members in a form of involuntary membership...*

SPREY, 1991.

Although **elderly siblings** may cause problems for one another, they can also extend support to one another in a social environment that does not always foster the development of social bonds (Connidis, 1995). Bonds between siblings typically extend throughout life and are reported to be second only to mother-child ties in intensity and complexity.

Most elders have a living sibling. The parents of today's elderly produced more children than did the elders themselves; any given married adult probably has more siblings than offspring. If the birthrate is now at the replacement level of two children per couple, we can expect there will be fewer children, and thus fewer siblings, in the future. In fact, the Baby Boomers will be the first cohort in history that has more siblings than children (Selzer, 1989). The family support system will be smaller in the years ahead, and for this reason alone, the felt responsibility of one family member to another is likely to increase with time. If there are no other resources for you, and you are my sister [or brother], can I *not* be there? Because adult siblings fall outside the nuclear family structure, their impact in the life course has been woefully overlooked by family researchers.

Exploring the sibling tie can highlight the importance of continuing family ties over time. Many family scholars have pointed out that there remains a conceptual distinction between feelings that siblings may harbor for one another and the obligations that are shared by virtue of family ties (Connidis & Campbell, 1995). When sibling ties are ranked by level of obligation within the family, the sibling tie is typically less binding than that of marriage or of parent/child, but is present nonetheless (Rossi & Rossi, 1990). The tie is important, and it is unique; siblings share biological and/or familial characteristics, values, and experiences, under comparatively egalitarian status (Robinson & Mahon, 1997). Given their shared experiences, siblings can be a major resource for life review among older adults (Hays et al., 1997).

Studies on sibling relationships have had somewhat inconsistent conclusions regarding sister/sister/brother/brother interactions. The variety of combinations of sibling units is nearly overwhelming, if we consider variables such as the marital status, birth order, proximity, number of siblings in the family, living (or nonliving) siblings and their birth order, stepsiblings, and so forth. Theory helps to identify some key, defining characteristics of being a sibling, however, to guide these investigations.

Connidis and Campbell (1995) established the hypotheses for a study on sibling relationships after conducting a major review of the literature on sibling relationships in middle and later life. Using interviews with 678 people over 55 years of age, the researchers wanted to understand more about the relationship of sibling gender, marital status, emotional closeness, and geographic proximity. Their conclusions, generally consistent with most of the less recent studies in the literature, are itemized in Table 5.1. Their findings imply that to understand the support and emotional closeness of family in later life, we must also understand sibling relationships. Because siblings are not considered to be extended family, their impact can be underestimated—both as providers of instrumental assistance and as assistants in maintaining a continuing sense of self when a sibling is in physical or emotional trauma, such as widowhood bereavement.

The elderly do, in fact, have brothers and sisters. In an earlier review of the literature by Cicirelli (1982), people reported that the percent of older people with siblings was from 78 percent to 94 percent. A more current review (Bank, 1995) indicates that siblings generally maintain contact with one another, and that contact increases in old age. In all of the studies it was quite rare for siblings to lose contact, and in no study did more than 10 percent of the respondents report they had completely lost contact with their siblings. Gold and colleagues (1990) reported that the majority of elder siblings view their relations with their brothers and sisters positively. Indeed, Gold reported that one of the greatest life regrets reported by elder siblings is a failed sibling relationship.

Older people are more likely to confront the death of a sibling than of any other kin, and that loss can be profound. The two highest times of interest and involvement in the life course in a

TABLE 5.1

Closeness, confiding, and contact among middle-aged and older siblings

Variable	Finding
Gender differences	1. Women's ties with siblings are more involved than those of men. 2. The greater emotional attachment of women to their siblings was confirmed. 3. Respondents with sisters only are closer on average to their siblings than those whose networks include brothers and sisters. 4. Women are closer to their brother(s) and their sister(s) than are men. 5. Telephone contact is more frequent if the highest contact sibling is a sister. 6. Women seem to have greater emotional investment in their ties to siblings and are more engaged in sibling ties—possibly due to an assumed level of obligation.
Marital status	1. Contact is more frequent between single siblings. 2. Emotionally closer ties among those whose closest sib is widowed than among those whose closest sibling is single. 3. Being single affects overall level of involvement with both the sibling network and the sibling seen most often, but does not alter feelings about siblings.
Parent status	1. Childless respondents confide more in their primary sibling confidant and in siblings overall than do parents. 2. Respondents with networks including parents and childless siblings confide in their siblings more than those whose siblings are all childless. 3. No greater emotional closeness to siblings among the childless. 4. Childless seem to have greater emotional investment in their siblings (higher levels of confiding).
Emotional closeness	A powerful relationship to confiding, telephone contact, and personal contact; emotional closeness appears to be a primary love/friendship binding tie.
Relationship over time; education; proximity; sibling number	1. Growing attachment to sibling network as a whole, over time. 2. Higher education is associated with greater closeness to closest siblings, but not sibling network overall. 3. Educational level inversely related to contact with sibling network overall. 4. Proximity enhances emotional closeness, but not to emotionally closest sibling. 5. Greater opportunity for selectivity within larger families. 6. Network size not related to overall closeness and confiding.

Source: Connidis, Ingrid Arnet & Campbell, Lori D. (1995). Closeness, confiding, and contact among siblings in middle and late adulthood. *Journal of family issues, 16* (6), 722–745.

sibling relationship is in youth and in late life. When an elderly person experiences the death of a sibling, the loss can be far more consequential than it might have been earlier in life (Hays et al., 1997). Parents die, children grow and leave home, friends die or move, and health becomes more frail, yet the sibling bond endures. The bond of siblings is reported to be more forgiving, mutually warmer, and more interested in one another in the last years of life (Bank, 1995).

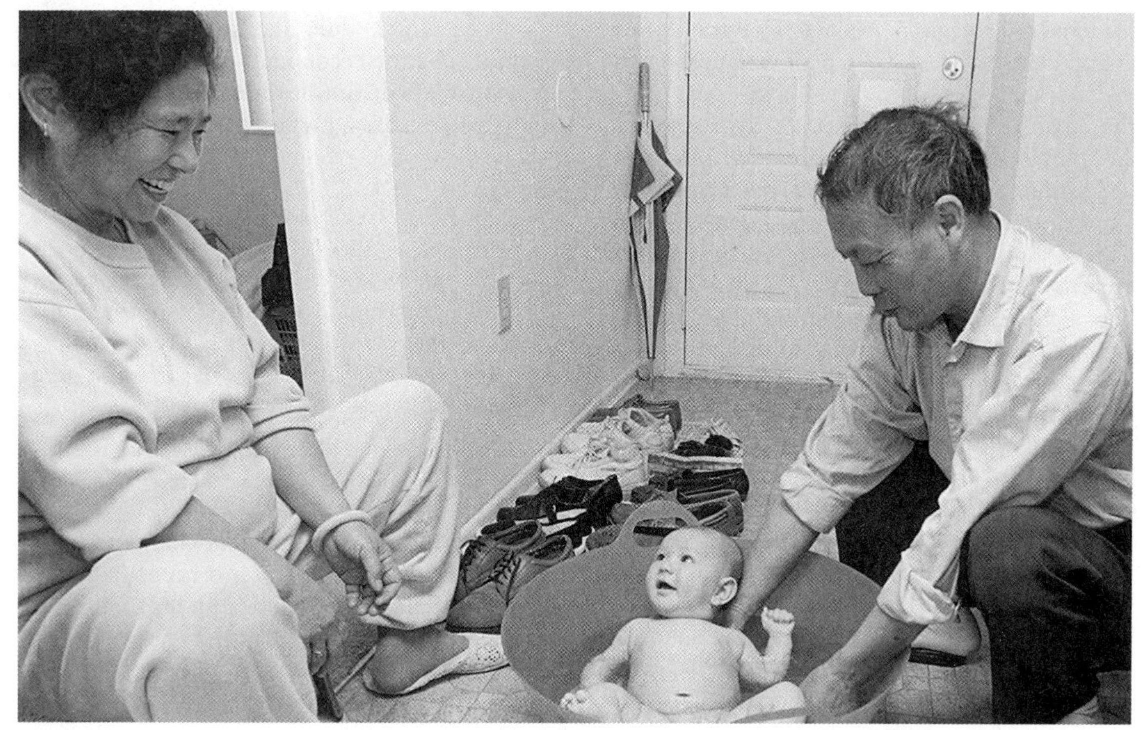

How to be a grandparent depends on one's health and age, whether grandchildren live nearby, family relationships, and ethnic customs. Many grandparents have close, indulgent relationships with their grandchildren.

VARIATIONS IN KIN RELATIONS

The demography of the kin system varies widely. Some older people have large and extensive kinship systems, with many relatives nearby, whereas other older people have managed to outlive siblings, children, spouse, and other kin. The relationships among kin members vary by sex, social class, and locale (urban/rural).

Gender differences are very apparent in family relationships. Females maintain closer relationships with other family members than do males. There appear to be stronger norms of obligation and feelings of attachment to extended family members among women than among men, as well as what might be called an *ethos of support* among women in a family (Connidis et al., 1995). Families with more sisters have an increased likelihood that parents—both fathers and mothers—will have assistance from their children. Having more brothers in a family decreases the likelihood among the men of being the primary care provider for a frail parent or parents. However, having more sisters in a family does not decrease the likelihood of being a primary care provider, but increases the levels of care to the parents (Connidis et al., 1995). This finding shows the extent to which family contact remains consistent and intact through the parents for many years after children reach adulthood.

Blue-collar families tend to have particularly close extended family ties, which members maintain by living near each other. Visits from kin often constitute the major, if not the only, form of social activity for such families. Although white-collar family ties are also fairly strong, such families are more likely to be geographically scattered by career opportunities. Contact is often maintained, however, in spite of distance.

Literature in gerontology is inconsistent in reported differences between rural and urban families. On the one hand, rural areas are shown to be bastions of traditional values, one being family responsibility and respect for elders. We can picture rural family reunions at which the aged are celebrities looking with pride at the family line of children, grandchildren, and great-grandchildren. In this picture, kinship ties are strong and meaningful. Small-town newspapers often reflect the apparent importance of family and neighborly ties by featuring articles on who has visited whom, who is in the hospital, or who went out of town to visit relatives.

Another picture of rural areas is one of poverty, isolation, and despair. In spite of the assumed traditional values, rural elders interact less with their children than do their urban counterparts. Compared with urban older people, rural elders have substantially smaller incomes, are more restricted in terms of mobility, experience poorer physical health, and have a more negative outlook on life. The outcome of social and demographic change in rural areas can be to isolate elders. Clearly, human service programs must be adequate to meet the needs of both urban and rural elders.

GRANDPARENTHOOD

The three-generation family is becoming common, and even four- and five-generation families are on the increase. Rossi and Rossi (1990) found, though, that two- and three-generational lineages are most common. About 80 percent of those over 65 have living children, and 80 percent of those, or 60 percent of all older people, have at least one grandchild. If one becomes a parent at age 25, one may well be a grandparent at age 50. If parenthood at age 25 continues for the next generation, the individual would be a great-grandparent at age 75, thus creating a four-generation family.

Note that middle age, not old age, is the typical time for becoming a grandparent. Most grandparents do not fit the stereotypic image of jolly, white-haired, bespectacled old people with shawls and canes; many are in their forties and fifties.

> *My grandmother was the radiant angel of my childhood, and, you know, now my grandchildren are just the same. They are the part of my life that is most joyous, that gives me most pleasure.*
>
> Grandfather (in Kivnick), 1982

The rapid cultural changes characteristic of the second half of the 20th century have profoundly affected the American family. Some analysts say these changes are negative for the family; some say the changes are for the better. Some analysts say they are *change*, without being necessarily positive or negative, but clearly being something to which people and society must adapt. In the tapestry of life, the color and design are variations brought about by change, but it is the continuity across generations that forms the fundamental shape and form. It is through that continuity that people learn how to be a grandchild, how to parent, and how to be a grandparent. The degree to which grandparents are involved in playing their role and just what type of role that will be with their grandchildren is significantly influenced by having known their own grandparents (King & Elder, 1997). Living with intergenerational relationships is critical to the passing on of that cultural and family continuity.

Studies of the meaning of grandparenthood show there are as many different ways of being a grandparent as there are family types and styles. Grandparents can be a point of reference and identity for the grandchild; they expand the age range and number of adult role models available to children. They can be the connection that provides a sense of historical and cultural rootedness for the child, and they can provide a secure and loving adult/child relationship for their grandchild (Kennedy, 1996).

For some, grandparenting is a time to have childish fun or to indulge grandchildren, or perhaps even a chance to reexperience one's youth—the **fun-seeker** grandparent. At the opposite end of the spectrum would be the more formal, distant grandparent—perhaps one who tries to be a role model or the repository of family wisdom—the grandparent children go to for the best cookie recipe or for stories about their parents, aunts, and uncles. For some, grandparenthood is personally meaningful because it represents the continuation of the family line—it provides a sense of purpose and identity and is a source of self-esteem as the keeper of family history. The grandparent role can be central to helping children maintain identity in stepfamilies. One grandparent might find great joy and meaning in the role of grandparent, whereas for another person, grandparenting has little relevant meaning.

For some grandparents, their role is essentially that of substitute parent. Because their adult child is unable or unavailable to parent—because of drug abuse, death, divorce, AIDS, a mental health problem, career choice, or a host of other modern-day complications—grandparents sometimes end up with full-time care of their grandchildren. This family form has grown over 40 percent in the past decade and is projected to continue to increase (U.S. Bureau of the Census, 1994). Some analyses predict that by the year 2000 approximately 125,000 children will have lost their mothers because of AIDS (Lee, 1995). Census data from 1990 suggest that two-thirds of children living with grandparents live in homes in which at least one of the child's parents also lives (Fuller-Thomson et al., 1997). This means that grandparents who have taken responsibility for raising grandchildren may also have responsibilities for (or the residential impact of) that child's parent. The stress of this complex set of relationships is enormous. One-third of grandparent caregivers report their health to have deteriorated since becoming primary caregivers, and a vast majority (over 72 percent) reported "feeling depressed" in the week prior to data collection in one major study (Minkler & Roe, 1993). Research has variously described grandparents who parent their grandchildren to be extraordinarily committed to child rearing; angry; in despair about their own child; guilt-ridden about their role as parent to their "failed" child; and frustrated regarding the imposition of unexpected child-rearing responsibilities in later life (Burnette, 1998; Kelly, 1997). The full range of these feelings is likely to be experienced, depending upon circumstances and personalities.

A number of support groups have emerged to provide instrumental and emotional support to caregiving grandparents to provide appropriate release for those frustrations, the depression, and the residual anger around the circumstance of their lives. Grandparents as Parents (GAP), National Coalition of Grandparents, Pacific Northwest Coalition of Grandparents Raising Grandchildren, and ROCKING/Raising Our Children's Kids are just a few.

Women are much more likely than men to look forward to the role of grandparent. Women often visualize themselves as grandparents well ahead of the birth of the first grandchild, and the grandmother role is positive and desirable to most women, even though it can make young grandmothers feel old. Men typically become grandfathers when their primary identity is still with the work role. Consequently, they may postpone involvement with their grandchildren until retirement.

In a classic study on grandparenting, anthropologist Dorothy Dorian Apple (1956) explored grandparent/ grandchildren relationships in 75 societies. She found that in societies where grandparents retain considerable household authority, the relationship between grandparents and grandchildren tended to be stiff and formal. In societies such as the United States, where grandparents retain little control or authority over grandchildren, the relationship is friendly and informal. Others have likewise observed that American grandparents, more than grandparents in other societies, engage in companionable and indulgent relationships with their grandchildren and usually do not assume any direct responsibility for their behavior.

One of the most representative samples of grandparents of teenagers affirmed many of these results. Grandparents often played a background, supportive role, helping most during times of crisis (Cherlin & Furstenberg, 1994). Among many families the role of grandparent is somewhat distant and does not include disciplining the grandchildren, for example, but in a family crisis, the grandparent is there with financial and/or instrumental support for the grandchildren. Additionally, even if they do not live with their grandparents, millions of American children receive childcare from their grandparents each day (U.S. Bureau of the Census, 1990).

Grandparents are the child's roots, a sense of belonging to a larger family and a larger community. Grandparents are there when things go wrong for the child—sometimes the child needs that protection.

GRANDMOTHER, QUOTED IN KRUK, 1994

One can conclude that grandparenthood carries meaning for some elders, but not for others. This meaning may be biological, social, or personal. The degree of involvement with grandchildren varies. Current evidence seems to indicate that in the United States, grandparenthood, for many, is not a primary role, although it is enjoyed by most. It may be a primary role, however, for grandparents who provide the majority of care for their families' children. Becoming a grandparent is not going to fill voids left by shortcomings in marriage, work, or friendships.

THE IMPACT OF DIVORCE ON GRANDPARENTHOOD

The consequences experienced by grandparents when their children divorce is currently a topic under study by sociologists and under legal scrutiny in the courtroom. If a couple divorces and the in-law is awarded custody of the offspring, grandparents often cannot enjoy the relationship they desire with their grandchildren.

In some families, grandparents are emotionally distant enough from their adult children's lives to maintain cordial relations with former in-law adult children. One study found half of the grandparents interviewed to be "friendly" with their child's former spouse. These grandparents tended to be friendly if the ex-spouse was a female, but they tended to lose contact if the ex-spouse was male, even if he had custody of the grandchildren. A recent study of grandparents and grandchildren of divorce indicated that grandchildren and grandparents saw their relationships in highly similar ways. They desired increases in time together as well as time together spent in specific activities The two groups associated emotional bonding with the grandparents' listening, keeping them safe, and gift giving. Grandparents felt a good relationship with the custodial parent was essential (Schutter et al., 1997). The study further identified "healthy" and "less healthy" subgroups. The healthiest subgroup was grandmothers and daughters or daughters-in-law, living in close proximity, with the grandmother a married, full-time worker. Grandparents who were related by blood to the custodial parent and had a good relationship with them were also more likely to have a healthy relationship.

Given the emphasis on individualism and social ties based on mutual interest, kinship can be complex in U.S. society. These social norms make the negotiation of kin relationships a necessary task. Good relationships with former daughters-in-law, for example, may determine whether grandparents can remain close to grandchildren. If informal negotiation fails, more people may be arguing in court for the right to spend time with a given child.

If for some reason grandparents are denied access to their grandchildren, they have traditionally had no standing in cases involving visitation and adoption of grandchildren. The courts have consistently upheld the supremacy of the parent-child relationship. Traditionally, a legal relationship between grandparent and grandchild existed only when both parents were incapable or dead, meaning that the courts had to judge the child's parents unfit before the grandparents had any rights.

Today, at least one legal precedent has been set; if provisions for visiting grandparents had been made prior to divorce, visitation is generally permitted after divorce. Thus, grandparents can, under limited circumstances, get visitation rights. (They have no rights, however, if parents choose to give their children up for adoption.)

Grandparents are increasingly pressing for rights with regard to their grandchildren. The recent growth of the "grandparent rights" self-help movement in North America suggests that a significant proportion of grandparents have concern about access difficulties and contact loss to their grandchildren following divorce or in other situations. There is currently insufficient social policy to address the phenomenon of grandparent-grandchild contact loss, although it has become an issue in the legal system for family mediators (Kruk, 1994). At this time, legal mediation is seen as the best possibility for resolution of grandparent-grandchild access problems.

We should also note that elders add new relatives to their kinship system when their adult children remarry. Remarriage, which may take place more than once, brings not only new sons- and daughters-in-law but may also bring stepgrandchildren. When older parents can maintain ties with their children's former spouse(s), grandchildren lead more stable lives. Grandparents who can remain flexible and friendly have the benefit of enjoying an expanded kinship system. This "new extended family" (Cherlin & Furstenberg, 1994) created by stepgrandparenthood may lead to close kin ties. Some grandparents report that there is no difference between stepgrandchildren and biological grandchildren. Often, younger grandchildren and those who live close will develop more involved relationships.

Social Networks

One stereotypical picture of old age is of a solitary person, in a tiny hotel room, staring silently into space. Another is of oldsters in a rest home, propped up in adjacent armchairs but worlds apart. Either way, the picture is one of isolation and loneliness. Do the elderly have friends—really good friends—they can count on? Simply stated, like other age groups, most do but some do not. Numerous factors affect the likelihood of close friendships in old age.

ELDERS AS FRIENDS AND NEIGHBORS

Friendship is extremely important in the lives of elderly people. Let us contradict one stereotype about friendships among elders by saying that most older people maintain active social lives. In one of the first major studies of friendship formation in widowhood, respondents were asked how many times in the past year friends had helped them with transportation, household repairs, housekeeping, shopping, yard work, illness, car care, important decisions, legal assistance, and financial aid. They also were asked how many times they had given help. Only 8 percent of the respondents indicated that they did not have a close friend. For the first close friend, 84 percent of the respondents named a woman. The average length of acquaintance with the friend was over 20 years; 81 percent keep in touch at least weekly (Roberto & Scott, 1984/85).

Note that the date of the Roberto and Scott study was the mid-1980s. It has only been in the past 20 years that the role of friendship in later life has been seen as an important enough factor in well-being in later life to be a topic of research. This is not necessarily because social science research is insensitive to later-life development. It is because, once again, we can see a consequence of longevity in the patterning of our lives. Friends have clearly always been important, however (as we were reminded earlier), the adage that "blood

Interactions with neighbors can provide companionship and be a source of connection for older people. These men meet regularly in a local park to "talk shop."

is thicker than water" is culturally ingrained, and it becomes easy to overlook the true impact that friends—particularly friendships of very long duration—have on our psychological and social well-being.

Roberto and Scott (1984/85) used equity theory to formulate hypotheses and analyze results. According to **equity theory**, which says that an equitable relationship exists if all participants are receiving gains, participants will be distressed if they contribute too much to, or receive too little from, a friendship. Equity is related to high morale, and, as expected, the equitably benefited women had the highest morale. An unexpected finding was that the overbenefited (those who received more help than they gave) had the lowest morale; receiving goods and services that one cannot repay may leave one feeling uncomfortable or inferior, resulting lower morale. Also unexpected was the high morale that existed among the underbenefited—those giving more than they received. Perhaps the underbenefited woman feels good that she does not need help and enjoys giving without receiving. The single women living alone compensated for lack of a marriage companion through extensive and meaningful friendship networks with other women.

A differentiation can be made between a confidant and a companion. A **confidant** is someone to confide in and share personal problems with, whereas a **companion** is one who regularly shares in activities and pastimes. A companion may be a confidant, but not necessarily. The objective of one study examining older women's friendships was to identify changes and stabilities in the qualities older women attributed to their close friendships (Roberto, 1997). They found that over time, women's interactions with friends did change, and the change was based on the woman's work, marital, and health status. Although those interactions changed, they also found that the essential elements of friendship—understanding, affection, trust, and acceptance—endured over time. It appears that the expressive domain of friendships in later life predominates (Roberto, 1997).

SOCIAL ORGANIZATIONS

Are elders "joiners"? To what rates do they participate socially in voluntary organizations? Many, in fact the majority, join and are actively involved in voluntary organizations (nonprofit groups that elders join only if they choose to do so).

Lodges and fraternal organizations, such as the Moose Lodge, Rotary, Eastern Star, and the like, are the most commonly joined volunteer associations. Membership in them tends to increase with age, and leadership positions are concentrated among older persons, perhaps because older members are more likely to be retired or have fewer family obligations with young children than to younger members. The second most frequently reported form of participation is in the church. Church-related activities involve more than attending services; they include participation in church-sponsored groups such as missionary societies and Bible-study classes.

Except for lodges and churches, other voluntary associations typically show a decline in participation with age. When social class is controlled, however, no decline is evident. This implies that being a "joiner" is related to a middle- or upper-class lifestyle, and aging by itself does not necessarily change this lifestyle.

Senior centers, as opposed to clubs, offer services and activities in addition to recreation. They additionally may offer libraries, music rooms, health services, counseling, physical exercise, and education. Many senior centers operate under the auspices of churches, city government, or private nonprofit agencies. Often, individuals who began senior centers in their own communities 20 years ago now find them successful and popular.

The demand for senior clubs and centers continues to rise. Someday every community may have a senior center, and it will be as natural for older people to use their senior center as it is for children to go to school.

NETWORK ANALYSIS

We can conceive of the combination of social ties—organization memberships, friends, neighbors, and family—as a **social network.** Each person has some kind of social network. The process of analyzing the strengths and weaknesses and the sources of various functions of an older person's social network, called **network analysis,** enables caretakers to tell whether social or health intervention might be necessary. A distinction might be made between social support and social network. **Social network** describes the structural characteristics of support relationships (e.g., size or composition). Social support, on the other hand, is assessed as a more qualitative aspect of the relationship, including how satisfied individuals are with the support they receive and whether supportive others understand them (Antonucci & Fuhrer, 1997).

In recent years, a great deal of research has focused on social networks. A study using the **convoy model** provides us with detailed information showing that older individuals are in frequent contact with both family and friends. The term *convoy* (Antonucci & Akiyama, 1987) is used to evoke the image of a protective layer of family and friends who surround a person and offer support. Convoys are made up of those family and friends who travel through time with the individual, with some members of the convoy traveling the entire way, some dropping out along the way, and some entering the convoy after it has begun. The average older convoy was reported in one major study of older persons to consist of about nine members who offer themselves as confidants, give reassurance and respect, provide care when ill, talk when upset, and discuss health (Antonucci & Akiyama, 1987).

The role of women as keepers of the network emerges in many ways when the networks of older people are examined. This finding is to some extent an effect of the difference in longevity between men and women. More older people are women, so women are more available as friends and family members. It is also due to social expectations and learning. Women tend to be more engaged in network support activities across the life span than are men. The caregiving role of daughters to aging parents has been well documented, as has the finding that married older people tend to maintain closest relationships with their same-sex children and siblings—a finding consistent with the **sex commonality principle.** Women play more central roles in the network of unmarried people (including widowed parents), a pattern referred to as the **femaleness principle** in network analysis (Akiyama et al., 1996).

A recent study of older people's networks (Akiyama et al., 1996) concluded that although older people tend to have more women in their network and receive more support from those women, elders are not necessarily closer—either psychologically or geographically—to the women than to the men in their networks. Their data also showed a noticeable shift from same-sex relationships to female-dominated networks when older people became widowed and required more support. When normative expectations for family member interaction were considered, the study concluded that relationship norms seem to be more powerful than sex norms; that is, the filial responsibility of a son to his parents is demonstrated by the son's interactions with aging parents.

Religion and Spirituality

The religious dimension of aging encompasses the spiritual, social, and developmental aspects of a person's life, and is an important dimension of well-being for the elderly. Efforts to study the relationship of the spiritual dimension to aging have been hindered by an inability of the research community to use consistent terms and definitions. Consequently, inconsistent conclusions abound in the literature. As more scholars become engaged in the study of spiritual development, however, a concerted effort has been made to share definitions and methodology.

> *I represent a Father in heaven who owns everything. That's one of the reasons I've gotten along so well. I haven't been worried about where the next dollar was coming from.*
>
> CHARLES, 101 YEARS OLD, 1992

Thomas (1994) conceptualized an intrinsic-extrinsic pole of religiousness for the individual in which the intrinsically religious find within themselves their ultimate meaning in life from religion. For these types, religion is the fundamental motive for living. The extrinsically religious use religion for more superficial social purposes or to justify their politics and prejudices. Their religion is extrinsic to their fundamental reason for being. Others have developed the concept of intrinsic-extrinsic religiosity by considering higher or lower levels of intrinsic **religiosity** (importance of structured religion to the individual).

Fehring and colleagues (1997) conceptualized the religious dimension by differentiating between **spirituality** and religiosity:

> *Spirituality... connotes harmonious relationships or connections with self, neighbor, nature, God, or a higher being that draws one beyond oneself. It provides a sense of meaning and purpose, enables transcendence, and empowers individuals to be whole and to live life fully. Religion, on the other hand, is a term used for an organized system of beliefs, practices, and forms of worship (p. 663).*

By differentiating these two concepts, the study was able to measure that religiosity (interaction with organized religion) and spiritual well-being (psychological sense of purpose and meaning) are independently associated with hope and positive mood states in elderly people coping with cancer. Subjects with high intrinsic religiosity and spiritual well-being had significantly higher levels of hope and lower levels of negative mood states than subjects with low spiritual well-being and low intrinsic religiosity. The researchers felt that subjects with high religiosity could use their religious patterns for coping (prayer, religious objects); and subjects with high spirituality were able to maintain a greater sense of wholeness than those with low spirituality (Fehring et al., 1997).

Church and synagogue attendance for older people exceeds that of other age groups (a measure of religiosity). People aged 65 and over are the most likely of any age group to belong to clubs, fraternal associations, and church-affiliated organizations such as widows and widowers groups, Bible-study groups, and volunteer groups serving the sick and needy. It is uncertain whether this is a cohort effect (i.e., people over 65 have been more religious throughout their lives than have younger age groups) or an effect of aging. Evidence for shifts in religiosity in aging is inconsistent: some studies find that religiosity changes significantly as one ages; others find that it does not (Courtenay et al., 1992). Studies including centenarians, however, indicate that among the oldest-old, "nonorganizational" aspects of reli-

Many people become more focused on their spiritual development as they age. For some, traditional religion and prayer are a powerful source of strength.

gion (less active aspects of religion such as beliefs, faith, and influences of religion on daily living) are more common than are the organizational aspects (Courtenay et al., 1992). This is likely due to more limited ability of the oldest-old to attend organized religious functions. These findings highlight the importance of the multidimensionality of the religion and spirituality.

The findings from Courtenay et al. (1992) might differ significantly for ethnic groups. More than 75 percent of all elderly African Americans are church members, for example, and at least half attend religious services at least once a week (Stolley & Koenig, 1997). Traditionally, religion and church have been powerful sources of social support for elderly African Americans—in fact, church attendance is the most significant predictor of both frequency and quantity of support received (Stolley & Koenig, 1997).

It is important to view elders in a multicultural sense. In a study of health-related decisions and the role of religion, Laurence O'Connell (1994) noted:

> *A healthy baby, a healthy marriage, a healthy sex life, a healthy set of social skills, a healthy appreciation of our mortality and so forth, are both humanly meaningful and religiously significant (p. 30).*

To this we would add that they are also *culturally* significant, and it might be difficult to disentangle culture, human meaning, and religion in this context. Individuals are multicultural, *and* cultural and ethnic groups are heterogeneous. Knowledge of the impact of religion for ethnic groups can be critical to, let us say, designing intervention programs that are culture specific. However, categorizing by ethnicity comes dangerously close to stereotyping by race. It is always necessary for the practitioner working with older people to remain sensitive to variations in cultural values, including religious and spiritual states and needs, as well as to individual differences within cultural groups.

Elders benefit from the services of religious groups that minister to the needs of the sick, frail, disabled, and homebound. Carl Jung said:

> *Among all my patients in the second half of life—that is to say, over 35—there has not been one whose problem in the last resort was not that of finding a religious outlook on life (Jung, 1955).*

This quote brings to mind questions about why and how and who enters a "spiritual journey" in the second half of life. The awesome challenges of facing loss, suffering, pain, and death; of finding ultimate meaning and purpose; of setting priorities and integrating the threads of one's life are possible reasons for such a quest. These are developmental tasks of aging, and religion may be useful in handling them. Jung's quote also brings to mind Erik Erikson's developmental concept of "integrity versus despair" discussed in Chapter 3: If a person can come to terms with life they have integrity; if not, they experience despair.

Strengthening Social Bonds

Although elders are not as lonely and isolated as stereotypes would have us believe, many live out their last years without the close emotional or social bonds that they need and desire. For some, such isolation may result from their inability to establish and maintain intimate relationships with others. For many, however, isolation results from the new social situation that old age brings. Changing family patterns means less need for the services of older members within the family. The trend toward smaller families means fewer siblings and children with whom to interact. Very old age may bring the loss of a driver's license and car, physically curtailing social opportunities. Physical disability and illness also can hinder one's social life, and if these events do not happen to one aged individual, they may happen to his or her friends. For other aged, social organizations may not be available to provide friends and companionship.

The concept of communal living is being emphasized in some retirement housing, designed with rooms clustered around a communal kitchen and dining room. People can then share meals together but find privacy in their own rooms. With some imagination, communal concepts could find further approval in the aged community and, in turn, enhance social relationships of the elderly who want to participate. Additionally, with aging Baby Boomers, communal living arrangements will be more cohort-appropriate.

Social, legal, and financial pressures on older people discourage remarriage. Many retirement programs pay the surviving spouse a monthly income that remarriage voids or reduces. Many older people experience pressure from children who may discourage them from remarrying for fear that, upon the parent's death, family assets will be in the hands of the second marital partner. Reluctance to marry out of respect for the deceased spouse poses another barrier to remarriage. Finally, old people may fear ridicule or condemnation if they choose to marry in old age. The barriers to marriage or remarriage can also become barriers to the formation of intimate relationships. But, as living together without legal marriage becomes a more acceptable lifestyle for young people, it also becomes more acceptable for the old.

Ways to become connected with other people take many forms. Widow-to-widow programs exist in many communities. These programs, which locate widows and help them to get together to share experiences, also provide legal assistance, social activities, and employment counseling. Churches are another source of counseling and other services for lonely people who can be assisted with making connections to others. We can strengthen social bonds and friendships through a genuine effort to provide these and other services and interaction that elders need.

Chapter Summary

Old or young, we all need intimacy and social bonds with others. Our social structure and values are such that old age can reduce opportunities for social interaction. Elders are at the latter stages of the family life cycle and may have experienced children leaving home, retirement, job changes, death or divorce of a spouse, death of dear friends, remarriage, and the birth and marriage of grandchildren. Despite these changes—or perhaps *because* of these changes—older people have the coping skills for getting through life's transitions. Connections with others—maintaining the ability to express intimacy, sexuality, and emotionality—are central to these coping skills.

In the area of social bonds, vast gender differences emerge. Women seem to be keepers of the support network—they are more involved with friends and family members when help is needed, and they themselves have more friends than do men. The bonds that men do have, however, are as emotionally strong as the bonds that women make. More women than men must cope with death of spouse and widowhood.

The importance of sibling relationships reemerges in later adulthood; aged siblings often provide support and companionship. Grandparenthood is a role that most elders experience; however, there are many different types of grandparenting, and the role of grandparent for most people is not a central one. The aged report themselves to be happier if they form intimate friendships with others. Neighbors and social organizations such as lodges, church, and senior centers are important sources of social interaction. Structured religion is a source of companionship, social stimulation, and spiritual support.

Key Terms

companion
confidant
convoy model
elderly sibling
equity theory
femaleness principle
fun-seeker
network analysis
religiosity
senior centers
sex commonality principle
social networks
spirituality

Questions for Discussion

1. What are the advantages and disadvantages of being married in later life? To being single?
2. Who offers the elderly the best chance of an intimate relationship, a family member or a friend?
3. What are the ages of those with whom you are most intimate? How much time do you share with your parents or grandparents, and they with you? How close to your parents do you expect to be in 10 or 20 years?
4. Imagine for a moment that you have just learned that your mother, living in a nursing home because of some cognitive impairment, is "being allowed" to have a sexual relationship with another facility resident. What is your emotional response? Should you do something about it? If so, what will that be? If not, how can you be certain that her best interests are being guarded?
5. As an older person yourself, how close will you want to be to your children or relatives? Who would you like to live with in old age if you were married? If you were single?

Fieldwork Suggestions

1. Attend a social function for older people, such as a club, senior center, or ballroom or folk dancing. Or attend a National Association of Retired Persons (NARP) or American Association of Retired Persons (AARP) meeting. What were the informal topics of conversation? What kind of interaction took place? What norms and values did you observe?
2. Interview two grandmothers and two grandfathers about the closeness of their relationships with their children and grandchildren. Include questions that explore how the relationships developed. How much interaction is there across the generations for these individuals? Why is the amount of involvement higher for some and lower for others?
3. Interview three older people about their relationships with siblings. What similarities do you find? Differences?

Online Activities

1. Search for resources for grandparents on the Internet. Look for AARP Grandparent Information Center; Grandparents as Parents; Grandparents who Care; National Coalition of Grandparents; and any other sources you can find. If you had a friend with sudden responsibilities for parenting their grandchildren, would you be able to provide information to them regarding these organizations?
2. See what kinds of Internet resources you can find that are designed to promote social contact

specifically for older people. Keep a log of your search path. How difficult was it to find information? How accessible do you think this information is?

3. Develop the idea for an Internet home page designed to promote social interaction among seniors. Remembering that older people as a group are very heterogeneous, incorporate in your home page various links to sources that might be interesting or useful to different types of interests.

6

Intimacy and Sexuality

Sex, Nursing Homes and Viagra: New Focus on Ongoing Dilemma

Jacqueline Stenson

Perhaps the one setting where sex is more of a thorny issue than the American workplace is in our nation's nursing homes.

And a Boston expert predicts that sex among elderly residents is going to become even more of a contentious issue for an aging population that now has Viagra, the wonder drug that is enabling thousands of older men and their partners to regain an active sex life.

For the most part, though, it's not the nursing-home residents who have hang-ups about sex. It's their kids, many of them unwilling to accept that their parents—who may have spent years without a companion—may now take full advantage of their new opportunities for socialization and sexual activity, according to Rosemary McDonald, a registered nurse who coordinates care for the elderly at the Brockton/West Roxbury Veterans' Affairs Medical Center in Brockton, Mass. Staff members often refer to her as "the sex nurse."

"Adult children are often very uncomfortable with their parents' sexuality," she said here Wednesday at the annual meeting of the American Geriatrics Society. "It's very hard for them. It's hard to perceive that your parents are still having sex."

Consider the case of an elderly woman with the brittle-bone disease osteoporosis who fractured her hip during sex. McDonald said that when the patient's daughter learned how the fracture occurred, she was outraged, demanding to know: "Why was she allowed to have intercourse?" Some people go so far as to insist that their parents be transferred to another nursing home to avoid contact with a consenting sexual partner. To this, McDonald response: "We cannot forget the word 'adult.' Sexuality is a basic human need. It's like food and water."

But even nursing-home staff can have difficulty accepting sexuality among consenting, mentally competent patients, particularly if a person has more than one partner, she said. And some staff members become outraged, and even ask that patients "be drugged," for engaging in behaviors like masturbation or reading pornography, she added.

While McDonald cited many instances where sexual activity in nursing homes is inappropriate—such as when patients aggressively pursue unwilling partners, when they expose themselves in public or when they are so mentally incapacitated that they may not know what they are doing—she said much sexual activity is perfectly normal and should not be subject to scorn, from staff or family members.

Part of the problem, she said, is lack of privacy. One nursing home she knows of had only one private room—the chapel. When staff members became outraged with a "dirty old man" frequently caught looking at pornography and masturbating, McDonald suggested that facility add some private rooms where patients could spend "uninterrupted time."

Sometimes, mentally incapacitated patients exhibit unacceptable sexual behavior, such as walking around unclothed or walking into an opposite-sex bathroom, but these patients need understanding and assistance—not condemnation or sedating drugs, she stressed.

Dr. Andrew Weinberg, who coordinates a committee on long-term care for the geriatrics group, agreed that sexual activity among the elderly is normal and needs to be addressed, not overlooked, in the nursing-home environment. "We need to take this seriously," he said. Attesting to the interest in sex among even the oldest of the old, McDonald recalled a recent conversation about Viagra with a 101-year-old male patient.

"If I had a sex partner," he said, "I'd be first in line."

The availability of the impotence drug makes dealing with issues of sexuality in nursing homes an even greater priority now, McDonald added.

The Need for Intimacy

Intimacy is the need to be close to, to be part of, and to feel familiar with another person. Old or young, we all need intimacy and social bonds with others. We may believe our ability to maintain close relationships is strictly a personal problem. However, from a sociological viewpoint, the social environment affects the maintenance of close or primary relationships, as well as the larger network of friends and of kin. The norms, values, and social structure of a society may either foster or retard the development of social bonds.

Social scientists have long discussed the positive relationship of connection with others and psychological well-being. Those with whom we are emotionally connected might be either friends—**achieved relationships**, or people whom we have chosen to be in our networks—or kin—**ascribed relationships**, or people in our networks over whom we have little choice (Adams, 1983; Adams & Blieszner, 1994; Antonucci & Akiyama, 1995; Blieszner & Bedford, 1995). The number of friends and active family relationships a person has traditionally has been viewed as an indication of how well an individual is aging. It must be remembered, however, that sheer number of interactions or connections is not necessarily an accurate reflection of the *quality* of those interactions (Adams & Blieszner, 1995). Psychological well-being is enhanced when the connections being maintained are positive and support the elder's ability to maximize potentialities and by interactions in which the elder's self-concept is positively reflected and maintained.

Adams and Blieszner (1995) identify **friendship relationships** in terms, first, of their process—the important attributes of the relationship; the level of enjoyment gained through the connection; and the activities conducted. Second, friendships are identified by structure, referring to the network size, how similar the network members are, and network density or the proportion of friends that know one another. **Family or kin relationships** are identified in terms of their *process*, similar to that of friendship networks; and of their *structure*, referring to family size and generational composition; marital and parenthood status; household size and living arrangements; and the functions members serve for one another.

Although most older people have strong social bonds of some sort, certain events are more likely to put constraints on their relationships. Disability and illness limit visiting, as does lack of transportation. Death takes friends and neighbors and, quite possibly, a spouse. At the stage in life when retirement brings free time for social interaction, the opportunities for it may be reduced. Malcka R. Stern experienced various losses, including her husband. She moved to a nursing home and is hearing impaired, but continues to reach out to others and respond to a warm social environment. Stern (1987) described her intimate group of friends in an article she wrote for the *Washington Post:*

> *When I count the many blessings accrued to me in my long life of 93 years, high up on the list is the fact that I am a resident in the Attic Angel Tower, a senior citizens' apartment complex in Madison, Wisconsin. There are about 70 of us, average age 85, mostly widows.*
>
> *We have a beautiful dining area, and when we all sit together at dinner—the one meal we take together—four of us to a table, we really present a picture of a group of elegantly coiffed and attired older women.*
>
> *True, at the tables lucky enough to have among them one of our few men, there always seems to be much more animated conversation and much more gaiety. We do indeed miss our men.*
>
> *Our group is impressive. We have among us professional women, all retired, of course, from all walks of life. Teachers, social workers, scientists. Many are widows of renowned professors, doctors, judges, lawyers and businessmen. In our midst we have talented artists, knitting and weaving experts, even a poet in residence.*
>
> *But lest we become too smug and too satisfied with our way of life, we all remember that attached to our apartment complex is the nursing home to which sooner or later we will all have to enter at the last stop. We don't talk about it very much. . . .*
>
> *Our friendships are warm and close. We have all experienced the same troubles, lived through losses of loved ones. Our own health fails. You complain to your neighbor about your arthritis and she doesn't say a word, but holds out her own gnarled and twisted hands. And we both smile and pat each other on the shoulder and go on about our business.*
>
> *I am very hard of hearing and often fear that I must seem pixilated when I respond inappropriately to someone's question. One does get tired of saying "What? What?" all the time. . . .*
>
> *Some of us go to a discussion group every week, and last week it was about grieving. We read James Agee's* A Death in the Family, *and then our group leader asked each of us to recall our first experience with grief.*
>
> *When it came my turn I talked about the death of my first child, my Barbara, a baby of 2 who died of diphtheria. I began to tell them and I couldn't finish the story. To my embarrassment, I burst into tears. It was 60 years ago. It was yesterday.*

Marital Status

The marital status of older people shapes a great deal of their roles, their patterns of interaction, and the social bonds they form. This section considers older couples and three categories of older singles: the widowed, divorced, and never married. An unknown percentage of older people live together without being married. Remarriage as a result of divorce or death of a spouse is becoming more common and is also discussed in this chapter.

BEING A COUPLE IN LATER LIFE

Being married is a reality for many older Americans; just under half (47 percent) of the population over 65 is married and lives with a spouse (CPS, 1996). Being married is far more common among older men than among older women. Life expectancy is longer for women, who therefore are more likely to be widowed than are men. Men are also more likely to be married to women younger than themselves. The total proportion of married people over 65 does not provide an accurate social picture, because 74 percent of men aged 65 and older are married, whereas about 40 percent of women in the same age group are married. In other words, older women are almost half as likely to be married as are older men (U.S. Bureau of the Census, 1996). In many respects, the older couple can be considered lucky. Most couples hope they can grow old together, but one or the other may die before old age.

A good deal of research evidence indicates that marriage is health-maintaining: married persons tend to have higher levels of well-being and better health than unmarried persons. Among men, marriage is associated with a lower risk of coronary heart disease, and socially isolated men and widowed women seem at particular risk of a fatal cardiovascular event. The longevity advantage of marriage is nearly always greater among men than among women, indicating that men gain greater health benefits from being married than do women (Preston, 1995; Gliksman et al., 1995; Goldman et al., 1995). Regardless of gender differences, however, the older couple seems to be happier, less lonely, and financially more stable than older single persons (Goldman et al., 1995). Together, they can usually live out their lives in a satisfying way and be a source of comfort and support to one another. If one's social ties have decreased because of retirement or disability, the role of spouse takes on even greater importance. The relationship can become the focal point of the couple's everyday life.

Physical and emotional intimacy and romance continue to the end of our lives.

The probability of an elder spouse providing caregiving for the other, more frail spouse, is very high for late-life married couples. This care provision can be deeply satisfying for both parties, as the caregiving can demonstrate a gift of love. It can also be extremely exhausting and stress producing, if the caregiving partner is her- or himself afflicted with any chronic illnesses. One particularly interesting study analyzed the quality of the marital relationship and the effectiveness of caregiving for a spouse with cognitive impairment (Townsend & Franks, 1997). The study found that people providing care to a spouse with cognitive impairment had a greater sense of effectiveness if the relationship was characterized by emotional closeness. On the other hand, emotional closeness did not mediate the sense of effectiveness when the frail spouse had a functional impairment—let us say, was incontinent, or unable to walk without assistance. In case of either functional or cognitive impairment, conflict had a direct, negative influence on a spouse's perceived caregiving effectiveness. In other words, marital emotional closeness is a critical component to understanding spousal caregiving effectiveness.

Either retirement or disability might suddenly precipitate a shift in the amount of time couples spend together. Disability is clearly not a planned-for event, and it might be expected that shifts in personal and couple identity and in other patterns would complicate a marital relationship. Research evidence consistently indicates, however, that retirement is a major transition, often requiring adaptation to the loss of work and reduced income, change in social status, and changes in identity (Sharpley, 1997). In fact, early gerontological literature emphasized retirement as a life crisis; however, more recent studies seem to indicate that, for most people, it is less a *crisis* than an *adjustment* (Hooyman & Kiyak, 1996). More recent literature describes retirement not as a single transition so much as a process including having friends who are retired, thinking about retirement, and making specific plans for being retired. Planning often includes investigating possibilities for part-time work following "retirement."

From a relationship perspective, retirement alters the interaction pattern of the couple. Prior to retirement, one or both partners may have been very active outside the home; consequently, the number of hours each week they actually spent together may have been limited. It is particularly important, given the current pattern of early retirement and increased numbers of years of healthy life following retirement, to understand about spousal relationships following this life transition. After years of separate jobs, the togetherness may need to be balanced with time apart.

Most current research indicates no trend of increased marital strife when a husband retires and his wife is not employed. In many such cases, marital satisfaction increases following the husband's retirement—a factor probably due to increased recreational shared time. A trend toward dissatisfaction and/or conflict was evident in a recent study on marital satisfaction among wives who were *still working* after their husband's retirement (Kausler & Kausler, 1996).

One common stereotype of marriage is that, after the early stages of romantic love, the relationship begins to deteriorate. Recent studies have found the opposite, namely, an increasing enchantment with each other in the later years. Marital satisfaction appears to follow an inverted bell-shaped trend—declining satisfaction after the initial years, leveling off in the middle years, and increasing again during the post-retirement years. Satisfaction may, in fact, return to its initial high level of the early marriage years, once couples have adjusted to their *new* relationship.

Couples in Retirement

People who retire involuntarily, not surprisingly, have been found to adjust more poorly to retirement than people who have planned for their retirement and have chosen the timing. This is in large part because the bulk of involuntary retirements occur when an individual has health-related disabilities and can no longer reasonably work full-time. More Type A personalities (people who attempt to control their environment and appear to be aggressive and ambitious on the job) are among those involuntary retirees than Type B personalities—the person who takes events more calmly and is not very assertive and ambitious in job-related situations (Kausler & Kausler, 1996).

The link between personality, work patterns, and adjustment at home in later life is evident in retirement. A survey in California indicated that voluntary retirees were more likely to exercise regularly, have lower stress levels, be in better physical condition, and report a higher quality of life than were involuntary retirees (Kausler & Kausler, 1996). The circumstance of the retirement, then, will have a direct effect on family relationships.

An inverted bell-shaped pattern also charts a husband and wife's opportunity to share time and common interests and to develop greater mutual respect and understanding. The time before the birth of their first child offers husband and wife maximum opportunity for mutual involvement and marital cohesion. As time demands for careers and parenting increase with children's ages and career responsibilities, couples spend less time together, and the relationship takes on a different quality than in its early years. The last child's leaving home and the retirement of the husband and wife once again allow time for greater involvement, shared activity, and marital cohesion.

Not all marital relationships become rosier with advanced old age. The deteriorating health of both husband and wife, for example, brings stressful challenges to a relationship. Outside intervention can help troubled couples in advanced old age. Too much stress, whether financial or health-related, is hard on a marriage at any age.

SINGLEHOOD IN OLD AGE

Older singles may be divorced, never married, or widowed. Only slightly over 5 percent of the aged are divorced and not remarried, and only 4 percent have never been married. The widowed

TABLE 6.1

Marital Status of Older People Living in the Community by Age, Race or Ethnicity, and Gender (Percentages)

	65–74		75–84		85+	
	Men	Women	Men	Women	Men	Women
White (N = 26,000,000)						
Never Married	5	5	4	6	3	6
Married	83	55	74	30	53	9
Widowed	8	36	19	61	42	83
Divorced	4	5	2	3	2	2
Black (N = 2,436,000)						
Never Married	4	4	6	5	—*	6
Married	67	39	60	27	—	16
Widowed	18	47	25	67	—	76
Divorced	11	9	9	2	—	2
Hispanic Origin (any race) (N = 1,005,000)						
Never Married	6	7	6	11	—	—
Married	78	60	69	26	—	—
Widowed	9	34	21	58	—	—
Divorced	6	10	3	5	—	—

*Based less than 75,000

Source: U.S. Bureau of the Census, "Marital Status and Living Arrangements: March 1989," *Current Population Reports*, Series P-20, No. 445, (Washington, DC: U.S. Government Printing Office, 1990).

make up the bulk of elderly singles. Thirty-four percent of all men and women age 65 and over are widowed (CPS, 1996) Fully 10.4 million women over 60 are currently widowed, whereas only about 2 million men are widowed and not remarried (U.S. Bureau of the Census, 1994).

THE WIDOWED

Table 6.1 compares the marital status of three age groups and compares males with females. In the United States, the differences between men and women have always been pronounced. Most white males at all age levels are married: 83 percent of those 65 to 74, 74 percent of those aged 75 to 84, and 53 percent of those 85 and over. Notice the very large percentages of women 85 and over who are widowed.

Widowhood is the predominant lifestyle for women who comprise the "old-old" (age 75 and above) and the "oldest-old" (age 85 and over). If 59 percent of all people 65 years of age and older are women, we can expect that, in the future, three out of four women will ultimately become widows. Only if a man lives to be 85 is there an even chance of his being widowed. Women essentially can plan to be widowed in their later life, and, given the numbers, perhaps women *must* include that possibility in their planning.

The transition from married to widowed status brings both personal and familial problems. The transition is not always successful. Statistics indicate that the widowed suffer higher rates of mortality, mental disorders, and suicide. Childless widows especially lack support. The feelings of loss after the death of a spouse are enormous, especially if the couple had been married 30, 50, or even 60 or more years. The empty chair and the empty place in bed reinforce memories of sharing family rituals. What does one do with the memories? How does one manage the grief? Many turn to other family members for emotional support; others simply suffer alone.

Loss of a spouse may cause the most difficult role change that a person must cope with in a lifetime. The widow has lost the support and services of an intimate person in her life. If she doesn't find substitute supports, she is on her own. Her social life will be altered. She, as a single person, may be either uninvited to, or feel uncomfortable, in social settings where she had once been welcome. She may lose contact with her husband's friends and relatives. She then must form new relationships and make new friends.

Official recognition of the event of widowhood typically begins with the funeral and the initial mourning period. The term **grief work** describes healthy confrontation and acknowledgment of the emotions brought about by death. Grief work for the widow takes time and may bring a temporary withdrawal from past social activities and responsibilities as she reassesses her life. Once she answers the question "Where do I go from here?" she can reengage in society.

Studies of widowhood typically characterize the period beginning about six months after the spouse's death as a reorganization stage different from the phase of intense grief that comprises the first few months after the event. Research on the later phases of coping with widowhood has focused on the importance of friends and family as sources of social support. The widow is particularly vulnerable with the early stresses associated with grieving, and support from friends and family is critical to help the widow maintain a sense of identity as she reassesses her life. The tight-knit structure of a family network seems indicated for this kind of support. The less highly structured network of friends has been associated with help on decisions for building a new life as a single woman. Not all support network interactions, however, are satisfactory.

Family dynamics, tight-knit or not, have both negative and positive aspects to them, as do friendship dynamics (Morgan et al., 1997; Shuchter & Zisook, 1993; Kanacki et al., 1996). To study supportive dynamics in widowhood, one study (Morgan et al., 1997) gave widows a diagram of concentric circles and asked them to place people who "have either a positive or negative effect on your life" into one of three circles: an inner circle for those who had the most effect; a middle circle for those who had effect but not quite so much, and an outer circle for anyone else who still had an effect. Although the researchers did not specify what the negatives and positives were, it allowed people to identify network members who did not have a positive impact at this time in the widow's life. Family members, it was discovered, were the primary source of both positives and negatives. Differences in the number of negatives were notable because they increased over time in both family and nonfamily segments of the network.

Clearly, the relationships of family and nonfamily serve different purposes in the process of grief work among widows. As Morgan and colleagues point out (1997), there is no theory to adequately address the finding of timing and the interaction of positive and negative support. Their research serves as an important reminder that assuming that personal networks are *positively* supportive is not necessarily accurate and can be myth generating, as is the belief that stressful events mobilize "positive support." Even so, research continues to support the finding that higher levels of perceived social support are related to lower depression scores for both widows and widowers (Kanacki et al., 1996).

The perception of having a supportive network, regardless of the contact and the amount of exchanges made, seems to serve a critically important function for widows. The *belief* that one is fully supported might be far more than half the battle. Changes, be they positive or negative, will naturally occur for the widow following the death of her spouse—reduced contact with friends of the husband or with in-laws, for example, and new and different relationships with children (Lamme et al., 1996).

Widowhood creates changes in the widow's support system beyond that of the absence of a spouse. In one longitudinal analysis of children's responses to their mother's widowhood, Roan and Raley (1996) found that contact increased between mothers and their adult children. This is a finding we would expect because adult children and their mothers have the intimacy of shared grief over the death of a father and death of a husband. Another study of parent-child communication shortly following the death of a parent-spouse found that both parents and children seemed concerned with protecting each other from the pain and sadness associated with the loss (Silverman et al., 1995). The study identified two types of families. In the open family, consoling and informing language was used. Less-open families used language to influence and to avoid feelings and confrontation with death. Two key points are relevant to all these studies, however: first, network contact is not necessarily always positive; and second, study findings are generalized and can mask the vast individual differences that exist.

The role of friends can be very important to the bereaved widow. Again, however, support can be positive or negative. One woman reported:

> *This business of people saying "You're doing so well:" I hated that. Or "You're so strong." Because I was really feeling terrible, and I needed someone to say, "Gee, it's really rough for you right now" (Morgan, 1989).*

Interviews with 300 widowed women in an urban community showed them to be self-sufficient in managing their daily lives. They did not lean heavily on anyone for help with the basic tasks of daily living unless they were in advanced age and/or experiencing poor health (O'Bryant, 1991). The research suggested that too much independence and self-sufficiency led to social isolation. Asking for help and giving help to others results in *interdependence,* which is the most valued lifestyle (Roan & Raley, 1996).

Different women react differently to the loss of a spouse. Women in traditional marriages, who see their role of wife as central and who invested their identity primarily in this role, suffer immensely. If the marriage was close, the loss cuts especially deep into all aspects of the survivor's life. The frequently experienced drop in income level experienced by widows can promote isolation and loneliness. Indeed, many widows have lower morale and fewer social ties because they are poorer than their married counterparts and are unable to interact in as many social events as more financially stable women can. Generally speaking, the higher the widow's personal resources, such as income and education, and the higher her social and community participation, the better she can cope with her status.

The process of adjustment to widowhood is a very complex path of redefinition of roles and self-concept. People may move back and forth between feeling secure and comfortable with their self-concepts or feeling quite the opposite or experience several feelings simultaneously. Those with previously happy marriages are more likely to consider remarriage or to make a successful life for themselves alone; in contrast, women whose marriages were not fulfilling are less likely to consider remarriage.

> *Darling, I am living half without you; half of me is dead.*
>
> BECK, 1965

Widowed women often describe their experience as one of transformation, not one of recovery. Van den Hoonaard (1997) named the process described by the widows "identity foreclosure" to refer to the sense of shift in personal identity reflected in their writing. Some examples of this foreclosure follow, in the voices of the women:

> *Who am I without Judd? Who will define my existence for me? (Seskin).*
>
> *My sense of self, to a great extent, became linked to being Leonard's wife... We reassured, validated, reinforced, and encouraged. We mirrored the best part of each other. I lost that mirror when Leonard died. It was a double death. When he had said, "You're wonderful," I believed him... But with Leonard gone, I felt paralyzed. It was as if he had taken a major part of me with him (Rose).*
>
> *"Sign here," the girl in the office of vital statistics said when I went to pick up a copy of your death certificate... "Right here. In the block that says widow of the deceased." The word pierced me like a lance and my sharp intake of breath was audible... Later as I walked home, I tried to give voice to my new label. Widow! Widow! I mouthed the word over and over and although I could hear it thundering in my head, no sound would leave my lips... Until two weeks ago, widow was only a word in the English language. Now it is me... (Dohaney, quoted in van den Hoonaard, 1997).*

A number of organizations offer outreach services to widows and widowers. They may be religious, social service, or mental health groups. The American Association of Retired Persons (AARP) has a program, Widowed Persons Service (WPS), in which volunteers who have been widowed 18 months or more are trained to reach out and offer support to the newly widowed. Participation in outreach programs can be a lifesaver for elders willing to seek help.

GENDER DIFFERENCES IN WIDOWHOOD

Family sociologists disagree whether husbands or wives experience greater difficulty in coping with the death of a spouse. A husband as the surviving partner of a traditional relationship may have the greater difficulty. He may have to learn the new role of housekeeper—learn to cook, to assume cleaning chores, and to host if he wants to entertain friends. Further, the widower is less likely than the widow to move in with his children, less likely to have a high degree of interaction with relatives, and less likely to have close friends. He is more likely to have somewhat increased interaction with sons, however, than is a widow with her sons. If the wife was the initiator of family contacts, her death typically lessens the widow's interaction with extended family members.

Statistics paint a grim picture for the husband who survives his wife. Widowers die four times as often from suicide, three times as often from accidents, 10 times as often from strokes, and six times as often from heart disease as do married men of the same age (*Widowed Persons Service Fact Sheet,* 1990).

On the other hand, the widow's situation may be equally difficult, both socially and psychologically (Stevens, 1995). Many widows (about half by some estimates) spend a significant period of time providing care to ill husbands before becoming widowed. They often have depleted social and emotional resources. Some social scientists believe that it would make good policy sense to shift a portion of Social Security benefits from the time both the husband and wife are alive to the time when there is only one survivor (Sandell & Iams, 1997). This might reduce some of the poverty that emerges with widowhood for many women.

The emotional costs of widowhood are high for all people. The long-term widowed men and women (five or more years) report more loneliness than married individuals, and women report less perceived life satisfaction (Lichtenstein et al., 1996). Health might be a factor in adjustment to widowhood. Women often show an "anticipation effect," indicated by elevated depressive symptoms just prior to the spouse's death. Although longitudinal analyses show that it is more stressful to be bereaved when young-old than when old-old, there are no age differences in how long it takes to feel well-adjusted again following a spouse's death. Adjustment to bereavement is multidimensional and includes personality, social, economic, and family history factors.

It seems that men and women change in different directions at the loss of a spouse. Men are often more "in search of others." They become more aware and appreciative of friends and relationships. Women, as the quotes above indicate, are more "in search of themselves." With time, they develop confidence, assertiveness, and independence. In general, widows were previously more wrapped up in the role of wife than were widowers in the role of husband. New relationships developed by each to allow more flexible roles and less dependency. Both sexes can find new excitement about the changes in their lives.

DIVORCED ELDERS

As the twenty-first century unfolds, divorce is a dominant social reality in the United States. In over one-third of all married-couple households at least one spouse had a previous marriage that ended in divorce or widowhood. Couples in a first marriage constitute one-quarter of black households and just under half of all white and Hispanic households (Holden & Kuo, 1996). Divorce among the 65 and older population, once uncommon, is increasing. In 1960 only 1.5 percent of women over 65 were divorced; in 1996, nearly 16 percent were divorced (Holden & Kuo, 1996).

Strains in marriage are complex and will not be dealt with completely in this review; however, it is important to keep in mind that marital strains are probably heightened by longevity. At the end of the 19th century, the average length of marriage when one spouse died was 28 years; now it is over 43 years (Troll, 1986). There have never before in history been so many couples attempting to live a lifetime with one another for such a long period of that lifetime. Rare and widely celebrated at one time, the golden wedding anniversary (50 years) is now reached by many couples, and although its occurrence is still celebrated and honored, it is no longer a rarity. To the extent that it is a rarity is increasingly due to the smaller proportion of marriages that last that long, but not because of the death of a spouse. One couple was overheard to be talking about celebrating 60 years of marriage between them: 22 years with his first wife, 20 years with her first husband, and 18 years together. This couple joked that the years were additive because they represented *experience* being brought to the present marriage. A new perspective on an old tradition is apparent at the close of the 20th century.

Each year at least 50,000 people over 60 years of age dissolve marriages of 30 to 40 years' duration. Additionally, divorce is projected to continue to increase. The overall rate has climbed in the last 30 years from 5 percent to 50 percent, and a high proportion of those divorces are taking place among the Baby Boomers—the cohort for whom divorce has become commonplace, and the next cohort to enter the aged population (Mulroy, 1996). For the elder who is remarried, the risks of that marriage ending in divorce are 10 times that of the elderly who is in his or her first marriage (Lanza, 1996). The consequences of these numbers are enormous. When one considers both widowhood and divorce, less than half of all women entering old age (65) in 2025 will be in a marriage.

Divorce is a particularly difficult event for older people. It is rarely a sudden development and might result from many years of deepening emotional disruption. Among people for whom marriage and the family have been both vocation and avocation, divorce is not only a failed promise but also a broken covenant (Lanza,

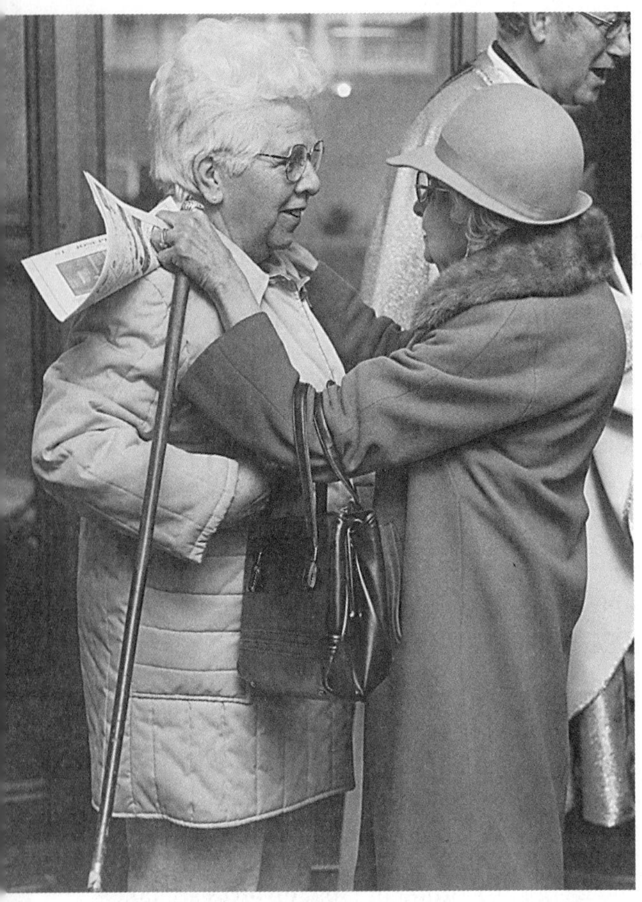

Friendships provide an important source of joy for everyone and can be especially important for elders with limited family contact.

1996). The social shame felt by some men and women at being divorced can be very powerful—particularly so among older women, for whom remarriage rates are very low. In her extensive study of divorced older women in 1988, Cain found that the length of marriage significantly contributed to postdivorce despair and slow recovery. Some women described feeling envious of widowed women they knew, as society knows how to respond to the needs of a widow, but is uncertain about those of the divorcee. There is little evidence of change over the past decade. Widows are more likely to have acceptance by peers, support of family, economic stability, and the anticipation of living alone than are divorced women (Lanza, 1996).

Not as much support exists for the divorced single person, male or female, as for widowed elders. Men have a higher probability of remarriage, but their friends are usually in longer-term marriages, and most of those friends were friends as couples. Adult children can have a difficult time dealing with the divorce of their parents after many years. Uncomfortable and complicated family interactions commonly erupt, and the isolation of one or both of the elder parents by children and grandchildren can result. Thanksgiving might seem less uncomfortable if *neither* grandparent attends; birthday celebrations for the grandchildren are more comfortably celebrated within the nuclear family only. There are few norms for dealing with the divorce of an older couple, for the divorcing couple or their friends, or for the kin network. These norms will, fortunately or unfortunately, become better evolved in the next few years, given the projected numbers of marriage dissolutions.

Though divorce has gained acceptance as a solution to an unpleasant or difficult marriage, at this point in history the impact of the increasing divorce rate in old age has profound impact on the financial status of elders and the conformation of kinship networks. Many of the changes in social interactions and patterns of relationship that are only now becoming worked out—relationships with ex-in-laws, for example—will become "traditional" in the next couple of decades, and new norms will emerge. Until that time, divorce is traumatic, both economically and emotionally.

Along with new social norms, social policy will need to catch up with the social reality of multiple marriages and single status through divorce in later life. Property reform and survivorship rules of public and private benefits have improved conditions of widowhood, but there is less protection against long-term economic consequences of past and future marital dissolution (Holden & Kuo, 1996).

THE NEVER MARRIED

The never married constituted a little over 4 percent of the aged population in 1996. Few people who were never married do so in old age—first marriages make up less than 10 percent of all marriages of elders. One might expect elderly singles who have never married to be unhappy and lonely, but the never married have typically adjusted to being single in their younger years and are well practiced in those skills of self-reliance and independence that make living alone a desirable and workable lifestyle.

Older people who have never married often have highly valued friends and relatives, including nephews and nieces. When these important people in their lives die or drop contact, the elders suffer greatly. Like all other subgroups of older people, however, the never married are a diverse group—some *are* isolated (sometimes by choice); others have many friends. Some wish they were married and feel they have lost out on something; others are happy and fulfilled with their lives and have no regrets.

REMARRIAGE

Today we hear a great deal more about the occurrence of late-life marriages. Remarriage in old age is becoming more common for two reasons: (1) more older people are divorcing, which places them in the remarriage market; and (2) remarriage has become more acceptable for the widowed. Although remarriage of widowed and divorced women over age 65 currently constitutes only 4 percent of all marriages (U.S. Bureau of the Census, 1996), remarriage seems to work well for most older people.

Many older people have had long, reasonably happy second (or third) marriages and are glad to have found another compatible partner. They do not take relationships or marriage for granted. Older singles in search of relationships try to meet partners at church functions, local clubs and organizations, parties, and dances. The extroverted might try video dating, computerized dating, or advertising in the personal columns of newspapers. Here is a sampling:

> *All I want is a kind, spiritual NS/ND/ND gentleman who has a house with a garden to grow vegetables. I am 5'7", 67 and into holistic health and metaphysics. I love nature and people, too.*
>
> *SINGLE WOMAN 60ish enjoys everything from opera to country, dining out, picnics, playing pool, horseback riding, swimming, reading and more! Would love to meet male with similar interests.*
>
> *An early 70's N/S DWM seeks the companionship of a woman who manifests spirituality and intelligence. A few of my interests are theatre, Dixieland jazz, and strenuous hiking. In 1994 I traveled to Europe and China. Please respond to . . . (*Santa Rosa Press Democrat, *"The Meeting Place," 28 February 1995, p. F3).*

Such ads indicate that the desire for courtship and meaningful relationships lasts a lifetime. Beginning in the 1980s, researchers called for more attempts to understand dating and mate selection in later life. However, we know little about the process of courtship in later life. Although we know that intimate relationships are important and that older people seek intimacy and meaningful relationships, we have not yet examined the process leading to remarriage.

A positive aspect of remarriage in old age is that children are grown and out of the house. The couple does not typically experience the great daily strain of being stepparents. An increase in the use of prenuptial agreements, developed by family lawyers, has helped to reduce potential for family conflict over inheritance. A greater number of attorneys are now familiar with issues of particular relevance to an older client: pension rights; whether both parties do or should have nursing home care insurance; clarity on issues around durable medical powers of attorney; tax issues; social security benefits; and insurance.

Some older people have bypassed remarriage because of concern for children's inheritance rights and competing filial obligations among adult stepchildren. Mediation before remarriage to establish clear understandings among all family members can help eliminate misunderstanding before it surfaces. Families are reassured, and the elders feel more secure in being able to develop their own late-life plans as a couple. Remarriage can enhance older partners' abilities to adjust to changes in physical competence by providing steady and caring companionship (Choi & Wodarski, 1996). Feeling cared for and being touched are important factors that enhance quality of life at any age, and perhaps they are most precious in later life when the possibility of being without them is so likely.

Sexual Relationships and Sexuality

Sexuality is not simply a product of biology. Sexual identity is a complex product of emotional, developmental, and cultural aspects of life—it is part of an individual's *identity*, and an important characteristic that is carried with us throughout our lives, over the life course. Being aware of the marriage of these aspects of life at all ages can help develop an appreciation for sex as an essential part of the relationship with oneself and with others (Drench & Losee, 1996; Kaye, 1993).

Developmentally, in childhood we learn in what ways our own boundaries are separate from those of other people. Understanding those boundaries is an important part of developing a solid sense of the *self*. In adolescence, the developing *self* learns to enter into relationships of love, in which the experience of being a separate individual is simultaneous with the experience of being emotionally merged. Sexuality is an integral part of loving and bonding. The continuing aspect of sexual identity remains a dynamic part of our self-concept throughout the life course. Over time the identity shifts and changes, but it remains a central aspect of our human condition. It remains central even if we develop a chronic illness, if a spouse dies, if we are surrounded by friends and family, or if we live alone and maintain a solitary life. Fundamentally, we are sexual beings.

Our sexual identity, as part of our self-concept, is dynamic—it changes over time in terms of behavior and of interest. Numerous psychosocial factors are involved: customs; personal characteristics; religious and social considerations; educational, financial, and vocational levels; partner availability; the nature and severity of organic conditions; mobility; and effects of medications (Drench & Losee, 1996).

Role models available to us as we grow into maturity are also critical. A survey of college students bears out this idea. Both young and middle-aged college undergraduates completed the Aging Sexuality Knowledge and Attitude Scale (Hillman & Stricker, 1996). Findings showed that greater *knowledge* about sexuality and the elderly was associated with more *permissive attitudes*. Most interesting, however, was the finding that the simple presence of a relationship with at least one grandparent was significantly and positively related to adult attitudes toward elderly sexuality. Those adults will bring their attitudes with them as they age and eventually become new cohorts of elderly.

SEXUAL INVISIBILITY

The sexuality of older people is largely invisible. This is partly because for many older people, sex and sexuality are intensely private matters. It is also from our cultural focus on youth; that which is not youthful (or new) is not functional and of no use. The myth that older people automatically lose interest in sex distorts perceptions of older people. It also influences older people's perceptions of themselves, because we generally incorporate our culture's attitudes, norms, and values into our self-concepts unless there is some other powerful validation for being "different." As a result, elders in our society are "sexually invisible." They are not viewed as being sexual. Therefore, any suggestion of sexuality is received with

Older people are often treated as asexual beings. This woman looks lovely, feels lovely, and is helping to change the image of later-life sexuality.

derision (What does he think *he's* going to do?), condescension (Did you see how *cute* he was around that young woman?), humor (Did you hear the one about the old guy who...), shock (How could a woman her age *act* like that?), or a deadly combination of all four. Simply stated, people generally do not put themselves in positions to be treated with scorn, therefore their sexuality becomes hidden. Invisible.

It is important to note that these assumptions need not be true, but simply believed.

R. A. FRIEND, 1987

PHYSICAL ATTRACTION AND YOUTH

The idea is commonplace that sexual tension is based mainly on physical attraction between the sexes, and very young men and women are the most physically or sexually attractive. Advertising, film, television, and stage promote the theme that good looks, youth, and sex go together. Models are generally young, and beauty contests usually involve those no older than their mid-twenties.

Many people consider only the young, perfectly proportioned body to be sexually attractive. The signs of age, especially when combined with obesity or socially unacceptable features, are assumed automatically to be unattractive. When people consider older bodies to be neither sexually stimulating nor desirable, the next step is to assume that no interest in sex or sexual activity occurs in old age. Assumptions can produce self-fulfilling prophecies in which old people internalize those cultural messages about themselves.

The self-fulfilling prophecy, however, might not always apply. Wilcox (1997) surveyed 144 men and women age 20 to 80 to determine their personal body attitudes. She found that self-esteem, health, and masculinity (an instrumental orientation) were positively related to body attitudes, but that these relationships did not differ by age or by gender. In other words, men and women with good self-esteem also had good body attitudes; that is, they liked their bodies. Eighty-year-olds with good self-esteem liked their bodies as much as 20-year-olds with good self-esteem. Wilcox suggested that **social comparisons** (Heidrich & Ryff, 1993) are an aspect of this body attitude. They describe a process by which people compare themselves with others who are having more difficulty along a particular dimension. This is a "downward" comparison, and might be a particularly functional adaptation for older adults in maintaining a good sense of body image.

ROMANTIC LOVE

Although romantic love has been variously defined, it has a number of generally accepted characteristics: idealization of mate, consuming interest and passion, fantasy, and desire for a blissful state of togetherness. Clichéd ideals—love at first sight and the idea that love conquers all—are often elements of romantic love. There is no inherent reason why only young people should have exclusive access to romantic love. Yet in all forms of media, romantic love is predominantly an emotion for young people. From Shakespeare's *Romeo and Juliet* to the present, passion and romance is primarily for young lovers. Perhaps the concept came to be associated with young people because they are the ones most often involved in mate selection. However, with the increasing divorce rate and with increasing life expectancy, mate selection often continues throughout life. The belief that only young people are capable of strong passionate feeling invalidates the passions of older people.

The concept of **sexual function for procreation,** which disassociates elders and sex, was embodied in Christian Catholicism by the teachings of St. Augustine (Feldstein, 1970). Accordingly, a woman's femininity was measured by her childbearing and mothering role. Likewise, a man's masculinity was measured by the number of children he fathered. Because of the association between sexuality and procreation, men and women beyond the usual childbearing years were believed to be asexual—most clearly so for women, whose ability to procreate ends abruptly with menopause. In current times, the sex act is considered an expression of love and happiness, with the reward being pleasure rather than children. Deeply rooted ideas take a long time to die, however. Some men still fear that a vasectomy will rob them of virility, and some women fear that menopause will rob them of femininity.

HOMOSEXUAL RELATIONSHIPS

Stereotypes of older gay men and lesbians are of lonely, predatory, pitiful outcasts in either homosexual or straight communities. Indeed, aging can be a particularly difficult course for gay men and lesbians. Psychotherapist Joel Frost (1997) states:

> *Negative myths and stereotypes about older gay men and lesbians, the dearth of positive older role models, continued discrimination in a heterosexist society, and developmental pressures without a clear model for gay aging make it especially difficult and complex for gay men and lesbian women. Indeed, many older gay men have to now struggle with being the age of the internalized homophobic stereotype of the "dirty old man" they learned to avoid when they were younger (p. 268).*

Relatively recent political and social discussion of the civil rights of gay males and lesbians has helped to highlight some of the discrimination faced by these groups (Boxer, 1997). Particularly among younger people, there is a good deal of social activism on behalf of issues relevant to gays and lesbians. The social and psychological circumstances for most older gays and lesbians is vastly different, however, than that of younger men and women. A study in the early 1980s (Dawson, 1982) estimated the United States population of gay men and lesbians over 60 to be 3.5 million people. These men and women developed their sexual identities and "came out" in times of social persecution and fear. They had few positive role models and were surrounded by highly negative stereotypic messages about themselves (Frost, 1997).

Developmentally and socially, most older gays and lesbians are charting new waters at the close of the 20th century, developing role models for younger adults in the process. It is a difficult course to chart; in addition to the impediments of social attitude and self-perception, many older people must address the ageism that still occurs in gay, lesbian, and bisexual communities (D'Augelli & Garnets, 1995).

Given the diversity and difficulty of generating representative samples for study, little is known about the older gay and lesbian population from a social science perspective (Michaels, 1996). Most information is anecdotal, based on partisan observations of regional or community proportion. For example, contrary to popular wisdom, recent research on families and relationships caution not to assume that being partnered is more developmentally appropriate or necessarily psychologically satisfying over being single for older lesbians and gays (Hostetler & Cohler, 1997). Clearly, research on aging in lesbian and gay male communities lags behind that of research on heterosexual aging. It is equally clear that the assumptions and theoretical frameworks used for one cultural group must be carefully challenged when applied to another.

Older lesbians and gay men typically live within a self-created network of friends, significant others, and selected biological family members. Herdt (1997) reported finding, however, that many people have fears about being alone in their old age. The possibility remains that as the Baby Boomer generation ages, new models of living in communities may become more common (Boxer, 1997).

In reality, the lifestyles and life choices of gay males and lesbians are similar to those of heterosexuals. In reports from older lesbians, although the respondents were suffering from ageism, sexism, and homophobia, they did not regret their sexual orientation. They were able, as are other groups of elders, to make a healthy adjustment and to live their lives with high self-esteem (Schoonmaker, 1993).

Research on Sexuality

The **Kinsey studies** of the sexual practices of men and women were the landmark studies on human sexuality in the United States, published in 1948 and 1953. Kinsey's findings were based on a huge oversampling of men recruited from homosexual bars, so the conclusions cannot be generalized to the larger population. The studies did, however, develop methods for conducting research on sexuality, and a great deal of research has followed Kinsey's stepping stone into aging and sexual behavior. A few of the more groundbreaking studies are explored here.

> *Erection is chiefly caused by scuraum, eringoes, cresses, crymon, parsnips, artichokes, turnips, asparagus, candied ginger, acorns bruised to powder and drank [sic] in muscadel, scallion, sea shell fish, etc.*
>
> ARISTOTLE, 4TH CENTURY BC

MASTERS AND JOHNSON

Masters and Johnson's studies of human sexual behavior were considered revolutionary for their time period, just as Kinsey's were for his; they studied not just sexual histories but also observed and recorded the physiological responses of couples having sexual intercourse. This research resulted in their first book, *Human Sexual Response* (1966). Their second book, *Human Sexual Inadequacy* (1970), is based on their treatment program for those suffering from sexual dysfunctions. Although the use of technical language is rather difficult for the layperson to understand, the discussion that follows is taken largely from a very readable book that interprets their work and is endorsed by them (Belliveau & Richter, 1970). One methodological problem relative to aging with Masters and Johnson's study is that most of their "old" subjects were between 50 and 60. They studied few individuals over 60.

Body processes slow down with age, but do not stop. Masters and Johnson found that if a middle-aged husband and wife are aware of these changes and take them into account in their lovemaking, there is no reason why pleasurable sex cannot continue. For men, the body processes affected by the aging process include the length of time needed to get an erection and the firmness of the erection. The ejaculatory expulsion of semen is less forceful, and the erection may be lost faster after ejaculation. In addition, it may take longer to have another erection. If the older man is aware that these changes do not signal the end of his ability to have an erection, he can relax and enjoy sexual activity.

According to Masters and Johnson, men over 50 have many advantages over younger men. Their ejaculatory control becomes better, and they can maintain an erection for a longer period of time without the strong drive to ejaculate. As partners, many women say that longer lovemaking is more satisfying—time allows for greater opportunity to bond emotionally during sex. Sex becomes, for these women, more an act of sexuality and emotional connection than an act of physical performance.

If [a woman]...is normally developed mentally, and well-bred, her sexual desire is small. If this were not so, the whole world would become a brothel, and marriage and a family impossible.

J. G. RICHARDSON, MD, 1909

The aging female is subject to all the negative attitudes of our society regarding women and sexual matters: the beliefs that a woman's sex drive is not as strong as a man's, that women are more passive, that women are not supposed to enjoy sex as much as men. These myths become even stronger in terms of the older woman—for instance, the myth that it is unnatural for women to continue sexual relations after menopause. Far less attention has been paid to sexuality in aging women than in aging men, in no small part due to the sexism of the male-dominated medical profession of the 19th and 20th centuries (Morley et al., 1989).

Masters and Johnson reported that it is natural and beneficial for older women to continue sexual activity with no long periods of abstinence. Older women do, however, experience a slowing process, just as men do. Vaginal lubrication occurs more slowly with aging and less lubrication is produced. While younger women take 15 to 30 seconds for lubrication, older women may take as long as four or five minutes. The clitoris becomes smaller with age, but it still receives and transmits sexual excitement. There is less increase in the size of the vaginal canal. And, with age, the lining of the vaginal walls can become thin. Older women, like older men, generally experience a shorter orgasmic phase.

Masters and Johnson reported an increase in the rate of masturbation in older women. Many women are widowed or divorced and isolated from male sex partners. Particularly among older couples, husbands may be ill and not willing to participate in sex. According to Masters and Johnson, many women who want release from sexual tension are able to provide it for themselves.

For women, as for men, aging has advantages. Postmenopausal women are no longer concerned about the risk of pregnancy or the side effects of contraceptives. They also may be free of the anxieties and pressures of motherhood. Menopause does not in itself blunt the human female's sexual capacity, performance, or drive. Masters and Johnson found no endpoint to female or male sexuality set by advancing years.

THE DUKE LONGITUDINAL STUDY

In spite of the small numbers of older people Masters and Johnson studied, their findings are of tremendous importance regarding the sexual *potential* of older people. But Masters and Johnson made no attempt to study just how many older people take advantage of their sexual potential and remain sexually active. The **Duke Longitudinal Study** tried to answer this question and to also assess the changes in sexual interest and activity that come with age (Verwoerdt, Pfeiffer, & Wang, 1969). The study, begun in 1954 at Duke University, still continues. One fascinating finding from this longitudinal study is that one in six of all people will become even more interested in sex as they age (Witkin, 1994).

In the Duke study, sexual activity was only one of many aspects studied in the lives of 254 older people. The sample was composed of nearly equal numbers of men and women whose ages ranged between 60 and 94. Four patterns of change in sexual activity were observed throughout the 10-year longitudinal study of 1954 to 1965: inactivity, sustained activity, decreasing activity, and rising sexual activity.

The researchers found a great deal of variability in sexual behavior among the aging individuals. Approximately 15 percent of the sample fitted into the rising category, whereas unmarried women were almost totally inactive sexually. Ten years did not greatly decrease the number of elders who were sexually active. About half of the men and women who survived into their eighties and nineties reported having sexual interest. Among men surviving into their eighties and nineties, continued sexual activity was not rare; and about one-fifth of these men reported that they were still sexually active.

The Duke study reveals enough sexual activity on the part of the old and the very old to illustrate the sexual potential Masters and Johnson found in older adults. On the other hand, the sexual *interest* of many Duke study participants exceeded their actual sexual activity. Although not clearly explained, this discrepancy was perhaps caused by ailing physical health, psychological reasons, or lack of an acceptable partner.

OTHER STUDIES

Starr and Weiner (1981) studied responses of older individuals to a lengthy questionnaire on sex and sexuality. Elders, even those in their seventies and eighties, reported being sexually active and stated that sex was as good or better than ever, though somewhat less frequent than previously in their lives. Three-fourths of the elders studied said their lovemaking had improved with time. The researchers challenge the Kinsey studies on the rapidity of decline of sexual activity with age.

Another opportunity for questionnaire response was provided by the *Consumers' Union* (Brecher, 1984); over 4,000 aged men and women responded. The responses indicated that age did not adversely affect enjoyment of sex and that most husbands and wives were currently having marital intercourse. Unhappy marriage reduced sexual activity for older couples, just as it did for younger couples. Rates of extramarital intercourse, though lower than those for younger couples, still occurred for the same reasons. Inattentive or uninterested spouses were major factors. Some couples had open marriages. Homosexual experiences were reported, some of which took place for the first time in old age. Such findings dash stereotypes of sexually inactive and uninterested elders. Many elders had struggled for sexual frankness and openness throughout their lives, fighting taboos that seem to have been more strict than those young people face today. Some elders had improved their sex lives over the years by breaking down psychological barriers; some had not. Some people regretted being so sexually uninformed when they were young.

Respondents found a variety of ways to compensate for sexual changes brought about by aging or poor health. They slowed down the lovemaking process, emphasized oral sex and manual stimulation of the genitals, and participated in lots of fondling and cuddling. Many reported that the sensation of touch was more important, meaningful, and appreciated than in their younger years. Some women used a lubricant to compensate for lack of vaginal moisture. The biggest problem for older, unmarried women was finding a partner; men their age are in small supply. Respondents generally showed a strong interest in sex and a large capacity for enjoying life.

Among the very old, biological studies of changes in the male reproductive system reveal these findings: need for greater direct penile stimulation to achieve erection, slower erection (but only a few minutes slower), briefer stage of ejaculatory inevitability, reduced amount of seminal ejaculation, and reduced need for ejaculation at each and every sexual contact. If a man becomes impotent, the cause is illness or disease, not aging. New knowledge and techniques are continually being made available in dealing with either impotence or premature ejaculation. In addition, sensations become less genital, more sensual, and more diffused.

In the aging female, sexual response changes include slower lubrication, greater need for direct stimulation of the clitoris, shorter orgasmic phase, and irritability of vaginal tissue and outer lying tissue with low levels of estrogen. These changes do not mean the end of one's sex life. Sexuality, it appears, is among the last of our faculties to decline with age.

A study in the *Johns Hopkins Medical Letter* reported that 70 percent of 68-year-old men and the majority (over 50 percent) of women in their seventies regularly engage in sexual intercourse. One of the most debilitating factors related to diminished sexual activity is the self-fulfilling prophecy in which the belief shapes the reality that sexual prowess diminishes with age. Knowing what changes to expect with aging as well as how to deal with those changes is a key to remaining sexually active. Understanding the relationship of sexuality and health is also important. At any age health problems such as diabetes, alcoholism, depression, or anxiety can interfere with sexual function.

Bretschneider and McCoy (1988) studied the sexuality of a healthy population of individuals between the ages of 80 and 102. The most common activities in order of frequency were touching and caressing, masturbation, and intercourse. Although 63 percent of the men had intercourse at least sometimes, only 30 percent of the women did. The researchers concluded that, for men, the frequency of sexual intercourse does not change greatly after age 80 compared to the previous decade. This suggests that physiological shifts have occurred already for the 80-year-old man, and that he has an available sexual partner—probably a wife. For either men or women in general there is no decade this side of 100 in which sexual activity is totally absent.

In general, findings on sexuality show that, given good health, a positive attitude, and an acceptable partner, even those in their eighties and nineties can remain sexually active. Physically disabled or terminally ill individuals continue to be sexual beings, too, and sexual counseling is now commonly available through hospitals and clinics to assist couples with physical disabilities or impairments. Sometimes people simply need reassurance that they are sexually attractive and capable, regardless of their physical limitations. It is relatively common for heart attack and stroke victims to report fearing that sexual activity may trigger a life-threatening episode. Information, knowledge, and caring for oneself and one's partner are primary aspects of a continuing and satisfying sexual life.

Improving Attitudes about Aging and Sexuality

In spite of society's general taboo on romantic love for older adults, many people look for romance. Many elders enjoy dating. They can and do talk about "steadies" and become possessive about their "friends" and partners. Indeed, retired older people may have more leisure time to dance, bicycle, eat out, and date than younger individuals, whose time is taken up with jobs and careers. Most dance clubs have a majority of members who are over 60 years old. Folk and country dancing, for example, can be vigorous exercise as well as fun, and an opportunity for romance as well.

The old double standard of aging is still so strong that a wife five years older than her husband is considered to be an "older woman," but a man five years older than his wife is not considered "older" (Lovenheim, 1990). In the past 20 years, however, a 50 percent increase in Amer-

Older men are more likely to be married than older women, but it is no longer uncommon to see a marriage between two older people. Sexuality and love persist throughout the life course.

ican women marrying younger men has taken place. Bureau of the Census data for 1990 shows that in 1970 only one-sixth of women married younger men, but in 1990, nearly 25 percent did (U.S. Census Bureau, 1994).

The patterns of sexuality across the life span represent a shift in normative attitudes about age. These changing norms affect later life sexuality. Change is in the air for the 21st century.

Once I asked Grandma when you stop liking it, and she was eighty. She said, "Child, you'll have to ask someone older than me."

GRANDDAUGHTER, 1998

REMAINING SEXUAL IN SPECIAL CIRCUMSTANCES

We come face-to-face with cultural taboos and social prohibitions with the topic of sex in nursing home settings. The topic has been generally avoided by research, and most information is anecdotal in nature, coming from nursing assistants and floor nurses in nursing homes. Much of the information is in the form of poking fun and expressing exasperation at the "problem" old man, or the "acting out" old woman.

Indeed, many old people continue to engage in sexual behaviors, despite the lack of marital partners and living circumstances that range from incarcerationlike, to the more affluent life-care communities. An anonymous study of sexual practices in 10 California life-care communities disclosed that sexual thoughts and activity were frequent (Richardson & Lazur, 1995). The interviews disclosed that the frequency and enjoyment of sexual activity in the past correlated with sexual patterns in the elderly years. The study, then, highlights that sexual patterns and attitudes do not change much over the life course. Those who enjoyed and sought out sexual opportunities earlier in life enjoyed and sought out sex in their elderly years.

What, then, of sexual interests and activity among people living in nursing homes, rather than the more affluent life-care communities? Most studies identify the barriers to sexuality among nursing home residents. Generally, sexual activity and interest in sex in nursing homes is seen as being problematic to both staff and residents, and in any one facility the "issue" is focused on particular individuals as the "problem" source.

It is very probable that cognitively competent older people handle their sexuality in a nursing home setting by private use of masturbation and by psychological repression. The sexual attitudes of nursing home staff were compared with those of the residents in one study (Lauman et al., 1994). It found that *residents* were more likely than *staff* to agree that sex is not needed for women after menopause or for men after age 65; that most people over 55 years of age masturbate some of the time; and that sexually active elderly people are "dirty." It is not coincidental to these findings that approximately 98 percent of the respondents were elders. In addition to attitudes about behaviors, 61 percent of the residents did not feel sexually attractive and did not think they would enjoy sexual activity if they had a partner (Richardson & Lazur, 1995). This form of repression is probably functional in most nursing home settings—it helps people to get past any felt need for sexual expression. It also illustrates, however, the sad loss of part of the human condition for nursing home residents. The lack of sexual contact hurts, as well as the lost sexuality. Most tragically, it is probably unnecessary, if alternative opportunities for the expression of sexuality were provided.

Living in the communal circumstances of a nursing home is difficult. Behavioral and psychological problems may result when residents are ridiculed or prevented from enjoying physical contact. When residents hold hands or say they want to marry, this may evoke laughter and sarcastic remarks, leading to humiliation. Treating an aged man and woman like children because they want to hold hands or embrace is insulting and robs those elderly of an important aspect of identity.

Nursing home administrators generally answer not to the elderly people in their facilities, but to the children of those elders. Adult children may have trouble accepting that their nursing home parent wants intimacy with another resident. Nursing homes can address this issue of sexuality directly in several ways, including

- Improving privacy ("do not disturb" signs, respected by staff)
- Educating staff about human sexuality in later life
- Helping to arrange for conjugal visits or home visits
- Encouraging other forms of sexual expression, such as hugging and kissing
- Evaluating complaints about sexual functioning
- Discontinuing medicines that may affect sexual function
- Providing information and counseling about sexuality to interested patients (Richardson & Lazur, 1995)

We all need to know that the possibilities for intimacy and enchantment with another continue to the end of our lives. Sex is for life. The frequency and vigor of sex may change with age, but sex in later life remains a critically important aspect of our self-identity, in whatever way it has formed for us over the course of our lives. Regardless of age, the loving expression of it says, "I value you. I appreciate you. I like having you in my life. I trust and want to touch you and be touched by you."

Chapter Summary

This chapter considers older couples and three categories of older singles: the widowed, divorced, and never married. An unknown percentage of older people live together without being married, but we do not directly address this important and growing phenomenon in this chapter. By the end of the first decade of the 21st century, when a new cohort begins to move into "elderhood," more information on the social significance of nonmarried partners will be available.

The myth that older people automatically lose interest in sex distorts perceptions of older people. Unhappy marriage reduced sexual activity for older couples, just as it did for younger couples. Seventy percent of men and 50 percent of women thought often about sex and physical closeness with the opposite sex.

Sex, feeling sexual, having intimate relationships, and being touched with care—caressed—are profoundly important human experiences, regardless of one's age. Old age separates people from marriage partners and sometimes from other relationships of intimacy, but old age does not mean asexuality.

Key Terms

achieved relationships
ascribed relationships
Duke Longitudinal Study
friendships
grief work
intimacy
kin relationships
Kinsey studies
Masters and Johnson studies
relationships
sexual function for procreation
social comparison

Discussion Questions

1. What are some differences between being a widow and being a widower? What are some similarities? Do you think that gender differences somehow shape the experience of losing a partner?
2. What are the advantages and disadvantages of being married in later life? To being single?
3. Imagine for a moment that you have just learned that your mother, living in a nursing home because of some cognitive impairment, is "being allowed" to have a sexual relationship with another facility resident. What is your emotional response? Should you do something about it? If so, what will that be? If not, how can you be certain that her best interests are being guarded?

Fieldwork Suggestions

1. Interview a person who works in a hospice program. What insights might this person give you regarding widowhood? Is what you hear consistent with your understanding of widowhood?
2. Talk with two people who have been widowed for several years. Ask that person about what their partner was like. *Listen* to the response.

Online Activities

1. Search for an Internet site with information on widowhood (try grief/ bereavement/ widowhood). Develop categories of the material you find: Who do you guess would use this site? What does the site market, if anything? What is the intent or purpose of the site?
2. Locate an Internet chat group specifically for older people who want to connect with other older people. What observations can you make about the site?

7

Physical Health and Well-Being

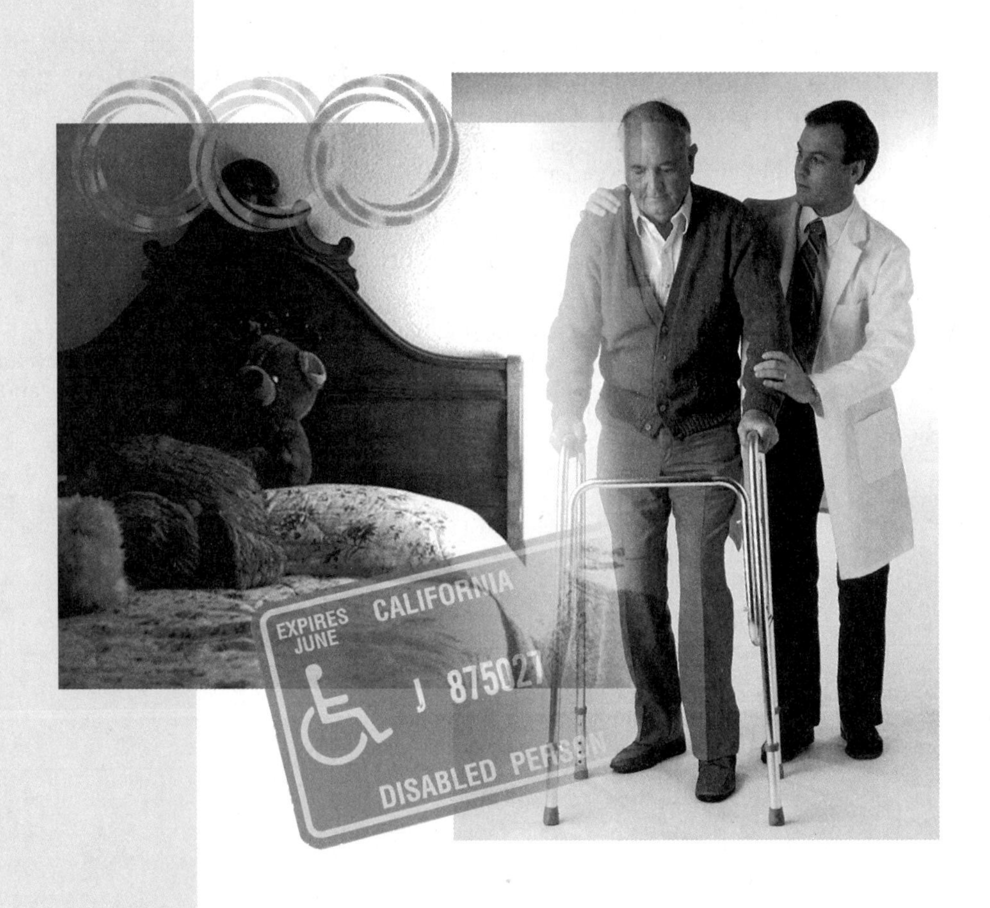

Tennis Champion, 94, Is Looking for His Match

Judith Scherr

Kenneth Beer takes a hard look at the man on the other side of the net. He bounces the ball once on the asphalt indoor tennis court and looks again as his 86-year-old foe shifts his stance.

Adjusting the white cap that covering his silver hair, Beer bounces the ball two more times, tosses it into the air and bears down with his racket, firing the yellow sphere neatly inside the right back corner of the court, well out of the challenger's reach.

Planning is key to the 94-year-old Hillsborough resident's tennis game.

"If you don't analyze your opponent carefully, why, he's going to analyze you and you'll lose," Beer said.

It took the nonagenarian three sets, lasting three hours, to beat challenger Bill Tuttle of Nevada City in the first round of the United States Tennis Association's National Indoor Tennis Championships for seniors last week at the San Francisco Tennis Club. Beer lost the second round, but won the right to play a consolation match last Sunday, which he won.

"These young kids are hard to beat," complained Beer with a good-natured smile, after the win against Tuttle, eight years his junior.

Beer, who plays in tournaments across the country—and who will be on the U.S. team in the 85-and-older division in international competition in Austria this summer—said it would be more equitable for him to go up against men his own age. The USTA has divisions for ages 70, 75, 80 and 85, but none for those 90 and above.

"We've been trying to get 'em to make a new category, but the national association says there's not enough of us," he explained.

When Beer first took up the sport, he was a pilot and wasn't thinking about competitive play.

"I found that exercise at the end of a trip was the best antidote for fatigue," said Beer, who flew 33 years for Pan American Airlines and piloted, among other aircraft, the famous Clipper ships that flew between San Francisco and China in the 1930s.

When the airline enforced a mandatory retirement rule at age 60, Beer didn't head for an easy chair: He started playing tournaments and has 72 golden tennis balls—for winning first place nationally—to show for his efforts.

Beer's achievements were recognized when he was inducted into the Northern California Tennis Hall of Fame several years ago. Among his greatest triumphs, said Northern California USTA spokesman Tom Carter, was when Beer captured two "grand slams" in 1988, winning the national championship in his age category on each of the surfaces—clay, hard court, grass and indoor—in both singles and doubles.

It's not a quest for trophies that drives him to the courts, Beer says, his eyes sparkling. Win or lose, he loves the competition. Getting ready for the challenge of the next tournament propels him to Peninsula Tennis Club almost every day to whack at least 500 balls shot from a machine.

"When you have an aim, you want to do something, you keep doing it and doing it. I've had friends just pass out and die because there is no longer a challenge," he said.

Tennis is not the only thing that keeps Beer's mind and body on the move. He skis and has an insatiable appetite for knowledge. He recently took up astronomy and enjoys using his computer. Beer refuses to let the modern world pass him by.

"I'm going to keep up. I'm not going to get caught short," he said, joking that his wife of almost 70 years says that he has "too many interests."

Sensible living has helped Beer stay in shape for tennis. If he has a pain, he rarely turns to medication.

"Nature gave us a pain to help us take care of ourselves," he said. "If I hurt myself, that's nature telling me to lay off, so I do."

Even after the three-hour battle for the win against Tuttle, Beer was not heading home to rest. He still had to prepare for the next day's match. So, after joining his friends for a little while, watching others play in the tournament, he went "to do a little practicing."

But he wasn't hungering for the next trophy. "I'm not much for thinking about records," he said. "I just think about the game tomorrow."

Underscoring a fundamental truth about biological functioning, the phrase "Use it or lose it" is often used to refer to physical abilities. What causes the decrease in physical activity that we see in people as they age? Is it inevitable?

Statistically, good health declines with age. However, we do not yet fully understand the role of the aging process in contrast to other factors that affect this decline. Poor diet, overeating, smoking, excessive drinking, misuse of drugs, accidents, and stress all affect our health. Some of the health problems that the elderly have may be an inevitable consequence of the aging process. Others clearly are not. Physical fitness and good nutrition are two factors that can slow the aging process.

To best fulfill their individual potentials, people of all ages, especially elders, need factual information about physical health and their body's changing dietary and exercise needs.

Aging is a gradual process beginning at birth. As guaranteed as biological aging is to all life, we do not know for certain what causes aging. For starters, we know that our life span is finite: we will not survive indefinitely. That period between birth and death, then, is our "life," no matter how long or short it might be. The **absolute human life span** is the maximum possible chronological age that the human can live. Although currently under debate, it is considered to be about 120 years for humans (Walford, 1983; Ross, 1996). Biologists believe that we are not programmed by our genes to live indefinitely, because aging is species-specific: the human maximum is around 120 years; the tortoise, about 150. Absolute life span of the domestic cat is about 30 years, and of the mouse, a little over 3 years. There may be a biological limit to the number of times human cells can divide and replace themselves, but, if so, we do not know what that limit may be or whether it is possible to extend it (Barinaga, 1991).

Did You Know . . .
Restricting food intake seems to retard aging in rats. Whether caloric intake restriction for humans would produce the same results is speculative, but some scientists believe that in the future the human life span can be increased.

A more useful measure of how long humans live than absolute possibility is the **mean human life span**, which is the chronological age by which

50 percent of humans will have died, according to statistical projection. That has been discussed somewhat when we discussed changing demographics, because it is the number that has most radically increased over the past century. Mean human life span in the United States is currently about 76 years, with gender differences of longer lives for women (approximately 81 years) than men (approximately 75); and ethnic differences, primarily based on the unequal distribution of wealth and access to health care in the United States.

As a person ages, his or her body parts may reach peak levels of operation or performance, and their functioning then remains constant or begins a slow decline. Some peaks are reached in youth, others in young adulthood or middle age, and some in old age if the potential of the younger years was never developed. Physical declines may result not from the aging process but from various pathologies (diseases), lack of proper diet and exercise, cigarette smoking, stress, or other factors. Some declines that have generally been attributed to the aging process can take place at very different ages or not at all once disease can be controlled.

This chapter will examine only that physical debilitation that is *correlated* with age. These physical problems generally are considered to be pathological or disease related, and may or may not be *caused* by the aging process.

The Aging Body: A Description

Many changes that take place in the body are observable: the skin loses its elasticity and becomes more wrinkled, the hair grays and thins out, and the body becomes less erect. Individuals get tired more easily and quickly. As early as the forties, the eyes begin to develop **presbyopia**, a condition in which near vision is impaired and the fine print of a book or newspaper becomes difficult to see at close range. Hearing loss may occur. As the aging process continues, teeth may be lost or gums may develop disease. In addition, an older person tends to gain body fat and to lose muscle strength, especially if he or she does not reduce caloric intake and maintain physical exercise. In most cases, the older people become, the fewer calories their bodies need. Further, the ability of the body cells to absorb calcium declines. This loss of calcium results in bones that are more brittle and more easily broken. Aging brings more wear and tear to one's bones and joints; thus, the likelihood of rheumatism and arthritis increases with age.

Some health declines are not as apparent. The capacity of the body to achieve homeostasis (physiological equilibrium) declines with age. This means that older people have greater difficulty "getting back to normal," biologically speaking, after a stressful event. Blood pressure and heart rates, for example, take longer to return to their prestress levels. Various organs operate at reduced efficiency: the lungs decrease their maximum breathing capacity; the kidneys decrease the speed at which they can filter waste out of the blood; bladder capacity declines; and the level of sex hormones decreases. The nervous system also changes; reflex action remains constant with age, but reaction time slowly declines. The digestive juices decrease in volume, consequently, the body takes longer to digest its food. The body's **immune system** decreases in its efficiency.

Although we know that these changes take place, we do not yet fully understand why they take place. In other words, we do not know what causes aging. Some gerontologists believe that aging is not an inherent process at all, but merely describes a "medley of unhappy outcomes" (Posner, 1995, p. 17). From this perspective, age is strictly the result of illness, and if we were able to keep ourselves completely disease-free, we would not "age."

A more useful understanding of aging, however, is to view it as a process in which bodily changes occur, and there is a general physiological decline in body functioning. This model of physical decline is somewhat offset, according to some gerontologists, by intellectual and psychological increases in competence. So, for example, at the very biological time one's metabolism is becoming less efficient, the person is intellectually and perhaps psychologically able to take more seriously the idea of self-care—being more attuned to messages from the body.

Biological changes such as slower reaction time or shifts in visual acuity can call into question the functional ability of older adults. One question often raised, for example, is whether older adults should be permitted to drive. Of the changes the aging body undergoes, visual changes are among the most pronounced. We know, however, that chronology (age by year) is a poor indicator of functionality (ability to function). Policy declaring that people at age 70, for example, could no longer drive would be grossly unfair to those 70-year-olds whose functioning is unimpaired. This is somewhat like declaring that 17-year-olds do not have the maturity or judgment to make quick, critical driving decisions, and therefore the driving age should be increased to 21. Although drivers aged 55 to 65 are the safest drivers on the road by almost every measure, after age 75, collision rates increase dramatically. What are the social implications of age changes that might endanger the safety of others?

Although physical changes may significantly affect the ability of some older adults to drive competently, improved structural changes in driving conditions would create a safer driving environment for older adults—larger road signs with more legible lettering, raised pavement reflectors, and so forth. As more and more of our citizens achieve late life, we will need to adjust traditional transportation practices to accommodate the mobility needs of this group.

All these physiological changes with age occur so gradually that they go unnoticed much of the time. The deterioration of body organs and systems with age may be fairly insignificant as it relates to an individual's ability to function independently, to get around, and to carry out normal activities. Nevertheless, the biology of aging is a process of decline.

CHRONIC AND ACUTE CONDITIONS

The key health problems facing middle-aged and older adults today are those that are chronic. Young people tend to have **acute conditions,** that is, short-term illnesses in which the cause is known and the condition is curable. Chicken pox, colds, and influenza are examples of acute diseases. In contrast, the number and severity of chronic conditions increase with age, whereas acute diseases decline with age. **Chronic conditions** are long term. Their causes are typically unknown. Even if the cause is known, cures are not available. The goal of chronic health care is control, maintenance, or rehabilitation. The five most prevalent chronic conditions affecting elders, in order of highest frequency are

1. Arthritis
2. Hypertension
3. Heart conditions
4. Hearing and visual impairments
5. Cancer
6. Diabetes

A chronic condition may or may not be disabling, depending on the type and severity of the condition. Loss of teeth can be considered a chronic condition, but is rarely disabling. A chronic condition may be progressively debilitating. Parkinson's disease is one example. An older person may have a number of chronic conditions but not be severely limited by any of them. Imagine the 65-year-old with mild arthritis, mild diabetes, minor visual impairment, loss of teeth, and a mild heart condition. Although this person has five chronic conditions, he or she may remain active, vigorous, and unaffected in a major way by any of them. Conversely, another older person might become completely bedridden by just one severe chronic condition.

Sometimes, the discovery of a medical cure for a disease can transform it from a chronic to an acute one. For example, some forms of cancer, now considered acute, were once thought to be chronic. Some chronic conditions do not seem to

TABLE 7.1

Functional Limitations by Age (Percent with Difficulty)

Activity	Age		
	65–74	75–84	85 and over
Walking	14.2%	22.9%	39.9%
Getting outside	5.6	12.3	31.3
Bathing/showering	6.4	12.3	27.9
Getting out of bed or chair	6.1	9.2	19.3
Dressing	4.3	7.6	16.6
Using toilet	2.6	5.4	14.1
Eating	1.2	2.5	4.4
Preparing meals	4.0	8.8	26.1
Shopping	6.4	15.0	37.0
Managing money	2.2	6.3	24.0
Using telephone	2.7	6.0	17.5
Doing heavy housework	18.6	28.7	47.8
Doing light housework	4.3	8.9	23.6

Source: U.S. Bureau of the Census, *Statistical Abstract of the United States, 1988,* 108th ed. (Washington, DC: Bureau of the Census, 1989), p. 109.

be the result of pathology (disease). Instead, they seem to be the result of the normal aging process. Several forms of arthritis fit into this category.

HEALTH STATUS

The majority of persons over the age of 65 are in fairly good health. The **health status of the aged** has improved throughout this century. Although the health status of the average 45-year-old and the average 65-year-old differ, this difference is not great. People do not reach age 65 and suddenly become decrepit. However, physical decline does become more apparent with advancing age. Those aged 75 and over usually have noticeable physical declines compared with the middle-aged, and those over 85 have even more noticeable declines. With advanced age come more numerous and longer hospital stays, more doctor visits, and more days of disability. But declines are typically very gradual.

Ninety-five percent of Americans age 65 and over live successfully or nearly successfully in the community; a smaller percentage are confined to institutions. Among noninstitutionalized elders, 86 percent has chronic conditions, but the vast majority of older people with chronic conditions suffer no interference with their mobility. Of the noninstitutionalized elderly with chronic conditions, which range from mild arthritis conditions to totally disabling ailments, 62 percent report no activity limitation whatsoever, 38 percent report some activity limitation, and 23 percent report limitation in a major activity (U.S. Bureau of the Census, 1996). Heart conditions and arthritis impose the most limitations on older people. Statistics that indicate that a high number of elderly suffer from chronic conditions hide the fact that most of the elderly manage quite well. The very old, those 80 years or older, are the ones who suffer most from disabilities.

Table 7.1 examines the functional limitations of older persons. Notice that those aged 65 to 74 have very few functional limitations and that those aged 75 to 84 do not, as a group, experience many limitations. And, although those 85 and over do have significant trouble managing everyday activities, a portion of them have no serious limitations.

Major Health Problems

Though people tend to assume that old age brings sickness, this is not necessarily true. Most of the major health problems of old age result from pathology, the presence of disease, the causes of which, in many cases, lie outside the aging process. Poor living habits established early in life, inadequate diet, and too little exercise cause some of the "diseases of old age." With preventive measures, these diseases can be avoided. About 75 percent of all deaths are caused by heart disease, cancer, and stroke. Death rates from heart disease have declined significantly over the last 20 years, due to medical advances, modifications to diet, reduced smoking rates, and better exercise habits. However, cancer deaths have increased, and cancer has its highest incidence in the elder population (American Cancer Society, 1996).

Differences in mortality are evident between black and white populations. Heart disease, cancer, and cerebrovascular diseases are the leading causes of death among those 65 and older for both races. The rates of mortality for African Americans are significantly higher: 5 percent, 17 percent, and 24 percent higher, respectively, for each of these conditions in 1990 (National Center for Health Statistics, 1994). These ethnic differences are due to the socioeconomic disadvantages experienced by African Americans, including income, education, and access to health care.

HEART DISEASE

Heart disease is a very general term covering many conditions. Some aspects of heart disease are pathological; that is, disease is present in the body. Other kinds of heart problems, although associated with aging, cannot be attributed to the aging process alone. Of all persons aged 65 and over, one-fourth (25 percent) are limited in their activities by heart conditions (U.S. Bureau of the Census, 1993).

The most widespread form of heart disease, **coronary artery disease** or **ischemic** (deprived of blood) **heart disease**, is now the major killing disease in the United States and in other industrialized nations as well. Its incidence increases with age, and it is *the* most common cause of death in middle-aged and older individuals. With coronary artery disease, a deficient amount of blood reaches the heart. This deficiency, which results from the narrowing of the blood vessels, damages the heart tissue.

Two major disorders of the circulatory system are **atherosclerosis** and **hypertension.** Atherosclerosis is one form of a group of cardiovascular disorders called **arteriosclerosis** (hardening of the arteries or their loss of elasticity) (Kausler & Kausler, 1996). Atherosclerosis occurs when fat and cholesterol crystals, along with other substances, accumulate on the interior walls of the arteries, thereby reducing the size of these passageways. The accumulation of some deposits of fat in the arteries seems to be part of normal aging; however, the increased incidence in Western countries of heart attack suggests that excessive deposits are linked to factors such as smoking and serum cholesterol levels that might be controlled by lifestyle changes.

Hypertension refers to excessive arterial blood pressure. It is present in about 40 percent of people age 65 and older and 25 percent of those in the 45- to 64-year age range (Kausler & Kausler, 1996). Hypertension can be treated with medications that rid the body of excess fluid and sodium. Factors associated with risk of hypertension include obesity, smoking, and excessive alcohol consumption. Additionally, some pain medications (nonsteroidal anti-inflammatory drugs) may increase blood pressure when taken over a long period of time. Hypertension is responsive to diet and exercise, so once again the issue of lifestyle choices emerges in relation to healthy aging.

Excess body fat has long been considered to be a risk factor in coronary heart disease, but the exact relationship is still unclear. A recent study of over 3,700 Japanese-American men from the Honolulu Heart program, age 71-93, suggests that the relationship of body weight to heart disease might be more complex than previously believed. The body mass index (BMI), or weight divided by height in square meters, is commonly used in research as an estimate of overall weight. The Honolulu Heart study found that among men, the waist-to-hip ratio (WHR) with elevated cholesterol (HDL-C) were more strongly related to coronary heart disease than was "predominantly peripheral fat accumulation," or excess weight accumulated more uniformly on the body (Huang, 1997). This study was of men; research indicates that risk factors among women are different than those among men, however, biomedical research on coronary heart disease experienced by women is still new and incomplete (Sonnichsen et al., 1993).

The solutions to difficult problems are oftentimes simple, logical, and wrong.

H. L. MENKEN, 1939

A major health problem associated with atherosclerosis is *thrombosis,* or blood clotting. Blood clots occur when undissolved fatty deposits in the arteries cut off the blood supply to the heart. Some of the factors that lead to atherosclerosis are thought to be a high cholesterol count, a diet high in refined sugars and saturated fats, high blood pressure, obesity, stress, hereditary factors, lack of exercise, and cigarette smoking.

Forrester and Shah (1997) argued recently for use of serum cholesterol as a screening test for preventing coronary heart disease (CAD) for a broader range of people than recommended by the American College of Physicians (1996). The guidelines state that screening is not recommended for men younger than 35 or older than 75; for women younger than 45 or older than 75; and "appropriate but not mandatory" for men between 35 and 65 and women between 45 and 65 (Garber et al., 1996). Forrester and Shah developed five arguments, based on reviews of the literature, in opposition to the ACP findings.

1. It is more cost-effective to prevent CAD than treat it after it is clinically apparent.
2. Elevated cholesterol in young adult men establishes increased CAD over the next 40 years.
3. Lowering blood cholesterol in young hypercholesterolemic persons would decrease rates of CAD over their life span.
4. Cholesterol lowering can be accomplished at low cost.
5. Cholesterol lowering is equally effective in women and the elderly.

Research that establishes treatment guidelines must be critically reviewed because those guidelines help establish recommendations that health insurance companies use to determine whether or not particular tests and treatments will be covered by a health policy. On an individual level, medical decisions are always probabilistic, with the uncertainty borne of the vast individual differences inherent among people as a group (Forrester & Shah, 1997).

Coronary artery disease can vary in its severity and in the area in the body of greatest damage. Older people are known to have increased risk of vascular disease in their legs (Vogt et al., 1992). This condition is strongly associated with increased disability, and particularly complicates symptoms of diabetes (Orchard & Strandness, 1993). If coronary heart disease results in deficient blood supply to the heart, heart tissue will die, producing a dead area called an **infarct**—the disease can lead to myocardial infarction, or heart attack.

Heart attacks can be acute, sudden, and painful—clearly identifiable; or they can be more subtle, creating a more generalized dizziness, weakness, confusion, or numbness. The symptoms have a broad range, and they are different in men than in women. Men and women have similar rates of heart attack after 65, but women are less likely to suffer this event before that age than are men. Even at younger ages, however, women are more likely to die from a myocardial infarction than are men—a fact that is still not clearly understood because of the limited research that has been conducted on women's health issues (Hooyman & Kiyak, 1996).

CANCER

In reality a group of several hundred diseases, **cancer** may affect the breast, the skin, the stomach, bones, blood, or other parts of the body. Its common characteristic is an uncontrolled, invasive cell growth at the expense of normal body systems. There may be numerous causes of cancer. Some are thought to be the inhalation or ingestion of chemicals, smoking, diet, and radiation. Although the basic cause of cancer is not fully understood, a living cell somehow becomes a cancer cell. This cancer cell then transmits its abnormality to succeeding cell generations. When the wild growth of cancer cells is not eliminated from the body, tumors develop.

Statistics have traditionally shown that the risk of cancer increases with age. The latest research, however, now shows that cancer mortality rates at very old ages decline precipitously (Smith, 1996). This finding is available only because of the number of people living into very old age. In 1960, there were 66 cancer deaths of people age 100 and over in the United States. In 1990, statistics showed that 12,340 people over the age of 100 died. Of them, 524 died of cancer—just under 4 percent of the total deaths (National Center for Health Statistics, 1994). The increasing numbers reflect the larger number of people living to 100 and beyond; the proportion of cancer deaths has remained the same over time. Different kinds of cancers peak at different ages: mortality for cancer of the liver peaks between ages 85-95; lung cancer seems to plateau between 80 and 84 years of age (Smith, 1996). Ovarian cancer incidence has been described to decrease beginning at about 75 years of age (Yancik, 1993).

Most people do not live to be over 85 years of age, however, and cancer remains a major killer of older people in the United States. Over one-half of all deaths from cancer occur in later life (age 65 and older). Thus, cancer is the second leading cause of death among the elderly and also a leading chronic condition among elderly. Many cancers are treated for some time before the reserve capacity of the elder is gone, or the elder has passed the 5-year point of "cure." This has implications for treatment: a 70-year-old woman, for example, has a remaining life expectancy of 15 years. If she has physiologic declines in addition to cancer, the impact on her ability to function in daily life is a major consideration (Cohen, 1997).

A recent study surveyed 1,647 elders with cancer to determine the impact of cancer on how well they could function and what was their utilization of health care (Stafford & Cyr, 1997). They measured limitations in the activities of daily living (ADLs)—such as getting out of a chair; and in the instrumental activities of daily living (IADLs)—going shopping, for example. Findings revealed that cancer increased the use of health care resources and modestly reduced physical function. Elders with cancer might require not only the care of an oncologist, but also the care of a geriatrician, to help determine appropriate services.

Three forms of cancer treatment are surgery, radiation, and chemotherapy (treatment with drugs). Some forms of cancer can be successfully treated and effectively cured, especially following early detection. For example, breast cancer, if detected early, appears to be one of these treatable forms. Other forms of cancer, such as lung cancer, are more difficult to diagnose at early stages and are therefore more difficult to treat.

CEREBROVASCULAR DISEASE

A stroke occurs when there is a disruption of blood flow to the brain. **Cerebrovascular disease,**

Exercise is critical for health in later life. Here an elderly woman who is unable to walk unassisted still achieves cardiovascular exercise as she bowls in a modified bowling alley.

more commonly called **stroke**, is predominantly a problem of old age. It is one of several chronic diseases that account for the greatest burden of physical disability and health care utilization in later life (Barker & Mullooly, 1997). It is estimated that more than half a million Americans have strokes each year; most are elders (Kausler & Kausler, 1996).

The most common cause of stroke is the same as that of coronary artery disease—atherosclerosis and arteriosclerosis. These conditions may result in either a malfunction or narrowing of the blood vessels serving the brain or in a blood clot blocking an artery that serves the brain. Two other causes of stroke are hemorrhage (bleeding inside the brain) and blockage of an artery serving the brain resulting from a clot that has broken off from a major clot elsewhere in the body. When brain cells do not receive blood from the heart, they die. The death of brain cells indicates the occurrence of a stroke.

The severity of a stroke depends on the area of the brain affected and the total amount of brain tissue involved. Strokes may affect various parts of the brain. When the left side of the brain is affected, the symptoms will differ from those that occur when the right side of the brain is affected. Depending on the particular area of the brain and the size of the area affected, paralysis in varying degrees, speech disorders, mental confusion, or memory impairment can result. Stroke is a leading cause of first admissions to mental hospitals because of the symptoms resulting from damage to the brain.

Rehabilitation for stroke victims is successful in varying degrees; much of the variance depends on the severity of the stroke. If treated promptly during the initial phases, the victim of a stroke has a better chance of recovery. Rehabilitation

and exercise training is now commonly prescribed for survivors of coronary artery and cerebrovascular diseases. The rehabilitation is remarkably successful. One study found marked improvements in exercise capacity and obesity indices and modest improvement in plasma lipids in older women, in addition to improved quality of life parameters (Lavie & Milani, 1997).

Rehabilitation from stroke and other life-altering diseases is also related to the personality of the individual with the disease. Morris and colleagues (1993) determined in an Australian sample of old people who experienced stroke that personality introversion and depression are associated with increased mortality following that stroke.

Stroke has become less lethal and disabling in the past 20 years, though no less common a disease. Debate rages in the medical world over whether reduction in mortality is due to hypertension control efforts or to treatment following the event (prevention or treatment). Both appear to be factors; a sharp decrease in the occurrence of coma among stroke cases occurred in the 1980s (treatment), and the reduced prevalence of hypertensive heart disease among new stroke cases (prevention) probably combine to reduce fatality (Barker & Mulloonly, 1997). The question, however, is an important one. The perspectives have implications for health care policy, which is increasingly determined by insurance companies. Is individual treatment the product, or are larger, more social-level programs most beneficial for prevention of disease?

ACCIDENTS

A health problem of major proportion is disability or death due to accidents. Although persons over 65 number 13 percent of the population, they represent 29 percent of all accidental deaths. Falls are the most common cause of accidental death among those 65 and over, followed closely by motor-vehicle accidents. Suffocation from an object that has been ingested, surgical and medical mishaps, fires, and burns are also major causes of accidental death among elders. The 90-and-over group has an alarmingly disproportionate share of deaths due to accidents in two of these categories: (1) falls, and (2) suffocation by ingestion of food (National Safety Council, 1993).

Such needless tragedy among advanced age groups illustrates a need for more preventive measures. A few concerned organizations, for example, have run "falls clinics" as a preventive measure. The annual incidence of falls is approximately 30 percent in people over 65 years of age, increasing to 50 percent in those over age 80 (Steinweb, 1997). About half of those falls can be attributed to accidents (toppling from a shaky ladder) and extrinsic causes (slippery floors). The other half are from causes such as lower extremity weakness, gait disorders, the effects of medications, or illness (Steinweb, 1997). A great deal of attention is now being focused on ways in which stability can be enhanced in older people, as a means for reducing the incidents and severity of falls. Some programs help people train for balance (Thapa et al, 1996). Much as we learned the balance as young children to walk, run, and/or skip on a railroad track or ledge, learning and relearning skills of balance can be accomplished at any age and have shown to be quite effective with elders.

There is a real danger with falls that a hip will crack. Because we instinctively use the hip to absorb most falls, and because bones are often weakened by osteoporosis, a hip fracture is a common ailment to be feared. One-third of women (those most likely to have osteoporosis) and one-sixth of men who live to age 90 will suffer a hip fracture.

About 90 percent of hip fractures are due to osteoporosis. Older women with smaller body size are at increased risk of hip fracture because of lower hipbone mineral density (Ensrud et al., 1997). Only 25 percent recover fully, and one in four die within six months of the injury (Schideler, 1994). Compared with women, older men hospitalized with hip fracture in one study were shown to have higher mortality and have more risk factors for osteoporosis. Like women, the men are usually fragile, with preexisting illnesses that contribute to an overall poor outcome (Diamond et al., 1997). Recovery can be slow and quite painful; some people never walk again, others gain mobility only with the use of a walker, and those that can heal well enough to resume a normal, active life often take years to do so.

Some other factors of age that contribute to accidental death or injury are failing eyesight and hearing; reduced muscular strength, balance, and coordination; and increased reaction time. If these limitations are combined with impaired judgment, the very old are especially vulnerable to accidents. They may try to lift loads that are too heavy or poorly balanced, or they may climb or reach overhead without sufficient strength to manage the task. Changes in automobile traffic conditions can happen too swiftly for them to react. The swallowing reflex diminishes with age, making choking on food or objects in the mouth, such as a safety pin, more likely. Danger signals of fire or leaking gas are not perceived readily, and the few minutes or seconds of delayed reaction often prove to be fatal. Accidental drownings of older persons result more often from activities around water rather than from actual swimming.

ARTHRITIS

Arthritis, which results from the inflammation of a joint or a degenerative change in a joint, is one of the oldest diseases known and is widespread today, affecting all age groups, but mostly older persons. There are numerous types of arthritis, with different causes, different symptoms, and differing degrees of severity. Rheumatoid arthritis and gout, though rare, are painful and troubling forms. The type of arthritis that most often poses problems for those 65 and over is osteoarthritis.

Did You Know . . .
Hayflick's experiments in the 1960s showed that connective tissue cells (fibroblasts) divided only about 50 times before dying.

Osteoarthritis, the most common form of arthritis, is fairly widespread in middle age and almost universal in old age. Most older people have some degree of osteoarthritis. The joints most commonly affected are the weight-bearing ones: the hips, knees, and spine. The fingers and big toe are also commonly affected. With osteoarthritis, elastic tissue (cartilage) becomes soft and wears away, and the underlying bones are exposed, which causes pain, stiffness, and tenderness. For some, osteoarthritis starts early in life and affects mostly the small joints. For others, osteoarthritis results from injury or vigorous wear and tear (the athletic knee is an example). It occurs later in life in the large or overused joints.

Osteoporosis

Osteoporosis, another potentially severe and crippling skeletal problem, is characterized by a gradual loss of bone mass (density) that generally begins between the ages of 35 and 40. The number of victims and the severity of the disease increase with advancing age. Millions of Americans suffer from this disease, and 75 to 80 percent of them are women. A severely compromised estrogen production has been associated with osteoporosis (Morgan & Kunkel, 1998).

Loss of bone mass can result in diminishing height, slumped posture, the "dowager's hump," and a reduction in the strength of the bones, which makes them more susceptible to fractures. The bones may become so weak that a sudden strain will break them.

The causes of osteoporosis are inadequate diet over a long period of time (lack of calcium is a major dietary factor), reduced absorptive efficiency due to an aging digestive system, cigarette smoking, lack of vigorous physical activity, and estrogen deficiency in women. But men can also get this disease, and fractures related to osteoporosis in men have higher mortality rates than in women (Diamond et al., 1997). The prevention of osteoporosis must be lifelong, with attention to nutrition and activity as well as the modification of risk factors such as smoking and excessive alcohol consumption (Johansson et al., 1993).

An initial cause of osteoporosis is a decrease or upset in hormonal balance. In menopause and old age, the body may not have enough hormones to maintain its calcium balance. Some medications, such as steroids, actually cause the development of osteoporosis, and this is a particular problem for older people who are likely to be on several medications for different medical conditions.

Osteoporosis can sometimes be slowed by a high-calcium diet. Some doctors recommend calcium supplements. The vitamin D metabolite calcitrol has been shown to help correct problems with calcium absorption and has been particularly useful with steroid-induced bone loss. There is growing evidence of the effectiveness of estrogen treatment for women following menopause (Mykyta, 1997). A new bisphosphonate, alendronate, is available by prescription in Australia. It has been shown to be effective in *increasing* bone mineral density in postmenopausal women (Chestnut et al., 1995; Adami et al., 1995).

National campaigns are mounted each year to teach about prevention of this disease. Weight-bearing exercise should start in younger years, as well as a good diet, and be continued in old age to slow this disease. Exercise has been proven to help maintain bone strength.

OTHER CONCERNS

Other health concerns more frequently found in older populations than younger ones are emphysema and chronic bronchitis (which often occur together), diabetes mellitus, and obesity. Emphysema is characterized by lung rigidity; thickening of the mucus of the bronchioles; and scarring of the lung walls. Smoking and inhalation of contaminants such as gases, industrial fumes, or traffic exhaust may increase the risk of emphysema. Bronchitis, on the other hand, is a condition in which the bronchial tube becomes inflamed and scarred, often resulting in chronic coughing and an excessive production of mucus. Acute infectious bronchitis is treated with antibiotics, but long-term management—appropriate for most elders—includes improving the airway passages through medications, providing supportive nutritional care, and maximizing the function of muscles supporting the respiratory process (Heath, 1993).

Type II **diabetes mellitus,** also called adult-onset diabetes, is a health-related problem that requires intervention and constant monitoring. Diabetes Type II is a cell insensitivity to insulin that impedes the transfer of glucose from the blood into the cell. The disease is developed late in life, and it is more mild pathologically than diabetes contracted in youth or late middle age. Often in late-onset diabetes, a change of diet may be sufficient to stabilize the condition. Symptoms of diabetes include increased appetite and urination, fatigue, decreased wound healing, and excessive thirst—but the symptoms might not be present in older people. Blood sugar might be temporarily elevated under conditions of illness or stress, so it is important to conduct glucose tests under conditions of reduced stress (Stolk et al., 1997).

Did You Know . . .
Increased serum insulin may be more strongly associated with decreased cognitive function and dementia in women than is cerebrovascular disease.

STOLK ET AL. 1997

One study with rhesus monkeys suggests an approach with humans: monkeys were provided a diet with 30 percent fewer calories than the control group but the same level of nutrition. It resulted in lowered blood sugar and insulin levels, compared with age-related increases in those markers in the control group of monkeys (Kemnitz et al., 1994). Although not considered a disease, obesity, which results from excessive food intake, strains the heart and exacerbates systemic disease factors such as emphysema, osteoporosis, and arthritis. About one out of three older adults is significantly overweight.

Biological Theories of Aging

Must we grow old? Is there any way to stop aging? Human beings have asked these questions for centuries. The longest-lived persons on record are Shirechiyo Izumi of Japan and Jeanne Calmet of France, both of whom reached 122 years. This figure, then, represents the **maximum life span** of the human species, the greatest age reached by a member of a species. Biologists refer to biological aging as *senescence,* often described as the onset of the degenerative process—a process that usually becomes apparent between the ages of 40 and 45. Graying at the temples, crow's feet around the eyes, and the need for reading glasses to correct nearsightedness (presbyopia) are among the early indicators that the process is underway.

Medical technology is slowing the aging process by increasing our fitness and vigor along with our **average life span,** the average age reached by the members of a species. No physician, or anyone else, has ever saved another's life—they have only prolonged it. A child born today has a life expectancy of approximately 80 years. Someday, life expectancy may be 120 or more years—a span the accommodation of which will require profound social and cultural changes.

The extension of life, although desirable, also challenges society to ensure that the quality of that life will justify the efforts to extend it. Why do we grow old? Although there are a number of biological theories of aging, there is, at this time, no one clear scientific reason why we age. Aging today is viewed as many processes, and the theories described here are not necessarily mutually exclusive.

Did You Know . . .
Alexander Graham Bell conducted a genealogical study of one family with thousands of descendants, and discovered that children of parents who lived to be 80 or older, lived about 20 years longer than children whose parents died before they were 60 years old.

KAUSLER & KAUSLER, 1996

AGING AS DISEASE

Aging may be entirely due to the disease processes in the body. If so, future medical science may be able to inhibit or eradicate **aging as disease.** By eliminating disease in the body as it occurs, medical intervention theoretically should be able to keep the body in good health indefinitely. Still, most scientists try to separate the aging process from disease, because people seem to age even when no disease is afflicting the body. Several ideas about the nature of aging have been put forth.

GENETICS

First, let us consider the genetics of aging. Scientific studies have demonstrated that human longevity runs in families. Investigations of twins confirm that human life span is inherited. Identical twins die within a relatively short time span of one another, whereas siblings have a greater variation in life spans. Evidence indicates that 10 to 15 percent of variation in age at death is genetically determined. Thus, the longevity of our parents and grandparents is an important indicator of our own longevity. A number of genetic theories have arisen to explain differential rates of aging. One group of theories is called **programmed senescence theories**. They emphasize internal "programs." Some genetic theorists presuppose a **biological clock** within us that begins ticking at conception. This clock may be in the nucleus of each cell of our body, an idea that advances the proposition that the body is "programmed" by specific genes to live a certain length of time.

Scientists once speculated that the biological clock was governed by a single gene. They now believe that thousands of genes are involved. The study of genetics became dramatically more sophisticated with the advent of genetic cloning and gene splicing; science is on the cusp of identifying for the first time the genetic factors in aging.

Do we really know that the human life span cannot be extended well beyond 100 years? What is the nature of the biological clock? How does it affect growth, development, and decline? Scientists in the fields of molecular biology and genetics continue to search for answers to these questions.

Related to the search for "longevity" genes is the search for genes that are responsible for hereditary diseases. More than 150 mutant genes have been identified. An example is the one responsible for a rare hereditary disease, a thyroid cancer. By the turn of the century, DNA tests are almost certain to be a part of medical exams. From a sample of the patient's blood, doctors will be able to spot genetic mutations that signal the approach of hereditary diseases and also breast cancer, heart disease, and diabetes. Today at least 50 genetic tests for 50 specific hereditary diseases are available. In the near future a genetic test for the breast cancer gene (BRCA1), which is responsible for 1 in 10 of all breast cancers will be available.

Genes are being identified at a rapid rate, including mutations responsible for Alzheimer's and colon cancer. Genes of neurodegeneration have been identified in the mouse in the form of a defect in a copper ion transporter (Mori, 1997). Most likely multiple genes are involved in Alzheimer's, and all these have yet to be found. Once a gene is found, laboratories work to develop a test to determine its presence or absence in the body. Discovering the genes of longevity in mammals cannot be far behind.

It is clear that there are multiple mechanisms to aging: it is a complex biological process that is characterized by disorder and decline and requires the approach of integrative biology, rather than the single-focus approach of a distinct biological discipline (Jazwinski, 1996). With the new support for research on the human genome, however, biogerontology has taken on an excitement.

Genetic "**error theory**" holds that errors in DNA molecules are looped back to become duplicated; thus any error introduced becomes replicated in the DNA, generating further errors, and finally leading to a lethal "error catastrophe" (Holliday, 1996). The errors can be introduced by radiation and heat, by chemicals such as alcohol, or by mutation. Although not yet strictly ruled out, recent research has concluded that "these studies culminated in a definitive demonstration that errors in protein synthesis do not increase during cellular aging" (Riabowal & Harley, 1995, p. 6). Holliday calls for the science community to keep an open mind to the idea of error catastrophe, because there are still many unanswered questions (1996).

IMMUNE SYSTEM

A most promising "programmed" theory about aging is the immune system theory. Many aspects of immune function decline with age, and this decline is related to many kinds of disease, such as cancer. If the body's immune system becomes decreasingly effective with advancing age, harmful cells are more likely to survive and do damage. The theory is that cancer and other diseases attack the body with advancing age because the body progressively loses its ability to fight off disease.

Some scientists are trying to revitalize the ailing immune systems of elders with hormone therapy, specifically the hormone DHEA. Studies of mice have shown that this hormone restored their immune systems to youthful levels in warding off certain diseases such as Hepatitis B. Experiments with testosterone show it to increase muscle strength and to counter anemia. In addition, AIDS research is bringing us more information about strengthening the immune system to help prolong lives.

A related immunological theory of aging suggests that as the body ages, it develops more and more autoimmune antibodies that destroy cells, even normal ones. As age increases, the immune system seems to increase its capacity for autoimmune reactions. Several diseases, such as midlife diabetes, are related to autoimmune reactions, thus leading to the theory that such reactions cause aging. The theory is criticized because most autoimmune diseases, in fact, begin to develop at younger ages, but the impact of their *consequences* affects the quality of life of elders.

The consequences of impaired immune function in old people include increased susceptibility to infectious disease, emergence of tumors, and increased autoimmune reactions (Wick & Grubeck-Loebenstein, 1997). For this reason, a distinction between **primary immunological change** (intrinsic decline of immune responsiveness) and **secondary change** (due to disease and environmental factors such as diet, drug use, physical activity, etc.) can help to develop treatment models.

CELLULAR THEORIES

A major group of theories, called "error" theories, direct attention to forces that damage cells (National Institutes of Health, 1993). If the forces can be controlled, the belief is that aging can be prolonged.

One of the oldest and most enduring "error" theories is the cellular theory of **wear and tear,** the idea that irreplaceable body parts simply wear out. The cell is viewed as a highly complex piece of machinery, like an automobile. Some organisms live longer because they maintain themselves more carefully. Those who live more recklessly will wear out sooner. This idea is difficult to test and ignores the fact that cells can repair damage caused by wear and tear.

FREE RADICALS

People seem to vary in their ability to fend off assaults to the body, such as smoking, too much fat, and alcohol abuse. Some smokers, for example, manage to live long lives with no apparent impact on their longevity. Winston Churchill is one example. Yet others who are very health conscious succumb to cancer or other diseases before reaching old age.

One explanation for variability in longevity is that some people are more susceptible to free radicals than others. "Free radicals" is a name given to overexcited oxygen molecules in the body that are searching for electrons to restore their status quo. The oxygen molecules are the byproduct of normal metabolism, produced as cells turn food into energy. A way to combat aging is to trap the damaging molecules before they can do harm. Free radicals invade cells throughout the body, mangling vital protein enzymes and membranes, and in general damaging the body.

Recent research is investigating the relationship of free radical theory to Alzheimer's disease. Harman (1995) hypothesized that Alzheimer's disease is caused by increased free radical reaction levels in brain neurons that over time advance patterns of cell loss. His conclusions suggest that the incidence of Alzheimer's may be decreased by efforts to minimize free radical reactions. Harman further recommends that antioxidant supplements taken by the general population may decrease the incidence of Alzheimer's in those who are destined to develop the disorder.

Researchers have discovered chemical agents that absorb free radicals and thus prevent cell and tissue degeneration. For example, a compound called PBN administered daily to aged gerbils restored the function of oxidized proteins in their brains. Their ability to run through mazes improved, and they had fewer strokes from brain damage. The next step is to develop compounds for humans. In the meantime scientists are looking to vitamin supplements such as A, E, and C as natural absorbers of free radicals.

Longevity: The Role of Diet, Exercise, and Mental Health

There is a saying that all people want to live forever, but no one wants to grow old. And there is another: If I'd known I was going to live this long, I'd have taken better care of myself! Research on longevity holds a fascination for all of us—wondering whether science can find the key to knowledge that would keep each of us on the planet awhile longer. The previous section covered some biological theories that hold promise for understanding the mysteries of aging. Scientists are also looking at some other factors—as well as diet and exercise, social, emotional, and environmental factors. There is no one answer to living a good long life.

Did You Know . . .
If the slowing of mortality rates achieved in rats by diet restriction is applied to humans, then the ***median*** *human life expectancy would approach the present* ***absolute maximum*** *of 120 years.*

FINCH & PIKE, 1996

DIET

Research has come up with some astonishing findings regarding diet and longevity. Scientists at the University of Wisconsin—Madison found that reducing an animal's usual diet by 50 to 70 percent could extend its life span by 30 percent or more. The animals not only live longer, but they also are healthier, exhibit less cancer and heart disease, have better immune systems, and have a much lower incidence of diabetes and cataracts (Devitt, 1991). Reducing a human's food intake by 50 to 70 percent might surely cause some serious interpersonal problems, if not physiological and psychological ones. Caloric restriction to the extent of the rat studies is not recommended for humans at this point, but some intriguing findings continue to emerge. It appears that disease and other pathology becomes delayed to the end of the absolute maximum life span of the animal. The animals remain remarkably healthy up to the point that they become ill and die. Morbidity has been delayed, and mortality has become compressed in these research animals.

"The outcome of caloric restriction is spectacular," stated Richard Weindruch, a gerontologist at the University of Wisconsin and a pioneer in this particular field. He has tested caloric restriction in animals from protozoa to rats to dogs to monkeys. The studies may be telling us we are tampering with fundamental aging processes. The animals act friskier and suffer fewer diseases. Tumor growth is reduced by at least 30 percent and some cancers are virtually eliminated. Thus, many usual causes of death are stripped away. A 22-year study of 19,297 men revealed that those at their ideal weight (determined by height) live longer than those who are only slightly above (2 to 6 percent) their ideal weight. Those men 20 or more pounds above their ideal weight suffered a major loss in years lived (Manson & Gutfeld, 1994). And from another culture, those who live on the island of Okinawa eat 60 percent of the normal Japanese diet. People live longer on Okinawa and have half the percentage of heart disease, diabetes, and cancer as on the main island of Japan. It would seem that by restricting food intake, scientists can cause age-sensitive biological parameters—such as DNA repair, glucose regulation, and immune functions—to work better and longer. The decline in the immune function is at the root of many of the health problems faced by elders. Flu, for instance, tends to be more severe with age because immune responses are less vigorous. Low caloric intake helps protect the immune response system.

Physiological change happens with age, but health and vigor are maintained through exercise. Many geriatricians now believe that physical flexibility is one of the most important keys to a healthy body in later life.

NUTRITION

Only in recent years have we begun to understand the inadequacies of the food eaten by the average American. Studies have shown that nutritional adequacy in early life is related to health and well-being in later life.

Dietary patterns in the mid-20th century turned away from raw fruits, vegetables, dairy products, and whole grains. For too many, today's diet still is high in cholesterol, fat, sugar, refined grains, and processed food, and low in bulk, fiber, and nutrients. Many recent studies give strong evidence of the relationship of diets high in vegetables and fruits with low incidence of various types of cancer and the relationship between type of dietary fat and coronary heart disease (Walter, 1997; Willett, 1994). Data pertaining to this matter show that older persons often have a low intake of important nutrients, such as calcium, iron, magnesium, vitamins B and C, beta carotine, thiamine, and especially folic acid.

In the 1990s, our awareness of the importance of fresh fruits, vegetables, and whole grains in our diet is increasing. Americans are decreasing their intake of salt, red meat, and saturated fat. The statistics presented in Chapter 1, showing reduced rates of heart disease, bear this out. Nutritional supplements, though controversial, are often recommended to older people whose diets might not provide adequate food-source nutrition. Additionally, specific nutrients have been associated with the enhancement of physical capability. For example, a recent study of older sportsmen found that vitamin C intake was associated with maximal oxygen uptake, as a measure of physical fitness (Chatard et al., 1998).

Research on diet continues to be productive, particularly using nonhuman mammals, in which the complexity of social and environmental variables along with the diet, can be controlled. The trace nutrient chromium, when given to rats, increased their life span by one-third. The chromium was thought to reduce the blood sugar level, which in turn reduces atherosclerosis and kidney disease (Schmidt, 1993). Results from studies like these provide suggestions for human dietary factors. Author of the best-selling book *Longevity,* Kathy Keeton, along with many health-conscious Americans, eats large portions of complex carbohydrates, especially pasta, because they are fat free and have a calming effect on the brain (Keeton, 1992).

Good nutrition, it must be remembered, is not necessarily only an issue of preference. Between 8 percent to 16 percent of old people in the United States have experienced food insecurity in a six-month period. This means that somewhere between roughly three and five million older people experience being hungry and/or not having access to a "nutritionally adequate, culturally compatible diet that is not obtained through emergency food programs" in a given six-month period (Wellman et al., 1997, p. S121). Though overall the economic situation of elders has improved in the past 25 years, not all Americans have made the same gains. Nearly six million older people were poor or near poor in 1994, and these numbers do not include those who are homeless or undocumented residents (Fowles, 1995; Burl, 1993).

As a group, elders fare far better than they did 40 years ago; as a result, hunger and malnutrition among the elderly has gone largely unnoticed by hunger advocacy groups. National hunger screening programs at the local level have reported elder malnutrition risk rates ranging from 25 percent to 50 percent (Wellman et al., 1997; Whitehead & Finucane, 1997). We can better understand the large proportion of at risk elders if we include those independent elders with confusion or memory loss; the one in eight elders experiencing appetite loss due to depression; elders with poor teeth and gums or misfitting dentures; and the one in five elders who has trouble with walking, grocery shopping, and preparing food. Malnutrition, and especially undernutrition, is a common and often unrecognized health risk among elders.

FUNCTIONAL AND BEHAVIORAL CHANGE

Physiological and sociopsychological factors can compound nutritional difficulties for the very old. Digestive processes slow down as part of the aging process. Dental problems can limit one to food that is easily chewed. Reduced keenness of taste, sight, and smell can diminish enjoyment of food and dampen the appetite. Physical handicaps, such as arthritis, can complicate the preparation and consumption of meals. Lack of transportation to markets poses further problems.

Less obvious, but also of great importance, are social and psychological factors. For example, a widow who has spent many years cooking for and eating with her family may find little incentive to shop and cook for herself when she is living alone. Older men living alone are even less inclined to cook for themselves than are women. Older adults on limited budgets who seldom leave their homes because of fear or disdain for shopping may settle for a diet of crackers, bread, or milk. Many have lost olfactory (taste and smell) acuity as well. Even those who live with families or in institutions may not find an atmosphere conducive to good eating habits. In some institutions, the hurried, impersonal atmosphere of meals served cold at 5:00 p.m. can discourage residents from eating as they should. And for those who do not live in institutions, we all know that American culture fosters the fast-food diet, which tends to be high in fat and lacking many needed nutrients.

PATHOLOGY AND DIET

Research on nutrition is now uncovering the way in which poor diet contributes to pathology (disease). Establishing the relationship between diet and disease is difficult, partly because the time that elapses before an inadequate diet results in disease can be substantial. Individuals may not be able to accurately remember their eating habits over a period of years. Nutritional cause and physical effect is difficult to determine.

Nevertheless, diet is increasingly being implicated as a factor in numerous conditions and diseases (Garber et al., 1996; Goldbourt, 1997). Saturated fat contributes to atherosclerosis. A lack of fiber in the diet is thought to be one cause of cancer of the intestine or colon. With a low-fiber diet, the cancer agent remains in the intestine for a longer period of time. High fiber protects against constipation, intestinal disease, gallstones, and cancer. Diverticulitis, an infection or inflammation of the colon, may be caused by a deficiency of vegetable fiber in the diet. Research has shown that various nutritional anemias are almost certainly the result of poor diet. Similarly, studies have shown that proper dietary programs can control 80 percent of the cases of diabetes mellitus. As we grow older, our metabolic rate slows down. We require less energy intake, or fewer calories. Because of reduced kidney function, elders should eat somewhat less protein to help avoid kidney strain.

> *It is the function of medicine to have people die young as late as possible.*
>
> E. L. WYNDER, AMERICAN HEALTH FOUNDATION, 1995

PHYSICAL FITNESS

A classic study of physical activity and health more than 40 years ago compared the incidence of coronary heart disease between London bus drivers and music conductors (Morris et al., 1953). Coronary heart disease was less by half among the conductors, compared with the bus drivers. The question arising from the study was: do specific occupations produce a differential effect on heart disease morbidity, or are healthier and more sturdy men selected for one job over another? From this study and others like it in the 1950s, grew research to assess the relationship of on-job and leisure-time physical activities and heart disease. The Framingham Heart Study in Massachusetts is one of the better- known studies of this type. More recent studies, armed with more sophisticated capabilities to measure biological functioning, replicate the findings that physical activity is positively associated with lower heart disease. Additional research establishes that physical activity is a component in rehabilitation following cardiac illness and reduces the risk of total mortality by 20 percent; of cardiovascular mortality by 22 percent; and fatal reinfarction (second heart attack) by 25 percent (O'Connor et al., 1989). Paffenbarger and Lee (1996) summarized the current state of research:

> *Since time immemorial, a physically active and fit way of life has been conceptualized as promoting health and longevity. But not until the 19th century did investigators use numerical quantification to show health benefits of physical activity by occupational categories demanding different degrees of energy output, and to demonstrate longevity differentials... (p. S12).*

Research shows that patterns of exercise throughout the life and even exercise at any point *during* the life produce positive physical and mental outcomes; *some* exercise is better than *none*. Exercising for the first time in later life is better than believing it to be "too late" and not exercising at all. For most older people, including those who are frail or ill, a program of strength training and flexibility exercises helps maintain mobility, improves quality of life, and prolongs independence (Buckwalter, 1997; Buckwalter et al., 1993). Loss of mobility is a significant cause of loss of independence among the elderly.

It is a myth that older individuals are unable to exercise or to profit from it. Actually, exercise helps maintain good health, improves circulation and respiration, diminishes stress, preserves a sense of balance, promotes body flexibility, and induces better sleeping patterns at any age. It is now clear that most old people benefit substantially from exercise. The person who exercises reduces the risk of heart attack and, should one occur, increases the chances of survival. Swimming, walking, running, bicycling, and tennis are all valuable and inexpensive forms of exercise. However, despite current publicity about physical fitness, some older people are not getting the exercise they need.

Much of the deterioration and many of the health problems and physical disabilities associated with age have been thought to be inevitable. However, many of the problems found in older people result directly from disuse of body systems, which results in decline. Disuse affects muscle mass, for example. Between the ages of 30 and 80, mean strength of back, arm, and leg muscles drops as much as 60 percent. Age-related changes in joints can lead to stiffness, which leads to limited range of motion (Buckwalter et al., 1993). These trends can be slowed and, in some instances, actually reversed with proper exercise (Hein et al., 1994).

We commonly associate youth with supple, strong, erect bodies and old age with weak muscles, drooped posture, and low energy. One study showed that aerobic exercises increased oxygen efficiency by 30 percent among 60- to 70-year-olds within six months of participation in a program (Seals et al., 1984). Older people can have dramatic exercise benefits from strength-training exercises. One study concluded that resistance exercise may forestall declines in strength and muscle mass for decades (Klitgaard et al., 1990). Their study found that even among frail elders, strength training leads to "life enhancing improvements such as increased stair climbing and walking speed" (Buckwalter, 1997, p. 131). Older individuals who participate in physical activity that constantly works the muscles will have a larger muscle mass than younger individuals who follow no physical fitness program. All unused tissues and functions atrophy. This can happen very quickly; it can occur in a matter of days while one is bedridden. With disuse, muscle tissue turns to fat tissue. Exercise prevents this from happening, but the exercise should be appropriate for the body's condition. For those who feel that high-impact aerobics are harsh, jarring, and harmful, low-impact aerobics may be ideal. Geriatric medicine should address these issues; unfortunately, there are not enough geriatric physicians in the United States at this time.

An older person does not have to run marathons or enter competitions to get exercise, feel better, and stay fit. Many programs offer more moderate degrees of exercise. Light forms of yoga, stretching, and relaxing exercises, and all kinds of dance and aerobics have been standard fare for elder fitness enthusiasts. People who exercise experience increased oxygen transport capacity, lung capacity, vital capacity, and physical work capacity (Huang et al., 1997). Body fat and blood pressure may decrease with regular exercise. Nervous tension also can be reduced with vigorous physical exercise. People who become sedentary and who overeat lay the groundwork for the development of disease. Complaints of aches and pains in joints and muscles, low-back strain, high blood pressure, and other symptoms could be eased or eliminated with a physical fitness program.

A recent research report demonstrates scientifically what for health enthusiasts has long been an article of faith: regular exercise can indeed prolong life. People who are active and fit can expect to live a year or so longer than their sedentary counterparts. For each hour of physical activity, one can expect to live that hour over—and live one or two more hours to boot. The study, the most comprehensive ever to relate exercise and longevity, tracked the health and lifestyles of 16,936 men who entered Harvard from 1916 to 1950. The subjects were followed until 1978, by which time 1,413 had died. Correlating death rates with exercise habits, the researchers were able to quantify, for the first time, the relationship between various amounts of physical activity and length of life. Regular exercise, the researchers found, is a critical factor in determining longevity. Men who walked nine or more miles a week (burning off at least 900 calories), for example, had a risk of death 21 percent lower than those who walked less than three miles a week. The optimum expenditure of energy seems to be about 3,500 calories a week, the equivalent of six to eight hours of strenuous bicycling or singles tennis. The Harvard men who worked out that much had half the risk of death of those who did little or no exercise. Moreover, the study showed that a lifetime habit of engaging in energetic activity three to four times a week could reduce the negative health effects of cigarette smoking or high blood pressure. It even partly offset an inherited tendency toward early death (Lee et al., 1995; Paffenbarger, 1984).

CHANGING EXERCISE HABITS

What are the constraints for elders of participating in exercise programs? The mantra "diet and exercise" has been repeated sufficiently that people of all ages surely understand the primacy of these two factors to good health and healthy aging. What, then, holds people back from participating in health-enhancing activities?

Constraints to exercise appear to be both universal and individual. One particularly useful study took a phenomenological approach by asking older people what they liked or did not like about their participation in an exercise program and the options offered them to participate (Whaley & Ebbeck, 1997). Some of the constraints that were voiced by elders were not those assumed by the researchers: "I don't like this activity—it's a women's class..." and "I want exercise with a *purpose*.... " Clear gender differences emerged. Men felt that classes offered were "for women" and were not appropriate for them. Women were more likely to cite health-related reasons for inactivity. Women are also more likely to live in poverty and to have more chronic illnesses than men; this affects women's ability to participate. In addition to these, more universal themes developed related to the **lived experiences** of the participants, which includes their histories and the social contexts of their life courses. Participating in an activity that has some product, like gardening, painting a house, or doing volunteer activity, seemed important to some study participants, whose life experience includes the Depression and a subsequent hard-work ethic.

There are many physical activities, something appropriate for every age group. Speed walking is an excellent routine for the middle-aged and elderly. Dr. William Evans at Tufts University in Boston reports that it is never too late to start a strength-training program. Study of participants 87 to 96 years old showed dramatic improvements after eight weeks; several no longer needed canes to walk and all experienced "three-to-fourfold increases in strength" (Evans & Rosenberg, 1991). Similarly, other experimental studies of nursing home residents lifting weights show them to greatly improve muscle strength, walking speeds, and mobility (National Institutes of Health, 1993).

The American College of Sports Medicine now recommends the following as a minimum exercise routine: some type of aerobic exercise for 20 minutes or more three times a week; and some form of resistance training at least twice a week that exercises all the major muscle groups in sets of 8 to 12 repetitions each (Segell, 1993, Part 1).

A study began in 1987 of almost 200 master athletes aged 40 and over who compete in one sanctioned event each year (e.g., runners, swimmers, field athletes) asks the question, "Just how old and how fit can one become?" The study is expected to continue for 20 years, but already it has predicted the following: (1) speed and muscle strength will endure longer than assumed, (2) athletic performance will not decline significantly until age 60, (3) death rate will be reduced, (4) falls and injuries will be reduced, (5) the heart and lungs will not have to lose function as quickly as previously thought, and (6) the incidence of osteoporosis will be reduced. In general, we have underestimated the ability and potential of older people.

Much as we have been told since childhood, to remain healthy in later life requires good genetic stock, exercise, excellent nutrition throughout one's life, and a healthy lifestyle.

The study also concludes to date that nothing can retard the aging process as much as exercise (Roan, 1993).

MENTAL HEALTH

The connection between physical well-being and mental health is strong. Most mental health professionals and geropsychologists recognize, in Niederehe's (1997) words "...that biological factors become more saliently intertwined with psychosocial ones in the mental disorders of late life, relative to typical problems of younger adults..." (p. 102). Biology and psychology have the paradoxical relationship of being the same and being different, simultaneously. Older people who are involved in aerobic sports—sports that increase the heartbeat and respiration—for several hours a week felt healthier and happier than people who were not involved in such exercise (van Boxtel et al., 1997). The subjective sense of being physically fit—feeling good about one's health and body—predicts better mental health (Niederehe, 1997). Being a happy, optimistic person in turn contributes to longevity. The 50-year study of Harvard graduates cited earlier (Paffenbarger & Lee, 1996) found the following:

- Men who cope well with emotional trauma live longer. Men who deny their feelings or intellectualize personal problems suffer more rapid declines in health after age 50.
- Optimists have better health in middle and old age than pessimists.
- Good mental health (one measurement was the lack of need to take tranquilizers) predicts successful aging.

A study by Costa at the National Institute on Aging found that a personality trait—"antagonistic hostility"—predicts premature death. This person is easily provoked to anger and is vindictive (reported in Segell, 1993). Other related personality characteristics have been determined by social scientists to be life shortening: repressed anger, depression, egocentricity, shyness, and various other negative attitudes (Morris et al., 1993; Shephard et al., 1995). One review of the study begun by Lewis Terman in the 1920s reported that the degree of psychological maladjustment was related to higher risk of all causes of mortality over a 40-year follow-up period. The review indicated that mental health problems were significantly more strongly related to deaths from injury and cardiovascular disease among men (but not among women). The finding was not mediated by alcohol consumption, obesity, or cigarette smoking (Martin et al., 1995).

In addition to longevity-limiting psychological characteristics, within any given age population will be those who are chronically mentally ill. Mental illness of any proportion is alarming and requires appropriate intervention, and it is anticipated that with the Baby Boom generation moving into late adulthood in the 21st century, the sheer numbers of people with chronic mental illness (as opposed to late-onset mental illness) will be large. To add to the possible load for mental health professionals, increased depression and suicidal ideation in older people with serious medical diseases has been documented (Niederehe, 1997). In some instances, the difficulty of letting go—of recognizing that death is nearby—can explain the sadness and depression. In other cases, however, it cannot be understood simply as the older person's psychological reactions to the experience of illness and must be looked at from a medical, as opposed to a mental health, perspective (Zeiss & Breckenridge, 1997). Medications often are a major issue to deal with in older adults, particularly in anxious older patients; shifts in medication tolerance and negative cognitive effects are part of a psychological symptoms complex associated with older adults (Beck & Stanley, 1997). If we expect larger numbers of people requiring mental health services in the future, we must train and prepare for that in the present.

A whole set of findings revolves around stress. In a nutshell, some stress may be a positive factor in life but too much of the wrong kind is bad. And those who are good at coping with stress will live longer. In the same vein, a good sense of humor helps, as well as a strong sense of self and purpose and a zest for life. The feeling that one is in control of one's life also adds years. Even in a nursing home, those who have choices and assert them will live longer.

In the presence of disease, "guided imagery" has been shown to lengthen life for some. Patients imagine their body parts getting healed—perhaps their immune cells are warriors fighting off the evil enemy. Or a totally healed lung is pictured in their minds. Here, positive mental attitude is used to get the immune system activated and fighting. Hypnotism, meditation, and other relaxation techniques are being used, with some success, to prolong life.

SOCIAL AND ENVIRONMENTAL FACTORS

The environment we live in plays a role in how long we live. Noise and air pollution, pesticides, radiation, secondary smoke from cigarettes, and other adverse chemicals in our air, water, and food bring disease and shorten life. The ultraviolet rays of the sun age the skin and can cause skin cancer. Living in an area of high crime can be life threatening. For rats, overcrowding in cages alters behavior and shortens life. Likewise, living in overcrowded cities may be harmful for humans.

A positive, hopeful, stimulating social environment adds years to life. Rats in cages with lots of wheels and mazes live longer than rats with no outlet for activity. Likewise, an active physical and mental environment is important for humans. Social class is correlated with longevity. Those with more money for health care live longer.

A shortened life is statistically correlated with the following: divorce (for men only); accidents (car, especially); a lifestyle that includes smoking, heavy use or abuse of alcohol or drugs, and too little or too much sleep; an imbalance of work and leisure; continual risk-taking/self-destructive behavior; and being a loner or a person without a confidant.

CENTENARIANS

Rather than study animals in a laboratory, some scientists have focused their attention on centenarians as a way of learning about longevity. Twenty-five or so centenarians, the "oldest-old," with a balance of white and black Americans, were in the Georgia Centenarians Study (Poon, 1992). With regard to personality and coping, the oldest-old scored high on dominance, suspiciousness, and imagination, and low on conformity—personality traits that served as protective functions. The centenarians were described as assertive and forceful. There were a number of extraordinary persons who wrote, published, performed musically, gave guided tours, invested in the stock market, earned a living, and coped well regardless of the adequacy of support systems. In terms of cognitive skills, they rated high on practical problem-solving tests, but lower on intelligence and memory tests. Religion was important and a common coping device: "I don't worry about the future; it's in God's hands," said Charles C., 101 years old.

Most of the centenarians were moderate, healthy eaters who did not go on diets. None were vegetarian; they did not smoke and drank very little; most ate big breakfasts. Surprisingly, they had high intake of saturated fat, especially the African American men who continued lifetime patterns of consuming pastries, soda, sugar, and whole milk. This speaks to the power of genetic predisposition; the frail and sick have died off, leaving behind a cohort with remarkable survival power.

The American demographer James Vaupel claims that genetic factors account for no more than 30 percent of variance in life spans, with the remaining 70 percent related to lifestyle and environmental factors (quoted in Kirkland, 1994). Beard (1991) found, in studying individual differences among centenarians, that long life was correlated with good health habits, stimulating physical and mental activity, spirituality, moderation, tolerance, integrity, and interacting with others. International studies of centenarians support the suggestion that heredity is important, but it explains far less about what constitutes the "sturdy disposition" of these survivors into a second century of life (IMSC, 1997). Further research of centenarians will provide us with more answers, and, in the decade to come, we will have centenarians from a wider range of cultures and lifestyles from which to gather information.

As science continues to document habits that increase stress and decrease nutritional and physical health, the wellness movement will gain strength, encouraging prevention and the adoption of good health-related habits. The long-term effects may well result in larger populations of older adults who will experience fewer debilitating illnesses and, as a result, higher levels of life satisfaction.

Chapter Summary

The health status of the population aged 65 and over is far better than most people would predict. Most elders are able-bodied and not limited in a major way by physical impairments—indeed, only 5 percent of people over 65 live in nursing homes or other long term care institutions. Poor health in old age is not caused by the aging process; lack of exercise, inadequate diet, stress, and disease are contributors. Heart disease, hypertension, cancer, strokes, and accidents are the leading causes of death. With the elimination of these and other factors, longevity would increase. Exercise and nutrition are vital in maintaining health and longevity; however, caution is given to avoid the pitfalls of "blaming the victim" for lifestyles not conducive to well-being in later life. Culture, life experience, historical time, and poverty levels each have an impact on choices made and choices available to each age cohort.

Wellness is the key emerging concept in the study of aging and in the planning for one's own aging. As the Baby Boomers enter late life in the 21st century, they will be the first generation to come into old age with a lifetime of information about the relationship of nutrition, exercise, and lifestyle choice on the aging process.

The wellness movement is based on anticipating and taking measures to prevent health-related problems as we age. Although modifying a person's lifelong behavior patterns is not always easy, it can be done. More and more of our young, middle-aged, and older citizens are losing weight, exercising, and monitoring their diets than ever before. Learning to avoid foods with higher levels of calories or fat, reducing hypertension, and discontinuing the use of tobacco, while simultaneously including a diet of nutritional foods and maintaining higher levels of physical activity reduces health-related risks in later life. Extending the number of healthy years of life, what has been called the **"health span,"** has become a viable goal for all Americans.

Key Terms

absolute life span
acute condition
aging as disease
arteriosclerosis
arthritis
atherosclerosis
average life span
biological clock
cancer
cerebrovascular disease
chronic condition
diabetes millitus
error theory
health span
health status of the aged
heart disease
hypertension
immune system
infarct
ischemic heart disease
lived experience
maximum life span
mean life span
osteoporosis
presbyopia
primary immunological change
programmed senescence
secondary change
stroke
wear and tear
wellness

Questions for Discussion

1. How long do you expect to live? How long did your grandparents or great-grandparents live? What are the causes of death among those in your family who have died? What are you doing specifically to enhance your well-being when you are in later life?
2. Examine your own lifestyle in terms of your everyday habits, exercise, diet, auto safety, smoking, drinking, and stress. How healthy will you be at age 80 if you are now 50? How healthy will you be at 80 if you are now 20 to 30?
3. Which biological model of aging makes most sense to you? Do you believe that the absolute maximum human life span can be pushed back to 150 years, or 200 years? Why or why not? What might be some social consequences of such longevity?

Fieldwork Suggestions

1. Survey a group of people who are older and a group that is younger to determine the kind and the quality of physical exercise they engage in. Which age groups are in better shape? Why?
2. Contact two people over the age of 65 at the close of the day. Have them list everything they ate. Evaluate the nutritional quality of their food intake.
3. Interview three people who work in health clubs to determine (1) how many people over 65 come into the club; (2) what the activities are of older club participants; and (3) what that person thinks about having older people working out. What level of training do these people have to work with older adults? Is the club you visited a place that you would recommend to your mother/father or grandmother/grandfather (or great-grandmother/father) to attend? Why or why not?

Online Activities

One intent of the exercises is that you become able to locate sources easily on the Internet. Another intent is that you develop a sense of discrimination about the information you find: to whom is it written/addressed? How difficult or easy was it to locate the information; and who do you think the primary users of the site are?

1. Locate the home page for American Associations of Retired Persons (http://www.aarp.org/index/html). What sort of practical health-related information does the site contain?
2. Log into Senior Com: The Source for Seniors (http://www.senior.com). This is a site designed to be used *by* seniors to promote their

health and well-being. Compare what you find, and the way it is presented, with the AARP site and with other sites for and about seniors.

3. Locate the best source of information you can find on the Internet related to nutrition for older people. How persistent did you need to be to find this source? Is it a site that older people might use? Is it one that someone who plans menus for a board-and-care facility might use?

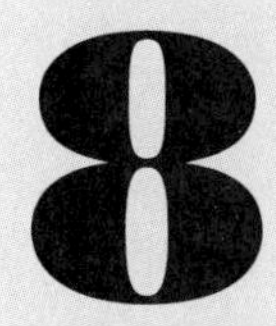

- The Concept of Retirement
- Age Discrimination in Employment
- Adjustment to Retirement
- Work and Leisure Values
- Expanding Work and Leisure Opportunities

Work and Leisure

Energetic Woman Takes Long Way Home

Maria Panaritis

Mary's been a Walker since birth, but she didn't become a walker until about 25 years ago.

That's when a transit strike transformed the 57-year-old commuter into a die-hard pedestrian, forcing her to end her workday with a 7½-mile walk home along the Schuykill River and into the city's historic Germantown section.

Now 82, Mary Walker still holds down a full-time job and still unwinds by slipping into a pair of Woolworth's sneakers and taking to the streets for her 2½-hour-long scenic stroll home.

"It's a little bit of a walk, but it's so beautiful that I enjoy every minute of it." she says. "I see people walking as fast as they can go, but that's not how I do it. I get home when I get home."

At any age, that kind of commute might be considered strenuous, if not crazy, especially in a society of automobile-enslaved individuals. At Mary's age, the long haul is downright extraordinary.

But Mary Walker is no ordinary woman. She holds down a job at one of the nation's largest banks with competence, diligence and vigor.

"Everybody's amazed by her," says her boss at CoreStates Corp., Philip J. Murray. "They're amazed at what she can do, and when they hear her age they're even more amazed. Everybody has an awful lot of respect for her."

Mary spends more than 40 hours a week in a ninth-floor cubicle of a skyscraper in downtown Philadelphia, toiling over the estates of recently deceased people.

Facing compulsory retirement 12 years ago at age 70, Mary bowed out of the business world. But she was soon offered the choice to return as a temporary employee, free to work as much—or as little—as she wanted.

"I love it," she says, her clear blue eyes glancing up momentarily from a shiny conference table. "I love the business world, and as my doctor said, 'Keep on working. It keeps your mind stimulated.' "

All year long, she hops on a train for a 20-minute ride into work. But from April to October she walks home, sizing up the weather on bad days and riding home only in a downpour. I like to get home feeling better than I started, full of fresh air."

She makes sure to admire cloud formations, remembering with each gaze how her mother used to point out animals and faces in the clouds. And she stops to smell the flowers and catch the sun sparkling on the winding river.

"You get to a certain age, you start to realize you don't want to rush through life," Mary says. "You want to savor it."

"I think people have a wrong conception of age," she says. "I don't think they realize you're not as old as your years. You appear as old as your years on the outside, but on the inside you feel just as young as in your teens."

Reprinted by permission of Associated Press.

The work ethic, like any ethic, is a set of beliefs and values that identifies what is good and affirms ideals of conduct. The work ethic historically has identified work with virtue and has held up for esteem a conflation of such traits and habits as diligence, initiative, temperance, industriousness, competitiveness, self-reliance, and the capacity for deferred gratification.

EKERDT, 1996, P. 239

As a social institution, retirement has been the major means of redividing the life span so that old age can be identified by a common dimension...[that is,] as a period of inactivity on a pension.

ANNE-MARIE GUILLEMARD, 1980

To work or not to work in old age: that is the question. The answer to this question has implications for both society and the older person. It also implies a choice that for many people is limited or nonexistent. Some people are forced to retire because of age discrimination or because of illness. Others must continue to work, often at menial jobs, because they cannot afford to retire. Further, the economics of supply and demand govern one's presence in or out of the job market. If there is a demand for your work, you stay; if there is not, you are encouraged to retire.

The issue of work and retirement is a thorny one. Retirees may either feel elated and free or devalued and depressed. Because of changes in routine, personal habits, and opportunities for social interaction, retirement can bring stress even when it is voluntary. Most older people generally make a satisfactory adjustment to retirement, given good health and sufficient income, but some do not have these benefits; and a minority are not satisfied with retirement, regardless of their health and financial status. *Retirement* is a dirty word to some; to others it represents freedom from a daily grind of work.

In this chapter, we will explore the options of retirement, analyze discrimination against the older worker, and examine the difficulties old people have in adjusting to retirement. We will also look at the meaning of leisure in our culture. When we are young, our time away from work is called "leisure"; when we are old, it is called "retirement." What is the difference?

The Concept of Retirement

The social definition of **retirement** has changed somewhat in the past half-century. For Atchley (1973) retirement is an event that occurs when a person definitively stops working and withdraws from the formal labor market. Numerous sociologists have since pointed out that some people withdraw from the formal labor market because they lack the health to continue working, because of age-related disabilities, or because they have become unemployed and are unable to find a new job. Retirement is quite different than struggling with the inability to work, and consequently being dependent on family, charity, or public welfare for survival. In this chapter, retirement will be seen from a social institution perspective: it is a person's departure from the major job of adulthood, with income replaced by a pension (Guillemard & Rein, 1993). Types of "retirement" vary enormously. It might be more useful to think of retirement as a life transition handled by different people in profoundly different ways (Mutchler et al., 1997).

Several conditions must be met for retirement to be a social institution. First, an economic surplus must exist that is sufficient to support former workers. Second, there must be a way in which that surplus is diverted to the former workers of society (through Social Security and pension programs, for example). Third, cultural values must support the idea of not working after a certain period of time; and fourth, people need to live long enough to have accumulated sufficient resources to afford retirement, or to be deemed "worthy" by society for support in nonwork (Morgan & Kunkel, 1998). When these conditions exist, a society supports retirement.

In 1900, nearly 70 percent of American men over age 65 were employed. By 1960, the figure had dropped to 35 percent; by 1976, to 22 percent; and by 1992, to 15 percent (see Figure 8.1). This figure is projected to be just under 15 percent by the year 2000 (U.S. Bureau of the Census, 1991). In 1992, the percentage of women in the workforce aged 65 and over was 9 percent; this number has remained fairly constant for the last two decades, but has experienced a 1 percent increase over the last five years and will rise further in the years ahead. Most of the labor force growth in the 1990s has and will come from increased participation by minorities and middle-aged and older women (Gall et al., 1997).

Economists and social scientists have collected a huge array of labor market statistics in the past 30 years and developed projections for future employment trends to determine the impact on economic support ratios and dependency. Table 8.1 shows Department of Labor projected trends in labor participation by older workers (1996). No particular pattern of change in the median age at retirement is projected into the 21st century for either men or women—the trends suggest a stabilization of the decrease of retirement age (Siegel, 1996). This is in marked contrast with the trends from the past 30 years in which the numbers of workers 65 and older markedly declined, as illustrated in Figure 8.1. The projected shifts suggest pronounced changes in the numbers of nonworkers and workers in the next half century, however.

FIGURE 8.1

Working less: Percentage of people aged 65 and over who still work

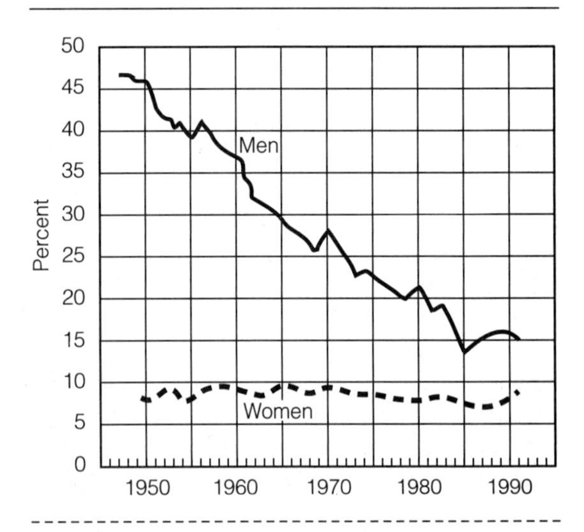

Source: Adapted from "Aging America," The Economist (16 September 1989): 18.

The ratio (per 100) of nonworkers 55 years of age and over is projected to rise from 31 in 1995 to 35 in 2010, then jump to 52 in 2030 (Siegel, 1993). There are presently more than three workers for every older nonworker, but in 2030 there are expected to be less than two workers for every older nonworker. Most of these older nonworkers are women—the economic support ratio for women will fall from more than 5 male and female workers for every female nonworker age 55 and over in 1995, to 3.25 workers for every female nonworker aged 55 and over in 2030 (Siegel, 1996). The future dilemma of support in retirement for older Americans is to no small extent an issue about women. The more women in the labor market, the more women will face retirement. Clearly, retirement as a social institution will encompass different social concerns in the 21st century than it did in the 1950s, when nearly all retirees were men.

TABLE 8.1

Civilian labor force participation ratios: 1994, 2000, and 2005

	Male			Female		
All Races	**1994**	**2000**	**2005**	**1994**	**2000**	**2005**
55–64	65.5	66.0	65.6	48.9	53.4	56.6
65–74	21.7	22.3	28.8	13.6	14.7	16.0
75+	8.6	8.2	3.5	4.0	4.3	

Source: Siegel, J. (1996). Aging into the 21st Century. National Aging Information Center. U.S. Department of Labor, Bureau of Labor Statistics, Office of Employment Projections. U.S. Administration on Aging, Washington, DC.

Cohort differences are likely to create changes in the actual patterns that emerge. These cohort differences have to do with economic and social status at the time that individuals prepare for retirement and then actually do so. Current workers in middle age were educated after the end of World War II, and retirement decisions are being made in a time of economic and labor market turbulence. For those who retired in the last 30 years, pension plans were less frequently provided, and social security benefits were lower than for middle-aged workers currently. Fewer retiring men had wives who were also in the workforce, and retirements did not have to be coordinated within a family. Because of longevity issues, fewer of the retiring workers in the past had elderly parents needing care. All these factors impact retirement decisions and the adaptation to retirement.

For most people in the United States, retirement is an expected life event. It has become a planned-for transition in adult life. Even though mandatory retirement has been abolished for many jobs, other factors are leading older men to favor retirement. On the other hand, more older women are entering or remaining in the workforce. However, not all workers retire completely: more than one of every five older Americans who retire return to work at least part-time.

In the agricultural era of the United States, few workers retired. Most workers were self-employed farmers or craftspeople who generally worked as hard as they could until illness or death slowed or stopped them. Stopping work, however, did not have to be abrupt. A gradual decline in the workload could occur simultaneously with a gradual decline in physical strength.

Older people who held property could usually support themselves in old age. For example, a homesteader who began to grow old and to experience difficulty in doing heavy work could usually pass the work on to family, retaining his or her authority as the children assumed more and more responsibility. Because he or she remained in charge, the older farmer did not have to quit producing entirely. No one could technically force "retirement."

Before 1900, few people lived past age 65. Those who owned property lived longer than those who did not own property or had helping family members. Older persons without economic resources had to do heavy work because of their need to support themselves. When they could no longer physically continue to work,

Self-concept for Americans is often tied closely to life's work. For some people retirement is a welcome respite after many years of work. For others it is a loss of daily companionship, income, and meaningful activity.

they often ended up in alms houses or died of malnutrition and neglect. The "good old days" were not good for many old people.

The Industrial Revolution brought many complex changes. Increased productivity created great surpluses of food and other goods. More people ceased being self-employed and went to work in large factories and businesses. Government and bureaucracy grew. When civil service pensions for government workers were introduced in 1921, the retirement system began.

In 1935, with the passage of the Social Security Act, all conditions for institutionalizing retirement were met. The law dictated that persons over age 65 who had worked certain lengths of time were eligible for benefits, and 65 became the age for retirement. Since then, employees in both the public and private sectors of the economy have retired in increasing numbers.

We also need a word about women's work pattern cohorts. Women born in the early 1900s were not encouraged to enter the workforce. A Gallup Poll in 1936 found 82 percent agreement for the statement that wives of employed husbands should not work (Burkhauser, 1996). Not until the 1960s did the concept of work outside the home as other than a temporary role for women develop. Even then, wives' employment was often seen as a supplemental source of money for "extras." Before the 1960s, the majority of permanently employed women were single. Married women tend to have interrupted work histories—entering the labor force and then leaving it upon the birth of a child (the "mommy track"). Thus many women in their old age today (the married ones, at any rate) do not have the extensive work histories that older women in the future will have, even though many of them worked temporarily outside the home during the Depression and World War II.

Now more than 95 percent of all adults expect to retire some day. Although retirement has become an accepted feature of modern life, one must question whether retirement is wise for everyone. Additionally, retirement may not be very meaningful for those people who are economically disadvantaged—many minorities and many women whose work-force participation has been discontinuous work into old age because of financial need (Calasanti, 1996).

THE TREND TOWARD EARLY RETIREMENT

A different trend is usurping retirement at age 65. More and more companies are encouraging employees in skilled, semiskilled, or unskilled jobs to retire before age 65 without a substantial loss of pension benefits. American industry, attempting to reduce the costs of senior employees, has steadfastly worked for early retirement and restrictions on work opportunities for older workers. Some businesses, such as the auto industry, have initiated **early retirement incentive programs (ERIPs)** in an effort to downsize the work force (Hardy et al., 1996; Hardy & Quadagno, 1995). In industry, retirement at age 55 is not uncommon and is typical at 62. This trend for early retirement is not among people in poor health. In 1993-94 the typical early Social Security beneficiary was as healthy and as wealthy as the typical same-age worker who did not retire (Burkhauser et al., 1996).

Early retirement has now become common in the white-collar world of work. Whether blue or white collar, most Baby Boomers say they would like to retire by age 55. Some (about 40 percent) want to retire between the ages of 56 and 65, and some, after 65 or never. The desire for and expectation of early retirement has increased over the last several decades. From 1950 to 1990 the median retirement age dropped from 67 to 63, however, this trend is projected to stabilize (Siegel, 1996), as shown in Table 8.1.

In 1961, early Social Security benefits were introduced. In the year previous to these benefits, over 79 percent of men aged 61 and nearly 76 percent of men aged 63 were in the labor force. In 1993 those percentages were 64 percent and 46 percent, respectively—despite improvements in mortality and morbidity (Burkhauser, 1996). In the 1970s, the trend toward making pensions and other benefits available before age 65 greatly accelerated, from the government's pension system, to other public and private institutions. One study indicated that those who were offered full pension benefits before age 65 were twice as likely to retire early. In contrast, in 1992, 38 percent of early retirements from large companies were the result of incentive offers. For the most part, companies were seeking to cut their payrolls and at the same time avoid layoffs.

Studies of companies and educational institutions show that most corporations do have early retirement inducements in their pension plans. Only a handful of organizations offer incentives to continue working beyond age 65.

A few businesses are beginning to question the policy of encouraging workers to retire at or before age 62. The labor pool of young workers is declining, and they sometimes cost as much to train as to retain the older workers (Cyr, 1996). Some companies are studying **late-retirement incentive programs (LRIPs)**. However, although most businesses are afraid that too many workers will take advantage of LRIPs, most workers still opt for early retirement. Incentives for early rather than late retirement are still the order of the day for business and industry. The only change is that many early retirees find the "good deals" not so good after all; buyout plans are growing skimpier, and good new jobs are hard to come by. The trend toward early retirement brings with it a number of complex issues.

OLDER WORKER DISCRIMINATION

Does age make a predictable, negative difference in job performance? Some early retirement incentives are offers that older American workers cannot refuse, and many older workers are wondering whether they are being subjected to disguised **early retirement discrimination.** For example, at the age of 56, a man who had worked for 31 years for a large manufacturing company was hoping to work 6 more years and retire at age 62. But his corporation, like many others across the United States, decided to trim its payroll and abolish numerous jobs, including his. The company offered him half-pay retirement for the next four years, provided that he did not work elsewhere. He accepted these terms out of fear that other jobs were not available to him.

A one-time incentive is not the same as an early retirement option. An early retirement option offers the employee the choice to stay or to go. In contrast, with the one-time incentive, the employee either accepts or gets laid off. For every employee who gladly accepts an early retirement incentive, another feels that he or she is being forced out the door. Under the **Age Discrimination in Employment Act (ADEA)**, all early retirements must be voluntary (Blouin & Brent, 1996). The question remains, What is voluntary? Do you leave of your own free will if your boss drops strong hints that you are not wanted and hints at a big bonus offer if you leave early? Or if you are told that in a year your job will be phased out?

Mandatory retirement was outlawed by ADEA with the exception of specific occupations falling under the **bona fide occupational qualification (BFOQ).** Examples include some law enforcement positions, air traffic controllers, and airline pilots. On the one hand, mandatory retirement for some occupations makes sense on the surface. On the other hand, the vast individual differences exhibited among people brings into question a law stating that age has a predictable effect on one's ability to perform (Morgan & Kunkel, 1998).

Employers are slowly starting to realize that jettisoning older workers can result in an irreparable loss of skills and expertise.

REDAY-MULVEY, 1996

Along with the multinational web of new global marketplaces, new forms of industrial competition are emerging "precisely at the time the population is aging" (Minda, 1997, p. 564). Downsizing, restructuring, reengineering, outsourcing, reduction-in-force (RIF)—all are terms common to the postindustrial work environment of the last decade of the 20th century. These management shifts were all part of an economic recovery between 1990 and 1998. However, while productivity and stock market indices have grown vigorously, median family incomes have remained stagnant, and average weekly earnings of most rank-and-file workers fell (Minda, 1997). Some economists and social analysts believe the newly emerged definition of work has created social changes as profound as those of the Industrial Revolution 200 years previous (Minda, 1997; Weaver, 1997).

In the United States, outsourcing and downsizing has shifted much work from permanent workers to contingent workers who are generally nonunion and lower paid than those they have replaced. Contingent, part-time workers often do not receive benefits such as health care and corporate pensions. Additionally, the risk of job loss is rising for workers 45 to 55—the age category that has suffered most as a result of corporate downsizing (Bureau of Labor Statistics, 1996).

The risk extends internationally. When Congress amended the ADEA to apply to United States companies abroad, it neglected to include the entire class of American workers working for foreign employers stationed in the United States (Madden, 1997). With increased globalization of the economy the protection of all workers, including older workers, becomes more complex and yet more essential.

The pattern of easing older workers out of the labor market cuts across all industrialized nations. In the Netherlands and France, less than 60 percent of the active male population between 55 and 59, and less than 20 percent of those in the 60-64 age range, are now part of the labor market (Reday-Mulvey, 1996). The rates are only slightly higher for Great Britain and Germany. It is not a problem unique to the United States—it is an issue related to the global economy. Downsizing, the 1990s version of permanent unemployment, has become a cause for older workers throughout the globe who have devoted an entire lifetime of employment to a single employer (Minda, 1997).

THE TAXPAYER VERSUS EARLY RETIREMENT

People are asking, "Can we afford old age?" Business and industry are pushing for early retirement programs, and these programs are sometimes a boon for the older worker. But there is an irony involved. Life expectancy is greater than ever, and the supply of younger workers is shrinking, creating a larger percentage of older workers. Social Security would be more likely to stabilize if older workers stayed on the job longer; and the government, contrary to many companies' wishes, is attempting to see that they do. The Social Security retirement age will gradually become 67 (in other words, the normal retirement age will be 67 for those reaching age 62 after 2022), and those taking benefits early will receive 30 percent less (they currently receive 20 percent less) than those receiving benefits at the normal retirement age. In this way, federal policy is encouraging workers to extend their work lives. But the incentives from business and industry are powerful in encouraging the older worker out of the market. Economics researchers make it very clear that most people respond to economic incentives in choosing to retire.

Early retirement has generally been interpreted positively. It is an indication that society is able to provide economic security for a large number of older people who no longer must be in the labor market. This in itself is a historic development. Additionally, retirement has been a positive force in avoiding generational conflicts between older, employed workers and younger workers, seeking employment (Morris & Caro, 1995). Despite its widespread acceptability, however, retirement poses problems for many older workers who find themselves unemployed.

Marty Denis (1996), in an analysis of early retirement from a corporate perspective, listed six advantages of early retirement plans:

1. They can reduce the need for massive layoffs.
2. Payroll costs can be reduced.
3. The number of senior, more highly paid employees can be reduced.
4. When done across-the-board (not targeted), employee morale may be preserved or at least not unduly disrupted.
5. Because of the release component, employment discrimination claims can be minimized, if not avoided.
6. Promotion channels can be opened so that other qualified employees can advance within the company.

The downside of early retirement, according to Denis, is that employers "may be deluding themselves about the overall effectiveness of these programs in cutting staff and, in particular, ridding employers of their less-productive employees" (Denis, p. 66).

When employees seek redress under the law for what they believe to be discrimination, they often do not win (Jacobs, 1998). In a retirement case heard by the U.S. Supreme Court in 1995 *(Lockheed Corporation v. Spink),* the Court supported the corporation. Lockheed had amended its retirement plan to provide financial incentives for certain employees to retire early. The plan required that participants receiving the early retirement benefits must release any employment-related claims they may have against Lockheed. Employee Spink was eligible for the early retirement package, but refused to sign the release. He retired without earning the extra benefits and subsequently sued Lockheed. The Court held that the Lockheed retirement plan was permissible, but introduced the concept of "retirement sham." If the payment of early retirement benefits is purely a sham, a court might find that the

Skills developed after many years of work can compensate for reduced physical agility or stamina of the older worker. In many jobs older workers are more productive than younger workers because they "work smarter."

plan assets were misused. Just how egregious the transaction must be to be considered a "sham" was not defined by the Court (Denis, 1996).

The economic incentives to business for introducing early retirement packages are strong. To keep older workers on the job and to thereby save Social Security funds, the government will need to strengthen its measures—to increase the amount of money older workers can earn without reducing their Social Security benefits, for example. And business and industry should try harder to find a place for the older worker, who may well offer a gold mine of experience, wisdom, and loyalty.

Unfortunately, workers near retirement seem expendable to most large-scale employers. But as the number and percentage of younger workers shrinks, private business may finally be motivated to retain and retrain older workers. It will take collaboration between the private and public sectors to reach the proper integration of policies that accomplish (1) an extension of the working life in order to manage human resources and to finance pensions; and (2) the development of well-protected and regular part-time work to sustain policies of gradual retirement (Reday-Mulvey, 1996). As the 21st century begins, a new definition of "work" is being forged, and hopefully it will represent a balance of the public interest with that of the private.

Age Discrimination in Employment

Age discrimination in employment starts long before the traditional time for retirement. Even those still in their thirties have trouble getting into some training programs and schools, such as flight school and medical school. The problem of job discrimination is severe for older workers in spite of federal laws that prohibit it.

The 1967 Age Discrimination in Employment Act (amended in 1974 and 1978) prohibits the following:

1. Failing to hire a worker between ages 40 and 70 because of age.
2. Discharging a person because of age.
3. Discrimination in pay or other benefits because of age.
4. Limiting or classifying an employee according to his or her age.
5. Instructing an employment agency not to refer a person to a job because of age, or to refer that person only to certain kinds of jobs.
6. Placing any ad that shows preference based on age or specifies an age bracket. *Exceptions:* the federal government, employers of less than 20 persons, or jobs where youth is a "bona fide occupational qualification," such as modeling teenage clothes.

Prior to 1978, the Age Discrimination in Employment Act protected employees from age 40 through age 64. The amendments adopted in 1978 extended that protection to age 70. Though all upper limits were removed for federal employees, the law does include exceptions that allow the federal government to retire air traffic controllers, law enforcement officers, and firefighters at younger ages. Nevertheless, the U.S. Supreme Court in 1985 ruled that the city of Baltimore could not force its firefighters to retire at age 55, despite federal regulations requiring retirement at 55 for most government firefighters. Other cities are easing their rules to allow firefighters, police officers, and other public safety employees to stay on the job until 65 or older.

Interpretations in the law can be subtle. In 1996 the U.S. Supreme Court upheld the suit of a 56-year-old worker who had been replaced by a 40-year-old worker, both ages of which are within the protected category of ADEA. In *O'Connor v. Consolidated Coin Caterers Corporation*, the Court ruled that the case was discriminatory because an older person was replaced with a substantially younger worker (Blouin & Brent, 1996).

Additional protection for the older worker was legislated in 1990 with the Older Workers Benefit Protection Act. Some companies required older workers to sign a waiver agreeing not to sue before they could qualify for an early retirement bonus. Now any waiver and release signed by an older worker going through a job transition must meet certain requirements. The agreement must be clear and concisely written, and the employee must have 21 days to decide whether to accept. Additionally, the agreement must clearly specify that the worker is waiving all rights under the ADEA (Blouin & Brent, 1996).

The protection of older workers has become necessary in light of downsizing and demand for high corporate profit margins, even in a time of economic growth. When layoffs are for legitimate business reasons rather than to eliminate one or more undesirable employees, or for eliminating those employees who are highly compensated, they are not legal. When actions are not legal, the onus is on the older worker to take his or her case to court—at enormous economic and emotional cost to the "retired" or otherwise laid-off worker. It is estimated that for every case that even gets to court (much less every case in which the worker wins the suit), there are 50 cases in which the unhappy worker did not sue (Abel, 1998).

AGE DISCRIMINATION IN THE JOB SEARCH

Age should not be a determining criterion in finding work. One's ability to do the job is what counts. Age discrimination in the labor market makes finding work more difficult. Preconceived ideas about aging by employers limits job opportunities (Burn, 1997). Because older workers have difficulty finding jobs, changing fields is even more difficult. The skills and energy of older people become greatly underutilized. More older people want to work than is commonly believed. One study found the following (Commonwealth Fund, 1993):

- As many as 5.4 million older Americans (55 and over)—one in seven of those not currently working—report that they are willing and able to work but do not have a job.
- More than 1 million workers aged 50 to 64 believe that they will be forced to retire before they want to.
- More than half of all workers aged 50 to 64 would continue working if their employer were willing to retrain them for a new job; continue making pension contributions after age 65; or to transfer them to a job with less responsibility, fewer hours, and less pay as a transition to full retirement.

Older persons who feel that they have been denied employment or have been let go because of their age can take steps to get their job back or to receive compensation by making a formal written charge of discrimination against the employer to the Wage and Hour Division of the Department of Labor. Individual cases of age discrimination are difficult to prove, however. In the investigation of the employer's hiring, firing, and retiring practices, the government tries to reveal a pattern of discrimination. For example, if an employer has hired a good many people over the past several years—but nobody over age 30—a pattern of discriminating against older workers in favor of younger workers may be documented. The older worker will have a better chance of winning if he or she hires a lawyer. A class-action suit may be filed if a number of job applicants feel they have been denied employment because of discrimination.

Resources that work diligently to help the older worker find employment are increasing. For example, in the past, employment agencies commonly violated the Age Discrimination Act by stipulating upper age limits or using words such as *junior executive*, *young salesperson*, or *girl* in advertising. Employment agencies also have been found guilty of failing to refer older workers to potential employers. Such violations, unfortunately, are still common practice. Now, however, employment agencies such as "Kelly Services: Encore" cater to people over 50 years of age. They advise older applicants that they do not have to give their date of birth on a resume, and they remind them that potential employers may not legally ask a person's age in an interview. Other employment resources are aimed specifically at elders. One example is Operation ABLE in Chicago, which has helped thousands of people between the ages and 50 and 70 to find work. It not only matches people with jobs but also teaches them skills such as word processing.

In the mid-1970s, Jobs for Older Women, a branch of the National Organization for Women (NOW), began analyzing refusals to hire older women. Employers often base refusal on an older woman's appearance: a department or clothing store may be worried about projecting a youthful image, or a certain restaurant may hire only young women who will wear skimpy uniforms. Older women are also rejected in favor of younger women for the more visible positions of bank tellers, receptionists, and other such jobs. The sad refrain is, "I'd love to hire you, but you just won't fit in." But employers may soon lack the personnel to meet their youthful standards. As the U.S. population collectively ages, older women will begin to outnumber younger women in the job market (Crispell, 1993). The percentage of women aged 55 to 59 in the job market was 55 percent in 1993, compared to 27 percent in 1950 and 46 percent in 1983 (Perkins, 1994). Middle-aged women, often heads of households, have had to settle for low-paying jobs with little chance for promotion. Age discrimination is well established by age 40 for women. One indicator is the large number of age discrimination lawsuits for women this age compared with men.

Women are in the labor force more continuously than ever before, yet women still earn less than men 35 years after the Equal Pay Act was signed into law. According to the U.S. Department of Labor, in 1998 women earned 76 cents for every dollar made by a man compared to 59 cents for every dollar a man earned in 1963 (U.S. Department of Labor, 1998). Minority earnings are equally disproportional; however, Department of Labor statistics indicate that women are laid off in a corporate downsizing before men of any color. The order of layoffs in downsizing is first, women of color; second, nonminority women; third, men of color; and finally major-culture men (U.S. Department of Labor, 1998). Business attitudes toward women will undoubtedly shift in the 21st century, given the increased amount of education, training, and work experience among women.

ON-THE-JOB DISCRIMINATION AND AGEISM IN LAYOFFS

Ageism in the labor market is deeply ingrained institutionally and culturally. Ageism in employment occurs in job categories of every kind. Studies of professionals, engineers, and scientists who are unemployed show age to be a significant variable in explaining their layoffs. Ageism is a factor in both blue-collar and white-collar occupations and for both sexes. Occupations in sales and marketing may suffer the most age discrimination, because they place more emphasis on youth and a youthful image than other occupations, as do occupations requiring physical stamina, such as construction. The computer software industry is notorious for age discrimination (Matloff, 1997; Computer World, 1997). Once out of work, older workers are likely to remain unemployed much longer than their younger coworkers and to find job hunting a nightmare. If they do find work, it is usually at a much lower salary and with fewer fringe benefits.

The number of age-discrimination charges filed with the U.S. Equal Employment Opportunity Commission (EEOC) has increased every year since the Age Discrimination in Employment Act went into effect. In 1997 more than 30,000 cases of age discrimination charges were filed with the EEOC, close to 20 percent more than 10 years prior, in 1987. Today, workers are even more likely to press charges if they feel they have been victims of discrimination. Complaints of age discrimination have been growing faster than those concerning gender or race. In these recession years, the large numbers of layoffs and reassignments have angered all workers, especially older ones. These layoffs have also been a factor in the large number of age-bias suits. Although few affirmative action programs address the concerns of middle-aged workers, a quirk in the age-discrimination law allows for jury trials, which seems to work in favor of those filing suits. In age-discrimination suits, jury members, who tend to be older, appear to see corporations as the "bad guys."

Age discrimination is still a tough charge to prove. In the last several years, thousands upon thousands of cases filed with the EEOC have led to only several hundred lawsuits, and not a high proportion have been won. However, in spite of mishandling many cases, the EEOC has obtained some very large settlements involving millions of dollars in back wages and pension benefits:

- Ceridian Corporation and Control Data Corporation will pay as much as $29 million to more than 300 former employees who claimed they were fired because of their age. The 1997 court ruling favored the employees, who accused the corporation of a pattern of discrimination by laying off older workers and replacing them with younger workers. The suit was begun in 1989; the proportion of the settlement required to cover legal costs will probably be one-third of the total amount (Ceridian, Control Data, 1997).
- Westinghouse Electric and Northrop Grumman Corporation settled two age-discrimination lawsuits in 1997 (Westinghouse Electric, 1997).
- A 78-year-old physician for the medical unit of the Los Angeles County Sheriff's Office was returned to his job after the county settled his claim that he was forced to retire (Jail Doctor Wins, 1998).
- A news correspondent got a settlement from CBS on age discrimination (Lambert & Woo, 1994).
- A California law firm settles an age bias suit (*Wall Street Journal*, 1997).

The cost in time, dollars, and personal stress required to pursue legal action is enormous. In addition, the line between discrimination and decision making for corporate well-being has become less clear. Some factors creating this lack of clarity include conservative court decisions, stockholder pressure for corporate high profit margins, and changing technology. In the past, courts have supported age-bias claims in which the layoffs had "disparate impact" on employees over the age of 40. Four federal appeals courts, however, have recently questioned the idea that people can claim age bias merely because an employer's actions had a harsher effect on older people. Instead, the courts have said, "older workers must now show that their employer intentionally discriminated against them" (McMorris, 1997, p. B1). In a job market in which technological skills are important, more recently trained people probably will have the most current skills unless the company provides appropriate employee training. If a company lays off workers based on up-to-date skill levels, or otherwise makes decisions that they feel further the economic stability of the corporation, is it age discrimination?

One particularly ominous struggle is taking place in the UK between nearly 200 Intel workers and Intel Corporation, the microchip manufacturer established both in Britain and in the United States. The workers have taken the unusual step of forming a pressure group (Former and Current Employees of Intel—FaceIntel) and publicizing their argument on the Internet. The concerns have to do with the firm's use of "ranking and rating" to assess employees. This ranks employees on "equal to" or "slower than" other employees, according to a moveable line determined by the company. Anyone receiving two out of three, or two consecutive "slower thans," is automatically put on a disciplinary corrective action program. Those who do not reach a target set by their manager face discharge.

The employees claim that a disproportionate number of people receiving "slower thans" are older workers and workers with disabilities—two groups protected by antidiscrimination laws in the United States. Intel denies the group's allegations, saying that it remains as flexible as possible in the face of the astounding competition in the microelectronics business. This competitive environment requires the company to have employees who can work under demanding circumstances. A random sample telephone survey by FaceIntel of the 1,400 laid-off workers reportedly found that 90 percent were over 40 years old, and 40 percent had some form of disability (Welch, 1997).

The following age-discrimination complaints are typical of those reported by older workers on the job:

- Position terminated: older people are told their jobs are terminated; when they leave, younger workers are hired in their places.
- Sales force downsized: the sales force is trimmed, and older workers are the ones eliminated.
- Retirement credits refused: older workers reach a certain salary level, and there is no more potential for salary (or pension) increases.
- Dropped for medical reasons: older people are told they are being dropped for medical reasons.

As suggested by the experience of workers in microelectronics, this list of age-discrimination complaints in the future might well include demands for competitively fast rates of precision movements and judgments.

In some cases older workers are passed over for promotion or are the first fired, sometimes to protect a company's pension funds, sometimes to save salary costs. The reasons for and means of discrimination against older workers vary. Employers frequently prefer younger workers—sometimes because of age prejudice, sometimes because younger workers will accept a cheaper wage, and sometimes because the company feels it will receive more years of work before it must pay retirement benefits. Employers in a tight job market can get by without giving substantial salary increases, because the older worker, afraid of unemployment, will settle for a low salary. The older worker is highly vulnerable in a tight labor market.

Health and life insurance fees, which tend to increase with worker age, constitute a supposedly inordinate cost of retaining older workers. The older, tenured worker also tends to receive a higher salary and more vacation time. Surely, companies could deal more creatively and tactfully with older employees. For example, many older people would gladly contribute toward their health and life insurance costs if it meant keeping a job; in turn, companies could be more realistic—and less paranoid—about the older workers' health concerns.

MYTHS ABOUT THE OLDER WORKER

Negative stereotypes of the older worker still persist. The older worker is thought to be accident- or illness-prone, to have a high absenteeism rate, to have a slow reaction time, and to possess faulty judgment. Stereotypes contribute greatly to on-the-job discrimination. Common **myths about the older worker** include the following:

- Older workers cannot produce as much as younger workers.
- Older workers miss more time than younger workers because of illness.
- Older workers lack physical strength and endurance.
- Older workers are set in their ways.
- Older workers do not mix well with younger workers—they tend to be grouchy.
- Older workers are difficult to train—they learn slowly.
- Older workers lack drive and imagination—they cannot project an enthusiastic, aggressive image.

Retention of older employees in the labor force will require some changes in employer attitudes. One study that looked at beliefs about older workers came to three interesting conclusions: (1) direct, frequent experience with older workers reduced negative beliefs for younger workers; (2) older workers had more positive beliefs about older workers than did younger workers, but even younger workers tended to have generally positive beliefs; and (3) older supervisors held more negative beliefs about older workers than did younger supervisors (Hassell & Perrewe, 1995). The third conclusion is rather surprising. The researchers suggested that age discrimination is so institutionalized, and so unconscious, that younger supervisors might have lower expectations with older workers and actually exaggerate or overreward their good performance. Older supervisors, on the other hand, choose to perceive themselves as valued members of the organization, and do not identify personally as an "older" employee.

Management needs to be concerned with dispelling myths about older workers. According to the U.S. Bureau of Labor Statistics, by the turn of the century there will be more than 17 million labor force workers aged 55 or older (Siegel, 1993). The impact of this process will be felt both by workers and by employees. Employers need to be aware of the following points:

- Healthy older workers may not cost more in medical benefits than younger employees who have children at home.
- Use of sick leave is more highly correlated with lifetime patterns developed at a young age than with age itself. A natural selection process operates to leave healthy older workers on the job. The less fit have quit.
- Older persons retain their mental faculties, they can learn new skills, and they are not necessarily more rigid.
- Older workers have fewer work-related accidents.

Age is not necessarily a determinant of the capacity to do well on the job. The fact that the age of the work force is increasing means that opportunities for a wide variety of interactions with older workers will increase. The more frequently younger people are around older people, the less negatively they see the elderly as a group, and older people are seen more positively—as individuals, some of whom are winners and some of whom are not.

OLDER WORKER PERFORMANCE

On-the-job studies reveal individual variations in the ability of older workers. Most importantly, however, such studies generally show that older workers are as good as—if not better than—their younger counterparts. One study indicated that older workers have superior attendance records (less absenteeism); that they are likely to be stable, loyal, and motivated; and that their output is equal to that of younger workers (Commonwealth Fund, 1993). The work ethic of older people tends to be very high, which leads to high job satisfaction.

Experience can often offset any decrements that come with aging. The ability to do heavy labor does decline with age, but this decline is gradual and jobs vary greatly in the physical strength they require. Furthermore, an older person in good physical condition is quite likely to outwork a younger person in poor physical condition. Studies of work loss due to illness show that workers aged 65 and over have attendance records equal to or better than that of most other age groups. The U.S. Bureau of Labor reports that workers aged 45 and over have better safety records than younger workers: the highest overall accident rates occur in the 18 to 44 age group (AARP, 1995).

Older workers may take somewhat longer to train, but considering their careful work, the investment in time should be worthwhile. Some firms who recognize this say the problem is not "How can I get rid of the older worker?" but "Where can I find more?"

Adjustment to Retirement

Just how difficult is adjustment to retirement? Though one myth claims that people get sick and die shortly after retirement, studies do not confirm this. Retirement in and of itself does not lead to poor physical health. Research shows, however, that adjustment to retirement can be difficult.

Financial problems top the list of reasons for unfulfilled retirement expectations. Those at a marginal or lower income level are affected most adversely by retirement. In fact, about one-third of retired men end up going back to work and many retirees worry that they will outlive their retirement funds (Szinovacz, 1996). Studies of retirement adjustment show varying results in terms of adjustment, satisfaction, and happiness. A general finding, however, is that a minority has serious problems with retirement, whereas the majority adjusts reasonably well. The message here seems to be that of continuity. The kind of person one has been does not change significantly just because of retirement.

Clearly, if one's retirement income is adequate, retirement has a much greater chance of success. Good health is also a critical factor. If the retiree has the money and physical mobility to pursue the lifestyle of his or her choosing, adjustment comes more easily. The importance of these two factors suggests that adjusting to the role of retiree depends more on physical and monetary resources than on mental set. Lifestyle is another factor: if a person is involved with family, friends, and activities, then adjustment is usually more successful. Conversely, if a person has nothing to do and no associates, then adjustment may be poor.

Willingness to retire and attitude toward retirement are also important factors. Naturally, reluctant retirees show negative attitudes toward retirement. Those who retire voluntarily are healthier mentally and physically than those who did not feel control over the decision to retire (Gall et al., 1997). A positive attitude toward retirement also depends on an individual's expectations. In general, those who expect to have friends and social activities, and who expect that their retirement will be enjoyable, usually look forward to retirement.

Gerontologist Guillemard (1993) identified five types of retirement patterns:

1. Withdrawal—Extreme reduction of social activity; long "dead" periods exist between actions performed to ensure biological survival.
2. Third-age retirement—Professional activities give way to creative activities (artistic creation, hobbies) and cultural improvement. (This term is commonly used in France. Life has three stages: childhood, adulthood, and **third age.** With each stage a new positive phase of living may begin.)
3. Leisure retirement—The focus is on leisure activities (vacations, trips to museums and other exhibitions, theater shows) with an emphasis on consumption.
4. Protest retirement—Characterized by political activism; much time is devoted to associations of the elderly to protect the interests of the retired.
5. Acceptance retirement—Acceptance of traditional retirement values; lengthy time periods spent in daily exposure to television and other forms of mass communication.

According to Guillemard, those with professional backgrounds tend to cluster in the second and third groups. Those with working-class backgrounds are overrepresented in the other categories.

Studies of white-collar/blue-collar differences in adjustment to retirement reveal various findings. Former top managers and executives can have difficulty adjusting because they feel a loss of power and status. On the whole, white-collar workers generally adjust fairly well because they have more resources at their command. Professional types, such as educators, often show a good adjustment to retirement. Because they are well educated, they tend to have interests and hobbies, such as community affairs, reading, travel, and art, that lend themselves well to retirement. Some professional people write or act as consultants. They seem to have many ways to spend their time fruitfully.

Blue-collar workers indicate a greater readiness to retire because their work may bring them less satisfaction. For example, a man or woman with a dull, routine factory job may look forward to leaving. However, studies show that those with the least education and the lowest incomes have the most trouble adjusting to retirement. Socioeconomic status has been found to have a major influence on retirement rates. The lower one's socioeconomic status, the earlier one retires. Individuals with less education who are employed in occupations characterized by low skills and labor oversupply tend to retire early.

Retiring persons face several adjustments that relate directly to retirement: loss of the job itself, loss of the work role in society, loss of the personal or social associations that work provides, and loss of income. In addition, events such as declining health or the loss of a spouse may coincide with retirement. When all these events occur at the same general time, adjustment is stressful and difficult.

RETIREMENT PREPARATION PROGRAMS

Retirement preparation programs can aid adjustment to retirement. Anyone who is employed would be wise to prepare for retirement, yet few people do much beyond paying into Social Security.

Retirement preparation programs are growing. In addition to traditional programs, "Outplacement companies" have been created to assist with layoffs and to offer assistance to laid-off employees (Marcellini, 1997). Most are offered by government agencies and by companies whose workers are covered by a private pension. These retirement programs fall into two categories: (1) limited programs that explain only the pension plan, the retirement timing options, and the benefit level associated with each option; and (2) comprehensive programs that go beyond financial planning to deal with topics such as physical and mental health, housing, leisure, and the legal aspects of retirement. Individuals exposed to comprehensive programs have a more satisfying retirement.

Favorable attitudes toward retirement are therefore associated with planning, company counseling, personal discussion, and exposure to news media presentations about retirement. People need to be socialized into postwork roles just as they are socialized into other roles. Anticipatory socialization, which prepares a child for adult roles, is also necessary to prepare an adult for successful retirement in old age. Retirement is prepared for in several ways: by saving money, by deciding what our goals are, by beginning to care for and improve our health, by forming meaningful relationships with a sense of permanence, and by expanding our interests so that work is not our primary focus.

Work and Leisure Values

Even though Americans are expected to retire, our traditional value system gives higher social esteem to those who work. In the past, leisure was an accepted lifestyle only for the extremely wealthy. Adherence to the traditional work ethic is not as complete as it once was. What value older people assign to leisure is a research question getting some interesting answers.

WORK

Before the Protestant Reformation in the 16th century, work had been regarded as a burden and something to be avoided (Weber, 1958). With the Reformation, religious reformers like Martin Luther and John Calvin taught that *all* work had an inherent dignity and value. In fact, diligence in the performance of work was part of the highest form of Christian behavior. This is the basis of America's **work ethic**, and it has remained strong through the centuries. Although no longer is work considered to be the direct glorification of God, the Judeo-Christian culture still highly values work for work's sake. The **work ethic** is a long-standing American tradition that it is immoral not to work. "Idle hands are the devil's workshop," a basic precept in the early American character structure, still influences our attitudes today. The current definition of the work ethic includes both strong value in hard work *plus* negative and disparaging views of others who may lack a strong work ethic (Mudrack, 1997).

To some, work is not a value in and of itself but is, rather, a means to identify one's social standing. It is not work that matters but having a job. Indeed, everyone knows that the general question, "What do you do?" requires a very specific answer: To have any status, one must name some type of occupation. Work provides a means of achieving self-identification and placement in the social structure. This very fact has made many American women second-class citizens, because work at home has not traditionally been considered an occupation.

A common theme in the literature—both popular and academic—is that the work ethic has declined. A frequently-quoted nationwide study in 1955 and again in 1980 reported a significant decline from 52 percent to over 33 percent of full-time workers in the United States who said they enjoy their work so much they have a hard time putting it aside. Additionally, workers who said they enjoyed hours on the job more than hours off the job declined from 40 percent to 24 percent. (Glen & Weaver, 1983-1984). This finding, however, probably reflected an increase in the cultural value of *leisure* rather than a decrease in the work ethic.

A follow-up to the study found that there were few fundamental changes in the work ethic in the United States from 1972-1978 to 1988-1993. The study found, in fact, that among white workers of both sexes in white-collar jobs, there is evidence for *increased* work ethic values (Weaver, 1997). Gender and ethnicity changes that did emerge were that more white females in blue-collar jobs and more white men in white-collar jobs said they would continue to work if they were to get enough money to live as comfortably as they would like for the rest of their lives. More women in white-collar jobs felt that people get ahead by their own hard work than by lucky breaks or help from others; fewer men and fewer women from all ethnic groups, however, reported being "very satisfied" with their jobs (Weaver, 1997).

Work matters to Americans. One problem with having a strong work ethic is that it may be difficult to reconcile it with retirement. Work attitudes can be so ingrained in retirees that they carry over to nonwork activities. A strong work ethic tends to be related to low retirement satisfaction. The least satisfied retirees tend to be those with high work values who do not perceive their retirement activities as being useful. Retirees with strong work values are not as active in social activities, because they have a hard time enjoying them. Although most eventually make a satisfactory adjustment, retirement can be one of the most difficult transitions in life.

Perhaps the work ethic only appears to motivate workers less because the line between one's job and "work" has grown less distinct than it once was. Choices in life course patterns are greater now than in the 1950s. Women might delay childbirth until their forties, first establishing themselves in careers. Men might choose to work less than full-time to mesh their work schedules with that of their wives in order to maximize time with young children. Those same men and women, having moved in a less lockstep manner through career ladders might have no interest in retiring at 55, or 60, or even 65. As technology changes the world of work in the United States, so too will changes emerge in the lifelong patterns of job and career among workers.

LEISURE

The traditional conceptualization of the life course is organized around realms of preparation for work, work, retirement from work; this is overlaid on a realm of marriage, childbirth, child rearing, grandparenthood, death. Traditionally, the male "specialty" has been in the work realm, and the female "specialty" has been that of home and children, with the understanding that movement between the two realms takes place in the process of living. This model is changing. Shifts in gender role expectations, work demands, longevity, and the needs for continuing education and training to update skills in a changing technology-driven marketplace have combined to shape this change. The model for the 21st century very likely will be one in which work comes and goes throughout the adult life course, as does recreation, as does education. The new model brings changes in attitudes toward the concepts of work and leisure activity.

A Gallup Poll revealed that 8 out of 10 adults of all ages think time is moving too fast for them. One benefit of retirement is having more time. The older the person, the more content they seem to be with the amount of time they have. Only 44 percent of those younger than 50 said they have enough time, whereas 68 percent of those 50 and older believed they had time enough for their tasks. According to the poll, all Americans wish they had more time for personal exercise and recreation, such as aerobics, hunting, fishing, tennis, and golf (47 percent); hobbies (47 percent); reading (45 percent); family (41 percent); and thinking or meditation (30 percent). Given more time, most Americans would relax, travel, work around the house or garden, or go back to school. **Leisure values,** that is, the acceptance of leisure pursuits as worthwhile, are becoming stronger.

Sociologists have observed that for the past several decades we have treated leisure as another commodity that is produced and consumed. The leisure industry is one of the largest segments of the American economy, and it keeps hundreds of thousands of persons employed. Ironically, Americans who become overly engrossed in working to attain the symbols and commodities of leisure must work harder to obtain them and often end up with less time to enjoy them.

In some segments of American society, older people are a visible and apparently contented leisure class as they accept the new lifestyles of the retired. The retirement community concept

Retirement can be a time to develop skills or specialties that were previously too time-consuming to pursue. Volunteer or part-time jobs provide tremendous life satisfaction for retirees.

has, no doubt, made the role of retiree more legitimate. Elders who choose the traditional symbols of leisure—the boat, recreation vehicle, or home in a warm climate with access to a golf course and swimming pool—seem to go beyond merely owning the symbols to enjoying the lifestyles that the symbols represent. These elders, it must be noted, are those with resources adequate to sustain this leisure lifestyle.

In the past, elderly Americans have been considered "invisible consumers," a segment of the population to be ignored by marketers (Oates et al., 1996). Their presence is now being acknowledged by virtually all institutions in the economy. On the positive side, recognizing elders as consumers gives them greater visibility and legitimizes their role as people enjoying life. On the negative side, consumerism directed at older people as a group often does not recognize that they are a diverse group whose needs and wants vary dramatically (Lee et al., 1997)

The sheer size of the over-65 age-group market, however, is gaining the attention of the commercial world. News that the mature market is growing and will likely have excellent incomes in the future from improved pension and retirement planning appears daily in bold print on marketing magazine covers.

Expanding Work and Leisure Opportunities

In spite of age discrimination and retirement eligibility, a substantial number of elderly are employed. Many middle-aged women are entering into the job force for the first time in their lives. Although men have been retiring in larger and larger numbers since the turn of the century, women have not. Indeed, although the labor-force participation of women 65 and over has remained at about 8 to 9 percent since 1995, middle-aged women have entered the labor market in increasing numbers.

More older people want to be employed full-time than are. Still, a more popular choice for older people is part-time work, but part-time jobs are relatively uncommon in many sectors. For example, professional, technical, administrative, and other high-paying jobs tend to be full-time. According to Social Security laws, those aged 65 to 69 are allowed to earn only up to a prescribed amount of income without a cut in their Social Security benefits. (The cut is one dollar off their Social Security for every two dollars earned.) And those younger than 65 suffer cuts at an even lower wage. These amounts are guidelines for many elders. Those who lack private pension coverage are more likely to continue working full- or part-time in their later years.

In one national-level study, workers of all economic status decreased their work hours gradually as their retirement approached (Choi, 1994). Not unexpectedly, the extent of work reduction was based on preretirement income, since reduced work reduces earnings. The study revealed the fluid relationship between work and leisure, especially during the early years of retirement. "For many workers," the authors concluded, "the transition from work to leisure is not a very finite process, at least in the early years of retirement" (p. 6).

Interest in work following formal retirement from a job seems to be related more to people's individual characteristics and their life goals than to postretirement income among those whose income is 50 percent above poverty level and higher (Toughill et al., 1993). Attitudes toward future employment among some retirees are very positive and among others, quite negative: people age as they have lived. Those who look forward to retirement and have planned their leisure activities for retirement do not want work and resent it if they feel compelled for financial reasons to work again. Others plan for continued work, either part-time or full-time, and find themselves frustrated to be rejected in job searches.

Where and how do older people find jobs they want? Although jobs are hard to find for any age group, they are especially so for elders. If an elder's original goal is to have leisure and a good-paying part-time job as well, opportunities may seem more limited when the actual time comes to get that part-time job. Older part-timers are on track for jobs that can seem quite disappointing for some people. For example, some retail outlets recruit elders, but the pay is minimal. Fast-food chains might offer a better wage, but the working conditions can be difficult—socially, physically, and psychologically—for some older people who are more accustomed to work in which they have a valued skill or knowledge base. The common occurrence of being paid less per hour as a part-timer for the same work as a full-timer can lead to low morale for part-time workers of any age

FULL-TIME WORK OPPORTUNITIES

An obvious and far-reaching way of expanding work opportunities for seniors is for private business and industry to keep their older workers and discourage, not encourage, early retirement. More older workers should be retrained and motivated to stay in the labor force.

Older workers who want to change jobs or branch out on their own need support in achieving these goals. Rather than retire, able elders sometimes shift their focus or their employers. A nuclear engineer may become an expert witness on nuclear power. A lawyer may leave a large law firm to set up practice on his or her own. A retired professor may become a lecturer, conduct workshops, or become a consultant. Consulting is a common job for "retired" managers, employers, and engineers.

Business leaders who look at demographics (shrinking young population, growing elders) have taken steps to hire older people. Days Inns of America currently employs many older persons; in fact, they are more than 30 percent of its labor force. Days Inns analyzed its Atlanta Center by comparing costs and benefits of hiring older versus younger workers. It found the following:

- After a half-day of computer familiarization training, older workers can be trained to operate sophisticated computer software in the same time as younger workers—two weeks.
- Older workers stay on the job much longer than younger workers—an average of three years compared with one year. This resulted in average annual training and recruiting costs per position of $618 for older workers compared with $1,742 for younger workers.
- Older workers are better salespeople: they generate additional revenue by booking more reservations than younger workers, although they take longer to handle each call for the reservations center.
- Older workers are flexible about assignments and willing to work all three shifts. (Commonwealth Fund, 1993, p. 17)

All in all, the president of Days Inns reports a very positive experience with hiring seniors as reservations agents. Other companies that recruit elders for full-time positions are Bay Bank Middlesex of Boston and Aerospace Corporation of Los Angeles.

Many elders turn to self-employment as a way to earn money. Creativity, initiative, capital, and sometimes past business experience are needed to start a business in old age. Still, self-employment is often easier than getting hired to work for someone else. Slightly over 40 percent of all employed elders are self-employed. One "retired" man at age 62 started a travel agency that eventually expanded into three more. At age 60, another started an equipment leasing business. Some retirees have businesses in arts and crafts, such as real grandfathers who make grandfather clocks.

A way of assisting older people in finding work is to encourage self-employment, whether by providing assistance for business start-ups or by providing the means for advertising and selling the goods senior-owned businesses make. One urban senior citizens' center established a shop to provide local artisans with a sales outlet for quality handmade goods. Rural towns, too, offer stores selling quilts, stitchery, wooden carvings, and other crafts made by local elders.

PART-TIME WORK OPPORTUNITIES

Some older people welcome the opportunity to work part-time, and companies such as McDonalds, Wal-Mart, and Walt Disney World all actively recruit older workers. Some retirees who enjoy young people have found part-time work in the summer at amusement parks (Harper, 1994). Some companies, such as Travelers Insurance at Hartford, Connecticut, and Aetna Life and Casualty, offer an early retirement program to the long-term workers who command the highest salaries. But Travelers hires back pensioned workers part-time when they are needed. Retirees are recruited regularly at "unretirement parties" hosted by the company. Open to all retirees is a job bank, which offers flexible part-time temporary work. The company profits by not having to train new workers and by not having to create new pension funds for them. Thus, one place to look for work is in the company that retired you (Commonwealth Fund, 1993).

The federal government has several small-scale work programs designed to aid retired persons by providing work to supplement their Social Security benefits. For example, the Green Thumb Program pays older people living near or under the poverty level minimum wage to plant trees, build parks, and beautify highways. The Foster Grandparent Program also employs old people near the poverty line to work with deprived children, some mentally retarded and physically handicapped, others emotionally disturbed. The older workers try to establish meaningful relationships with the children. For their efforts as foster grandparents, elders receive an hourly wage, transportation costs, and one meal a day.

Work opportunities could expand if employers were more flexible in scheduling the hours and days older employees worked per week. Management consultants have suggested that workers aged 55 and over be allowed gradually shrinking workweeks, with final retirement not occurring until age 75 or later. Another suggestion is that companies allow employees the option of reducing their workload to two-thirds time at age 60, one-half at 65, and one-third at 68. Still another alternative would allow the older person near retirement to work six months and to "retire" for six months, alternating work and "retirement" periods until permanent retirement. **Flexible work/retirement** plans enable older persons to gradually retire and at the same time remain productive on the job even into their seventies and beyond, if they desire.

Part-time work is sometimes possible through **job sharing.** Job sharing has generally been found not only to please workers by giving them more options, but also to benefit employers. One employer stated that it increases productivity: "When people know they're working only two or three days a week or only up to four hours a day, they come in all charged up. You can bet they're much more productive." Job sharing increases job interest, lowers absenteeism, and gives the company a decreased turnover and increased morale, which result in greater productivity. Employers' arguments against job sharing are (1) people may have less commitment to part-time work than to full-time work; and (2) training and administrative costs might increase because of the greater number of people involved (Kane, 1996). Neither of these points are borne out in the literature (Turner, 1996).

RETRAINING

If new technology makes older workers obsolete, they should have options for updating their knowledge and skills. In the past, people assumed that professionals and their skills naturally and unavoidably became obsolete. Now, however, **retraining** and midcareer development programs have proven effective, and national training programs have trained older workers as successfully as younger workers, despite the fact that these training programs could work harder to consider the unique problems of adult retraining.

Career development programs for middle-aged and older workers are far too few. In our society, which generally punishes those who make job changes, the older worker who changes jobs loses most of the retirement benefits from his or her previous job. People would have much more career flexibility if retirement benefits were transferable. They would feel freer to change jobs, and companies would be more inclined to hire the middle-aged. For those whose careers require working so intensively that one becomes hardened and emotionally drained, spending a few years in a related field would actually increase one's effectiveness in the original career, if one chose to return to that field of work.

Under Title V of the Older Americans Act and with the help of the Job Training Partnership Act (JTPA), older workers are receiving some job training. The JTPA offers special training programs for economically disadvantaged older workers aged 55 and over; 3 percent of the funds allotted to the act must be spent on such training. Some businesses are offering more than severance pay to laid-off workers—a chance to start a new teaching career. Pacific Telesis, Chevron, AT&T, Rockwell, IBM, and Kodak, as a part of their severance program, pay tuition and expenses for retirees to go back to school to become teachers in kindergarten through 12th grade. At PacTel, managers with undergraduate degrees in math or science who are bilingual are given priority (Severance Offers Chance to Teach, 1991).

Other diverse businesses offer continuing education and retraining. General Electric and AT&T have classes to teach employees the latest changes in technology. Pitney Bowes has a retirement educational assistance program in which employees and their spouses over age 50 are eligible for tuition reimbursement up to $300 per year per person, continuing for two years after retirement for a maximum of $3,000 per person. These same retirees often become teachers for classes at Pitney Bowes (American Association of Retired Persons, 1990). The examples given here may be a "drop in the bucket," but they serve as examples of how older people can be retrained, reeducated, and encouraged to stay in the workplace.

LEISURE OPPORTUNTIES

As we discussed previously, Americans generally use leisure for keeping busy with something, so that we rarely *relax* or refresh ourselves. Time away from work at any age should be a time for *being,* not doing. We all need conditioning to learn to be, to express our individual talents and interests, and to find fulfillment in the pleasure of self-realization.

Boredom does come with nothing to do, but real leisure is self-satisfying. Meditation, reflection, and contemplation are fun when divorced from the necessity to do them. Playing with ideas, trying to resolve puzzles, or brainstorming new inventions can be relaxing and pleasurable. A group of older citizens could meet daily for lunch to share their ideas and experience: "We solve the problems of the world, but no one listens." All of us have undeveloped personal resources, talents, and abilities that could be realized. We need not limit our self-development only to what is necessary to hold a job. For example, a particular college professor likes to sit quietly and speculate. Students coming to her office say, "I see you are not doing anything." Much that can be enjoyed cannot be seen!

We should try to see the role of retiree as a valid and legitimate one, well deserving of leisure in its real sense. Our work values need to be examined and put into perspective. Passively watching television, a common activity of both young and old, is hardly a form of self-realization. Our educational system, both formal and extended, should prepare us not only to work, but also to find fulfillment as human beings.

Chapter Summary

Retirement has not always been characteristic of American life. Ceasing work at a given age and receiving a pension has become more and more common for Americans after the Great Depression when Social Security was enacted. Most now expect to retire and many take an early retirement. Orientation to work and leisure are important factors influencing the older person's decision to retire. The older person with a strong work ethic who enjoys status and friends on the job may continue working. Age discrimination operates against older people in employment. There are negative stereotypes of older workers. Employers may want more years of work than the older person has to give. "Youth cult" values encourage hiring the young instead of the old. Finding work in old age can be difficult.

Many factors affect one's adjustment to retirement, and the capacity to enjoy leisure is not a given. Sufficient retirement income appears to be of great significance in retirement. Work and leisure opportunities for elders in our society could be greatly expanded. More part-time options and gradual retirement programs would give older persons more choice, and hence, satisfaction with postcareer plans.

Key Terms

age discrimination in employment
Age Discrimination in Employment Act
bona fide occupational qualification (BFOQ)
career development program
early retirement
early retirement discrimination
early retirement incentive programs (ERIP)
flexible work/retirement plans
job sharing
late-retirement incentive programs (LRIPs)
leisure values
myths about the older worker
retirement
retirement preparation program
retraining
third age
work ethic

Questions for Discussion

1. Are we becoming a more leisure-oriented society?
2. Do you see positive or negative values (or both) in retirement communities that place great emphasis on leisure activities?
3. Why would someone want to continue working beyond age 65?
4. Will discrimination in jobs on the basis of age ever be eliminated? Why or why not?
5. What do you envision for yourself in old age in terms of work and leisure?
6. Imagine yourself isolated in a cabin in the mountains for two weeks with only pencil and paper—no visitors, television, or radio. Would you enjoy it?

Fieldwork Suggestions

1. Study adjustment to retirement by talking to four retired people about their adjustment.
2. Go to a senior center in your community and talk with older retired people about what would induce them to return to work. Are you able to draw any conclusions from your discussions?

3. Interview two older people who have remained in their professions—entrepreneurs, lawyers, writers, teachers, executives, managers, or doctors, for example. Why do they continue working? Do they have any "retirement" plans?

Online Activities

1. Look up FaceIntel on the Internet to assess their position in terms of older workers. See if you can find an Internet response to this pressure group by Intel.
2. Locate a Web site with current age discrimination cases in the state in which you live. Who sponsors the site? How accurate to you believe the information is? How easy or hard was it for you to find it?
3. You are a career counselor, providing assistance to a 57-year-old male who was recently laid off by a nationwide hardware chain. His former job was inventory control for 6 stores in a certain region of the country. What Web sites on government programs and services will you access for information on his behalf? (Hint: Begin with Web sites for Pension Benefit Guaranty Corporation and the Social Security Administration.)

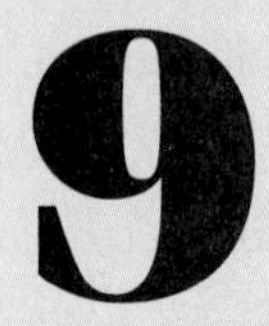

Financial Status

Social Security or (Social) Insecurity?

Medical Expenses in Old Age

Private Pensions

Lifestyles of the Poor

Finances and Lifestyles

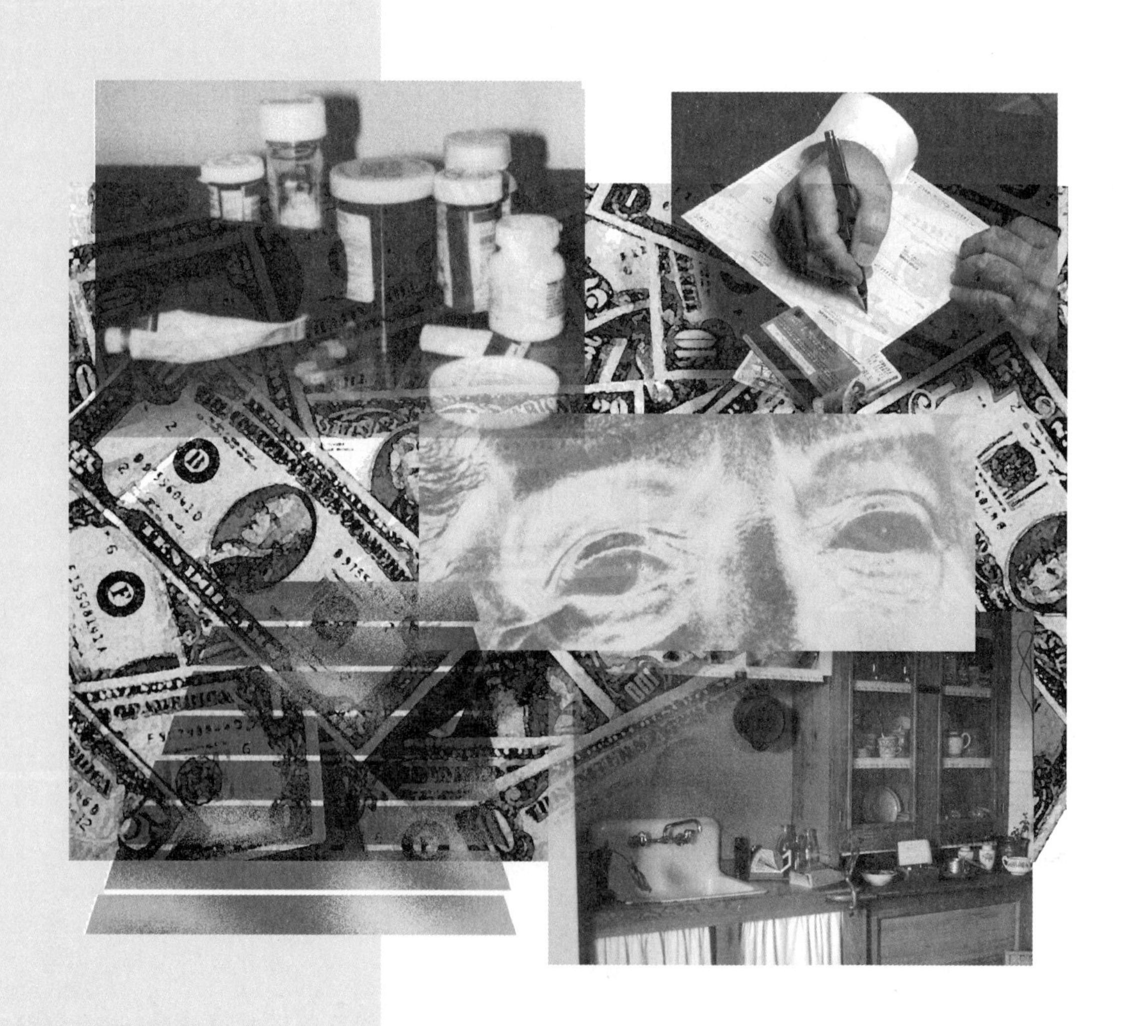

Poverty Major Cause of Seniors' Poor Health

USA Today

Older people living in poverty are more likely than their middle- or upper-class peers to experience declining health as they age. This more rapid decline in health not only threatens the quality of life of older persons, but increases significantly their risk of entering a nursing home.

According to Raymond Coward, dean of the School of Health and Human Services, University of New Hampshire, Durham, low-income elders are at much higher risk of developing difficulties performing routine activities of daily living like bathing, preparing and eating meals, doing light housework, or shopping for groceries. Less education and advancing age also were found to contribute to the increased risk to health, but low income had the most powerful influence.

Coward, along with colleagues from the University of Florida, Gainsville, and the University of North Carolina, Chapel Hill, monitored the health of more than 800 adults over a 30-month period. Each of the subjects was 65 or older at the beginning of the study, lived in a community setting, and was in good health. Specifically, none reported any difficulties performing routine activities of daily living. Half of the sample, however, had incomes that were below the Federal poverty threshold.

"At the same time that low-income elders are experiencing greater declines in their health, they also have fewer financial resources with which to cope with this poorer health," Coward points out. It is not simply a lack of access to quality care that contributes to their condition. "Poor diets and nutrition, the greater likelihood of poor health habits, including smoking, greater exposure to occupational hazards and unsafe workplaces, and unsanitary living conditions can accumulate and take their toll in life."

The Health Care Financing Administration estimates that 58 percent of public health care dollars are spent on the elderly. and the most recent edition of the *Encyclopedia of Aging* states that "persons age 65 and older account for about one-third of annual U.S. health care costs. . . . "

Thus, the more rapid decline of health among low-income elders may contribute unduly to rising national health care costs and is a significant concern to public officials.

"To improve the circumstances of future cohorts of elders, we must act now to reform social and economic circumstances in the United States, so that current generations of low-income persons do not suffer a lifetime of deprivation, inevitably leading to increased poor health in old age," Coward maintains.

Poverty profoundly shapes later life. Opportunities for education, preventive dental care, nutrition—all are linked by underlying social conditions shaped by income.

During the first 50 years of the 21st century the number of people over 65 years of age will increase by 63 percent. The number of people over age 85 will increase by 35 percent (Siegel, 1996). New models of intergenerational exchange are being forged even as this is written. Family financial relationships in the 21st century will not look like those in the 19th and the 20th centuries.

In the early 1900s, older Americans were almost all poor or near-poor. They faced a variety of economic hardships that were not justified, given the generally high standard of living among the rest of the population. With the advent of Social Security and other pension programs, the financial status of the elderly has improved throughout the 20th century. Changes in Social Security in the 1960s and 1970s provided more comprehensive coverage. Still, the bulk of elders live relatively modest lifestyles. To cope with inflation, a big problem in the 1970s and early 1980s, the U. S. government raised interest rates. In the early 1990s when a recession hit, interest rates were dramatically lowered. Interest-sensitive monies are savings accounts, bonds, and utilities stocks—those very institutions in which elders' have invested their savings and pension.

Financial Status

The financial status of the *average* older American is relatively favorable and the extent of poverty is less than among the rest of the population (U.S. Bureau of the Census, 1996). The household income of those over age 65 is not much different than the average for all adult households. The median income of older people in 1995 was $16,684 for males and $9,626 for females. In terms of real median income (adjusting for inflation), these figures represent a slight decrease in real income from 1995 of 1.7 percent for men and a decrease of 0.1 percent for women (Administration on Aging, 1997). Households with families headed by people 65 and older had a median income in 1996 of $28,983. A pronounced economic disparity exists: ethnic distribution of this median income is $29,470 for whites, $21,329 for African Americans, and $21,068 for Hispanics. Approximately one in every six households headed by an elderly person had incomes of less than $15,000; 40 percent had incomes of $35,000 or more (American Association of Retired Persons, 1997). The average household income of people over 65 is higher than that of young adults (18–24), but lower than that of middle-aged people (35–64) (Kutty, 1998).

Figure 9.1 charts median income for families by age of household head. Notice that the decline beginning between age 50–54 continues on throughout extreme old age. This income reduction does reflect a real decline in household income, but it overstates the difference because of greater noncash benefits and smaller household size of older households (Siegel, 1996).

On average, the poverty level of elders has improved over the last several decades. The poverty rate for persons aged 65 and older declined from 24.6 percent to 10.8 percent between

FIGURE 9.1

Median family unit income, by age of head, 1990

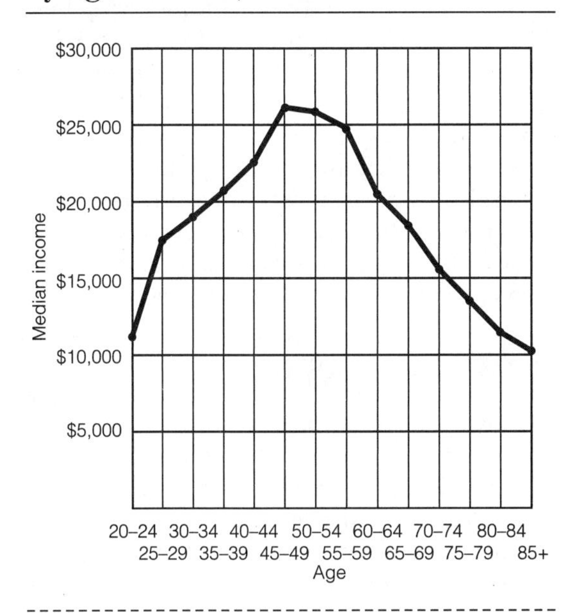

Source: F. Schick and R. Schick, *Statistical Handbook of Aged Americans* (Phoenix, AZ: Oryx Press, 1994), p. 213.

1970 and 1996, slightly less than the rate for people 18-64 (11.4 percent) (AARP, 1997; U.S. Bureau of the Census, 1993; HCFA, 1996). Table 9.1 shows the projection for the reduction of poverty to increase, slowly, into the next century.

Another 2.4 million (7.6 percent) of the elderly were classified as "near-poor" (income between the poverty level and 125 percent of this level). These elders have been variously described as near-poor, deprived, or **economically vulnerable.** To most persons, such income is inadequate to have a full life. All together almost one-fifth (18.4 percent) of the older population was poor or near-poor in 1996 (AARP, 1997). Table 9.1 shows the projection for the reduction of poverty to increase, slowly, into the next century.

A major reason for the increased income (reduction in poverty) of elders over the past two decades is that Social Security payments are

TABLE 9.1

Income of persons 65 years and over living in the community as a percentage of the poverty level: 1990, 2005, 2020

Income	1990	2005	2020
Total percent	100	100	100
Less than 100 percent	17	13	7
100–140 percent	18	14	9
150–199 percent	13	12	9
200 percent or more	52	61	75

Source: Siegel, J. (1996). *Aging into the 21st Century.* National Aging Information Center, U.S. Administration on Aging: Washington, DC.

higher because of automatic cost-of-living adjustment. Additionally, more women are now covered. The number of young and middle-aged women in the workforce who pay into the system has steadily increased since the 1960s. As these women retire they receive greater benefits than did women from previous generations.

> *The moral economy of a society is its set of beliefs about what constitutes just exchange: not only about how economic exchange is to be conducted...but also...when poor individuals are entitled to social aid, when better off people are obligated to provide care, and what kinds of claims anyone—landowners, employers, government—can legitimately make on the surplus product of anyone else.*
>
> DEBORAH STONE, 1988

DIVERSITY IN FINANCIAL STATUS

Analysis of recent census data suggests that the spread of wealth is great among older people. That means that those 65 and over have a great diversity of rich and poor. Additionally, income is not equally distributed among ethnic groups. One of every 11 (9.4 percent) of elderly whites was poor in 1996, compared to one-fourth (25.3 percent) of elderly blacks and almost one-fourth (24.4 percent) of elderly Hispanics (AARP, 1997). Women of any ethnicity are particularly likely to be or become poor in old age, as are African Americans, people living alone, very old people, those living in rural areas, and most especially those with a combination of these characteristics (Siegel, 1996).

Equalizing effects of Social Security are more than outweighed by private pensions and asset income (interest on savings), which are received mainly by those in the upper-income brackets. Table 9.2 shows the distribution of income by age. Again, the numbers belie the unequal distribution of income among races and among males and females. Inequality throughout life is cumulative and becomes magnified in old age. In other words, the advantages of good education and/or good jobs leads to better pension coverage and savings in the later years (Crystal & Shea, 1990).

Women and ethnic minorities are discussed in more detail in Chapter 14. Their financial distress is a function not only of aging, but also of education, race, and past employment. Poverty has declined over the past several decades, but not extraordinarily, given the state of the economy. Gerontologists are concerned that older Americans are being unfairly blamed for the country's huge economic deficits. The myth that all elders are down and out has transformed into the myth that elders are well-to-do and depriving the young of their fair share. Most older people are struggling in the lower- to middle-income ranges. If the benefits of Social Security were backed out of that income, many more of America's elderly would move into poverty. The new trend toward decreased government support for social welfare places the well-being of this population in a precarious and insecure position.

HOME OWNERSHIP

The overwhelming majority of the American population saves little for old age, does not maintain significant savings accounts, and does not hold other financial assets. However, around 78 percent of the elders owned their own homes in 1996, a figure that is 12 percent higher than a decade before. Although more older people own their homes than do younger adults, the problem for older home owners is to remain in their homes

TABLE 9.2

Income[1] distribution of unrelated individuals 60+ by age

Age	No income	Under $5,000	$5,000–$9,999	$10,000–$14,999	$15,000 $19,999	$20,000–$29,999	$30,000–$49,999	$50,000–or more
Total 60+	2.4	15.8	33.2	17.0	10.3	10.7	7.1	3.5
60–64	3.8	14.9	21.1	15.3	12.0	15.2	12.0	5.7
65–74	2.0	14.7	31.9	18.2	11.4	11.5	7.0	3.4
75–84	2.2	16.7	38.6	17.0	8.9	8.6	5.4	2.7
85+	2.6	19.1	40.9	14.8	7.5	7.2	4.9	2.9

[1]Includes wage or salary income; net nonfarm self-employment income; interest, dividend, or net rental or royalty income; Social Security or railroad retirement income; public assistance or welfare income; retirement or disability income; and all other regular sources of income.

Source: Population and Housing Patterns Among Older Americans (1996). Selected Statistical Tables Based on the 1990 Census of Population and Housing. National Aging Information Center. Administration of Aging, Washington, DC.

and stay financially solvent. The percentage of income spent on housing, including maintenance and repair, in 1995 was higher for older persons (34 percent) than for the younger consumer population (27 percent), However about 80 percent of older home owners in 1995 owned their homes free and clear (AARP, 1997). Many older people are "house rich and cash poor"—that is, they have minimal monthly income, but many thousands of dollars in equity in their home. The greatest asset for most elders is the value of their home.

In 1988, the federal government introduced a plan of **reverse mortgages,** whereby a loan is made against home equity owned by the borrower. A borrower (the home owner) increases indebtedness while drawing-down the equity in the home. The loan does not require monthly repayment and becomes repayable when the borrower ceases to use the home as a principal residence, which may be when he or she moves (to long term care, for example), or dies. At that time the home is sold, and the lender (government and/or its agent) receives the value of the loan plus interest.

It is estimated that more than 600,000 elderly home owners living in poverty could be raised above the poverty line if they obtained a reverse mortgage (Kutty, 1998). One study sponsored by the U.S. Department of Housing and Urban Development estimated that the poverty rate of elderly households could be reduced by three percentage points by means of reverse mortgages (Kutty, 1998; Sawyer, 1996).

Reverse mortgages are only of value for those elders who strongly desire to age in place—that is, those who wish to live in their present home until their death (or a move). If an older person were willing to move, selling the home and investing the proceeds in an income-generating asset would make more sense from a strictly economic perspective (Kutty, 1998). Most older people, however, are strongly motivated to remain in their own homes for as long as possible. Houses are memory holders: one's *lifescape* is contained in a home. Familiar surroundings, including of the familiarity of a neighborhood—even one that has changed over time—are comforting. For many elders, a reverse mortgage option can provide exactly the right payoff: the investment in a home over all those years is paying off for them in their old age, assisting them to remain solvent, in the space of their choosing. For others, it is an option they chose not to take; still others have fewer options than this.

A number of elders own mobile homes, which are typically lower in cost than houses. Many people have found the mobile-home park lifestyle to be an affordable one. A summary of mobile-home facts and figures reveals the following:

- Almost half the residents of manufactured housing are age 50 or older.
- More than one-third of manufactured home residents are retirees or part-time workers.
- More than 90 percent of older residents own their manufactured homes; 23 percent own their lots.
- More than half the older residents of manufactured homes live in mobile-home parks.
- States with the most manufactured homes are California and Florida.
- Average price for a single-section home in 1992: $20,600; for a multisection home: $37,200. (Glasheen, 1994)

These figures speak for themselves as to the popularity of mobile homes among seniors and their affordability. However, in many areas of California, elders are called "prisoners of paradise," because their rents have escalated at a frightening pace. Mobile-home owners and even condominium owners who pay maintenance fees are subject to cost increases over which they have no control. Older people would benefit from legislation controlling these costs.

HOME RENTAL

A renter is more subject to inflation, enforced living conditions, involuntary moves, and other forms of control by others than is a home owner. In 1995, of the 20.8 million households headed by older people, 22 percent were renters. The median household income of older home owners was $21,629; the median household income of older renters was $10,151 (AARP, 1997). Some cities have adopted rent-control ordinances to help people, like elders, living on fixed incomes, but such policies are rare.

Social Security or (Social) Insecurity?

The United States has had a strong work ethic since its inception. In 1929, the U.S. stock market began a steep decline into a crash. Subsequently, in 1931, many large financial institutions failed, and the United States entered the Great Depression. This was perhaps the first time as a nation that Americans were faced with the reality that hard work, diligent savings, and good citizenship were not enough to keep one from economic disaster. Good people—admired political and community leaders, as well as ordinary, hard-working blue-collar folk—became economically ruined overnight. The collapse was like a house of cards: businesses failed; factories shut down; people lost jobs; banks repossessed properties for which loan payments were not being made; then many of the banks failed, taking the savings of ordinary and extraordinary people, alike, down with them. The poverty rate in the United States was tremendous, and older people were among the very least competitive applicants for whatever jobs were available. The extent of economic interdependency was clearly driven home to the average U.S. voter. It indeed might take more than hard work, good values, and trust in the institution of banking to protect oneself economically, and society as a whole had an obligation to help out those who were most desperate.

The United States was one of the last modern, industrial nations to introduce a major public system of social insurance against old-age dependency. By 1935, 27 other countries already had well-developed national retirement systems. **Social Security** began in 1935 to counteract the effects of the Great Depression. It was designed to provide, in the words of President Roosevelt, "some measure of protection...against poverty-ridden old age." The intent of the first Social Security Act was to provide a safety net for those most vulnerable to desperate poverty. It was assumed that pensions and personal savings would support people in their later years. However, in 1994—about 60 years after the act was first passed—40 percent of all income received by older people was from Social Security (Hooyman & Kiyak, 1996).

Social Security was designed to supplement pensions or retirement savings, rather than to provide the total income of aged people. Although everyone seems to agree that Social Security should not be and was never designed to be the sole source of retirement income, for most people it continues to be just that. If it were not for Social Security benefits, nearly half of our aged, rather than the current 12.4 percent, would live in poverty. In general the lower one's income level, the more important Social Security becomes as a component of the household budget. It is the most common source of income for all races (Figure 9.2). For either blacks or Hispanics, Social Security is much less likely to be accompanied by other forms of income. Obviously, for the individual with no income from earnings, savings, stocks and bonds (asset income), or pensions, Social Security is a much higher percentage of the total income (Crenshaw, 1992). Under these circumstances, there is no universal agreement on the adequacy of the benefits or the appropriate level of benefits. Social Security benefits currently begin at age 65, but they may begin at age 62 if the recipient chooses to accept 20 percent less per month.

The Social Security Act of 1935 required that employer and employee each pay 1 percent on the first $3,000 of the worker's wages. (Workers in 1991 paid 7.65 percent of their paychecks into Social Security.) Congress eventually amended the act to extend benefits on the basis of social need in addition to earned right. Amendments

FIGURE 9.2

Receipt of income of aged from various sources, by race and Hispanic origin: 1990

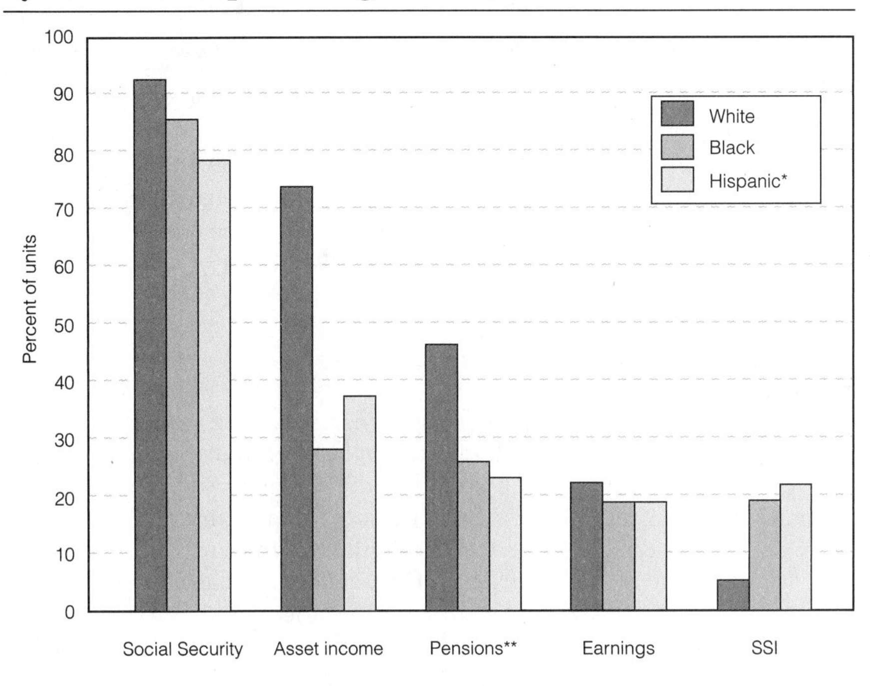

* Persons of Hispanic origin may be of any race.
**Includes private pensions, government employee pensions, and Railroad Retirement.
Source: F. Schick and R. Schick, *Statistical Handbook of Aged Americans* (Phoenix, AZ: Oryx Press, 1994), p. 212.

adopted in 1939 made certain dependents of retired workers and survivors of deceased workers eligible, too. In 1960, amendments extended benefits to all disabled persons. Over the years, the amount of money a retired person may earn before forfeiting part of the benefit has also increased.

WORKER TO NONWORKER RATIOS

Social Security operates on a principle of sharing: some individuals die before they are able to collect benefits, whereas others live long enough to get back much more than they contributed. The ledger supposedly balances. However, the increasing percentage of elders and their increasing life expectancy has greatly strained the Social Security system.

In 1945, for instance, 42 workers paying into Social Security supported one retiree. Today, each retiree is supported by just three active taxpayers. In about 30 years, the huge Baby Boom generation will begin to retire, creating even bigger strains. In the year 2030, there will be only two workers for every retiree. Most citizens believe that their payroll taxes go into a kind of insurance pool, which is held and invested until the day they retire. In fact, Social Security taxes are transferred almost immediately to retirees: The system takes money from workers and hands it to retirees. Americans have been receiving far more than they and their employers ever paid into the system. Most young people now will collect less after retirement than they contribute over their working lives (Roberts, 1995).

Dependency ratios describe the proportion of workers to nonworkers. The **total ratio** is the number of people under 18 plus the number of people 65 years and over per 100 people 18 to 64. The assumption is obviously somewhat flawed, because it assumes that people under 18 and over 65 are not part of the labor force, although it does provide a picture of economic trends. The **child dependency ratio** is the number of people under 18 per 100 people 18 to 64; and the **elderly dependency ratio** is expressed as the number of people 65 years and over per 100 people 18 to 64 (U.S. Bureau of the Census, 1996). Table 9.3 shows current and projected dependency ratios.

TABLE 9.3

Projected total, child, and elderly dependency ratios: 1995 to 2050

Year	Total	Children	Elderly
1995	63.7	42.8	20.9
2000	62.4	41.8	20.5
2010	60.2	39.0	21.2
2020	68.2	40.4	27.7
2030	78.7	43.0	35.7
2040	79.7	42.1	36.5
2050	79.9	43.9	36.0

Source: U.S. Bureau of the Census (1996).

SOCIAL SECURITY ADJUSTMENTS

Social Security benefits do rise with the cost of living. This change was brought about by Social Security amendments instituted in 1972. Under the current law, this **cost-of-living adjustment,** or **COLA,** occurs automatically whenever there is an increase in the Consumer Price Index in the first quarter of the year (in comparison with the same period in the previous year). Effective January 1995, for example, Social Security benefits increased 3 percent based on the 1994 increase in the Consumer Price Index from the previous year. However, even with the COLA provision, many who now receive Social Security are still living below the poverty line.

How to keep Social Security solvent has been a major issue over the last decade. Some changes in Social Security have been made to restore the system's fiscal health. In 1983, compromise amendments were painfully worked out by a bipartisan committee and were subsequently adopted by Congress. For example, since 1988 college students between the ages of 18 and 22 can no longer draw benefits on a deceased parent who paid into Social Security.

Changes in the system were seen as necessary to keep it from defaulting. The question of how close the Social Security system is to bankruptcy is more complex than it appears to be. Social Security is said to be heading for bankruptcy because it uses earmarked taxes and has a trust fund. Other federal programs (such as education and defense) have no earmarked taxes and no trust fund and would therefore never be perceived to be bankrupt. Those other federal programs are represented in the Congressional budgetary process—a process by which program needs are presented and the budget is lobbied for by legislators, along with budget requests from other programs. Social Security was designed to be free from year-to-year political winds, and therefore designed as a "pay-as-you-go" system. Essentially, Social Security will only become bankrupt and unable to pay benefits if taxpayers are unwilling to raise taxes to pay for those benefits—the benefits that "spread the cost." It is necessary for voters to make that specific decision for Social Security (as opposed, for example, to the budget for education) because of its special status (Feldstein, 1997).

Adequate income for later life is critical, but savings and assets are unequally divided in society, reflecting income inequality during the working years. For those with adequate resources old age can be a profoundly rewarding time.

A more radical suggestion is to eliminate social security all together and instead to require mandatory IRAs; in other words, privatize retirement benefits (Roberts, 1995). This plan would replace today's pay-as-you-go program with a funded system of individual accounts invested in the stock market (Wildavsky, 1997).

The unknowns are enormous: to completely privatize is to tell citizens "you're on your own," rather than to spread the risk through an insurance program model (social security) and help each other. On the other hand, banking regulations since the Depression have been enacted to radically minimize the possibility of a similar collapse in the future—so presumably, the individual's mandatory investments would be protected from such disaster. The bottom line in the emerging debate is what sort of social contract the nation wants: to what extent does a nation consider itself responsible for the well-being of its citizens.

INEQUITIES IN SOCIAL SECURITY

Under Social Security, people under age 65 and between ages 65 and 69 are penalized for working, although after age 70 there is no penalty on wages earned. Earned income is subject to both income and Social Security taxes, although Social Security payments are subject to neither. Nor is there a penalty for income earned through capital gains or interest on savings. In the end, the system is more beneficial to those who have money than to those who do not; however, it is far more critical to the economic quality of life for those with fewer resources.

Salaried workers are penalized the most by the present system. Older workers who need money often settle for hourly part-time jobs at minimum wage or even less so their wages will not be docked. In fact, most federal government employment programs for elders provide income only as a supplement to Social Security and pay minimum wage or less. Military, federal, and state government and other pensioned retirees, however, generally face no penalty against their pension earnings after retirement, because salaries and wages are the only income subject to the penalty.

Congress has considered reforming the Social Security law to eliminate the ceiling on earnings. However, this change has never been enacted. The reluctance of Congress to remove all limits on extra benefit income is due in part to uncertainty as to the effects of such a move. Congress has reasoned that an older person who could earn more than the yearly amount of unpenalized income probably does not need full Social Security benefits, thus reducing the strain on the system for the benefit of others. But this ruling works a hardship on those making a very modest living. Further, if there were no ceiling, it might reduce the number opting for early retirement by keeping them employed full-time. All that would ease the strain on the system.

Still another criticism of Social Security involves the two-career family. The law favors one-earner households. Working couples pay up to twice as much in Social Security taxes as single-earner families, yet they seldom collect twice as much in benefits. For example, a woman who has contributed throughout her working years may find that, because of her lower earning capacity, she may fare better with 50 percent of her husband's benefits than with 100 percent of her own. Another problem: Divorced men and women, particularly those who have not worked outside the home, may be left totally unprotected. To draw on an ex-spouse's benefits, a man or woman must have been married to that spouse for 10 years. Divorced women suffer more than divorced men because they are more likely to have worked at home and to not have paid into Social Security. Clearly, as discussed previously, this inequality will become less viable as a policy issue as women who have been in the labor market throughout their adulthood begin to retire.

ASSISTANCE FROM POVERTY

The definition of **poverty** for purposes of social policy is framed in terms of inadequacy, yet what is adequate might be **absolute** (having less than an objective minimum); **relative** (having less than others in society); or **subjective** (feeling one does not have enough to get along) (Hagenaars & de Vos, 1988). Poverty, then, must be understood in its political context, which is dynamic and changing over time. At one point in time, keeping citizens from starving to death might be the bottom line social objective (absolute adequacy) for a society. At another time nutritious food, adequate safe shelter, and access to information for decision making is the bottom line objective (relative adequacy). The difference in the values of those two times is primarily economic—economic strength and stability drives social policy, and to some extent, social values. It is an important concept to bear in mind while making the difficult trade-offs in cutting the budget pie.

The poverty threshold in the United States was set in the 1960s by estimating a minimally adequate food budget and multiplying by a factor of three, because research from the 1950s indicated that families spent about one-third of their income on food. Since the 1960s the threshold has been modified in prices, but not for standard of living (Meyer & Bartolomei-Hill, 1994). Table 9.1 presents projections into the next century for people living below, at, and above the poverty level.

A federal program formerly known as Old Age Assistance, which was intended to aid those not covered adequately by Social Security, was renamed **Supplemental Security Income (SSI)** in 1974. Instead of being managed by local offices, it is run by the Social Security Administration. Funds, however, come not from Social Security, but from general U.S. Treasury funds. The program provides a minimum income for elders, blind, and disabled by supplementing Social Security benefits if they are below the amount stipulated by SSI. In essence, it is a guaranteed annual income, and that is very important for those who get little or no Social Security. The monthly amounts vary from state to state.

The federal SSI program makes no allowances for special circumstances. The amount is clearly defined, calculated by subtracting an individual's or couple's income from a guaranteed level. In addition to income, individuals must pass an asset test: couples have countable assets (those that "count" in the defined allowances) of less than $2,500, and singles must have less than $1,500 to be considered eligible. Excluded in this are the value of an owner-occupied home, a car needed for transportation to medical treatment or to work, life insurance valued at less than $1,500, and personal property or household furnishings valued at less than $2,000 (McGarry, 1996).

The SSI program is designed to be a safety net for the poorest segment of the population. Although called "supplemental," benefits decrease substantially if the person or couple has other sources of income. The program has been strongly criticized because it does not consider differences in the cost of living between states, and it allows for no flexibility for special circumstances. It has been estimated that only 56 percent of the elderly who are eligible for SSI presently receive benefits (McGarry, 1996).

Medical Expenses in Old Age

Medical expenses rise with age. Although elders represent only 13 percent of the population, they spend 25 to 30 percent of the money used for health care. Contrary to popular belief, Medicare and Medicaid do not cover all medical expenses when one is over age 65. Actually, these programs do not cover many chronic conditions, leaving the individual to pay for treatment. The "Medicare Handbook" lists the following expenses as not covered:

- Routine medical checkups
- Dental care and dentures
- Over-the-counter drugs and most prescribed medicine
- Eyeglasses and eye examinations
- Hearing aids and hearing examinations
- Routine foot care
- Most immunization shots
- Custodial care in the home
- Custodial long term care (nursing homes)

Examine the list carefully. The program's coverage excludes most parts of the body that tend to change with age and require care. As medical costs rise, one's standard of living declines.

Did You Know . . .
Medicare and Medicaid are expected to grow by over 10 percent annually over the next 5 years; they will have the fastest growth rate of any other part of the federal budget. Together they are [projected] to constitute one-third of the federal budget in 2002.

LYNCH & MINKLER, 1997

MEDICARE

Medicare is a part of the Social Security system; those who are eligible for Social Security benefits are also eligible for Medicare. The vast majority of those people are elderly. Medicare is the main insurer of persons over 65 years of age. Medicare hospital insurance (Part A) covers 95 percent of the elderly, and 98 percent of those people have supplementary medical insurance (Part B) as well (Health Care Financing, 1990). Medicare requires deductibles and 20 percent coinsurance for most services, which must be paid for either by Medicaid if the individual meets the financial criteria; supplemental private insurance (Medi-Gap) purchased by the individual; or the individuals themselves pay the deductibles (Ettner, 1997). **Medicaid** has traditionally provided medical coverage for poor and highly disabled people.

Two interacting factors cause concern for the solvency of Medicare: the growth of the over-65 population and medical costs. People enrolled for Medicare coverage increased from 19.5 million in 1967 to (projected) 38.1 million in 1996—a 95 percent increase. Medicaid recipients increased by 275 percent (this proportion includes an increase of 86 percent in dependent children). The number of **dually entitled** persons (people covered by both Medicare and Medicaid) amounted to nearly 6 million in 1995 (Health Care Financing, 1996).

Steadily rising medical costs threaten both the Social Security system and the elderly individual. Some examples: Medicare skilled nursing facility payments increased from $7.1 billion in 1994 to $9.1 billion in 1995—an increase of 28.2 percent and due in no small part to longevity. That increase is projected to continue. Home health agency benefit payments for Medicare grew from $12 billion in 1994 to $15.1 billion in 1995—a 25.8 percent increase. Medicare hospice expenditures have significantly in-

TABLE 9.4

Medicaid recipients/trends: 1995 to 1997

	Fiscal Year					
	1975	1980	1985	1995[1]	1996[1]	1997[1]
	In millions					
Total[2]	22.0	21.6	21.8	36.2	37.5	38.7
Age 65 years and over	3.6	3.4	3.31	4.2	4.4	4.6
Blind	0.1	0.1	0.1	0.1	0.1	0.1
Disabled	2.4	2.8	2.9	5.9	6.2	6.5
Dependent children under 21 years	9.6	9.3	9.8	17.6	18.2	18.7
Adults in families with dependent children	4.5	4.9	5.5	7.8	8.0	8.3
Other Title XIX	1.8	1.5	1.2	0.6	0.6	0.6

[1]Estimated

[2]Eligibility categories may not add to totals as some recipients are classified in more than one category during the year and due to the exclusion of unknowns.

Sources: Health Care Financing Administration, Bureau of Data Management and Strategy: Data from the Division of Medicaid Statistics and the Office of the Actuary: Data from the Office of Medicare and Medicaid Cost Estimates, 1996.

creased, from $1.4 billion in 1994 to $1.9 billion in 1995—an increase of 35.7 percent (Health Care Financing, 1996)!

In 1967 national health costs, including Medicaid, were $51 billion, or 6.3 percent of the gross national product. By 1995, total Health Care Financing Administration (HCFA) outlays were $248.9 billion—16.4 percent of the federal budget. Although the elderly are increasingly scapegoated as causing the national budget deficit, note in Table 9.4 that nearly 18 million dependent children under 21 received Medicaid benefits in 1995. That represented 52 percent of the Medicaid budget in that year; by 1997 the number was projected to be nearly 19 million children. The 4.6 million people over 65 receiving Medicaid represent only a little over 12 percent of all recipients.

Medicare has two parts. Part A, called Hospital Insurance, covers a portion, averaging about 50 percent, of short-term hospital bills. Most people on Social Security pay no premiums for Part A. In 1994, hospital insurance paid for all covered services for the first 60 days in a hospital, except for a deductible of about $700. For days 61 to 90 in a hospital, Medicare pays a portion and the older patient pays a daily coinsurance amount. If you need inpatient skilled nursing or rehabilitation services after a hospital stay, Medicare pays for up to 100 days. Medicare does not pay for "custodial" care given in a facility that lacks appropriate medical staff. Some hospice care is also covered. If the recipient is confined at home, Medicare can also pay for limited visits from home health workers.

Part B, called Medical Insurance, consists of optional major medical insurance for which the individual paid a monthly fee of about $40 in 1994. Medical insurance helps pay for necessary doctor's office visits, outpatient services for physical and speech problems, and many medical services and supplies that are not covered by Part A. After the patient pays a deductible, medical insurance pays 80 percent of covered services.

To qualify for Medicare payments under Part A, hospital care must be "reasonable and necessary for an illness or injury." For this reason, the most common health needs of seniors, such as routine checkups, drugs, and dentures, are not covered. In addition, the program places both a dollar limit and a time limit on what is covered. Other restrictions and limitations get rather elaborate. Suffice it to say that many frail, sick elders pay thousands of their own dollars for medical care. Medicare does not usually cover all expenses, especially for long-term, chronic conditions, and private insurance plans such as Blue Cross, Kaiser, and EmCare cover only portions of either office visits or a hospital stay. Therefore medical expenses can get costly, and a person may be just a major illness away from financial disaster.

PAYING FOR MEDICARE SERVICES

Fee for Service

Of the 38 million Medicare beneficiaries, nearly 90 percent are using a traditional **fee-for-service** model. They pick their doctors, and Medicare pays a set fee for each service. Most beneficiaries also purchase private supplemental insurance to pay for uncovered costs. It can become an expensive proposition, even with Medicare assistance. The Public Policy institute of the American Association of Retired Persons recently found that over 2 million elderly people at or below poverty line are using 50 percent of their yearly income *or more* for medical expenses that are not covered by Medicare (Stamper, 1998). These expenditures went for things like prescription drugs, outpatient care, and premiums for private supplemental insurance.

Health Maintenance Organizations

One alternative to fee-for-service is the **health maintenance organization** (HMO), also called managed care, in which approximately 11 percent of elders are currently enrolled (Nelson et al., 1997). In this model, the HMO agrees to cover all of an individual's medical needs for a **capitated** (all-inclusive) payment for all Medicare-covered services (Liu, 1995).

In the managed care model, the elder can use only the doctors and facilities on a limited list, but there are often additional benefits such as a broader range of coverage for pharmaceuticals and the convenience of avoiding a confusing bureaucratic billing system. ("This is not a bill, but you owe X dollars.") Concerns with the HMO model have been that, in an effort to control costs, access to needed care will be restricted. Some people fear that more costly services will be rationed, resulting in unequal access. Recent studies on service access have borne out some of those concerns. Vulnerable subgroups, such as the nonelderly disabled, the oldest old, people with functional impairments, and people in poor health or worsening health, seem significantly more likely to report access problems than the general population (Nelson, 1997; Brown, 1993; Ware, 1996). The authors of one major study on health provision models concluded that access to home health services is particularly problematic in the managed care model and that HMOs need to address the needs of frail and more vulnerable Medicare beneficiaries more effectively (Nelson et al., 1997).

Point-of-Service

A third option for Medicare services is called **point-of-service**, in which beneficiaries can visit doctors outside the network but must pay an additional cost. Another option that is growing in popularity is the **preferred provider organization (PPO)**, in which the beneficiary can visit any doctor in the health care network without a referral, or see doctors outside the network at an additional cost. Medicare pays the PPO a set fee for all services for a set period of time.

The **provider-sponsored organization (PSO)** is quite new. Owned and operated by doctors and hospitals (as opposed to health insurance companies in the HMO model), PSOs are organizations similar to managed care plans in which Medicare pays the health plan a monthly fee for each recipient. In the **Medicare medical savings account**, to go into effect around 1999, a high-deductible insurance policy provided by Medicare is combined with a tax-free medical savings account to help pay the deductible. At the end of the year, the beneficiary keeps any unused Medicare money.

Privately Contracted Fee-for-Service

The final option for Medicare services is the **privately contracted fee-for-service**, in which the beneficiary may visit any doctor or purchase any health plan, but pays extra for uncovered or expensive services (Serafini, 1997).

Beyond question, those with greater financial resources have a more broad range of options for health care services in later life. Because Medicare is an **entitlement** (provided categorically on the basis of age, not need-based), people with higher income pay the same as people with limited income in terms of dollars, but that percentage of their income is much less.

MEDICAID

Extremely low-income individuals who qualify for SSI are also eligible for Medicaid in most states in the nation. Two groups of people qualify: the categorically eligible and the medically needy. The categorically eligible are people with certain characteristics (aged, blind, disabled, or a member of a family with dependent children that is headed by a female or in certain cases by an unemployed male) (Ettner, 1997). The medically eligible must have a limited income and minimal savings, excluding one's home and automobile, household goods, and $1,500 in burial funds. For those who qualify, Medicaid helps pay for a wide variety of hospital and other services. Medicaid often pays for services Medicare does not cover, such as eyeglasses, dental care, prescription drugs, and long term nursing home care.

Note in Table 9.5 that more than half of all Medicaid funds are distributed to children and young people under the age of 21. Only 12 percent of the funding is spent on people over 65, although nearly two-thirds of Medicaid support for long term care is for elders (Kaiser Commission on the Future of Medicaid, 1996). Currently, federal law requires states to cover nursing-home care for very poor elderly people judged to need that care and gives states the option (which all states take) to cover people above the poverty level but without resources for long term care (Feder et al., 1997). Federal law allows but does not require states to cover long term care at home or in the community. States have the option to cover personal care; however, New York is the only state which budgets much funding for this type of care (Health Care Financing Administration, 1996).

TABLE 9.5

Medicaid recipients/demographics: 1995

	Percent Medicaid Distribution
Total recipients	100
Age	
Under 21	51.5
21–64 years	31.5
65 years and over	12.2
Unknown	4.8
Sex	
Male	36.5
Female	58.5
Unknown	5.0
Race	
White	45.5
Black	24.7
American Indian/Alaskan Native	0.8
Asian/Pacific Islander	2.2
Hispanic	17.2
Unknown	9.7

Source: Health Care Financing Administration, Bureau of Data Management and Strategy: Data from the Division of Health Care Information Services, 1996. Table compiled by the National Aging Information Center, Washington, DC.

MEDIGAP POLICIES

"Medigap" insurance policies are popular among elders who can afford them. In spite of continually rising policy costs, a majority of those on Medicare are estimated to also have a **Medigap policy.** Such policies are sold by private companies to help cover the "gaps" in health care protection for which Medicare does not provide. Prior to 1992, insurance carriers could sell any benefits they chose as medigap so long as minimum benefit requirements were met. The range and costs were enormous. In 1992, federal legislation was implemented to standardize policy benefits. Any company that sells medigap coverage must offer policy A (a specified package of core benefits). Policy A is the starting point for policies B through J, with policy J having the most comprehensive coverage. Prior to standardization a typical policy paid out a maximum of $500 per year, compared to $1,250 or $3,000 after (Roha, 1998; Rice et al., 1997).

The required core benefits include:

- Daily Medicare copayment of $191 for hospital days 61 through 90, and $382 for days 91 through 150
- Full cost of up to 365 additional hospital days during your lifetime
- 20 percent copayment of Medicare's allowed amount for doctor charges

Table 9.6 provides a summary of the differences in each policy level. The policy level, as well as the company providing the policy, needs to be carefully chosen by the consumer. For example,

TABLE 9.6

Medigap policy benefits summary

	Summary of coverage
Policy A: Core benefits	· Daily copayment of $191/day hospital days 61–90; $382/day hospital days 91–150 · Full cost of hospital days up to 365 additional hospital days during one's lifetime · 20% copayment for doctor charges
Policy B	· Core benefits *plus* · Annual $100 Part B deductible for doctors' fees
Policy C	· Core benefits *plus* · Annual $100 Part B deductible for doctors' fees
Policy D	· Core benefits *plus* · Copayment for skilled nursing-home care, days 21–100 ($95.50/day) · Foreign travel emergency care · Up to $1,600/year short-term custodial care
Policy G	· All of D *plus* · 80% difference between doctor charges and Medicare approved payment
Policy H	· Core benefits *plus* · 50% cost of prescription drugs up to maximum of $1,250/year; $250/deductible
Policy J	· Core benefits plus · Annual $100 Part B deductible for doctors' fees · Daily copayment for skilled nursing-home care, days 21–100 ($95.50/day) · 50% outpatient prescription drugs costs up to $3,000/year, after $250 deductible · $1,600/year for short-term custodial care at home following surgery, illness, injury · 100% difference between doctor charges and amount approved by Medicare · $120/year for preventive health screenings · 80% cost of emergency care during foreign travel, $250 deductible

Adapted from: Roha, Ronaleen R. (1997). *Kiplinger's Personal Finance Magazine*, p. 107–108.

policy C appeals to many seniors, but the cost from most carriers is often greater than the benefit. Policy H might be best if significant prescription drug expenses can be anticipated, but the cost of the policy must be balanced with its benefit. Additionally, consumers will find wild price differences, even within the same region: for example, the cost of policy A ranged from $436 to $1,032 for a 65-year-old man in California in 1998 (Roha, 1998).

For the first six months after signing up for Part B of Medicare, a person can buy *any* medigap policy sold in their area. After that time, the insurance provider has the option to turn down an applicant.

Did You Know . . .
New federally legislated medigap insurance provisions will take place in 1999. People who lose their coverage through no fault of their own or who move away from the area covered by the plan will have 63 days to buy any plan labeled A, B, C, or F, regardless of their health. Also: new high-deductible versions of policies F and J will be available at the turn of the century. They will provide the same coverage as present ones, but will be much less expensive because each will have a $1,500 deductible.

NO PLACE TO GO

The aging population is the major determinant of increasing nursing home admissions: the number of elderly requiring long term care is expected to double by 2025. Currently, 46 people per 1,000 over 65 are nursing home residents, and the proportion increases to 220 per 1,000 among those 85 and over (Hicks et al., 1997). Double those proportions will represent a substantial, if not alarming, increase in costs and need for facilities. The out-of-pocket costs for nursing home care have also dramatically increased. In 1980, the nursing home industry consumed 8.1 percent of all spending for personal health care services, at $17.6 billion. In 1994, those costs came to $72.3 billion and accounted for 8.7 percent of all personal health care expenditures (Levitt et al., 1996).

For many older Americans, the cost of long term health care is insurmountable. In a few months a couple can use up all their assets. If their income is sufficiently low, they can apply for Medicaid to cover nursing home care. This is a devastating experience, and one that more commonly occurs to the oldest-old (those aged 80 and over), to women, and to those living alone.

In terms of medical coverage, the forgotten minority is those elders whose income is just above the Medicaid cutoff, yet too low to cover the cost of nursing home care. Medicaid is administered by states; eligibility and dollars per month coverage vary widely. In Delaware, one of the best states for coverage, nursing homes are well reimbursed: therefore, good homes are available and willing to take even "heavy-care" patients. In contrast, a study of working- or middle-class Florida residents just above the Medicaid level of eligibility found that these elders were experiencing severe emotional, physical, and financial hardships trying to cope at home. Nursing home care, unavailable or unaffordable, was urgently needed for many (Quadagno et al., 1991).

With no adequate government programs to pay for nursing home care, older patients suffer, as do hospitals and frustrated care providers. Many low-income elderly patients who cannot get into nursing homes remain in hospitals even if they no longer need the expensive hospital care. Hospitals that keep older patients for longer periods than Medicare or Medicaid will fund rack up huge losses. The "boarder elderly" problem affects about 25 percent of the nation's hospitals, with urban hospitals hurt the most. Seventy-five percent of hospitals say that finding nursing homes for their "boarder" patients is difficult. Although "buyers" regularly visit some hospitals shopping for "profitable" elders on Medicare or Medicaid to fill their nursing homes, they have trouble finding them.

The message here for older people is this: Do not stay too long in a hospital or nursing home

Although not created to be so, Social Security has become the most common source of income for all ethnic groups in the United States. If not for Social Security, nearly half of the aged would live in poverty.

unless you can pay for it yourself. If you are poor and there is no government subsidy, nobody wants you and there is nowhere to go.

Private Pensions

A pension is money received upon retirement from funds into which an individual usually has paid while working. Some employers have plans to which the employee contributes; others have plans to which the employee does not have to contribute. An employee may have both a pension plan and Social Security or only one of these programs. On the average, **private pensions** provide a much lower percentage of the income of elders than Social Security (which is, overall, 38 percent of the income of elders).

Private retirement plans created in the 1980s have become popular, such as Individual Retirement Accounts (IRAs) and 401(K) pension plans. These plans transfer more of the retirement costs directly to the individual employee. For cost-cutting reasons, U.S. employers, in droves, have eliminated traditional pension plans in which they footed the bill. These plans guaranteed retirees a specific income based on salary and length of employment. Many employers offer no substitute; the others offer 401(K) plans or similar types of individual plans (IRA's), which may or may not have a limited contribution by the employer. There is a definite shift away from fully paid health care for retirees by private employers.

Tax incentives further encouraged this avenue of retirement planning. However, the Tax Reform Act of 1986 eliminated some tax advantages, and uncertain interest rates (on which IRAs are based) have made these alternatives less reliable over the long term. When interest rates were high in the 1980s, the IRA and 401(K) (along with other savings plans such as certificates of deposit) were seen as good sources of supplementary income to Social Security or employer pension plans. When interest rates came down in the early 1990s, these saving plans did not seem as good or as reliable as they were in the 1980s. Also the earnings can be tied to the stock market, which carries risk for the individual who is participating. In any case whatever is in the account when the worker retires is what he or she gets. And if it runs out before the retiree dies, too bad. One good thing is that a worker who changes jobs can take the IRA or 401(K) along—they are portable—unlike the company-sponsored pension.

PROBLEMS WITH PENSIONS

Numerous gaps exist in private pension plan coverage. Temporary or part-time employees do not typically have a pension plan offered by their employers. Some companies simply have no pension plans. And to be eligible for pension benefits in many companies, the individual must have worked for a considerable number of years. Thus, the person who changes jobs every 7 years might work for 40 or more years but accrue very small or no pension benefits from any job. The worker who changes jobs several times will typically get less in total pension income than a long-term worker, even if both earned the same pay, worked the same number of years, and were in similar pension plans.

In spite of a pension reform bill passed in 1974, many loopholes in pension plans continue. Before the Pension Reform Act of 1974, a person who lost a job before retirement might have lost all the money he or she had paid into the company's pension fund. The Employee Retirement Security Act of 1974 established minimum funding for private pension plans and offered termination insurance to protect employees if their company ended the plan for any reason.

Congressional investigation of private pension plans has revealed that many workers, after a lifetime of labor rendered on the promise of a future pension, found that their expectations were not realized. In some instances, people were laid off in their late fifties or early sixties, just previous to their retirement, and lost their pensions in the process. In other instances, corporations changed ownership—a small chain of independently owned grocery stores, for example, rotated ownership among key family members every eight years or so. Each "sale" provided a legal loophole for the company to eliminate or otherwise alter the pension fund. As more giant companies fall on hard times, retirees face a wave of broken promises. General Motors is one such company among numerous well-known large companies (Karr, 1993). For companies that go bankrupt, later never comes.

Did You Know . . .
A study on the status of elderly single women in 6 industrialized countries (France, Germany, the Netherlands, Sweden, Switzerland, the U.S.) concluded that the Netherlands and Sweden seem to have the best record in preventing poverty among older single women. France's position is next, with elevated poverty in the 75 or older age group. Germany is a greater distance behind, with Switzerland in close proximity to Germany. The U.S. ranks last for its protection of older single women.

JURG K. SIEGENTHALER, 1996

Lifestyles of the Poor

What does poverty mean to you? You might say it is low spendable income, and that would certainly be true, but how does income translate to lifestyle? It is the housing in which you cannot live, the food you cannot afford, the stores in which you cannot shop, the medical care you cannot get, the entertainment you cannot enjoy, the items (color TV, VCR, car) you cannot possess, the clothing you cannot buy, the places you cannot go, the gifts you cannot give, the holidays you cannot celebrate. These and other deprivations are the essence of poverty.

Inner cities and rural areas both contain disproportionately high shares of the older poor, yet the elders' lifestyles are different. About four million people in the United States are poor and old. Each day, about 1,600 people aged 65 years old enter this group.

Did you Know . . .
A study of 225 homeless people in London in 1997 revealed: Two men became homeless before they were 10 years old; 5 men and 4 women first became homeless in their 70s; more than 75% of women and 50% of men had been in one town since becoming homeless; heavy drinking was not a problem for many respondents; more then 2/3 demonstrated or reported mental health problems.

PAYNE & COOMBES, 1997

Rather than a sudden displacement from an upper- or middle-class economic situation to a lower class, the overall picture of the aged poor is typically a descent from a lifelong lower economic class to the lowest, culminating in total dependency on a government paycheck that is far too small.

HOMELESS ELDERS: AN URBAN DILEMMA

Close to three-fourths of all older U.S. residents live in urban areas. Of these urban seniors, nearly half live in central cities. Although younger people are more likely to abandon a deteriorating city area, older people are more attached to their area; for both emotional and financial reasons they are not as likely to move to the suburbs. Urban issues such as crime, pollution, transportation, housing, and living costs in a large city are the issues of older people. The bulk of the older population in a central city lives in neighborhood communities, often racially and ethnically homogeneous–ethnic enclaves of European, Hispanic, or Asian ancestry.

A new feature of poverty in the 1980s and 1990s has been the large number of homeless elders. Though homelessness received considerable media attention, formal studies of the homeless focus more on the young than on the old. Crane, in a widely-quoted review of three studies on homeless elderly people, found agreement that catastrophic causes for homelessness were rare. Risk factors were more commonly discharge from an institution; release from prison; or being exploited and abandoned by family members. The studies each profiled older people who had "lifelong difficulties with other people, lack of a supporting family, poor education and lack of job skills, and personal problems such as alcohol abuse and criminal behavior" (Crane, 1994, p. 633). Additionally, among New York City homeless elderly people, psychological trauma following a relationship breakdown or bereavement were listed as causes.

Whether portrayed as derelicts, as victims of misfortune, or as people burdened by structural forces beyond their control, the image of homeless people as reflected in most court opinions is one of weakness, helplessness, and despair.

DANIELS, BUFFALO LAW REVIEW, 1997

Older men and women suffer homelessness in essentially the same way. Often labeled "bag ladies," homeless women cannot afford even the most inexpensive shelter. They often shun the confinement of an institution and carry their few possessions with them, eating from garbage cans or wherever they can get a free meal. Their very existence says something profoundly tragic about the role of elders in our society. For older, homeless men "skid rows" are common living environments. Estimates are that one-fifth of the homeless live in such areas. A skid-row resident is essentially homeless, even though he or she may not live exclusively on the streets. When they can afford it, they get cheap accommodations in run-down hotels or boarding houses. Typically, the men live on the street, periodically abuse alcohol or other drugs, may be physically or emotionally impaired, lack traditional social ties, and are poor.

Marginal and poor elders also live in **single-room occupancy (SRO) hotels**. The Tenderloin area of San Francisco fits the stereotyped image of the decaying central city. Although unique in some respects, it characterizes sections of all large cities. The Tenderloin is primarily a residential neighborhood where most inhabitants occupy cheap single rooms in apartment buildings, rooming houses, and hotels. The area seems to house society's discards; it is a dumping ground for prisons, hospitals, drug programs, and mental institutions.

Some SRO residents are alcoholics; others are lifelong loners, detached from larger social networks. Both men and women, reluctant to trust, tend to present a "tough" image and protect their privacy. The death rate is high in the Tenderloin, with common causes of death including malnutrition, infection, and alcoholism, all of which hint at neglect, isolation, and loneliness. In spite of the negatives, some elders seem to like the independence and privacy that a hotel room in the Tenderloin can offer, much preferring their SRO quarters to an antiseptically clean room in a nursing home.

A survey of 485 aged SRO residents in New York City had similar findings. Many of the elderly residents had weak family ties, strong preferences for independence, and long-standing attachments to central city neighborhoods. The SRO hotel, although run down, was an acceptable solution for housing because more "standard" accommodations were not affordable (Crystal & Beck, 1992). Some are able to find meaning and purpose in life despite rough circumstances; others are not.

Jason DeParle (1994) provided an excellent summary of the history of SROs in the United States:

> *They sprung up in downtowns during the early part of the century to house railroad workers and other transient laborers. Over time, many of them deteriorated into slum housing for drifters, drinkers, and the mentally ill. Then came developers, who, enticed by cheap land, razed the skid rows and replaced them with gallerias and office towers. Over the past several decades, as many as a million cheap hotel rooms have been destroyed (p. 53).*

Some cities have begun to view their SROs as a community resource for the prevention of homelessness, rather than as a community liability that should be demolished (Sheppard, 1997). Residents of SROs are, after all, only a short step away from living on the street. Perhaps the specter of people sleeping in doorways and camped out in alleyways will become too great an ethical burden for the public-at-large, and society will see fit to fund social programs to address homelessness.

PROBLEMS FACING RURAL ELDERS

Rural is defined by the U.S. Census Bureau as territory outside places of 2,500 or more inhabitants. It includes ranches, farms, other land, and towns that are smaller than 2,500 persons. The term *nonmetropolitan* is much more general and refers to counties that are not metropolitan. A metropolitan county (or counties) contains an urban area of 50,000 or more and the surrounding counties totaling at least 100,000 people.

Elders in rural areas represent all social classes. Some are owners of large farms or ranches; others own oil fields, factories, businesses, or have been professionals such as doctors, lawyers, and teachers. Their only commonality may be a love of the rural lifestyle, which in itself varies from the South to the Midwest to the North and East coasts, and varies by population density. Some rural areas contain small towns; others, acres and acres of farms and ranches with no towns for miles.

In 1996, the 10 states in the United States with the highest poverty rates for people over 65 were Mississippi (20 percent), Tennessee (20 percent), the District of Columbia (19 percent), Arkansas (19 percent), South Carolina (19 percent), Louisiana (18 percent), Alabama (17 percent), North Carolina (16 percent), Georgia (16 percent), and South Dakota (15 percent). Note that with the exception of South Dakota, the elder poverty rates are highest in the southern states. All areas represented except the District of Columbia are agricultural states and have large rural populations of individuals who lived a marginal lifestyle as farm workers, existing on Social Security as their only source of income when they retire, if they have even that.

The lifestyle of the rural poor is potentially more isolated than that of the urban poor. The older person may live miles from town or from neighbors. Housing in rural areas is often more run down than in urban areas and it is more likely to be substandard. Lack of a formal transportation system plus lower income profoundly impacts the older rural person's access to services as well as to specialty health care services, friends and family members, and ability to participation in social activities in more distant regions (Alexy & Belcher, 1997; Johnson, 1996).

Incomes for rural elders are often lower than those of their urban counterparts. Compared with urban elders, a greater percentage of rural elders is poor and an even higher percentage is **near-poor.** This is especially true in more southern states, yet income in and of itself may not be the most appropriate indicator of this group's well-being. The rural elderly have a somewhat lower cost of living and tend to be more satisfied and more able to make do with what they have. Rural elders are likely to have lived 20 or more years in their communities; they have commonly developed low expectations with regard to services, both social and medical, but they generally have greater community connections than their urban counterparts.

Rural and urban elders construe health differently, with rural persons more tolerant of health problems (DePoy & Butler, 1996). Age, education, and marital status are apparently less related to a sense of life satisfaction among elderly rural women than are social factors over which they have no control, such as their standard of living, or community changes (Butler & DePoy, 1996). One study concluded that rural women seem to feel less entitled to question their life satisfaction ("my lot in life") than do urban women of the same age ("why me?"). Expectations and comparisons, in other words, shape people's perception of quality of life, and female rural elders in this study expected less (Butler & DePoy, 1996).

Rural African Americans generally tend to be particularly economically disadvantaged. In general, their incomes are substantially lower than their rural white counterparts. For example, in 1987 the poverty rate for nonmetropolitan older African Americans was 46.5 percent compared with 12.6 percent for whites (Spence, 1997). The disparity becomes even greater among those in the oldest-old category. Sixty-eight percent of rural African American women lived in poverty, compared to 21 percent of their white counterparts in the early 1990s (Bould et al., 1989).

Government-sponsored low-income housing is less available in rural areas. Rural residents are likely to migrate to cities simply to improve their housing circumstances. Yet retirement complexes in large cities often do not offer a viable way of life to longtime rural dwellers. Many rural elders do not really want to sacrifice the advantages of rural living, such as peace and quiet and long-time friendships, for better medical care and a more modern home. Studies of rural life tend to document a marked resilience and strength, based perhaps on a lifetime of expectations of self-sufficiency ranging from growing one's own food to sewing one's own clothing. Interviews reveal rural elders to be self-sufficient, proud, and able to survive on small Social Security checks.

"The devil wipes his tail with the poor man's pride."

JOHN RAY, *ENGLISH PROVERBS*

"It is life near the bone, where it is sweetest."

H.D. THOREAU, *WALDEN*

A PIECE OF THE GOOD LIFE

In reflecting on what old people deserve in later life, we must conclude that they deserve a fair share of the "good life"—respect, dignity, comfort, and resources for experiencing new or continuing pleasures. Actually, a select number of aged in our society's upper echelons are doing quite well, having amassed great assets over their lifetimes. But they account for only 5 to 6 percent of the population aged 65 and over. Many elders, especially those at the very bottom of the economic ladder, struggle to enjoy—or to simply get—their piece of the American pie.

One obstacle to attaining this good life is that older people typically have less income in retirement than when they were working. A rationale for this is that the older person is not doing anything; therefore, little money is necessary. However, this rationale is based on an image of the elder as too frail to be involved and active. The image can become self-fulfilling. Actually, the retired person with plenty of leisure time needs an adequate sum of money to enjoy it. During our working years, we spend eight hours per day on the job; we spend more time traveling to and from work; we spend still more time preparing for our workday and resting up from work. After the working years, one may justifiably need more money for pursuing leisure activities, such as travel, school, and hobbies. Elders without money most commonly fit the negative stereotypes of aging.

Businesses in cities and towns recognize the modest means of many older persons and offer discounts of all kinds. Local programs provide seniors with token assistance, such as free banking service and discounts in theatres, restaurants, and transportation. In the Richmond, Virginia, area, for example, local merchants initiated a **senior discount program.** All elders who wanted to participate were issued photo identification cards. After nine months, over 600 merchants and over 19,000 older people were participating. The AARP has a national discount directory, and some cities have a "Silver Pages" section of the Yellow Pages that lists special services and shops that cater to the "senior citizen."

Discount programs also serve to stimulate the concept that purchasing goods and services is a good idea. The programs were initiated for elders whose life experience included the Great Depression and two world wars—a far different cohort than the aging Baby Boomers. Boomers will need little encouragement to consume. They grew up exposed to "new and improved" as a near-religious mantra. Marketing incentives to stimulate spending will probably no longer be necessary as the Word War II generation of elders gives way to the Baby Boom generation shortly after the turn of the century.

Chapter Summary

The poverty rate for persons aged 65 and older declined precipitously from 1970 to 1996, in no small part due to the benefits of Social Security. Women, ethnic minorities, those who live alone, and the oldest-old comprise 90 percent of the elderly poor. Most old people, however, are not desperately poor, but struggling in the lower- to middle-income ranges. If the benefits of Social Security were backed out of their income, many more of America's elderly would move into poverty.

Under Social Security, people under age 65 and between ages 65 and 69 are penalized for working, although after age 70 there is no penalty on wages earned. An income tax levied on higher-income Social Security beneficiaries resulted in about 20 percent of people on Social Security paying taxes on their benefits. Supplemental Security Income provides a minimum income for elders, blind, and disabled by supplementing Social Security benefits if they are below the amount stipulated by SSI. It is designed to assist the very poor.

Food, shelter, personal safety, health, and the opportunity to be socially interactive are minimum requirements for a good quality of life. It is the responsibility of the society as a whole to provide for all of its citizens, including those poor elders whose fortunes have changed, and those desperately poor elders who have never experienced comfort and security.

Key Terms

absolute poverty
capitated
child dependency ratio
cost-of-living adjustment (COLA)
dependency ratios
dually-entitled
economically vulnerable
elderly dependency ratio
entitlement
fee-for-service
Health Maintenance Organization (HMO)
Medicaid
Medicare
Medicare medical savings account
medigap insurance
near-poor
point-of-service
poverty
preferred provider organization (PPO)
private pension
privately contracted fee-for-service
provider-sponsored organization (PSO)
relative deprivation
reverse mortgages
senior discount programs
Social Security
SRO Hotels
subjective poverty
Supplemental Security Income (SSI)
total ratio

Questions for Discussion

1. What is the general purpose of Social Security for older persons?
2. What are some loopholes in pension plans?
3. Why do older women have more financial problems than older men do?
4. Within the population of elders, compare the urban poor with the rural poor.

Online Activities

1. Locate Quotesmith (*www.quotesmith.com*) on the Internet to determine the range of medigap policies in your state and specifically in your region. If you were seeking medigap insurance for your parent or grandparent, in what way would you use this resource? Find three other sources of information on medigap insurance (Hint: Check out AARP, HCFA, the insurance commissioner's office in your state).
2. You represent a 75-year-old man whose wife is in long term care. They own their own home and have a savings account of approximately $120,000. Locate a site or sites with information on Medicare, Medical, Social Security, and/or other information that would help you give your client some primary points in making economic plans.

10

Living Environments

Housing Options

Nursing Homes

The Omnibus Budget Reconciliation Act of 1987 (OBRA)

Living Environments

My New Small Town

F. Champion Ward

North Branford, Conn.

I had assumed my retirement community—call it Sycamore Woods—would be like a hotel, a base for excursions, with anonymous transients in the next room. No so. It is more like a small town. You know and meet everybody daily at the mail room, bank and stores, on surrounding roads and trails, at Saturday night movies in the community room and, if female, at the hairdresser's. There is even traffic: carts coursing through the corridors, dodging ambulatory but unsteady pedestrians.

Indeed, intimacy extends further here, induced by a swimming pool, common dining room and hobby groups: cabinet makers, trailblazers, bird watchers and poetry lovers.

Nor is government lacking. An elected residential council calls the loftier shots, hears complaints (however trivial), negotiates with the owner and forms subcommittees to oversee the library, planting of patio borders, display of art in the corridors and the food. There is even a "town meeting," at which views are aired, awkward amendments put forward and decisions occasionally reached.

Before moving in, I wondered what one would talk about at Sycamore Woods. The answer was soon clear: Sycamore Woods. No small town ever took itself more seriously. And self-preoccupation is intensified by the presence of a large number of strong-minded former executives, professors, nurses and doctors. During their life work they formed a habit of command, which is now directed at the less far-reaching affairs of Sycamore Woods.

If this suggests an inescapable and intrusive atmosphere, it has yet to materialize. We are free to welcome or avoid any or all neighbors or activities. This might have left us feeling crowded or lonely if our fellow residents had not proved to be an interesting and congenial lot. Rather, my wife and I have made many ninth-inning friends, and it is easier to entertain here than it was in Greenwich.

This may be the last American generation consisting largely of married couples, now in the autumn of long lives together. The mutual loyalty and determined cheerfulness are moving. The health—physical or mental—of one partner is often impaired, but brave fronts are gallantly maintained, fortified by the unfailing solicitude of other residents and the staff.

Comparison with old elephants, retreating into the jungle to expire together, is inviting. But I've avoided black humor since enduring the reproachful reception that greeted my suggestion that Sycamore Woods be renamed "The Semi-Finals." Meanwhile, a recent spell in drydock due to repairs to sundry body parts may appear to bear out de Gaulle, "Old age is a shipwreck." But I still like to think that Santayana got it right when he wrote that "The last years of life are the best, if you are a philosopher."

Think of the one place where you can be yourself, surrounded by the things that mean the most to you, live in the way you prefer, and shut the world out when you feel like it. There are lots of names for it, but they all mean the same thing—home. In this chapter, we will discuss the problem of housing, which to some may mean a home or to others may mean only a shelter. Psychologically, there may be a big difference between *housing* and *home.*

One of the most important challenges facing the nation now and into the 21st century is that of providing safe, adaptable, quality, affordable housing for the growing elderly population. Between now and the year 2050, the population of people over 85 is expected to quadruple, from 5 million to 20 million. Shifts of this magnitude in the age distribution of a population require that a responsible society work to understand the social implications of that shift and prepare for the well-being of its citizens.

Housing is one area that profoundly affects the quality of life of an individual, and especially among special-needs populations, it requires careful study and policy-level response. This chapter will consider issues of income and affordability; competence and opportunity; needs for adaptability (of houses, of people, and of social policy); the emotional power of the meaning of home; and options, both current and future, for housing for older people.

Living Environments

Housing—where a person lives—is a primary key to the quality of life of that person. Housing is comfort, safety, community, memory, and connection to family and the larger community. This is especially so for older people living on fixed incomes and those who are becoming frail and less mobile. The diversity of the aged population underscores the need for many housing options. Compared with other industrialized nations, the United States has been very slow to acknowledge the housing needs of its older citizens and slower yet to offer the needed options.

The housing market for older people is continually changing as the older population ages and grows. Elders need appropriate housing that offers safety and comfort in a convenient, desirable location and at a cost within their budgets. Gerontologists are increasingly concerned with the effect of the **living environment** on older people—not only in terms of the house structure, but also in terms of the environmental context. The features of a residential area and its surrounding community help to determine whether an older person is going to be happy. Because older people are typically in their homes many more hours per day than younger people are, it is important that their living environments make a positive, meaningful contribution to their lives.

DIVERSITY IN LIVING ARRANGEMENTS

The kinds of problems elders face in housing depend to an extent on the location and type of housing they have and on their personal circumstances, such as their health and marital status. The majority (67 percent) of older noninstitutionalized people lives in a family setting, according to the U.S. Census Department of Health and Human Services data (1997). About 81 percent of older men and 57 percent of older women live in families—usually with a spouse (Figure 10.1). The number of people living in a family setting, of course, decreases as widowhood increases. Single people tend to choose to live independently until there is a specific reason not to do so, which generally occurs when they become more physically frail with age. In fact, the elderly, whether single or married, are the least likely to change residence than any other age group. In 1994, only 6 percent of people 65 years old and older had moved since 1993, compared to 18 percent of people under 65 (Administration on Aging, 1997).

FIGURE 10.1

Living arrangements of persons 65 and over: 1995

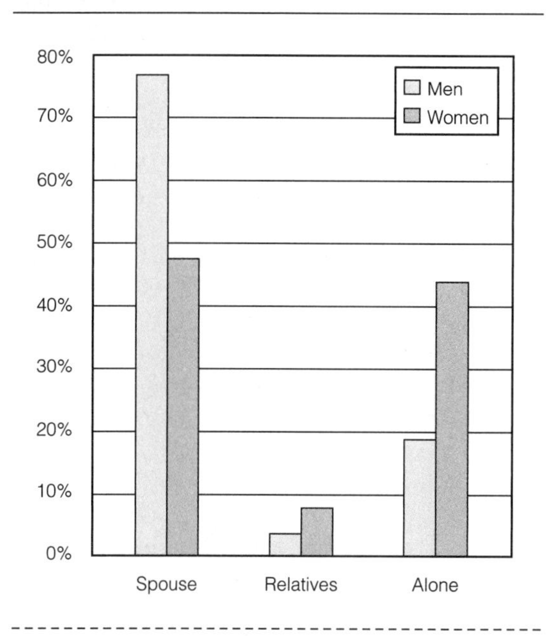

Adapted from: Administration on Aging. Department of Health and Human Services, 1997.

> *In the home are objectified both self-identity and social identity. Patterns of living, social norms and values, together with personality and biographical experiences, are hardly more clearly expressed anywhere else than in the home.*
>
> EKSTROM, 1994

About 7 percent of older people (6 percent of men and 8 percent of women) in 1995 were not living with a spouse but were living with children, siblings, or other relatives. An additional 2 percent of men and 2 percent of women, or 567,000 older people, lived with nonrelatives in 1995. About 30 percent (nearly 10 million) of noninstitutionalized older people lived alone in 1995—that represents 7.6 million women and 2.3 million men, or 42 percent of older women and 17 percent of older men (Administration on Aging, 1997).

A modest increase in the rate of home ownership for elders occurred in the 1980s whereas home ownership rates slightly declined for young adults, minorities, and other first-time buyers. Rates of home ownership for elders in the 1990s stabilized, or, according to some reports, declined slightly. In 1995, 78 percent of elders owned their own homes. For elders, these statistics reflect both better health (enabling elders to live in their own homes longer) and a better financial situation (enabling elders to afford homes of their own). The percentage of income spent on housing by those older home owners, including maintenance and repair, was higher for older people, at 34 percent, than for the younger consumer population, at 27 percent of income in 1995 (Administration on Aging, 1997).

The older population is scattered throughout the United States, although some areas and states have disproportionately high numbers. In 1996, just over half (52 percent) of people over 65 years of age lived in nine states: California (over 3 million); Florida and New York (over 2 million each); and Texas, Pennsylvania, Ohio, Illinois, Michigan, and New Jersey (over 1 million each) (Administration on Aging, 1997). The 65-plus population increased by 14 percent or more in 11 states between 1990 and 1996: Nevada (45 percent); Alaska (42 percent); Hawaii and Arizona (23 percent each); Utah, Colorado, and New Mexico (17 percent each); Wyoming, Delaware, and North Carolina (15 percent each); and Texas (14 percent) (Administration on Aging, 1997). Inner-city areas with high percentages of elders typically house those who have "aged in place." In such areas the people have aged along with their houses.

Older people tend to reside in ordinary houses in ordinary neighborhoods, rather than in institutions or in age-segregated housing. Thus, the housing needs of elders are obscured because many are dispersed and invisible as a distinct group. Those who live alone tend to have fewer financial resources than married couples, and their housing tends to be of poorer quality. Single men have the poorest housing, in spite of having higher incomes than single women, who, after fulfilling roles as homemakers, often seem to have more of an emotional investment in their housing.

AMERICA'S OLDER HOMELESS

Some elders have no home at all. Homelessness was addressed in Chapter 8 in more detail, but this chapter on housing addresses the problem once again.

Although the *proportion* of men who are homeless is declining because of the increased number of women and children in this situation, the *number* of homeless men is increasing. It is estimated that over 3 percent (5.7 million) of people in the United States was homeless between 1985 and 1990.

The population of homeless Americans has an "unacceptably high risk for preventable disease, progressive morbidity, and premature death" (Plumb, 1997). A study of 55 chronically homeless older men in Seattle found them to have serious health care needs. They were also subject to violence and crime and faced loneliness and frail health brought about by a history of poor nutrition, overconsumption of street drugs, and alcohol. In general, these homeless men had profoundly inefficient networks of social and emotional support (Goering et al., 1997).

Public homeless shelters provide the homeless a temporary sanctuary, but rigid routines and the loss of self-esteem suffered in such places are not conducive to encouraging a sense of community. Older homeless women are increasing in number and proportion and, like the men, they often suffer from histories of antisocial behavior and/or mental health problems (Daniels, 1997). Outreach agencies such as Project Rescue in New York and the Hostel Outreach Program in Ontario have been successful in providing respite and health care to homeless elders. However, little funding is available for such programs, and special-project funding is more often targeted to the severely mentally ill or to homeless families—groups that can be systematically categorized—than to the larger issue of homelessness and poverty (Daniels, 1997; Buhrich & Teesson, 1996).

We on the street have long recognized that Social Services operates under the policy of "don't make it too easy for them." ...A county caseworker told me that before she could process my application I must bring in receipts from all the people I'd panhandled from so she could total my monthly income. But my personal all-time favorite is "provide proof of no income."

"KIM," HOMELESS VOICES, 1997.

Across the United States, cities are now preparing for the consequences of the 1996 welfare "reform" bill called the Personal Responsibility and Work Opportunity Reconciliation Act. This act was designed to force people to work, it's underlying assumption being that poverty and homelessness is an individual responsibility that can be addressed by getting a job. Some policy analysts fear that this legislation will radically increase the number of homeless persons in the next 10 years, placing even greater strain on existing health, food, and shelter programs (Hwang et al., 1997; Golberg et al, 1997).

Additionally, the welfare reform bill of 1996 was accompanied by cuts in social programs that left holes in the safety nets available for people living on the streets—both the chronically homeless, and the "temporary" homeless (Plumb, 1997). In the next 10 years, just what will the status of the elderly homeless and near-homeless be? Given their yet greater reduced opportunities for employment, it is difficult to project. The future of these vulnerable groups depends greatly on the political climate and emergence of leadership.

GRAMMA IS DETERMINED TO AGE IN PLACE

A home of one's own fosters the maintenance of personhood and integrity. A home not only provides shelter, but also is a symbol of permanence and identity. The loss of home is devastating to one's being. Along with the loss of self is often the loss of friends and neighbors, loss of support, and loss of a platform from which to reach out and restructure one's life. When bodies age, the desire to remain settled and safe is strong. Homeless elders symbolize the tragic nature of a competitive society where the less fit are ignored and neglected. Lack of a place to call home in one's old age is tragically incomprehensible.

DISSATISFACTION WITH HOUSING

Compared to the homeless, those who have a place to live are doing well and counting their blessings. Yet older people can be dissatisfied with their housing situations for a number of reasons.

PERSONAL CHANGES

It is generally not until people are in the oldest-old age group (85+) that the more profound effects of aging begin to affect the ways in which they can live comfortably in their homes. However, for a significant minority of elders, acute or chronic health conditions will necessitate a change in their housing (Frolik, 1996). Among those people, a decline in strength and vigor makes it inappropriate to remain in their current living situation.

Changes in one's life may lead to being in a home that does not match one's needs. First, as the older person's needs change, a house may become too large. A large proportion of older individuals are widows or widowers living alone. When a house that once was the appropriate size for a family is large and empty, a smaller house or an apartment may be more suitable. Its size makes it easier to maintain, and it *feels* less empty.

Those with physical disabilities may not want to put their energies into keeping up a big house.

One person's castle is another's prison. Housing is appropriate for an elder if the person wants to be there, and if it is physically and psychologically safe.

Limited mobility and agility make it hard for older people to climb stairs, stand on stepladders, use bathtubs, and reach high cupboards. The person who loses a driver's license due to failing health or as a result of forgoing car ownership may be unhappy if the home is also isolated from friends and stores.

FINANCIAL CHANGES AND INCREASING MAINTENANCE

Shrinking personal finances can lead to difficulties in paying required housing costs. The older, retired person may have only half the income he or she received when working. For home owners, property taxes and insurance premiums can take huge proportions of a fixed income. Among renters, sizable rent increases may force a move to less adequate housing. The housing costs of taxes, insurance, and repair will increase, but at least property resale, over which the elder has no control, will not result in higher monthly payments for the home owner.

The home ages with the person. Older people may have lived in their homes 30, 40, or more years. The older house requires more maintenance; hiring others to perform the work is often costly. Leaking roofs must be repaired, appliances made usable, lawns mowed, and windows washed. Housing that requires little upkeep is ideal, but there is a risk that older people will not do necessary home maintenance. An estimated 10 to 15 percent of elders live in dwellings that are substandard.

The amount of money spent annually on the upkeep of a home is less for home owners age 65 and older than it is for younger homeowners. Average home maintenance costs for people 60 and younger is about $466 annually; that cost drops to about $145 for home owners 75 and older (Kausler & Kausler, 1996).

DESIRE TO PURSUE LEISURE

Old people who have no financial or health problems may wish to relocate closer to recreational amenities. Some want milder climates; others want to live among those in their own age group. Those who choose to migrate, who must go through the difficult decision of whether or not to uproot, often select a retirement community or center. Many such places exist, especially in Florida, Arizona, and southern California, where the climate is mild; but there are others scattered across the United States.

According to an AARP study quoted by Braus (1994), the most common reasons older people gave for relocating are:

1. Want to be closer to family, 15 percent
2. Want a change, 10 percent
3. No longer able to afford current housing, 9 percent
4. Buying better housing, 8 percent
5. Retirement, 7 percent

Not included in this list, but a very important factor in the decision to relocate, is the physical inability to continue to live in the present environment. Whatever the reasons for deciding to relocate, there are a number of issues associated with making the move. Four of those issues are discussed here.

SHORTAGE OF APPROPRIATE HOUSING

The availability of adequate housing for elders is, in some communities, woefully inadequate. One of the biggest shortages is in low-cost, or **public housing**. Demand far exceeds supply in all areas of the United States. Those with low incomes—for example, those who must live entirely on Social Security or Supplemental Security Income—often live in substandard housing. Government housing programs for elders lost their funding in the 1980s, due to budget cuts.

The National Affordable Housing Act of 1990 incorporated some provisions to help older home owners. A home equity provision allows use of home equity to make home repairs (Redfoot & Gaberlavage, 1991). The equity provision is available to all home owners, regardless of income. Budget constraints at the federal, state, and local levels, however, offer little hope that other funds for housing will be forthcoming. In 1997, the status of Section 8 housing was considered fair game in the battle for budget balancing, as lawmakers struggled between the ideological issues of the degree of governmental responsibility to provide its citizens with safe housing. Section 8 housing is rental assistance to specific properties, many of which are "project based," and provides assistance to more than 20,000 properties containing an estimated 3 million units across the United States (Wells, 1997).

One suggested model is that project-based subsidies be replaced with tenant-based assistance—that is, that federal assistance be provided to the individual, who then locates his/her own housing, rather than subsidizing builders and housing project management. The weakness in this argument is that the private sector will have no incentive to build inexpensive housing. Sister Lillian Murphy is president of nonprofit Mercy Housing, Inc. which operates about 3,000 units for low-income elders and families in eight states. She fears that housing for the poor will virtually disappear if there are no incentives for the for-profit industry. "The market has never served the poor, [and] it never will," she said. "If [for-profit companies] are not getting the subsidies, they will walk away" (Wells, 1997).

To allow elders to remain in their original homes, some states provide property tax relief by not taxing property after the owner is a given age. When the older person dies, the tax bill is deducted from the estate. A second option, discussed at greater length in a previous chapter, is the Home Equity Conversion Mortgage Insurance program, or reverse mortgage plan. Both tax savings and reverse mortgages, however, require the individual to own their own home.

A shortage also exists in housing to meet the special needs of the oldest-old. Ideally, the physical structure of a house for the older person would include wide hallways and doors to allow wheelchairs to move freely; protective railings and dull-surfaced floors to reduce the probability of falls; low-hung cabinets for easy access; increased brightness in lighting fixtures to accommodate reduced visual acuity; and acoustical devices to increase the volume of doorbells and telephones.

The very-old have little physical tolerance for extreme temperatures; thus, the thermal environment must be carefully regulated. The house should have no change of levels, not even a step down into a living room. Walk-in, sit-down showers rather than bathtubs are a must. Nearly as important as services and facilities of the living environment is the **surveillance zone**—the visual field outside the home that one can view from the windows or glass doors inside. A surveillance zone provides an important source of identity and participation with one's environment. The concept has implications for location, design, and landscaping.

Housing designed without consideration for the special needs of the elderly is just as inadequate as housing built on an unstable foundation or housing with inadequate plumbing.

UPROOTING

Relocation is difficult whether it is voluntary or not, because it involves leaving close friends and associates as well as a familiar environment. It also poses the uncertainties of change. Older people, like everyone else, have quite varied emotional experiences to forced moves; however, making a move that one has not fully chosen—moving with regrets—can have a particularly powerful emotional impact on the elder.

Most studies on the emotional impact of voluntary and involuntary moves made by elderly people have focused on stress. Stress has to do with loss of control. It is the emotional experience of being unable to manage a situation or changes that occur and of the struggle to reshape those changes to gain a sense of competence. A complex blend of emotions, or feelings, are present in the stress of changing one's home, most especially if that change is not fully voluntary. Issues having to do with security, attachment, belonging, estrangement, anxiety—all are connected to the emotional meaning of *home*.

Mats Ekstrom (1994) developed categories of emotional states that people in his study experienced when they were forced to move from the place they called home (See Table 10.1). Coping with stress requires a reinterpretation of the *meaning* of the stressful situation, and it requires the development of a plan of action designed to remedy the situation. The person must *reinterpret* feelings of mistrust, self-estrangement, guilt and sorrow, and—most centrally—of violation, or adjustment to the stress of the move will not happen. Ekstrom provides the poignant story of a man who was required to make an involuntary move:

> *For Mr. Peterson his home was intimately associated with who he was. In spite of the fact that his wife had been dead for several years, little had been touched. Her bed was in the same place as before, the furniture arrangement had not been changed, the ornaments had not been moved, and in the kitchen and linen-cupboard things were ordered in the way that she had ordered them. In conjunction with the move he had to dismantle all this, and he never felt able to put it together again. Several months after the move what had been his home was still largely packed in boxes that stood all over the new flat. The furniture was scattered here and there, and only in the bedroom were there curtains and pictures on the wall. His relationship to his new flat was an alienated one, at the same time as he felt that his life had been encroached upon by the landlord, for which reason he felt deeply violated. Mr. Peterson finds it hard to hold back the tears as he speaks: "They took my home away from*

TABLE 10.1

Emotions described by an elderly population being forcibly relocated

Emotional Experience of . . .	Definition
Stress	Feeling the lack of resources to cope with, and possibilities of escaping from, considerable problems, demands and/or threatening situations. Exposure to potentially stressful situations, and also the capacity to handle them, is dependent on social context, and dispositions and patterns of actions developed over time
Trust & security	Related to the degree of dependability, continuity, stability and anonymity of the social environment in which one lives
Belonging, self-estrangement, meaninglessness	Related to the capacity to set our imprint on the environment through creative, self-expressive action; realize our thoughts in various objects; realize our possibilities of living in a place, and in the presence of objects, to which, over time, we have established a deeper relation
Guilt, shame, pride, dignity	Indirectly, also joy and sorrow; created when we regard ourselves through other people's eyes and reflect on our actions in light of other people's values and expectations
Violation	Direct exercise of power, insult and infringement of social identity; vulnerability to such actions is socially determined

Adapted from: Mats Ekstrom (1994). Elderly people's experiences of housing renewal and forced relocation: Social theories and contextual analysis in explanations of emotional experiences. *Housing studies, 9* (3), 369–391.

me... I was forced to take apart the home we had, and I'll never be able to put it back the way it was... I live in a furniture depository and I'm never really happy" (p. 388).

Mr. Peterson's story demonstrates the importance of the home environment—the relationship of things, of placement, and of space to memories. *Home* has deep emotional meanings for us all, and the management of those emotions might take more resources than any one individual—especially one who is experiencing the losses of the physical self—has to give it.

MIGRATION

More than 60 percent of older people living in their own homes have lived there 20 years or longer (Redfoot & Gaberlavage, 1991). Living in an area for a long time fosters a feeling of neighborhood integration and security and closeness to friends and family. Yet many older persons can and do move, some very happily.

Retirement communities have sprung up throughout the country, advertising their amenities for the "golden-age lifestyle." It must be kept in mind that most older people do not move at all until it becomes absolutely necessary for them to do so because they are unable to thrive in their present housing. This is projected to be particularly true for the newest cohort of older people, born between 1925 and 1942 (Brecht, 1996). By the end of the 1990s, almost all the marketing efforts and retirement services were directed to those born before 1924. The "new generation" of elders are those born between 1925 and 1942, and their needs and interests will be different than those of their predecessors (Clark et al., 1996).

Amenity relocation (moving to an age-homogeneous community for one's retirement pleasure) is a concept made real by an industry specializing in building living. Most housing built in the 1960s and 1970s offered no nursing care or assistance with daily living. The communities focused on hospitality services such as meals, housekeeping, transportation, and activities. They targeted the newly-retired (Brecht, 1996). In the 1980s and 1990s the age of those moving into independent living units was typically in the late 70s and early 80s, rather than the late 60s and early 70s (Newbold, 1996). That elder population requires a different approach to facility amenities than did the first wave of retiree-relocators.

Among those who do move, a first move typically occurs around retirement for the young-old. In any five-year period, about 5 percent of the population over age 60 makes a long-distance move. Long-distance moves are more popular among "sixty something" couples who have both the financial resources and the desire to relocate during their early elder years. Some retirees have planned their move for years and have vacationed in the place to become their home many times. Though the reasons for relocation vary, they typically involve the attractive leisure amenities retirement communities offer—whether it is arts and crafts, music, golfing, boating, fishing, tennis, or social activities. Elders from the northeast and midwest still migrate toward the sunbelt of the west and south.

Migration may be either permanent or seasonal (Newbold, 1996). For several decades now, Sun City, Leisure World, and other large retirement communities of the sunbelt states have offered housing and amenities at reasonable prices. Over half the popular retirement communities are in southern states or in the southern parts of other states. The northern and western states of Michigan, Wisconsin, Minnesota, Oregon, and Nevada also have clusters of retirement communities. Florida still has the largest percentage of elder residents of all states.

Some older persons are **snowbirds,** living in the north for several months during the summer and going south for the winter. The opposite, those who live in the south and move north in the summer, have been labeled **sunbirds.** Sunbirds have been understudied, yet the tendency for older Arizona residents to leave in the summer is comparable to the tendency of older Minnesotans to go south during the winter. Demographers find a trend toward the snowbird eventually making a permanent migration to the South, then becoming a sunbird. Seasonally migrant elders compared to nonmigrants are more likely to be married and retired; they also have slightly higher levels of education and backgrounds as white-collar workers. Amenity relocators generally hear about retirement areas from relatives and friends, and they generally visit the community before moving to it.

Some people do move, but not that many. The popular belief that Snowbelt seniors will flee to warmer climates if they can afford to obscures the reality that only 5 percent actually move away from their community. Most projects attract residents from within a six- to seven-mile radius (Olson, 1998).

The 1990 census repeated the 1980 census in finding that more older persons live in the suburbs than in central cities. Declining health and the need for health care are often associated with migration to suburban areas. Given the closing of rural hospitals and the inadequacy or nonexistence of rural health care systems, worry about well-being often acts as a strong stimulus for an unwanted move to the city. The young-old who do not have to worry as much about health care tend to migrate to rural areas. The old-old tend to come to the suburbs or city from rural areas for necessary social and medical services.

INTEGRATION VERSUS SEGREGATION

The issue of **age-integrated housing** versus **age-segregated housing** concerns whether one would rather live in age-segregated communities, and thereby threaten an elder's ties with the larger society; or whether it is better to be integrated into the larger with greater opportunity for interaction among all age groups.

Age-concentrated retirement housing has strong support from middle- to high-income elders. Interviews with elders in three apartment buildings with low, medium, and high densities of older adults revealed that residents associated high-density senior citizen housing with larger numbers of friends, more active friendships, and slightly better morale (Hinrichsen, 1985). However, the hypothesis that age-concentrated housing is the best and most desirable situation has not been proved conclusively. Another study, in contrast, revealed that living environments with high densities of elders had little effect on morale, either positive or negative.

Many elders live in age-concentrated housing because they like the accommodations and amenities. Others are simply in "old" neighborhoods: age concentration is high because everyone has lived there for many years. They do not, by choice, limit their interactions to other old persons. Researchers conclude that, in general, though age-concentrated housing is a desirable alternative for some, it should not serve as a guide for housing policy at large. Some sociologists are predicting more age integration in the years to come (Riley & Riley, 1994). If the young-old stay in the job market longer and continue their activities of middle age, they will not gravitate toward age-segregated housing. Some social critics view age-segregated housing as a means of insulating older people from the ageism in the larger society. Here again, if ageism decreases, one would predict a decline in age-segregated housing.

Housing Options

We can view types of housing as ranging on a continuous scale from independent to dependent. Living in one's own home is the most independent lifestyle; living in a hotel-type residence is semi-independent; and living in an institution is the most dependent lifestyle.

Generally speaking, the more dependent the new lifestyle, the more difficult the adjustment. Sometimes the problem in institutionalized group housing is not the quality of care provided, but the fact that the older person really does not want to be there. Many people are dedicated to a lifestyle of self-reliance and self-direction and have little tolerance for the regulations of a nursing home. They might prefer better food and shelter, but not in exchange for the freedom to decide their life's course. A truly independent person might choose to live on a menu of eggs, beer, and ice cream in a cockroach-infested hotel, rather than live in a nursing home.

On the other hand, an isolated, frail, disabled elder might welcome the safe haven of institutionalized care. Acknowledging the diversity in age, personality, and health of those age 65 and older opens up more and more housing alternatives for older people. The needs and requirements of the young-old in good health are vastly different from those of frail elders in poor health. In this section, housing options for both the young-old and the oldest-old are considered.

Nearly every study affirms the conventional wisdom that older people strongly prefer to age in place, to grow old within familiar territory that has provided a context for their lives, whether they live in single family dwelling, elderly housing complexes, or naturally occurring retirement communities.

SYKES, 1990

AGING IN PLACE

Most people do not move from their own homes until they must do so for reasons of safety. The image of retiring and moving to Golden Age Village is just that: an image. Some people do retire and move; indeed, in some states elderly migra-

Aging in place has profound psychological meaning for some elders. It is sometimes difficult for families to balance their needs for the elder to be safe and cared for with the elder's needs to age in place/die in place.

tion is a growth industry. Retirees are viewed as the ultimate "clean industry" (Clark et al, 1996). Moving does not reflect the first choice of most new retirees these days, however. Most people go to great lengths to remain in their own homes—a home not associated with being old, frail, or of having special needs. That home is the home of memories and is often associated with the self-concept of mature and responsible adulthood. **Aging in place** has become a popular phrase reflecting the pattern of staying in one's home as long as possible despite increasing frailty and its associated problems.

American elders have moved less frequently each year since World War II (Golant, 1994). About 84 percent of people age 55 and older say they want to stay in their longtime homes rather than move to senior housing. When they are forced to move, 63 percent prefer to remain in the same city or county and only 11 percent prefer to move to a different state. "Their dominant preference is to stay in their homes, and not move, never move—stay there forever," said Lea Dobkin, a housing specialist with AARP.

Many older people already live in informal retirement communities known in the senior housing industry as **naturally occurring retirement communities (NORCs)**. These are buildings or neighborhoods where the residents have aged over the years. There are many cases in point, both in the suburbs, the rural Midwest, and inner cities (Newbold, 1996). The neighborhood, like the individual, goes through a life cycle of young to middle-aged to old.

Aging in place is not always easy. As people age into their eighties and nineties and beyond, more and more tasks may pose difficulties, even for those in good health—writing checks, driving a car, shopping, or bathing. Public or private agencies must be available to provide services that elders themselves and their families and friends cannot provide. Home-nursing services and homemaker services, including cooking, housecleaning, bathing and grooming assistance, laundry, and transportation might be required. Also, social services may be needed for emotional health and support. In many communities, volunteers telephone older people once a day to check on their health and safety. These calls are especially important for those living alone.

DOWNSIZING

The move to a smaller home, say a condominium or a mobile home, if it is in the same town or general area, is a form of aging in place. The reasons for such a move were discussed earlier in this chapter: The upkeep is easier, taxes are lower than for a large house, and the location may be more convenient.

Mobile homes, typically smaller than conventional homes, can provide a comfortable living environment. Perhaps the most significant factor in opting for a mobile home is related to its affordability. Mobile homes provide older adults with a sense of home ownership, privacy, and security.

Life in a mobile home may not be without problems, however. Historically, the quality of mobile homes has been suspect. In the past, owners have had little success in influencing manufacturers to correct deficiencies. There has been general agreement that, overall, the quality of mobile homes has improved in recent years. In a move to protect mobile-home buyers, recent congressional proposals would require that buyers be provided with a five-year warranty, building (manufacturing) standards be raised, and "mandatory" funds designed to pay for repair costs not reimbursed by unscrupulous or bankrupt businesses be required from state funds.

An additional potential problem for the majority of older mobile-home residents is related to the fact that they must purchase space in a **mobile-home park** where they have little control over actions made by park owners. Problems include space rental increases and restrictive rules.

Enough people live in their RVs (recreation vehicles) the year around for the term **full-timing** to have evolved. This is one more choice that older people have. Some fulfill a lifetime retirement dream when they "hit the road" in their RVs and see all the places in Canada, the United States, or Mexico that draw them. It is a lifestyle that has not gone unnoticed by sociologists and gerontologists.

ADULT DAY CARE

Adult day care offers medical and social services at a center to elders who commute from home. Many service providers call their programs "frail elder programs," to avoid the comparison and association of child-care centers with programs for adults. Centers may be nonprofit organizations, government-run centers, or for-profit organizations run by insurance companies such as Elderplan. Multipurpose senior centers provide health care facilities where older persons are brought in the morning and taken home in the afternoon. These might be day hospitals that offer medical or psychiatric treatment or day care centers that provide social and recreational services. People who can avail themselves of adult day care actually reduce their risks of hospitalization—probably due to the greater physical exercise and mental stimulation achieved by the programs.

Some nonprofit organizations provide multiple services to elders. Through the Older Americans Act, the federal government now funds a number of multipurpose senior centers. One such organization, the Minneapolis Age and Opportunity Center, largely government-funded, provides services such as daily meal deliveries, laundry, and transportation. *A Touch of Home* in Rochester, NY, provides respite and socialization opportunities for frail elderly and their caregivers. The program is an example of other small nonprofit agencies that provide "therapeutic recreation that emphasize opportunities for success in a structured, safe and fun environment" as well as transportation, sometimes a meal, personal care, and transportation (Tracy, 1996).

Frail elder programs are especially critical for people who choose to continue living in their own homes, or who are living with a spouse or adult child caregiver. The socialization and care provision offered can make the difference in whether or not an individual can continue to live independently. The Touch of Home program in Rochester grew from a small program in the basement of a church in 1990 to services at three locations in the region, providing services to over 60 people by 1996. The need is undeniably there; however, the funding to support programs and subsidize program costs for individuals and families is stretched very thinly among competing social services programs.

Insurance programs are now being offered to assist the older person in staying at home. Such plans are becoming affordable and workable. A variation of the health maintenance organization (HMO) is the SHMO—social health maintenance organization. Elderplan in New York, Kaiser in Oregon, and Seniors Plus in Minnesota offer health insurance programs that provide personal care and household assistance services at home or in day care settings.

A new variation of health insurance policies offers LCH (Life Care at Home). Insurance agencies are tailoring LCH insurance policies that cover medical and personal costs for the older person who wishes to stay at home. One must proceed with caution in purchasing a LCH plan because the LCH involves a large initial entry fee, a monthly fee, and at least a one-year contract. Such private long term care insurance policies are expensive and may have restrictions that limit coverage.

The On Lok Health Center in San Francisco, patterned after the day care system in England, provides day care services to elders in Chinatown. A van with a hydraulic lift transports the elderly to the center, where each day begins with exercise and reality orientation. People are introduced to each other in both English and Chinese. On Lok assumes responsibility for providing all services needed by the functionally dependent. If not for On Lok, the participants would need institutional care. Though the cost per person for this service is about the same as that for institutional care, the psychological benefits and the social facilitation make the service well worth the price.

GRANNY UNITS AND SHARED HOUSING

A housing concept currently being proposed and enacted on a limited basis in the United States is actually an old concept to the Japanese and Australians: the **granny unit,** also called the granny flat or elder cottage. A granny unit, by U.S. definition, is a small living unit, built on the lot of a single-family home, where adult children can care for aging parents. Older people can also install granny units in their backyards. They can rent their home or their granny unit for income or trade for services such as nursing or homemaking.

Advocates of the granny-unit concept, such as the American Association of Retired Persons (AARP), often must fight zoning laws in some towns and cities. Areas zoned for single-family homes may not welcome added granny units. The desirable features of granny units are that they allow the older person a choice of living independently. If the older person can live in a granny unit rather than in the adult child's house, there is more privacy and freedom for everyone. The "granny flats" experience in Great Britain suggests that "they have an important but limited role" in enabling people to live close to their families (Tinker, 1991). But, despite cost and regulations, this housing alternative is gaining support in more countries worldwide.

ADULT COMMUNITIES

Many towns and cities have **adult communities** for those over age 50. Typically, children under 18 are prohibited from living in these places; court cases have upheld the legality of the age limit. Adult mobile-home parks with age limits on younger persons are also quite popular. An adult community may have a grocery store, bank, medical clinic, and convenience stores within its boundaries. The sizes of adult communities within cities vary. A recent trend is for older folk with interests in common (for example, artists or gay retirees), to form their own communities.

Retirement Cities

Some people seek out age-segregated **retirement cities.** One of the largest and most well known of the many retirement cities is Sun City, begun in Arizona in 1960. In the late 1990s there were Sun Cities in California, Illinois, Nevada, South Carolina, and Texas with around 100,000 people calling them home. The cities are known for their broad range of activities and social resources for residents: championship golf courses, state-of-the-art recreation facilities with swimming pools and exercise equipment, classes and social clubs that address almost every interest from piano, to bicycling, to model railroads and beyond.

The intent of commercially developed retirement cities such as Sun City and Leisure World, is to provide an environment fostering a sense of community through leisure activities and the environmental setting. That setting often includes hiking and biking trails and beautifully landscaped grounds.

For many people, activities shaped around children in the home and friendships forged in the workplace have created the heart of their social network. When children leave home and jobs are left behind for retirement, the need for a renewed social network often becomes apparent. For people with the economic resources, retirement cities provide an option offering that new community. In the words of Sun City promotional material, "We attract people like you—people who value their community, their friends, their lifestyle."

ASSISTED LIVING

Assisted living (or assisted housing) typically refers to community-based residential housing of some type (apartment, condominium, or semi-communal living), including supportive services to assist in the activities of daily living. It is designed to serve the needs of the more frail person who wants to live in a homelike setting, but requires some assistance to do so. This level of care is a fairly new concept. Elders requiring assistance with their daily living tasks formerly had only the options of hiring home assistants or moving to skilled nursing facilities, in which by law, "all needs" are to be provided for. The assisted-living philosophy is one of individualizing and maximizing the elder's independence, privacy, and options.

It is a clear "hands-off" approach: People will be provided whatever assistance they need to maximize their independence. This is in stark contrast with the philosophy of skilled nursing care, which is to be "hands on," providing people assistance with all their needs. Assisted living services generally include meals and the option of eating in a dining room setting or eating in one's room, housekeeping, transportation, and help with everyday tasks like bathing and grooming.

Growth in assisted living has come about because investors can see the emerging market and the potential for profit. It is, in fact, currently the hottest senior housing market. In 1996, construction for assisted living accounted for 54 percent of all senior housing built in the United States (Murer, 1997). Assisted-living development is estimated to reach $33 billion in revenues by the turn of the century, with nearly 4.1 million beds (Olson, 1998).

In the mid-1980s hospitality corporations such as Marriott and Hyatt made substantial investments in long term care, which had previously been seen as a health care or hospital arena. This somewhat legitimized the industry for other investors. In a recent analysis of assisted-living facility development, Olson (1998) reported that "In the past 24 months there has been a tremendous increase in the money available to develop senior housing... A large part of this capital comes from Real Estate Investment Trusts (REITs) seeking to diversify their portfolios." Wall Street and bonds also provide development funds, but the majority of financing comes from conventional sources such as banks (Olson, 1998). Financing provides the structures; the cost of the services are purchased, separately from rent, by the resident. Not surprisingly, most of the facilities generating the greatest amount of excitement are designed for upper- and upper-middle income elders.

Some funding is available for housing for the truly low-income elderly—those with annual incomes of about $15,000 or less. Section 42 of the Internal Revenue Tax Code provides for a low-income housing tax credit to corporations investing in low-income elder housing. Some communities use Community Development Block Grants to build low-income housing; still others look to other federal programs such as the HOME Program, established under the National Affordable Housing Act of 1990 (Nolan, 1997).

Problems arise in the options for building low-income assisted-living housing for elders because of the need for *assistance*. Services must be funded separately, because for low-income elders those costs cannot be passed on to the resident. Some developers have used a new Medicaid home- and community-based waiver that allows for the financing of health care services in an assisted living setting (Nolan, 1997). Other areas simply compete with local service providers for the limited funding available to provide living assistance to the poor.

"In its current state of development, assisted living is a Cadillac: nice to have but affordable to a relative few. Unlike a Cadillac, though, assisted living is more than 'nice to have'; it is becoming a necessity for many elderly Americans who are, nevertheless, unable to afford it. Aging but still living independently, in need of support services but a long way from needing skilled care, they are natural customers for assisted living. Is gaining access to it beyond hope for them?"

NOLAN, 1997

Board and care homes are similar to the old "mom and pop" operation in a large family home where unoccupied bedrooms become available to boarders. Relatively little attention has been paid to board and care facilities, which are variously referred to as residential care facilities, adult congregate living, rest homes, adult foster care, personal care, care facilities, and group homes (Garrard, 1997). Usually, the board and care facility offers a bedroom in a private home, whereas an assisted living facility offers self-contained housing units. Operators of board and care homes are typically middle-aged women who live in the homes with their spouses; many of the operators have worked previously as nurses or aides in health care settings (Kalymun, 1992).

Sunrise Retirement Homes and Communities is the country's largest operator of assisted-living centers, operating more than 30 such communities (Estrada, 1994). When a husband-wife team started their first Sunrise Center by renovating a nursing home, the term *assisted living* did not exist. Now more than 2,000 elders live in their centers. One example of their efforts is the Sunrise Retirement Home near Washington, D.C., a three-story "Victorian mansion" with 42 one- and two-room units The building has the feeling of a country inn with a fireplace, large bay windows, and a sunroom filled with wicker furniture. Residents' rooms are grouped around common living rooms and lounges. In 1997, units rented for $2,000 to $3,000 a month, which includes housekeeping, meal services, and minor medical care.

Did You Know . . .
More Americans are concerned about financing long term care than about paying for retirement (69 percent to 56 percent)?

NATIONAL COUNCIL ON AGING AND JOHN HANCOCK MUTUAL LIFE INSURANCE COMPANY. MILLER, 1997

CONTINUING CARE RETIREMENT COMMUNITIES (CCRCS)

The **continuing care retirement community** (CCRC) represents an upscale form of congregate housing that requires a strong commitment on the part of the resident. CCRCs, also known as **life-care communities,** require a large entry fee ($50,000 to $500,000), monthly fees of $500 to $2,000 (depending on the area of the country, quality of housing, and number of services available), and commitment to at least a year-long contract. In return, the entrant is provided with housing, health care, social activities, and meals. Few CCRCs are currently being built because they are large (typically with a budget of $50 to $70 million per project) and the financing is complex (Olson, 1998).

Housing options will be developed if a market is perceived to be there. For example, some universities are now investigating CCRCs for alumni and faculty. According to a plan developed for Davidson College in South Carolina, residents will be able to audit classes, use campus libraries and sports facilities, and become involved in other ways with the university campus life (Olson, 1998). Part of the exchange, aside from providing a profitable and valuable service, will be that the increased investment in the university's well-being by the CCRC residents' involvement will result in an increase of bequests to the university.

The entire life-care industry has grown dramatically in the last few years. Dozens of big-name developers and corporations have built or plan to build CCRCs and other assisted living senior residences. The options are marketed in very sophisticated ways, and there is a growing concern for the need to protect older consumers.

Legislation has been passed in many states to protect the older consumer. Contracts and rental agreements are regulated, and most states have certification and registry requirements. California and Florida, for example, require extensive disclosure statements prior to certifying facilities; Indiana and Colorado require that the potential resident receive copies of such disclosure statements. Those considering life-care communities must protect themselves as much as possible by examining the facility and contract very carefully before signing.

Nursing Homes

Meeting the needs of the infirm is the responsibility of society, not just the responsibility of service providers, the government, or their families. Here we will consider what nursing homes can offer. How well they meet needs ultimately depends on how well the public informs itself concerning the problems of nursing homes and the rights and services to which residents are entitled.

Who Needs a Nursing Home?

Nursing homes are becoming large-scale operations. Since 1985, the number of nursing homes decreased by 13 percent while the number of beds increased by 9 percent (DHHS, 1997). The number of nursing home residents was up only 4 percent between 1985 and 1995, however, despite an 18-percent increase in the population aged 65 and over. Before this 1995 finding by the Department of Health and Human Services, the utilization rates had kept pace with the increase in the elderly population (DHHS, 1997). People are *not* aging in the same way they did 25 years ago.

The typical nursing home patient is female, white, widowed, and over age 80. Most of the residents come to the facility from another institution, usually a general medical hospital, rather than from their own homes. Most nursing home residents have multiple problems such as arthritis, heart trouble, diabetes, or vision/hearing impairment. In addition to physical impairments, there are often mental health problems, such as disorientation (confusion), impulse control (anger), and emotional affect disorder (depression). People living in nursing homes generally require assistance in dressing, eating, toileting, and bathing.

Making the Decision To Move

Whether an older parent, relative, or friend will need nursing home care can often be anticipated some months before the individual actually enters the facility. The limitations in behavior brought on by chronic illness or age may be progressive as well as irreversible, usually allowing the individual and the family time enough to make a thoughtful and careful selection of homes and to ease the transition from one living arrangement to another.

Unfortunately, too few people are willing to entertain the possibility of a nursing home and simply wait for circumstances to force a quick, hurried decision, usually one filled with emotional trauma for all concerned. Statistics indicate that the typical nursing home patient enters the facility from a hospital rather than from a private home. This signifies that nursing home care has become a necessity rather than a choice. Families often burden themselves for long periods of time trying to care for an elderly parent who could receive care as good or even better in a nursing home. They often associate guilt, and even shame with any attempt to consider nursing home care until the need becomes absolutely critical.

Families can anticipate eventual need and involve all members in the decision-making process. Everyone concerned, including friends, can discuss the advantages and disadvantages of nursing home care and share the task of gathering information and visiting facilities. Families can and should discuss these problems in an atmosphere of mutual love and concern. The older person "dumped," without discussion or plan, in a nursing home after a sudden medical crisis may well feel deserted and hurt.

Did You Know . . .
The annual cost to companies for lost productivity from eldercare responsibilities was $17 billion a year in 1995—that is $3,142 per employee in America.

WALL STREET JOURNAL, 1995

Finding a Nursing Home

Over 30 percent of the population in one national-level random-sample study would rather die than move to a nursing home (Olson, 1998). Some professionals and family caregivers might add that the other 70 percent simply do not know about daily life in a nursing home, cost notwithstanding.

Many nursing homes provide fine patient care and make special efforts to meet the psychosocial needs of their residents. Others are skilled in the delivery of medically related services but lack the foresight, knowledge, and skill to address the psychological and emotional needs of their residents. The better facilities generally have long waiting lists, so early planning is essential to eventual placement.

There are resources that can assist in the search for the right nursing home. The local Council on Aging and the local chapter of the state Health Care Association can provide the locations of licensed facilities in the area and factors to consider in choosing a home. The local ombudsman program maintains a list of all formally reported complaints made by or on behalf of people who are residents of long term care facilities. The Office of Nursing Home Affairs can provide information on characteristics of good homes. Finally, the local chapter of the Gray Panthers typically has a nursing home committee; various other watchdog groups publish information on how to choose a nursing home.

The following was compiled by social workers and nursing home professionals as preliminary ideas about how to select a nursing home.

- Make at least two visits to a particular nursing home, once at a mealtime and again in midmorning or midafternoon. Visit several other facilities, so you can make comparisons.
- Make sure you know what the basic rate covers. Investigate extra charges for professional services and medications.
- Take time to observe interactions among staff. Does there seem to be an easy relationship, or do you pick up any tension? The more staff seem to like one another, the greater the probability that the environment is a happy one for residents, too.
- Extend your observations to interactions between staff and residents. Are you comfortable? Do staff extend beyond courtesy to each

resident, and seem to have a genuine regard for each person (you, after all, are "company" and "company manners" might be on display)?

- Ask to see a copy of the month's menu. Is it varied and interesting? Does the food on the menu actually get served? How is it served? Have breakfast, lunch, or dinner in the facility. How was it? How did it make you feel?
- How many hours a month does a registered dietician spend in the facility? Experts believe four hours a week should be an absolute minimum.
- Is there a registered nurse on duty on the afternoon and evening shifts? This is required by law for facilities of 100 beds or more. All facilities with more than six beds should have an RN on the daytime shift.
- Is there an activities director (required by Medicare certified facilities)? Talk to him or her. What are the reasons for specific activities? What is the range of activities, and how often do they occur? Are there activities for bedridden residents? What are they? Do they seem interesting to you?

Death is a dramatic, one-time crisis while old age is a day-by-day and year-by-year confrontation with powerful external and internal forces, a bittersweet coming to terms with one's own personality and one's own life.

ROBERT BUTLER, 1994

Life in a Nursing Home

Virtually all of us are either directly or indirectly affected by nursing home care. Although at any given time only 5 percent of the nation's elders are in long term care institutions, this figure is deceptive. About 1.5 million residents were receiving care in 16,700 nursing homes in 1995. Almost 90 percent of those residents were aged 65 or older, and more than 35 percent were aged 85 and older (DHHS, 1997).

Families are also affected. Nine out of 10 children can expect that one of their parents (or their spouse's parents) will spend time in a nursing home. Nursing home populations are projected to increase from the 1990 level of 1.8 million to 4 million within the next 24 years—an increase of well over 50 percent (DHHS, 1997). That means that a lot of people are going to be directly and indirectly affected by the quality standards of nursing homes.

The question remains: Are all homes as bad as we imagine them to be, or is a bad nursing home relatively rare? It turns out that this question is not an easy one to answer. For starters, we can easily identify truly negligent care, but can we identify good care—"quality" care? The very concept is laden with personal judgments—good quality in Mr. Jones' estimation might not be good quality from the perspective of his wife. Bad care, on the other hand, can be obvious to the observer, or more subtle and not immediately apparent. Nursing home violations cover a broad range of conditions, just a few of which include residents being tied in chairs for hours at a time; lack of an activities program; bedridden elders lying in urine-soaked bedding; unappetizing and possibly undernourishing meals; and the use of Styrofoam drinking cups and plastic utensils, which impose a hardship on those with tremors and arthritis. Where is the line between *bad* and *good enough, all things considered?* What about *quality?*

Measuring Nursing Home Quality

Identifying the specific dimensions of nursing home quality in a way that makes sense to professionals, consumers, and policy makers is a relatively new research endeavor (Table 10.2). In a major qualitative study, Rantz and associates interviewed people with a variety of experiences in providing nursing home care to determine the variables they used to assess nursing home quality (1998). The people interviewed represented a range of responsibilities in long term care, including administrators, nurses and activity directors, social workers, ombudsmen, state regulators,

TABLE 10.2

Factors in nursing home quality

Nursing home care components	Good care quality	Bad care quality
Environment	· Clean · No odor · Maintained · Bright/good lighting	· Odor of urine/feces · Shadowed, lighting poor
Care and treatment	· Attentive, caring, residents listened to · Treated as individuals · Restorative care, ambulating · People up, dressed, clean, and well cared for · Food is good	· Residents unkempt, exposed, not clean, unshaven, disheveled, clothes dirty, poor nail care · Complaints from residents about care, lying in urine, not being taken to toilet
Staff	· Knowledgable, professional · Busy interacting and working with residents · Open and listens to family · RNs involved in care · Education encouraged · Low turnover	· Interact inappropriately or ignore residents · Vistors can't find staff
Milieu	· Calm but active and friendly · Presence of community, volunteers, animals, and children · Residents engaged in age- and functionally-appropriate activities	· Chaos? · Residents screaming and no one paying attention · Unfriendly atmosphere · An institution, not a home
Central Focus	· Residents and Family	· Surivival of agency · Leadership void · Financial gain without regard or understanding of services needed by residents

Adapted from: Rantz, M., et al., 1998. Nursing home care quality: A multidimensional theoretical model. *Journal of nursing care quality, 12* (3), 30–49.

professional home care staff, and hospice and mental health personnel.

It seems apparent that quality nursing home care is something that cannot be legislated. The difference between "good enough" and "high quality" takes an organizational philosophy—a dedication to providing *care* in the nursing home. *Caring* incurs meeting individual needs, and meeting individual needs incurs a good deal of knowledge and understanding about the individual being cared for. This, in turn, requires a low ratio of residents per staff person, and an organization dedicated to the mental as well as physical well-being of its guests. At the turn of this century, money holds quality of life hostage for the care of many of America's elders. As a nation, the United States has not made elder care a priority.

Did You Know . . .
Medicare will provide

- Only skilled nursing and rehabilitative services
- Only in Medicare approved nursing homes—fewer than 10 percent of existing facilities

Medicare Nursing Home Benefits provide

- First 20 days paid 100 percent by Medicare
- Additional 80 days, patient pays $92/day; Medicare pays remainder
- Beyond 100 days, patient pays all nursing home costs

The economics of nursing home management introduces another whole range of problems. The government reimburses nursing homes through two systems, both of which can be corrupted by dishonest owners. On the flat-rate system, the nursing home is paid so much per patient. The operator who wants to make a large profit on this system keeps costs as low as possible by providing cheap food, having as few registered nurses on the staff as possible, and providing no physical therapists or psychiatric counseling. Healthy residents are the most desirable under this system.

The second system is called the cost-plus system. Here, the nursing home is reimbursed for its costs, plus a "reasonable" profit. The way to make money under this system is to pad the bills—in other words, the government is billed for more goods and services than the facility received, or billed for goods and services never delivered. Doctors and nursing homes gain if doctors perform "gang visits," stopping just long enough for a quick look at residents' charts and perhaps to visit briefly with people. The government is then billed as though each resident had a separate appointment—a task that would take days rather than hours.

The debate over whether proprietary (for-profit) homes offer a lower quality of patient care than nonproprietary (nonprofit) homes goes unanswered. One study, using strict quality control measures, found no difference in the quality of care between profit and nonprofit facilities (Duffy, 1987). Other analyses disagree, observing that not-for-profit facilities generally have greater concern for the psychological and spiritual development and well-being of their residents (Rosenkoetter, 1996). Close to three-quarters of all nursing homes, however, are operated on a for-profit basis.

Who speaks for the frail, sometimes confused residents who are not objects of a television news exposé? Ombudsman Programs are an independent, federally and state mandated nonprofit agency charged to advocate for long term care residents. Employing a staff of well-trained volunteers, this agency investigates and resolves complaints from and on behalf of residents of nursing homes. The agencies, though seriously underfunded by federal and state sources, provide a critical watchdog role. In one northern California county in 1997, the three-person-staff, 20-volunteer program handled 1,052 cases, including over 200 abuse cases. Volunteers made 1,429 visits to long term care facilities in the region and contributed 5,155 volunteer hours (OPSC, 1998).

Those in the business who are really concerned about elders and provide quality care deserve credit. Credit also must be given to all the honest doctors, pharmacists, nursing home inspectors, social workers, and therapists. A number of nursing homes are excellent by any standards. The Jewish Home for the Aged in San Francisco is considered to be among the best. The living quarters resemble rooms in a nicely furnished college dormitory. Virtually all residents are out of bed and dressed. The home has a beauty shop, and there are many activities and opportunities for therapeutic exercising on stationary bicycles and other equipment. "They take care of me from head to toe," said one resident.

NEW TRENDS IN NURSING HOMES

The majority of nursing home residents have disabling mental health conditions, such as depression, Alzheimer's disease, or a history of mental illness. As a result, many nursing home residents present behavior problems, such as agitation, abusiveness, or wandering. Nursing home care presents an increasing challenge for staff, family, and residents alike. In the past, the health care system provided scant rehabilitation for frail elders and held low expectations for older people in nursing homes. Now, however, there are positive new trends for both the physically and the mentally disabled.

Those over 65 are more likely than any other group to suffer strokes, lower limb amputation, hip fractures, and heart disease. With rehabilitation, many can achieve a level of independence that allows frail elders to live in their own homes. Rehabilitation units represent a departure from the traditional nursing home. One nursing home with a rehabilitation unit revealed that 57 percent of its residents were discharged after an average stay of three months in the unit. The unit had a team composed of a geriatrician, psychiatrist, physical therapist, social worker, nurse, occupational therapist, and nutritionist. The conclusion was that patients discharged "quicker and sicker," without rehabilitation, are likely candidates for relapse and readmission. The rehabilitation unit brought a sense of triumph to all who participated (Adelman et al., 1987).

It is estimated that 65 percent of all nursing home residents have at least one mental disorder (Lantz et al., 1997). The mentally ill, who present far more behavioral problems than other nursing home residents, need rehabilitative services. Such services have been found to be generally effective. But, according to Shea and associates (1994), fewer than 25 percent of nursing home residents with a mental disorder actually received such services in the year of the study. Obviously, although services for those who receive them tend to be somewhat effective, much more must be done to provide the quality and quantity of services for those who need them. It has been argued that nursing homes, in fact, should be mental health facilities. A more in-depth preparation of staff is necessary, and a wider range of mental health professionals must be utilized to meet these needs.

Family and community involvement can improve life for elders in a nursing home. Both resident-only counseling groups and resident/family counseling groups reduce anxiety and increase feelings of internal control for those in institutions. Family members who strive to keep family connections, offer optimism for recovery, and help the resident to maintain dignity can do much to uplift spirits. Family members tend to judge a nursing home not so much by its technical care as by its psychological care. The views of involved family members provide the staff with good feedback that hopefully can lead to improvements. Families of nursing home residents are often unfamiliar with ways to assist their relatives. Nursing homes that establish a "partnership" with families in sharing responsibilities for the nontechnical aspects of care enhance the psychological and emotional welfare of the resident as well as that of family.

Residents' Bill of Rights

The 1987 Nursing Home Reform Act required all nursing homes to post a "Residents' Bill of Rights." It gives patients the right to:

- Choose a personal physician and be informed in advance about treatment;
- Be free from physical or chemical restraints;
- Have privacy (though not a private room);
- Obtain prompt resolution of grievances concerning the behavior of other residents;
- Participate in social, religious, and community activities that do not violate the rights of other residents;
- Enjoy confidentiality of records;
- Receive needed services;
- Complain without reprisal;

- Examine the results of the most recent survey of the facility by government inspectors; and
- Have immediate access to a state or local long-term care ombusman.

The Omnibus Budget Reconciliation Act of 1987 (OBRA)

With the enactment of the **Omnibus Budget Reconciliation Act of 1987**, the nursing home industry became one of the most highly regulated environments for health care delivery in the United States. In addition to tightening survey and certification procedures, the act strengthened patients' rights when planning their care and making treatment decisions. Other requirements, such as written care plans, mandated nursing assistant training, and the employment of certified social workers, were designed to upgrade the quality of patient services and to insure their participation in planning their care.

OBRA also intensified requirements for survey teams making routine and unscheduled audits. As a result, many past procedures, such as placing patients in restraints without medical authorization or denying patients full disclosure of their medical records and diagnoses, and failing to assure patients of their rights may become grounds for censure or, ultimately, the closing of a facility by regulatory agencies. Although OBRA does not purport to correct all problems related to the quality of care, it represents a concerted effort to upgrade and enrich services to institutionalized elders.

Enforcement of the provisions of OBRA is generally left in the hands of State Health Departments that are generally woefully understaffed, which results in only occasional audits of nursing homes to ensure that OBRA mandates are being carried out. Although it is hoped that the enactment of OBRA has led to a higher quality of care for residents, empirical evidence does not confirm that those outcomes have been achieved.

Chapter Summary

Theoretically, there are many acceptable kinds of housing currently available to those who must relocate. Reality, however, does not keep pace with theory. Old people are often forced into housing that is inadequate or that needlessly increases their dependence.

Most prefer to live in their own homes where possible, but others enjoy the stimulation of living in retirement communities, shared housing arrangements, community care retirement centers, or similar living environments. For older adults with limited incomes, public housing or mobile homes may provide a practical alternative. Although the percentages are declining, many continue to live with relatives—usually a daughter or son and their families. Regardless of the type of living situation, most prefer to remain as independent as possible.

For those who decide to relocate (either voluntarily or involuntarily), problems may arise with respect to housing shortages, downsizing, decisions over whether to live in an integrated or segregated environment, or finding a community in which to live that is compatible with their lifestyles. Relocation is never a simple matter, although under optimal conditions it can enhance both the lifestyle and life satisfactions of those who elect to do so.

For a small percentage of older adults—those who are debilitated—the nursing home is often the only viable housing option. The lack of personalization often creates dependency and the loss of personal freedoms for the resident. OBRA legislation was enacted to increase the quality of life in nursing homes by providing for resident input and by offering a broader range of higher quality services.

Everyone needs a home. The older we get, the more important a safe harbor becomes. Home is not just a place to exist, but a place to be. More needs to be done to meet this most important psychological requirement. We all deserve to live out our lives in dignity, pride, and comfort.

Key Terms

adult community
adult day care
age-integrated housing
age-segregated housing
aging in place
amenity relocation
assisted living
board and care home
continuing care retirement communities (CCRCs)
downsizing
full-timing
granny units
life-care community (LCC)
living environment
mobile-home park
naturally occurring retirement communities (NORCs)
Omnibus Budget Reconciliation Act of 1987 (OBRA)
public housing
retirement city
snowbirds
sunbirds
surveillance zone

Questions for Discussion

1. Identify at least three reasons that adequate housing is important for older adults.
2. Think of your parents as older adults. In what type of housing environment would you like to see them live? Why? Imagine that you are 70 years of age. Where would you like to live? Why?
3. What are some of the issues associated with living in public housing? What steps would you take to increase the quality of public housing?
4. What are the disadvantages of living in a segregated community? Advantages?
5. What would you look for in selecting a nursing home for your father or mother? What alternatives, other than the nursing home, would you consider? Why?

Fieldwork Suggestions

1. Visit a senior center and interview at least three older adults. Ask each of them where they live, who lives with them, and how satisfied they feel about their housing. Do you find any themes in their responses? How consistent are the responses to material presented in this chapter?
2. Visit a public housing complex in your community. What are your first impressions? Talk to residents to find out how they feel about living there. Interview the director of housing with a focus of identifying the positives and negatives associated with that particular complex.
3. Visit a local nursing home. Using the guidelines from this chapter, list the major strengths and weaknesses with respect to how the environment promotes quality of life for residents.
4. Visit an assisted-care living complex. What is the living environment like? What is the apparent functional level of the people you observed? In what way does this environment differ from your observations of the nursing home environment?

Online Activities

1. Locate the home page for the American Association of Homes and Services for the Aging. What resources do they have that would give you information if your private nonprofit agency were interested in building an assisted-living complex for poor elders in your community?
2. Your parents live 500 miles away from you, their closest adult child. Your mother requires extensive caregiving, and your father is very weakened from a recent heart attack. You fear that his exhaustion in trying to care for your mother will kill him. You feel that the family needs to consider placing your mother in a nursing home. Use the Internet to search out the information you need to bring to a family gathering that is being held to discuss, "What will we do with Mom?"

11

Mental Health

The Psychology of Aging

Learning and Memory

Alzheimer's Disease

Caring for the Mentally Ill

Good Mental Health

OLD IS NEWS

Aging Outrageously

Jerry Carroll

Phyllis Diller is putting up a fight. "You want me to grimace," she tells the photographer. "I don't want to grimace. They don't make Roseanne grimace. I would like a nice picture for a change. I really would. I made up my mind. I want a nice, human picture, please. For a change."

But in the end, old trouper that she is, she gives in. The photographer gets that open-mouth a-ha-ha-HA look that goes with the laugh that sounds like too many years of whiskey and cigarettes.

That's her stage persona but not the real her. Diller, 79, has a big capital investment in her face and she's proud of the results. When she began her career as a comic at the Purple Onion in San Francisco in 1955, she was plain and gawky, a shy 37-year-old housewife from Alameda and mother of five.

Phyllis Diller said she wanted a nice portrait of herself but in the end she cracked up

Now, 42 years and 17 plastic surgeries later, she says she looks much better than when she was young. Decked out in chic black and white polka dots, Diller was promoting her upcoming nine-day tour of Northern California.

"I had a complete face-lift when I was 55. Nose job, eyes, the neck. Boom, that was the big difference. A lot of people start much younger, but I think it's a big mistake. You can stretch the skin only so far."

That ditzy character on stage, the one who makes fun of the husband, Fang, and cracks the mother-in-law jokes, is a far cry from the smart, sophisticated Diller you meet in private. The shyness is long gone ("I'm a corrected introvert"), replaced by a take-charge tartness.

"There's no such thing as a dumb comic. You might not like him and he might be a lousy comic, but he's still bright. A lot of them are geniuses. Joan Rivers is a Phi Beta Kappa. Comics see everything at a different slant. They see way beyond the surface of things and they see the different twists, the connections and the reasons and meanings, the what's-it-all-about-Alfie. And they analyze everything."

Husbands are in the act but not in real life. She was married twice, but both died. Same with the lawyer with whom she had a 10-year affair. Her current beau is an 89-year-old Wichita investor. "I guess I should get a boy toy."

Diller has made concessions to age.

She doesn't do as many dates as before and has knocked off tours to places like Australia. "I used to be much busier, insanely busy. I used to work 90 percent of the time. Every night. In the old days, it was two shows a night, which is really hard. I don't want to be that busy anymore.

"Hell, I'm gonna be 80 in July. I wanna watch the birds and the bees and the flowers. But I have a reduced staff now. My daughter Stephanie is it. She's responsible for making my home like I always wanted it. I had other people, but they wouldn't grow flowers. Everything is just perfect now."

Psychologists continue to unravel the effects of aging on the mind. The ultimate fate of an elderly person was once considered to be senility—whatever that meant. No one was surprised if Grandpa forgot where he put his glasses, that cousin Herman was coming to visit, or even that he was married. No one became too alarmed if old Mrs. Jones down the street saw angels in the sky or was hiding in a cave because she thought the world was going to end in six months. The reasoning went, "This is what happens when people get old—their minds go. At the very least, they become set in their ways, stubborn, and cranky." Nonconformist, bizarre behavior was tolerated and rationalized: "What can you expect at her age? Old age must take its course. What can you do but accept?" These ideas about old age still persist. Today, scientific evidence suggests that declining mental health is not a natural consequence of the aging process. The vast majority of people aged 65 and over is in good mental health. If they are not, specific causes other than the aging process itself usually can be pinpointed. This chapter will examine the psychology of aging and the most common mental health problems of older adults.

The Psychology of Aging

In this chapter, we will discuss areas traditionally covered in the behavioral aspect of the psychology of aging. These are changes with age in perception, motor performance, intelligence, learning, memory, and personality. Gerontological psychologists also study changes in the brain and central nervous system. Many psychologists have backgrounds in physiology, biology, physics, math, or some combination thereof. Others are more interested in personality characteristics and social behavior and, thus, may have social psychology backgrounds.

In the psychology of aging, one must distinguish between **age-related changes** and **biologically caused changes**. For example, a scientist may find a positive correlation between age and depression—the older the age group, the higher the incidence of depression. In this case, depression is an age-related phenomenon. Once this statistic is staring the scientist in the face, the scientist must interpret it. Can the scientist say that the biological aging process causes depression? Certainly not without further investigation. What would be some possible causes of the correlation? Are society's values the cause? Are there cumulative stresses that some persons resist in their younger years but to which they finally succumb in old age? How do events such as retirement, poor health, or the death of a spouse affect aging? There may be other possible causes for the correlation.

The important thing to remember is that some psychological states that initially appear to be caused by the biological aging process are, upon closer examination, really related to age, in which case the scientist must look further for the cause of the correlation. For example, studies of the incidence of depression in the United States show some surprising and contradictory results. Several studies found the highest rates of depression in young adults and elders, but not in middle-aged groups. In contrast, in three other studies the oldest group showed a lower rate of depression than all younger groups, when variables such as income, socioeconomic status, and gender were held constant (Lewinsohn et al., 1997). A social scientist must go beyond assumptions; preconceived notions should undergo objective testing.

Did You Know . . .
Lower limb strength is a predictor of performance on cognitive tests. Strength loss results from muscle atrophy, which is caused by a loss of fibers and, to a less extent, reduction in fiber size. Anstey & Williams (1997) report that muscle fiber reduction is caused by denervation and reinnervation of individual fibers caused by continuous loss of motor neurons in the spinal cord, which is part of the central nervous system. Age-related changes in the central nervous system are also associated with memory, reaction time, and cognition.

COGNITIVE PROCESSES

Cognition is what we think about a situation. It is our awareness of the world around us—how we absorb stimuli and information and how we make sense of it. Our perception of a cause is related to our behavior in various situations. Did you see the traffic accident? Did you hear the crash? Do you know who was at fault based on what you saw? What was your response? How quickly did you react? Cognitive processes involve the use of our senses, our arousal, attention, information processing, reaction time, and motor performance. Gerontologists want to know whether people see and hear situations differently based on their age: Does attention span or speed change? Is information processed in an altered or different way due to aging?

Psychologists have compared our brains to computers. Information enters our brain, is coded, and then is stored at various levels. If our brains are working efficiently, we can retrieve information when we need it. This section deals with cognitive functioning. First, the basic senses, sensory memory, and steps of information processing are described; second, studies of intelligence are reported; and, third, learning and longer-term memory are analyzed.

BASIC COGNITIVE FUNCTIONS

Information processing in the brain is a complicated matter. The loss of memory that many people assume will occur in later life seems to be more highly related to *individual differences* as well as the *context* in which human development occurs than with age itself (Luszcz et al., 1997; Lewinsohn et al., 1997). But memory loss does seem to occur. Some of the complex processes having to do with thinking, remembering, and making judgments (perceiving) are discussed in the next sections.

THE SENSES

Sensation is the process of taking information in through the senses. **The five senses** (vision, touch, hearing, smell, and taste), that relay environmental information to the brain generally lose acuity with age, therefore one set of pathways in which information is gathered for processing by the brain is modified as we age. Vast individual differences exist, however. Some very old people, however, experience no sensory declines. The social and psychological consequences of sensory declines can be enormous, and it is the old-old—those over age 75—who are more likely to experience noticeable declines than are the young-old, or those between 65 and 75 years of age.

Older persons vary in how they deal with sensory loss. Some persons can compensate for losses in one area by stressing enjoyment from another. For example, a person losing vision might choose to focus on an existing appreciation of symphony music. Compensation by habit and routine is probably even more frequent. Though adaptability may vary, most older people can compensate very well for minor sensory losses. For example, loss of visual acuity can be compensated for with corrective lenses, more light, less glare, and clearly printed reading material.

Those who care for the elderly could easily respond inappropriately to such sensory decline: Why fix a nice meal for one who cannot taste it, or why take a vision-impaired elder outside? Rather than encouraging withdrawal, sensory decline might challenge caretakers to find ways of enhancing life for those who have suffered losses. Perhaps the person might like spicy Mexican food, or stronger hugs, or a windy day, or a warm fire in the fireplace. Sensory decline may call for stronger responses on the part of the caretakers, rather than weaker ones.

SENSORY MEMORY

Each memory starts as a sensory stimulus. You can remember certain aspects of things you see and hear for only a fraction of a second. This initial short-term sensory experience is called a **sensory memory**. Sensory memory takes in large amounts of information so rapidly that most of it gets lost. Do you recall what is on a one-dollar bill or a dime? Could you draw the details? Much information that passes through sensory memory is never processed to a storage place in the brain because we cannot pay attention to everything hitting our senses. Although not as well studied as other memory phases, research indicates that the amount of visual information one can handle at a time seems to decline with age.

ATTENTION

Paying attention is an important part of information processing. **Selective attention** is focusing attention on the relevant information while inhibiting irrelevant information. If we pay attention to a stimulus, the experience moves from our sensory memory to be stored in our working memory. If we are distracted—unable to focus a specific stimuli among many—our ability to code the stimulus into memory is impaired. Compared to sensory memory, working memory can handle a very small amount of input. We vary in the capacity of information that can get to our working memory at any one point in time. Very old people have a reduced capacity to absorb stimuli into working memory and thus to maintain concentration over a long period of time.

Studies of **divided attention** (doing two things at once such as watching television and reading) show that when divided-attention tasks are easy, age differences are typically absent. But when the tasks become complicated, age differences emerge. Attention studies show that older people are more distractible and are less able to disregard the clutter of irrelevant information than are younger people. Age-related differences in vigilance also exist (Wolters & Prinsen, 1997). Older adults tend to have lower physiological arousal (Mutter & Goedert, 1997), which lowers their alertness. Vigilance does not appear to be age related unless the task is sustained over an extended period of time, when, beyond age 60, fatigue can result in notable performance loss.

PERCEPTION

The process of evaluating the sensory information carried to the brain is called **perception**. Individuals may perceive the same stimuli differently; further, the same person may react differently at different times. **Sensory threshold** is the minimum intensity of a stimulus that is required for a person to perceive it. Mood, activities, and personality may all influence perception.

Sensory decline affects perception significantly. If a person is unable to hear parts of a conversation, for example, the content of the conversation is more likely to be misunderstood. Perceptual differences among age groups are frequently reported, but research does not explain the reason. The differences may be caused by biological changes, or they may be age related. Social isolation also tends to affect perception; therefore, isolation, not aging per se, may cause perceptual changes.

Some skills become enhanced with age. Age can ripen and enchance the interpretation of music, compensating for reduced physical agility.

PSYCHOMOTOR SPEED

A person first experiences the environment through the five senses; second, a person perceives what is happening; and third, a person may react. A physical reaction to stimuli is called motor performance. Motor performance may be simple, that is, a reaction requiring very little decision making or skill. Pressing a button to turn on the television and turning off a light switch are simple motor skills. Some motor performance, such as dancing, riding a bike, playing tennis, or driving a car is more complex.

Very old drivers, for example, may be affected by changes in vision and hearing. Their vision does not adapt as rapidly to dark, and they are more affected by glare. Additionally, older people take longer to read road signs. The processing of information is slower from the point of sensation (seeing the sign) to the perception (its meaning registers, and action is taken). Researchers suggest designing cars with older adults in mind: headlights with less glare, well-lit instrument panels, easy entry, and so on. They recommend large letters on signs with pictures if possible. Training programs for those with sensory declines are also advised.

Though it is common belief that older drivers are hazardous on the road, older drivers have far fewer accidents than do younger drivers. This is due in part because older people seem to exercise greater caution (reduced speed and greater conscious awareness given to the task), drive fewer miles, and drive at less hazardous times than do younger people.

One aspect of motor performance is reaction time—the length of time between the stimulus and the response, directly related to psychomotor speed. Studies show that reaction time increases with age, at about age 26 for some tasks and not until the seventies for other tasks. The general slowing of behavior with age is one of the

TABLE 11.1

Variables hypothesized to be related to slowing of information processing in old age

Genetic-biological factors	· Changes in sensation acuity
	· Changes in physiological arousal to stimuli
	· Changes in attention
	· Changes in motor capacity (stiffness; reduced strength)
	· Lower levels of physical activity
	· Changes in blood flow to the brain leading to neural malnutrition
	· Changes in the central nervous system
	· Changes in cortical levels of the brain
	· Gradual loss in brain mass
	· Neural/metabolic changes
	· Decline in physical health
Cultural-social factors	· Changes in self-esteem and self-confidence
	· Lower levels of mental activity
	· Lessened familiarity and experience with the task
	· Lifestyle characteristics, such as divorce, lack of travel, lack of stimulating environment

most reliable and well-documented age-related changes. This includes slowed **psychomotor speed** and the resultant lengthened reaction time. The more complex the task, the greater the difference in reaction time by age, generally speaking. However, individuals can differ substantially; for example, an individual 70-year-old might respond more quickly than a 30-year-old.

A noted researcher in the field of cognition has introduced two terms to categorize the variables affecting cognition:

1. **Cognitive mechanics**—the hardware of the mind—reflect the neurophysiological architecture of the brain. It involves the speed and accuracy of elementary processing of sensory information.
2. **Cognitive pragmatics**—the software of the mind—reflects the knowledge and information of one's culture. It involves reading, writing, education, professional skills, and life experiences that help us master or cope with life (Baltes, 1993).

The first term represents the genetic–biological influence and the second represents the cultural–social influence. Table 11.1 itemizes the biological factors, biological mechanics separately from the cultural–social, pragmatic, factors associated with he slowing of information processing in old age. The cultural–social factors tend to be more reversible than the genetic–biological ones.

Many of the variables in Table 11.1 do not accompany universal aging. Physical pathologies (e.g., high blood pressure) do not go hand-in-hand with aging. Neither does reduced activity. Aerobic exercise and other forms of physical activity have been shown to increase blood flow and increase speed of reaction. Activities such as tennis and dancing are helpful. Physically fit older people have shorter reaction times than less fit young adults (Foley & Mitchell, 1997). Practice at a task can compensate for slowness. Many a grandchild has been amazed, for example, at the speed with which a grandparent can peel a potato or whittle a wooden object.

The slower reactions of older people apparently has more to do with changes in the mental processes of interpretation and decision rather than at the initial level of sensory input (Thomas, 1992). In other words, the course of slowing has a lot to do with the brain and central nervous system (CNS). Vast individual differences exist, and not every older individual experiences a slowdown in reaction. It is a pattern of aging that has many exceptions.

The implications of CNS slowing for the everyday life of the older person are various. Experience and familiarity are great levelers—giving the older person an edge on the job or at various tasks at home. Very old people may need more time to get a job done, and they may need to be more cautious to avoid accidents. A speedy reaction is needed to avoid falling objects, to drive a car safely, to escape a fire, to get across a busy street, or to play a good game of ball. Many older adults would benefit from education or retraining to minimize the consequences of reduced cognitive efficiency. Environmental modifications may be in order—for example, stronger lighting, brighter colors, grab bars, hand railings, door handles as opposed to knobs, louder telephone rings, larger sturdier step stools. And people should not be so ready to assume that if an individual cannot think quickly, he or she cannot think well. That is a form of ageism.

INTELLIGENCE

As we compare the learning abilities of babies, elementary students, college students, or people in general, we find that within each group, some people are better able to learn than others. **Intelligence** was conceptualized by Guilford (1966) in three dimensions: *content* (figures, symbols, words); *operations* (memorizing, evaluating, coming up with solutions); and *products from the operations* (relationships, systems, implications). The dimensions are measured by various tests to determine an individual's "intelligence."

Although tests have been devised to measure one's intelligence quotient (IQ), the validity of such tests has been debated for years. They have been variously criticized for being ethnocentric (biased toward the major culture), sexist (biased toward boys/men), and ageist (inadequate measures of applied knowledge) (Cunningham et al., 1998). The jury is still out, even as tests become more clearly defined for diverse populations. Two major questions about IQ tests arise: (1) Is there any such thing as intelligence? and (2) Do IQ tests really measure intelligence?

The tests actually measure a number of specific intellectual abilities. Twenty-five **primary mental abilities** have been established, composed of five primary and independent abilities: number, word fluency, verbal meaning, reasoning, and space. Tests of six or so secondary mental abilities—skills composed of several primary abilities—have also been identified. Most research focuses on two secondary mutual abilities: fluid and crystallized intelligence (Schaie & Willis, 1996).

Intelligence Tests

Intelligence is most often measured by a standardized test with many multiple-choice items on vocabulary, reasoning, and the ordering of numbers and spaces. Using such a test represents the **psychometric approach** in contrast to other tests that examine thought processes—the quality and depth of thinking and the ability to solve complex problems (the **cognitive process approach**).

The most widely used psychometric test of intelligence for older adults is the Wechsler Adult Intelligence Scale (WAIS), developed in the 1950s. This test compensates for increasing age. The test norms assume declining speed with age; an older adult can perform worse than a younger adult and still have the same IQ! Critics point to the fact that this test emphasizes skills learned in school and not skills of everyday life. For this reason, all things being equal, the test favors the younger adult. This test has been revised (WAIS-R) and is used widely in clinical settings; however, its accuracy is still hotly debated.

Another IQ test, the Primary Mental Abilities Test (PMA) has often been used to examine adult intellectual development. The WAIS test measures a "verbal intelligence" aspect that involves comprehension, arithmetic, similarities, vocabulary, and the ability to recall digits; and a "performance intelligence" aspect that involves completion, block design, and assembly of objects. On the performance scale, speed is important. Bonus points are awarded for rapid solutions.

Crystallized and Fluid Intelligence

Both the WAIS-R and the PMA include tasks that evaluate fluid and crystallized intelligence. **Crystallized intelligence** is a measure of knowledge you have acquired through experience and education. Vocabulary tests are a clear example. **Fluid intelligence** refers to innate ability—the information-processing skills described in the previous section. Each of these types of intelligence taps a cluster of primary abilities. No standardization test measures one alone, although a given test can emphasize either crystallized or fluid intelligence (Kaufman & Horn, 1996).

We once assumed that a decline in intelligence with age was to be expected. Scientists now question this assumption. Longitudinal studies have found that some IQ components such as verbal skills remain stable with time and some can even increase with age. Schaie (1996) reported that virtually no individuals show deterioration on all mental abilities, even in their eighties. At age 60, 75 percent of subjects maintained their level of functioning on at least 80 percent of the mental abilities tested (as compared to seven years prior). More than 50 percent of those aged 80 had maintained 80 percent of their mental abilities over the seven-year period.

Fluid intelligence does appear to decline some with age, whereas crystallized intelligence does not. Similarly, the verbal scores of the WAIS show no declines with age, whereas the performance scores do decline with age. The high verbal score and declining performance score of older adults is so consistently found that it is called the **classic aging pattern** (Thomas, 1992). The drop in fluid intelligence indicates a decline in the ability to process information and complete tasks in an efficient manner, and might reflect the complexity of age-related changes in functions such as sensory and perceptual skills, or something as simple as lack of practice or fear of tests. More than likely, changes reflect a combination of both: neuropsychological shifts with age, plus the context of the individual's life.

Age and Intelligence

To understand fully what happens to intelligence with age, we need to know exactly what primary mental abilities decline with age and why. We need to know at what age any onset of decline happens and what is the rate of that decline. We need to know whether such changes are inevitable and whether they can be reversed. And we need to account for individual differences. Schaie (1996) found that it is not until people reach their seventies that declines in intelligence take on significance, and then speed of response is the major decline. Perceptual speed may be the most age-sensitive mental ability. Older people are as proficient as ever when it comes to situations that demand past experience or knowledge—given that they have enough time.

Though cross-sectional, "one-shot" studies of different age groups often find that older people have lower IQs than younger people, such studies may not acknowledge that young adults may have benefited from upper-level schooling. Many of the elderly studied in the 1950s and 1960s had not attended either high school or college. Some had had no formal schooling at all. Thus, cross-sectional studies that infer a decline in IQ with age are suspect. Test makers should distinguish between actual IQ (the quotient the test actually measures) and potential IQ for the young as well as for the old.

Intelligence tests must be used with caution. IQ tests measure specific skills to generalize about an all-inclusive concept of intelligence. Their results may be biased, and scientists must continue to investigate why, how, and in what direction such instruments are biased. The evidence today supports the finding of little decline with age in skills that one acquires through education, enculturation, and personal experience. We do not really know what happens to IQ as one approaches extreme old age, say after age 85. Although researchers believe that IQ begins to decline at some point in very old age, they have yet to determine the typical course it follows.

An example of problems with cross-sectional IQ studies: The new generation of elementary and secondary students today are not performing as well on standardized tests in their general education as their predecessors. If this translates into lower scores on IQ tests, then it will appear that IQ *increases* with age because older generations today do better at test taking. To avoid the problems in cross-sectional research, longitudinal studies are essential.

A few words of caution, however, about longitudinal studies: Sample size is generally small. The repeat presentation of material, which brings about improved performance, can produce a learning effect. In other words, people generally get better at tasks repeated several times. That does not mean their IQs have necessarily increased. Additionally, the people from whom the final measures are obtained are survivors: They are more robust and healthy than were those who died over the duration of the study. In one major study on intelligence and aging, only one-sixth of the sample was still living after seven years (Savage et al., 1973). One must be aware of the research methodology employed and recognize that any one study is bound to have some inadequacies in addressing issues of age-related changes.

A new area of intelligence study is practical problem solving. The Everyday Problem Solving Inventory (Denney & Palmer, 1987) has been used to measure the ability to solve problems such as a grease fire breaking out on top of the stove. When the problems are familiar to older people, they do very well on these tests, although not necessarily better than middle-aged adults. Many gerontologists and psychologists believe that tests measuring decision making in real-life situations are more accurate measures of the intelligence quotient in adulthood.

Further research is needed to clarify the relationship between age and intelligence. A theory of terminal decline or "**terminal drop**" has been proposed by a number of gerontologists (Kleemeier, 1962; White & Cunningham, 1988). According to this phenomenon, a precipitous decrease in cognitive functioning is related to the individual's distance from death rather than to chronological age. "Critical loss" in cognitive functioning is supposedly experienced up to two years before death. The theory is controversial and has not been fully substantiated by research.

Learning and Memory

Learning and memory, important components of mental functioning, are separate yet interrelated processes. When an individual can retrieve information from his or her memory storage, learning is assumed to have occurred; alternatively, if someone cannot remember, it is assumed that learning has not adequately taken place.

LEARNING

Learning is the process of acquiring knowledge or understanding. For purposes of psychological research, scientists speak of learning in terms of cognitive processes, which are intellectual or mental. As in studies of intelligence quotients, learning is measured by tests of performance, particularly verbal and psychomotor performance. Again, the same sort of question surfaces: Do such tests really reflect learning?

Let us consider two general questions related to age: Do learning skills change with age, and how do older people's skills compare with younger people's? The answers to these questions depend on the skills being learned and the conditions under which they are being learned. Up until 1960, and even later, members of the scientific community generally assumed that learning declined with age.

Many factors affect learning abilities. *Pacing* (the rate and speed required for learning) is an important factor. Older adults learn better with a slower pace; and they perform best with self-pacing. They also do better with a lengthened time to respond. Another factor is *anxiety*. Some studies suggest that older adults are more uncomfortable with the testing situation and therefore experience increased anxiety. The *meaningfulness* of the material makes a difference, too. Older people do better when nonsensical or abstract syllables and words are replaced with actual, concrete words. They tend to be more interested if the material makes sense to them. Further, they are more susceptible to *distraction*. *Motivation* and *physical health* are contributing factors as well. Here again the factors in Table 11.1 may inhibit learning. The finding that younger adults are better learners than older adults should be viewed cautiously. Under certain conditions, older people can learn as well as or better than younger people.

MEMORY

Memory varies enormously among individuals of all ages (interindividual differences), and types of memory vary greatly in the same person (intraindividual differences). There appears to be a very slight and progressive deterioration in memory efficiency as people grow older, however the extent of this deterioration remains controversial.

Four types of memory have been identified by researchers. They are diagrammed in Figure 11.1 and are as follows:

FIGURE 11.1

Levels of memory

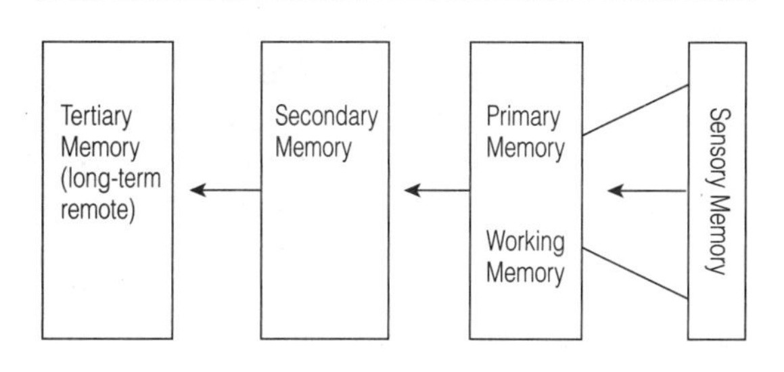

1. *Sensory memory*. Sensory memory is the initial level at which all sensory information is registered but not stored. It is fleeting, lasting less than a second, unless deliberate attention is paid to the information and it is transferred to primary memory (see previous section on Basic Cognitive Functions). Countless numbers of stimuli bombard us every fraction of a second in our waking hours.
2. *Primary and working memory*. Primary memory is our current consciousness. We have only a small capacity to deal with what is being paid attention to at the moment. It may be forgotten rather quickly—for example, a phone number or joke; or it may be transformed for longer storage. The processing of our current sensate information is our working memory.
3. *Secondary memory*. Secondary memory, once called recent memory, refers to remembering the details of everyday life—friends' telephone messages, directions to the new shopping mall, the movie you saw last week, what you studied for the exam, what you need to do at work, and so on. It is the major basis for the research on memory. Hundreds and hundreds of studies are reported in this area.
4. *Tertiary memory*. Tertiary memory is long-term memory, sometimes called remote memory. It is the stored facts and words, learned years ago—the past life experiences such as weddings, births, deaths, and episodes from childhood. Tertiary memory is studied much less often than secondary memory.

The findings on sensory memory have been described earlier in this chapter. The findings on the other levels of memory follow.

PRIMARY MEMORY AND WORKING MEMORY

Primary memory shows little change with age. Once information is stored in primary memory, people of all ages seem equal in being able to recall it. But age differences are found in **working memory**, or the processing of sensory stimuli to give it meaning and get it transferred to longer-term storage. If information does not get to storage, it cannot be recalled. Two examples of using working memory are (1) remembering a phone number given to you orally long enough to dial the number a few seconds later, or (2) unscrambling letters of a word in your head. Some researchers believe that working memory is vital to understanding declines in the cognitive functioning of older adults (Bechara et al., 1998). Neuropsychologists generally believe that a major portion of age-related decline is due to decreased speed of working memory to process information. Research on working memory is relatively new but holds great promise in solving some of the mysteries of the mind.

Secondary Memory

Research indicates that **secondary memory** is another major source of age-related decline. Younger adults are superior on tests of secondary memory, which is the major memory function in everyday life. The processing involved is deeper than primary memory, enabling recall to take place over a longer period of time. If the processing is too shallow, a person will not be able to recall the information a year, month, or even a day later.

Numerous kinds of memory tasks have been developed to study secondary memory. For example, in "free recall," people are given 20 words and asked to recall as many as they can in any order they wish. The results from hundreds of studies are that younger people do better on this task. There is great variation with the type of task and pace involved. In tests of "recognition," people are given a list of 20 words to look at, and then given a list with those 20 words plus 40 new words. They are then asked which are old and which are new. Older people do as well as but not better than young people on this test. On some memory tests, such as those that require the subject to recall facts out of context, older persons do worse than middle-aged persons.

Starting somewhere in middle age, many persons suffer from "tip-of-the-tongue"(TOT) syndrome, which places them on the verge of recalling a name, date, or event and unable to do it. Later, when they are not trying to remember, they will recall the information. Older adults experience more TOTs, and come up with more blockers (related words) during the TOT than do younger adults (Brown & Nix, 1996). In old age, interference hinders secondary memory. For example, if a neighbor rings the doorbell while an older person is reading the paper, he or she may forget what was just read. Studies suggest that eliminating distractions could optimize short-term memory for the older person. Still some older people have excellent memories.

Older people do not usually have to engage in free recall because they have external cues, such as date books or notes of reminders on the refrigerator. A psychometric test situation may not have "ecological validity" in a real-life setting. A good deal of recent research focuses on natural memory, which includes studies of autobiographical memory. Most people believe they can remember where they were on the day of a particular, historic event, such as the start of the Gulf War, or the destruction of the Challenger. These searing historical moments are called "flashbulb memories," but they seem to be no more accurate three months later than any other memories (Small, 1995). Instead, "flashbulb" memories serve as "benchmarks in our lives that connect personal histories to cultural history" (*Science News*, quoted in Small, 1995).

Did You Know . . .
It is possible, according to sleep scientists, that we sleep in order to organize efficient cortical representations of experience. Information acquired during the day is compared

with older memories, and both new and old memory become somewhat modified in the process.

SEJNOWSKY, 1995

Tertiary Memory

Information is stored for years in tertiary, or long-term, memory. The study of this memory has some problems. For instance, if the person constantly recalls the old days, say, going to college, is it still tertiary memory compared with someone who has not thought about his or her college days for years? Some people may retrieve certain events of the past often, whereas others never do. Another problem is to know the accuracy of long-term memories. Researchers often have no way to validate the memories.

One method of study is to ask people of all ages about a historic event—such as a major earthquake, or a popular television show. Typically, no age differences exist in these studies. Some autobiographical information can be verified, like naming high-school classmates, for example. Again, no age differences appear in tertiary memory. What does appear to change with age is perceptual speed, or the speed at which long-term memories are processed and retrieved. When perceptual speed was controlled in one major memory study, all age-related differences in the working memory span were eliminated between young adults and older adults (Fisk & Warr, 1996). The speed of retrieval, not memory itself, is the difference.

Exercising the mind is important. Learning and recalling what is learned (in other words, keeping the mind active and stimulated) is a good way to preserve memory. Learning and memory are related; memory is the ability to retain what is learned. The more one learns, as a general rule, the more one can remember. Reading books, talking to friends, and seeking new activities are fun ways to exercise the mind at any age. People adapt differently to recent memory loss. Some might compensate very well by carrying a notepad to jog the memory—keeping a written record of phone numbers, plans, and appointments. Another person might give in and permit what he or she perceives as "senility" to become a self-fulfilling prophecy. As is so often the case, positive attitudes and self-evaluations can lead to constructive, corrective actions.

Part of the mind/spirit's effect on healthy aging is direct and conscious. The extent to which we regard ourselves, take care of ourselves, determines whether we eat right, get enough sleep, smoke, wear seat belts, exercise, and so on. Each of these choices is conscious decisions of the mind, and control probably 90 percent of the factors that determine our health.

WILLIAM SCHOTANUS, 1997

Memory retrieval skills may decline with age if they are not used. If used, memory will be maintained or even improved throughout one's lifetime. Memory expert Tony Busan (1991) advocates the use of mnemonics, that is, memory techniques to improve memory. One technique is to use a vivid imagination, calling forth wild, colorful, and exaggerated images, even sexual ones, and associating them with important dates or items on a shopping list. A second technique is to use a linking system with a special list of key words to which all other items are linked.

Many studies of memory view the person as a machine that senses, acquires, processes, stores, and retrieves information. Using this image, older adults generally show a pattern of decline in the speed and efficiency with which they can process, store, and recall information. Movement from one "task center" to the next requires a complex set of psychoneurological communications. Error at any one of the points will create disruption in the remaining processing points. So, for example, if a person misinterprets the initial sensory information, it is moved to short-term memory (acquired), processed, stored in long-term memory, and ultimately retrieved inaccurately. Likewise, error might be introduced at any point along the way in the process.

If, however, the image of cleanly-oiled machine is substituted to an image that excludes speed and includes philosophy of life and the ability to integrate a lifetime of experiences, the older person makes gains with age. There may be a trade-off—losing some details but gaining the broader outlook. This has been referred to as the race between the bit and the bite, with older adults giving up the bit for the bite. We have only just begun to explore the potential of the aging mind.

PYSCHOPATHOLOGY AND THE MYTH OF SENILITY

Psychopathology is the study of psychological disease or, in other words, of mental disorders. Some mental disorders have a physical cause; others seem to be entirely emotional in nature. In still others, the physical and emotional aspects seem intertwined. A specific diagnosis, though difficult, is critical in the treatment of patients at any age.

Unfortunately, the term **senility** has been used as a catchall term for any mental disorder of the elderly. Any symptoms of confusion, anxiety, memory loss, or disorientation readily receive this label, and the labeling is done by people of all ages, including elders. Senility, however, is not an inevitable consequence of growing old. The word masks both the possibility of multiple causes of certain mental disorders and the fact that treatment for them may be available. In some cases, for example, persons diagnosed as senile actually suffer from thyroid deficiency. Thyroid hormone treatment eliminates the "senility." In other cases, the "senile" patient may be suffering from anorexia or emotional problems that antidepressant medication can alleviate.

It is particularly problematic when doctors and other health care professionals accept the myth that the elderly become senile as a result of the aging process. This erroneous belief forms the basis for ignoring an older person's complaints, rather than attempting to diagnose the problem thoroughly. This tendency is not from disregard for the older person's well-being; medical professionals are generally inadequately trained in geriatrics. In reality, the symptoms of "senility" have many causes. Older patients can show confusion and disorientation as a result of infection, pneumonia, heart failure, heart attack, electrolyte imbalance, anemia, malnutrition, or dehydration—to name only a few causes. Older people more often have cognitive contraindications to drugs than do their younger counterparts, and they are more likely to be taking a multiplicity of drugs, including such "benign" over-the-counter drugs as decongestants. Depression may also be a reason for **pseudosenility**. Most mental illnesses can be more precisely described—and thereby treated—than the label "senile" suggests.

FUNCTIONAL DISORDERS

A reference book by the American Psychiatric Association (1994), designed to improve the diagnosis of psychiatric disorders, is the *Diagnostic and Statistical Manual of Mental Disorders* (4th ed.), called *DSM-IV* for short. Psychologists use the term **functional disorder** to denote emotional problems of psychological, rather than physical, origin that interfere with daily functioning. Such disorders are more serious than the emotional problems (such as those based on widowhood or other loss) previously described. To differentiate among functional disorders, psychologists use the following terms: *anxiety disorders, depressive disorders, personality disorders, affective disorders,* and *schizophrenia.*

ANXIETY DISORDERS

Anxiety is a cluster of feelings of uneasiness, nervousness, tension, or dreading the future. Trait anxiety is related to the individual's personality, and state anxiety is more related to a transitory situation. Persons with **anxiety disorders** tend to be anxious, rigid, or insecure personality types. There seem to be no age differences in either trait or state anxiety, as measured by psychological tests. Anxiety disorder, which is a clinically significant form of neurotic anxiety, is quite low for elderly people (Kausler & Kausler, 1996). Among those elders with this disorder, however, it can be debilitating—especially when it is undiagnosed and assumed to be the result of aging.

Did You Know . . .
Problem-solving deficits *(the ability to formulate and execute a plan) are significantly related to depression and anxiety among older people. This contrasts with unselected populations, for whom* problem orientation *is more important for psychological well-being than problem-solving skills.*

KANT AND ASSOCIATES, 1997

Generalized Anxiety Disorder

When a person becomes so anxious that fear and dread of things or events begin to impair his or her ability to function, a **generalized anxiety disorder** is present, exaggerating any real danger. An older person may fear being robbed or mugged. Consequently, he or she may not leave home; the person may get dozens of locks and constantly check them. Psychotherapeutic intervention would help this person face the threat—if actual—rationally and realistically.

Obsessive-Compulsive Disorder

A person obsessed with one act, such as washing hands, walking back and forth across a room, looking for something, or touching something, exhibits **obsessive-compulsive disorder**. Persons who continually wash their hands may think they are dirty when they are not. The "dirt" may be internal—for example, repressed feelings of guilt that need to be resolved.

Phobia

A **phobia** is a fear that displaces fears that a person cannot face. Claustrophobia, the fear of being closed in, may, for example, mask a more potent fear, such as fear of death. Numerous kinds of phobias can manifest numerous fears, and left untreated, phobias can be especially limiting for an individual whose life circumstances include other limits, such as physical frailty or impaired vision. Social phobias, characterized by the fear and avoidance of situations where an individual is subject to the scrutiny of others, have been shown to be more than 10-fold higher among first-degree relatives, implying a biological basis (Stein et al., 1998). A clear understanding of the relationship of biology with all phobias still eludes psychologists.

DEPRESSIVE DISORDERS

Many people of all ages are depressed at times. A depressed person feels sad, has low self-esteem, is lethargic, and believes that life is confusing, hopeless, or bereft of meaning. Physical symptoms of **depressive disorders** may be insomnia or difficulty in sleeping, loss of appetite, or the inability to concentrate. Depression can be triggered by the death of family members, the loss of memory, or other disappointments accumulated over time. The person may or may not have had bouts of depression throughout his or her life. Most people over 65 who suffer from depression are not receiving any formal psychiatric treatment.

It is a common belief that older adults suffer from depression more than do younger adults. This belief, much like the belief that memory loss is a function of aging, is a myth. Early studies indicated that as much as 65 percent of the older population suffered from depression. It is now recognized that the tests used to obtain those scores were not valid for an older population. For example, emotional symptoms ("I feel sad") were included with physical symptoms ("I have difficulty sleeping"). Among younger adults, a strong relationship exists between feelings of sadness and lack of sleep. Among older adults, it is now recognized, this relationship does not exist *necessarily*. More recent studies reveal that roughly 15 to 20 percent of older people suffer from mild (but noticeable) depression, and only 1 to 2 percent are clinically (severely) depressed (Kausler & Kausler, 1996). The incidence of clinical depression among older people (1 to 2 percent) is actually lower than among younger adults, at 4 percent (Richardson & Hammond, 1996; Kant et al., 1997).

Depression can be treated, but first it has to be recognized. More mild forms often spontaneously disappear, but more severe (clinical) depression requires treatment. Treatment for older adults variously includes psychotherapy, especially cognitive therapy; chemical antidepressants—which can be problematic if the individual is taking any other medications; the administration of electroconvulsive therapy (ECT); or a combination of these treatments (Kausler & Kausler, 1996).

"'Don't say bleed,' says the Hypochondriac's First Aid Book, 'say hemorrhage.' This tongue-in-cheek advice sums up much of the hypochondriac's problem: it isn't that he or she imagines symptoms that don't exist; it's that they greatly overestimate the seriousness of those that do."

TRISHA GREENHALGH, 1997

Hypochondria

A hypochondriac is someone who is overly concerned about his or her health. The person generally has bodily complaints for which no physical cause exists. He or she may be depressed, fear physical deterioration, need attention, or be otherwise expressing emotional issues through a series of somatic (body-oriented) complaints. Although the complaints may be real, the appropriate treatment involves dealing with the underlying emotional problem.

PERSONALITY DISORDERS

We age into the people we have been through our life course. **Personality disorders** are not characteristics of older people, but are characteristic of a group of people, *some of whom have aged into late adulthood.* This distinction becomes important when treatments are considered: A psychotherapeutic treatment plan for a young adult is not any more appropriate for an older adult than it is for a child.

Personality disorders are believed to occur in approximately 10 percent of the adult population, yet they are seldom diagnosed in primary care settings (Hueston et al., 1996). People who have developed extremely rigid styles of coping that make adaptive behavior difficult or impossible fall into the category of having personality disorders. People with personality disorders typically have held long-standing, maladaptive, and inflexible ways of relating to stress and the environment throughout adulthood. We can describe a number of personality types that lend themselves to disorders.

The *paranoid* personality is extremely suspicious and mistrustful, preoccupied with being alert to danger. A person with this personality tends to be stubborn, hostile, and defensive.

The *introverted* personality tends to be a solitary person who lacks the capacity for warm, close social relationships. Situations that call for high levels of social contact are especially stressful for the introverted individual.

The *antisocial* personality is characterized by a basically unsocialized behavior pattern that may conflict with society. Such people have difficulty with social situations that require cooperation and self-sacrifice.

These personality types and others involve behavior from childhood or adolescence that has become fixed and inflexible; for each, certain situations cause stress and unhappiness.

AFFECTIVE DISORDERS

Affective disorders are sometimes called "mood disorders" because depression and mood swings are typical. *DSM-IV* uses the term *bipolar disorder* to describe behavior that includes both a depressed phase, of sadness and slowed activity, and a manic phase, characterized by high levels of excitement and activity. An individual generally first manifests this type of disorder in his or her twenties and thirties. *Depression*, without the manic phase, is more common. Depression is most severe as an affective disorder; as an anxiety disorder, it is moderate. Some event—a great disappointment, for example—sets it off. For the older person, depression might follow the loss of a spouse or the onset of a terminal illness. In nonclinical depression, feelings of melancholy are normally appropriate for the situation; normally, the feelings will eventually wane. An inappropriate duration of depression and intense, continued sadness mark clinical depression.

SCHIZOPHRENIA

Schizophrenia, another category of functional disorder, is more complicated, severe, and incapacitating than any of the disorders previously described. It may affect up to 1 percent of the general population (American Psychiatric Association, 1997). Typically suffering serious disturbances in thinking and behavior, schizophrenics are often unable to communicate coherently with others. Their language seems to be a means of self-expression rather than communication, and their talk is filled with irrelevancies. Feelings have no relation to verbal expression: fearful topics may be discussed with smiles; a bland topic may incite rage. Schizophrenia is characterized by an impaired contact with reality, at least during the disorder's active phases, and it often takes the form of hallucinations or delusions.

Late-life onset of schizophrenia is fairly rare; typically, the sufferer has evidenced the disorder in earlier years. Surprisingly little is known about the treatment needs of patients who remain symptomatic and functionally compromised in late life, despite the debilitating effects of the illness (Bartels, 1997). Older people with schizophrenia often develop cognitive impairment that seems similar to, but less severe than, Alzheimer's disease (Davidson et al., 1995). Postmortem studies of tissue from patients who were chronically hospitalized with schizophrenia, however, show notably little neuro-degeneration or other pathology to explain the impairment (Arnold & Trojanowski, 1996). We apparently are not yet close to understanding the path of this devastating form of mental illness in late life.

ORGANIC MENTAL DISORDERS

Organic disorders arise from a physical origin that impairs mental functioning. About 11 percent of older adults are believed to have mild disorders of this type (Vasavada et al., 1997), and geriatricians estimate that 6 percent of Americans over 65 have severe intellectual impairment based on physical causes. This rises to 20 percent for those over age 80 (Cohen, 1990), with some estimates as high as 50 percent.

The difficulty in assessing dementia prevalence is partially due to the many different paths of brain disorder, including reversible and irreversible dementias with a multiplicity of causes and symptom clusters (Bowen et al., 1997). The diagnosis of dementia overlaps with a recently described mild cognitive impairment CIND, or "cognitive impairment, no dementia," which previously was believed to be a mild, initial form of dementia (Graham et al., 1997). **Dementia**, defined by geriatrician Bruce Robinson (1997) is

> *...an acquired syndrome of progressive deterioration in global intellectual ability that interferes with the individual's ability to function in social and occupational roles.* ***Global deterioration*** *is...impairment in memory and at least one other cognitive category [such as language or visual/spatial ability] (p. 30).*

An acute organic brain disorder is short-term and reversible. An infection, heart condition, drug reaction, liver condition, or malnutrition may cause an acute disorder. Anything that interferes with the nourishment of the brain—the supply of oxygen or food by the bloodstream—can produce an acute disorder. If not treated promptly, it may become chronic.

Chronic organic disorders are brain disorders with a physical cause for which no cure is known. Thus, such disorders characterize an irreversible, chronic, and progressive deterioration of the brain. One should not assume, however, that

The ethical issues of the potential for a sitting President to become a victim of Alzheimer's disease engaged a nation when former President Ronald Reagan's Alzheimer's disease was made public.

these disorders go hand in hand with old age; they do not. Organic brain disease is so debilitating for the minority who suffer it that we should direct our efforts to finding cures, rather than merely fostering acceptance. Of those with chronic brain disorders, 50 to 60 percent are living at home rather than in institutions and are being cared for by relatives and neighbors. More geriatric services would be helpful to all concerned.

The two manifestations of organic brain disorders are delirium and dementia, which are general terms for two syndromes or symptoms of organic brain disorders. Delirium is characterized by a lack of awareness about oneself and the surroundings, hallucinations, delusions, and disorientation. Caused by the atrophy and degeneration of brain cells, dementia was once labeled as senility and was thought to accompany normal aging. Now no longer recognized as "normal," symptoms of dementia can result from many disorders. However, causes for many types of the disorder still remain a mystery. More than 10 forms of dementia have been identified—for example, years of alcohol abuse can lead to dementia. However, the largest contributor by far is Alzheimer's disease.

In the early stages of dementia, emotional responses to ordinary daily affairs, previously handled without difficulty, may be extreme to inappropriate. Memory, judgment, social functioning, and emotional control are impaired. Problems become more difficult to solve, and decisions become harder to make. One may lose interest in life and become apathetic or irritable. Further declines come as one has trouble receiving, retaining, and recalling new information. A newly acquired fact may be forgotten in minutes: a person may forget, for example, what he or she saw on a television program minutes after the program ends. As time passes, progressive disorganization of personality follows, accompanied by disorientation with respect to time, situation, and place. Some patients can no longer recognize even family, friends, and neighbors.

Did You Know . . .
Alzheimer's disease is a major public health concern. It was added to the list of leading causes of death in the United States beginning with mortality data for 1994.

Alzheimer's Disease

The most common form of chronic organic brain disease, accounting for 70 percent of all such disease, is **Alzheimer's disease.** It is estimated to affect four million middle-aged and older persons in the United States. The standardization of diagnostic criteria has helped make estimates of the prevalence of this disease; however, estimates continue to vary widely, from 3% to 11% of those 65 years and older (Hoyert & Rosenberg, 1997).

In 1995, the disease was named on 41,419 death certificates for people of all ages, and

40,836 of those were people 65 years old and older. In 1995, Alzheimer's disease was the fourteenth leading cause of death for all ages combined, and ninth for people ages 65 and older (Hoyert & Rosenberg, 1997). The risk of developing Alzheimer's disease during one's lifetime depends on disease incidence and on life expectancy. The *incidence* of Alzheimer's disease (number of people who contract the disease) does not appear to be increasing. Its *prevalence*, however, (proportion of people in a population) has increased because it is more commonly developed in later life, and more elders are living into late life. It seems to be more common among women than among men.

The Framingham Study estimated the lifetime risk of developing Alzheimer's disease and dementia based on their longitudinal population studies. For a 65-year-old woman, the lifetime risk was calculated to be 12 percent; for a man the same age, the risk was 6.3 percent. The cumulative risk was much higher from age 65 to 100, at 25.5 percent in men and 28.1 percent in women (Seshadri et al., 1997).

Named after the German physician Alois Alzheimer, who, in 1902, diagnosed the condition in a 51-year-old woman, the disease was thought to be rare and was relatively unknown as late as the 1970s. In the 1980s, it emerged as the fourth leading cause of death among adults. As a result of this disease, the brain gradually atrophies, shrinking in both size and weight. Neurons are lost, fibers become twisted in the neuron cell bodies, and abnormal masses develop. Affected individuals gradually lose their memories; their thought processes slow; their judgments are impaired; they develop speech disturbances; and they become disoriented. In the disease's more advanced stages, the individual suffers emotional disturbances, delusions, deterioration of personal and toilet habits, failing speech, and finally total loss of memory. This disease, which heightens anyone's fear of brain disorders, is tragic for all concerned.

The major symptoms of Alzheimer's disease are gradual declines in cognitive functioning (memory, learning, reaction time, word usage), disorientation, declines in self-care, and inappropriate social behavior such as violent outbursts. In the beginning the symptoms are mild and may mimic depression or mild paranoia, but they often develop into profoundly disruptive behaviors.

Extremely disruptive behaviors have been termed **catastrophic reaction**, a reaction occurring when the organism is unable to cope with a serious defect in physical and cognitive functions (Goldstein, 1980). The catastrophic reaction is defined as "short-lasting emotional outburst characterized by anxiety, tears, aggressive behavior, swearing, displacement, refusal, renouncement, and/or compensatory boasting," which are embedded in physical and mental shock (Tiberti et al., 1998).

The cure for Alzheimer's disease continues to elude scientists, who hope to approach a cure by understanding more about it's cause. The cause of the disease in 10 to 30 percent of people with Alzheimer's has been identified as genetic, and the fields of molecular biology and genetics currently lead the way into the 21st century for hope to finding a cure. Geneticists have discovered mutations in three different genes—APP, PS1, and PS2—which are associated with increased production of a protein that accumulates in the plaques of both "sporadic" (late onset) and familial cases of Alzheimer's disease (Hass & Selkoe, 1998).

Did You Know . . .

Leaves from the ginkgo tree have been used by Chinese herbalists for several thousand years as a cure for memory problems. Research at New York Institute for Medical Research has recently found that 27 percent of people with Alzheimer's disease who took a 40-milligram ginkgo tablet for one year showed improvements in memory and social behavior. The improvements were equivalent to a 6-month delay in the progression of the disease. The results are comparable to the two drugs currently on the market to treat Alzheimer's disease.

HEALTH, 1998

In 1993, the genetic risk factor for late-onset sporadic and familial Alzheimer's was found to be in the apolipoprotein E (apoE) e4 allele. An eightfold risk of developing the disease exists among those with this allele, compared to those bearing the common e3 allele (Corder, 1993, reported in Lamb, 1998). This breakthrough has been further developed to explore possibilities for accurate diagnosis, but reports recently published indicate that apoE genotyping does not provide sensitivity or specificity sufficient to be used alone for diagnosis (Mayeux, Richard et al., 1998).

Some medical experts think it unlikely that Alzheimer's disease is the result of a single, underlying cause. Genetic tracing is only part of a broad range of approaches targeting Alzheimer's disease, and research on all fronts must continue until cause and cure are determined. Exploring the possibility of environmental toxins, searching for a virus, looking at causes for the penetration of the blood-brain barrier—all of these factors continue to be explored in the search for a cure to this horrendous disease.

Among the most intensive areas of therapeutic intervention are currently the role of cholinesterase inhibitors (Tacrine HCI; donepezil; metrifonate), the possibility of hormonal control (especially estrogen), the effect of anti-inflammatory agents, and other approaches such as antioxidants, calcium channel blockers, and nerve growth factor (D'Epiro, 1996).

Because a prevention or cure for Alzheimer's disease has yet to be discovered, attention must be directed toward improving the functioning of the ailing person and helping family members to cope. The disease is gradual and progressive; the length of survival ranges from 2 to 20 years. Several stages are involved—some say seven stages: (1) normal; (2) forgetfulness; (3) early confusional; (4) late confusional; (5) early dementia; (6) middle dementia; and (7) late dementia.

Did You Know . . .
The University of Kentucky Nun Study has found that women who scored poorly on measures of cognitive ability as young adults were at higher risk of Alzheimer's disease and poor cognitive function in late life. Of those nuns with confirmed Alzheimer's who died, 90 percent had low linguistic ability in early life, compared with only 13 percent of those without evidence of the disease.

National Institute on Aging, 1996

In the first stages, cognitive declines are not readily apparent. A midway stage is characterized by recent memory loss and personality changes. For example, a person may become hopelessly lost while walking to a close and familiar location. Abstract thinking can also become impaired; the difference between an apple and an orange can become confusing, for example. Ailing individuals are typically aware of their intellectual decline, becoming anxious, depressed, or angry.

The next stages of Alzheimer's disease advance the deterioration of thought processes. Further memory loss and drastic mood swings are common. Speaking may become difficult, and paranoid symptoms may appear. During this stage, complications often force the patient to relocate to housing where care is provided. He or she may have trouble remembering close family members.

The final stage is terminal and usually very brief, lasting one year or less. Though many Alzheimer's patients at this stage stop eating and communicating and are unaware of surroundings, years, or seasons, they are still sensitive to love, affection, and tenderness. This is an enormously stressful time for friends and relatives; at this stage, they are most in need of support groups and counseling.

MULTI-INFARCT DEMENTIA (MID)

Rising from problems with blood flow to the brain, this vascular dementia is caused by a series of small strokes (infarcts) that damage brain tissue over time. The disease is typically chronic, and a person may live with it for many years. For most, impairment is intermittent, occurring when a stroke occurs. The strokes are so small that one is unaware of them. A patient may have sudden attacks of confusion but then recover. Another may remember something one minute, then forget it the next. Gait difficulty, urinary incontinence, and palsy may accompany dementia symptoms. The brain area in which the stroke occurs corresponds with the impaired ability.

ALCOHOLISM

Lifelong alcoholism or the onset of alcoholism in late life may yield changes that indicate a dementia syndrome. For example, chronic alcoholism may cause Wernicke-Karsakoff's syndrome, a type of dementia resulting from the lack of vitamin B_{12}, which results in memory loss and disorientation.

CREUTZFELD-JACOB DISEASE

Creutzfeld-Jacob brain disease, though less common and much more rapid than Alzheimer's, follows a similar course. Within a year, the cerebral cortex degenerates to a fatal point in the sufferer. Scientists suggest that an infectious agent, possibly a virus, may be involved.

PARKINSON'S DISEASE

Parkinson's disease, which can lead to dementia, affects close to one million individuals in the United States. Rarely diagnosed before age 40, it increases in prevalence in those between the ages of 50 and 79. Tremors and rigidity of movement characterize the disease. Parkinson's progresses through stages, and some sufferers are eventually confined to bed or a wheelchair. Between 20 and 30 percent of patients develop dementia. Parkinson's has been treated with some success using the drug L-dopa, which relieves symptoms but is not thought to slow the progression of the disease (de Rijk et al., 1995; Turjanski et al., 1997).

HUNTINGTON'S DISEASE

A rare disease, Huntington's disease is inherited as a defective gene. Its most famous victim was Woody Guthrie (1912–1967), a popular folksinger and composer. The disease starts unnoticed in one's thirties or forties and proceeds over a 12- to 15-year period, ending like Alzheimer's disease with total deterioration of memory and bodily functions.

Caring for the Mentally Ill

Care for mentally ill elders can be provided in clinical settings of mental health professionals, hospitals, institutions for the mentally ill, nursing homes, or the homes of relatives. Some environments are supportive of mentally ill elders, whereas others are hostile or indifferent. Those who are mentally ill, whether living in group homes or boarding homes, have been shown to benefit by

1. Activities to keep people busy, such as music, dance, cards, and handiwork
2. Activities oriented to the larger community—even if that means having a cup of coffee at the local café
3. Programs and goals of reducing dependency and getting people out of a conforming, passive rut

For families caring for the mentally ill elderly at home, the burden can be great. Caretakers can expect no expanded government programs in the immediate future; if anything, programs are being curbed. Gerontologists are looking to volunteer programs and family support groups to help the elderly infirm and their families. Fortunately, support groups for caretakers of patients with Alzheimer's and other dementias are often available and highly beneficial.

Community networks—cadres of "good people"—have been tremendously helpful by forming volunteer programs designed to consider the unique needs of mentally ill elders and in organizing the assistance of friends, other residents, and family members. Through network building, programs can expand to involve churches, schools, and senior citizen groups in caring for the mentally ill in institutions or at home.

Peer counseling is a somewhat similar concept. Older persons are trained by a professional to reach out to other elders in need of mental health services. These volunteer peer counselors are taught to deal with a variety of problems, to offer advice, and to serve as a bridge, through referrals, to more formal mental health services. In some communities, peer counselors have organized hotlines for elders in crisis. Support for these programs is tight, however.

The costs for care of people with impaired mental functioning can be enormous. This care has historically been provided either (1) solely by family members, (2) by state-run institutions, (3) by a combination of family and state, and (4) in community-based living environments, such as board and care homes. In an effort to reduce public spending, California led the nation in the 1970s in closing its state-operated living facilities for people with special mental functioning needs, including people who are developmentally disabled, mentally ill, and those with some forms of dementia. Theoretically, those special-needs people were to move to smaller, more homelike community care living situations run by the private sector. Public moneys were to go directly to the individuals needing the services rather than to institutions providing the services. Elderly people with dementia and those who had lived in sheltered housing for some time were a large number of people requiring community-based housing.

A scandal erupted in California in 1998 with the publication of a previously-suppressed report prepared by the state's Department of Social Services suggesting that grave problems were found in the care of those community-based mentally disabled people. The report cited numerous cases of the horrendous treatment of people, highlighting inadequate and inappropriately trained staff and a lack of appropriate oversight by state licensing agencies (Lempinen, 1998). In its attempt to reduce state spending, California had created a model of care for this vulnerable population in which concern was shifted from that of the well-being of individuals, to concern for a robust profit margin. It is just this scenario—from inadequate care to the suppression of the finding for political reasons—that is a major concern for gerontologists.

Good Mental Health

Most older people have good mental health. One safeguard against emotional debilitation in later years is good mental health in youth and middle age. Many mental disorders in old age represent continuing problems that have gone untreated. A second safeguard against emotional debilitation in old age is to maintain an active interest in life and to keep one's mind stimulated. A third safeguard is to seek professional health care services when they are needed.

Getting mental health care is less likely in the older years. Ageism in mental health perpetuates the myth that mental illness in old age is untreatable. The problems of younger persons have often received more priority in mental hospitals, community organizing, and other care organizations. Older people are also more reluctant to seek help. But the mental health of the elders is beginning to receive more attention. More geriatric specialists are offering encouragement and assisting those older individuals with mild emotional problems or more severe disorders. Sharp criticism has occurred of the application of psychotropic drugs to mental health problems of older people. Older persons do not have to tolerate depression, anxiety, or other disorders any more than younger persons do, nor must they be drugged into zombielike states in lieu of appropriate therapeutic attention. Depression and anxiety are pathologies that can be treated and cured.

At every point in our lives, we can have the goal of maximizing our potential. Even a person in a very debilitated mental state can generally respond to help. For example, individuals suffering from advanced organic brain syndrome can benefit from "reality orientation": reviewing the day of the week, one's location, and one's name. Human contact, a touch or hug, also adds meaning to life.

Caretakers in the field of mental health can work toward maximizing a patient's potential. In the On Loc Nursing Home in San Francisco, even the most impaired attend programs, form friendships, and are encouraged to attend music groups, old movies, and arts and crafts workshops. They are fully dressed in street clothes every day, even though most are incontinent. In this hospital, the worker's goal is to help patients reach and maintain maximum functioning potential. With a constantly deteriorating patient, specific goals may have to be adjusted downward; but if the goal is to see Mrs. Smith smile, or to hear Mr. Juarez sing, the task remains rewarding.

Community Mental Health Clinics (CMHCs) are mandated to serve the old as well as the young, yet a disproportionately small number of older persons use these services. Medicare pays only a minimal amount for outpatient mental care. A tragic irony exists in that although nursing homes represent a major setting for mentally ill elders, they receive, for the most part, inadequate mental health care in these homes. Geriatric mental health is an evolving field desperately in need of growth and improvement.

Chapter Summary

The psychology of aging is a broad field covering cognition and its many aspects: perception, sensory input, information processing, psychomotor speed, intelligence, learning, and memory. Older persons generally suffer a decline, in reaction time, but not necessarily in intelligence, learning, memory, and other areas. Mental health problems may be functional (have no physical basis) or organic (have a physical basis). Functional disorders may be moderately debilitating, as with a temporary emotional problem, or they may be quite severe, as with a psychotic breakdown. The most common form of organic brain disease is Alzheimer's disease. The bulk of the aged are in good mental health. A substantial minority of elders need mental health care by a professional.

Key Terms

affective disorders
age-related changes
Alzheimer's disease
anxiety disorders
biologically caused changes
catastrophic reaction
classic aging pattern
cognition
cognitive mechanics
cognitive pragmatics
cognitive process approach
crystallized intelligence
dementia
depressive disorder
divided attention
fluid intelligence
functional disorders
generalized anxiety disorders
information processing
intelligence
learning
memory
obsessive-compulsive disorder
organic disorders
perception
personality disorders
phobia
primary memory
primary mental abilities
pseudosenility
psychometric approach
psychomotor speed
schizophrenia
secondary memory
selective attention
senility
sensation
sensory memory
sensory threshold
terminal drop
tertiary memory
the five senses
working memory

Questions for Discussion

1. How does age affect intelligence, learning, and memory? How would you design a training program that would permit the capable older worker to retrain under the least stressful circumstances and to demonstrate capability?
2. What personality variables would you choose to examine in a longitudinal study of adults throughout their lives? Why?
3. What emotional problems do you anticipate in your old age based on your present personality?
4. How would you respond to being told you had a chronic brain disease?
5. Why do high numbers of older men commit suicide?

Fieldwork Suggestions

1. Put in earplugs and wear a thick pair of gloves as you go through your daily routine. Note the loss of sensory perceptions and how these losses influence your ability to function and to do things for yourself. Are you treated well by other people? Are you hesitant about going out in public? How long are you able to withstand the sensory loss? Did you find any ways to compensate for it?
2. Call your county mental health agency to find out what services are available for elders.
3. Interview a mental health worker. Ask him or her what mental disorders older people seek treatment for. Is there a percentage breakdown?

Online Activities

1. Locate the Internet site for the Alzheimer's Disease and Associated Disorders Association (ADRDA), and research two therapeutic treatments for the disease. Are you able to tell whose perspective represents the information you have found? (Was it developed by academicians or by a pharmaceutical company, for example?) How useful is the level of material to you?
2. Find all that you can about *learning*, from as many different sources as possible. Keep a journal of your search: Which locations are the most useful? Was it easy, or more difficult for you to gather a range of material? Did your search provide you with cross-cultural resources? Cross-species resources?
3. Develop a list of Internet address links that you would use if you were designing a home page on learning and memory in later life.

12

The Oldest-Old and Caregiving

Long Goodbye

John B. Judis

My mother died this summer in a nursing home after two severe strokes. Her death saddened me, but it also brought a certain relief, not simply because it ended her suffering, but because it alleviated my fears that I would have to choose between my mother's welfare and my children's.

In the winter of 1993, my mother phoned me from a hospital room in Chicago. She sounded dazed. When I called her regular doctor, he told me that she had blacked out and fallen on the pavement several nights before and she had suffered a concussion. He assured me that she would soon resume her normal widow's life of friends and volunteer work. Still worried, I decided to got to Chicago to see her. When I arrived the next week, she had been transferred to the renowned Chicago Rehabilitation Institute.

Her doctor there pulled me aside and told me that my mother was no longer capable of living by herself. She couldn't walk fifty feet unaided without falling, and her mental capacities had deteriorated to such an extent that she couldn't balance a checkbook. I was completely taken aback—several months before she had seemed fine—but when I went to her apartment that night, I discovered ample confirmation of what the doctor had said. My mother had always been the most fastidious and organized of people—a wet ring left on her coffee table by a glass could drive her to distraction. Now, though, her apartment looked like a bag lady's, with unopened bills and magazines still in their subscription wrappers piled on the floor and strewn over chairs.

As my mother's only child, I was now suddenly responsible for her. My wife and I decided she should move to an "assisted care facility" in Maryland near us, where we could visit and watch out for her. But when I told her what the doctor said and what we thought she should do she was adamantly opposed. But after several weeks of bitter argument she finally gave in, partly because she had no choice, but also because she fell again at the hospital and went through another spell of not knowing where or who she was.

Over the next three years, she continued to rage against her fate and sometimes me. Like many older people who lose their independence, she became obsessed with her money and possessions. While she never accused me or my wife of stealing from her, she believed everyone else around her was. Knowing that I was worried about her finances, she would taunt me by threatening to go on a shopping spree at Tiffany's. She became increasingly confused about who exactly I was. She knew my name and could give a capsule summary of my life, but as I became her guardian, rather than vice versa, she seemed unsure about what our relationship was. She would tell me about "our son John," as if I were my father. One day she asked me when she was going to meet "my new wife," as if I had ditched her for my current wife. When I called doctors or administrators, I'd have to stop myself from saying I was "Ruth Judis's father" rather than her son.

I discovered that even doctors who treat the elderly often have little sensitivity to illnesses like the one my mother suffered. Before her concussion, my mother told me she had complained to her internist in Chicago of weakness and fainting spells; he told her she was depressed and prescribed Prozac. Her first doctor in Maryland could never understand my mother's status, which initially lay somewhere between full independence and a nursing home. Both of these doctors refused to accept "Medicare assignment"—they charged more than standard Medicare rates—and her doctor in Chicago insisted my mother fill out her own forms. Both doctors dropped my mother as a patient when she was no longer able to visit their offices. In fact, the only doctors who seemed to understand her condition were geriatric specialists attached to institutions, where she was transferred in November 1994 after a severe stroke left her paralyzed on one side.

When the Republicans took over Congress after the 1994 elections, I had a few guarded hopes. I gave those up pretty quickly during the debates over Medicare and Medicare funding. As I discovered, about 40 percent of the money Medicaid spends is for elderly nursing home inhabitants who exhaust their life's savings. Where I live, the average nursing home costs about $50,000 a year. And that doesn't include doctors bills, Medigap insurance, and whatever else a resident might need. (My mother's wheelchair cost over $1,000.) At that rate, even an upper-middle class family would soon exhaust its savings.

Many nursing homes (like the Manor Care near me, whose parent company's CEO is a prominent Montgomery County Democrat) won't accept Medicaid patients at all.

This July my mother suffered a final stroke that left her without speech and seemed to rob her of any remaining incentive to live. Like many elderly people, she had already made it clear to her doctor that she would not want any extraordinary measures taken to keep her alive. She died about a month later. I plan to take her ashes back to Chicago, but they sit now in my backyard, a reminder of the difficult and unhappy days she and I endured over the last three years.

As the population of the old-old has mushroomed, caregiving to an older person within a family setting has become more common. Informal caregiving usually precedes and sometimes accompanies or replaces the formal caregiving offered by hospitals and other institutional settings. We have no clear-cut norms or customs dictating care for older family members who need help in caring for themselves. This chapter examines the oldest-old population and the caregiving that is offered in a family context.

The Oldest-Old

Recently, researchers have begun separating old-age groups in their studies. As early as 1974, Bernice L. Neugarten identified more than one category of older persons: the young-old (age 65 to 74) and the old-old (age 75 and over). Before that, studies considered all the elderly together, obscuring important differences and offering little insights into the social realities of the **oldest-old.** Other terms for the oldest-old have also come into use, and they may have slightly different meanings: the very old, the extreme aged, the dependent elderly, and the frail elderly.

These terms, often used interchangeably, need to be clarified when they are used. There is no clear-cut time at which gerontologists all agree that one joins the "oldest-old." The discussion in this chapter reflects that fact. Here age 75 and over and age 85 and over are both used at different times to identify the oldest-old, depending on the studies cited. As longevity and the proportion of very old elders increases, however, "oldest-old" more commonly refers to those 85 and over, but it has not yet standardized.

Figure 12.1 shows the percentage distribution of four age groups among those 65 and over, the two oldest groups being 85 to 94, and those 95 and older. People aged 85 and older are the fastest-growing segment of the older population, currently representing 15 percent of the older population (all Americans 65 years or older). Table 12.1 shows the projected number of people 65, 75, and 85 and older for approximately the next 100 years. Note that the number of people over 85 years of age will be more than 5 times as great in 2100 as in 1995; the number will be nearly one and one-half times greater in 2100 than in 2050. The table shows there were 3.8 million people 85 years and older in 1995 in the United States—a huge number, relative to existing social policy (Social Security Administration, 1997).

Another 46 percent of the older population were in the 75- to 84-year range in 1997. By the year 2000, those age 75 and over will comprise 48 percent or nearly half of the aged population. Thus, the needs of elders from 75 and older will weigh more heavily in the future as their number and percentage of the population increase. As a society we will need to provide a viable lifestyle for this burgeoning group. People do not necessarily decrease in functional ability with age, however.

PHYSICAL HEALTH

The 75 to 84 age group is, by and large, healthier and happier than stereotypes would have us believe. In fact, the general consensus seems to be that physical losses in old age do not begin taking a heavy toll until after age 85. The 85-and-older group uses approximately 10 times as many hospital days as those 45 to 64, whereas those 75 and over use about 4.5 times as many (U.S. Census Bureau, 1993). An 85-year-old is two and a half times more likely to enter a nursing home than is a 75-year-old.

FIGURE 12.1

Four age groups of elders in 1997

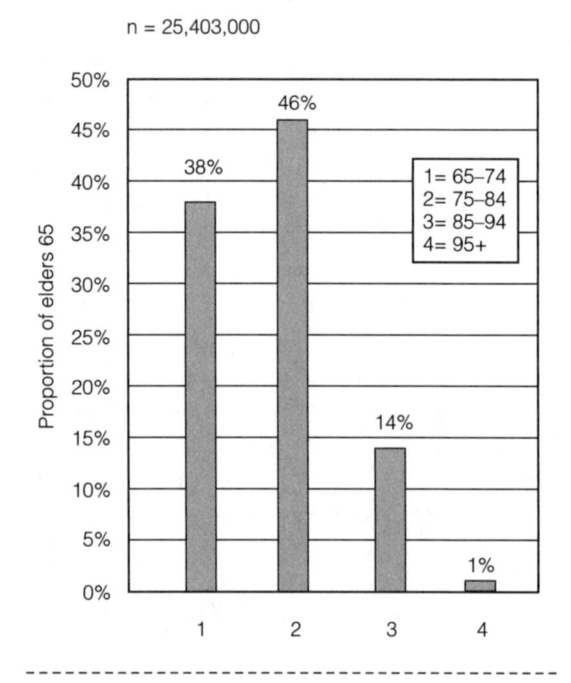

Source: United States Census Bureau, Aging Studies Branch, Population Division, Washinton, DC.

In one of the first longitudinal studies of the health well-being of elders (median age just under 89 years), conducted in the 1980s, only moderate declines in mental, physical, and daily living functions were found over a 10-year period (Palmore et al., 1985). The findings contradict the gloomy view at that time that the old-old experience rapid decline. In the 1990s, a mere 20 years

TABLE 12.1

United States aged population, projected

Age in years	1995	2000	2025	2050	2075	2100
	In millions					
65 and over	34.2	35.4	60.8	74.1	83.7	89.9
75 and over	15.1	16.8	25.1	39.3	45.9	50.6
85 and over	3.8	4.4	6.3	14.7	16.9	20.1

Source: Social Security Administration, Office of Programs: Data from the Office of the Actuary, Washington, DC.

after the first wave of the study cited above, it is clear that traditional views of aging need rethinking. It is now recognized that people who do not suffer from illnesses or severe impairments can exhibit a broad range of healthfulness and well-being. People in their nineties and older are often very healthy and robust—and the population of centenarians grew by 160 percent in the United States during the 1980s (Perls, 1995).

Did You Know . . .

Among people 65 to 79, women seem to have a slight advantage over men in cognitive abilities. A gender crossover *seems to occur between the ages of 80 and 89, however, after which men are on average higher than their female counterparts. This occurs because men who are cognitively impaired generally die earlier than do women, leaving mainly mentally intact men to live into later life.*

THOMAS T. PERLS, 1995

The health of the oldest-old is a basic concern. A critical measure of health is whether a person can manage daily activities alone, or whether the help of others is required. A measure of **functional ability** is the ability to do **personal activities of daily living** (PADLs or ADLs) without help. These include bathing, eating, dressing, toileting, transferring oneself in and out of a bed or chair, and walking or getting around inside the home (see Figure 12.2). A second measure of functional disability is the ability to do **instrumental activities of daily living** (IADLs) such as shopping, housework, money management, and meal preparation (see Figure 12.3). Less than half of the oldest-old (85 and over), need some help in performing ADLs, and about 60 percent need help with IADLs.

The oldest-old have a number of common chronic disabling conditions. The most common problems are bone and joint problems, heart disease, vision and hearing problems, mental impairment, drug intoxication (from prescribed drugs), falls, and urinary incontinence. Selected chronic conditions of those under age 75 and over age 75 are shown in Table 12.2.

In spite of these numbers many of the oldest-old have no *functional* limitations: that is, their chronic diseases do not keep them from living alone and doing their own personal and household chores. A recent study of people over 85 years of age and living in home settings found good to excellent functioning in mental and social domains, with the largest functional impairments having to do with physical functioning (Krach et al., 1996). Common chronic diseases in this group were arthritis, hypertension, and cardiac problems. The elders in this study reported that they needed visiting nurses, home health aides, and help with shopping and transportation to maintain themselves.

Robust aging is sometimes called "successful aging." It refers to aging while maintaining good mental and physical status. The most robust aging people have certain characteristics in common: they report far greater social contact than those who are not aging well; they have better health and vision; and they have experienced fewer life events in the past three years than their less well compatriots (Garfein & Herzog, 1995).

The implications for society of robust longevity are vastly important ones. As a result of better ways of life and medical advances, the "new" model of living into very old age might work to compress morbidity, mortality, and

FIGURE 12.2

Activities of daily living (ADL) index

Physical Self-Maintenance Scale (PSMS)

Subject's Name ______________________ Rated by ______________________ Date __________

Circle one statement in each category A–F that applies to subject.

A. *Toilet*
1. Cares for self at toilet completely, no incontinence
2. Needs to be reminded or needs help in cleaning self, or has rare (weekly at most) accidents.
3. Soiling or wetting while asleep more than once a week.
4. Soiling or wetting while awake more than once a week.
5. No control of bowels or bladder.

B. *Feeding*
1. Eats without assistance.
2. Eats with minor assistance at meal times and/or with special preparation of food, or help in cleaning up after meals.
3. Feeds self with moderate assistance and is untidy.
4. Requires extensive assistance for all meals.
5. Does not feed self at all and resists efforts of others to feed him/her.

C. *Dressing*
1. Dresses, undresses, and selects clothing from own wardrobe.
2. Dresses and undresses self, with minor assistance.
3. Needs moderate assistance in dressing or selection of clothes.
4. Needs major assistance in dressing, but cooperates with efforts of others to help.
5. Completely unable to dress self and resists efforts of others to help.

D. *Grooming* (neatness, hair, nails, hands, face, clothing)
1. Always neatly dressed, well-groomed, without assistance.
2. Grooms self adequately with occasional minor assistance, e.g., shaving.
3. Needs moderate and regular assistance or supervision in grooming.
4. Needs total grooming care, but can remain well-groomed after help from others.
5. Actively negates all efforts of others to maintain grooming.

E. *Physical Ambulation*
1. Goes about grounds or city.
2. Ambulates within residence or about one block distant.
3. Ambulates with assistance of (check one) a. another person ____ b. railing ____ c. cane ____ d. walker ____ e. wheelchair ____
4. Sits unsupported in chair or wheelchair, but cannot propel self without help.
5. Bedridden more than half the time.

F. *Bathing*
1. Bathes self (tub, shower, sponge bath) without help.
2. Bathes self with help in getting in and out of tub.
3. Washes face and hands only, but cannot bathe rest of body.
4. Does not wash self, but is cooperative with those who bathe him/her.
5. Does not try to wash self, and resists efforts to keep him/her clean.

Source: Adapted by M. Powell Lawton, Ph.D. Director of Research, Philadelphia Geriatric Center, Philadelphia, from *Older Americans Resource and Assessment Multidimensional Functional Assessment Questionnaire.*

FIGURE 12.3

Instrumental activities of daily living (IADL) scale

Name ______________________ Rated by ______________________ Date __________

1. Can you use the telephone
- without help, 3
- with some help, or 2
- are you completely unable to use the telephone? 1

2. Can you get to places beyond walking distance
- without help, 3
- with some help, or 2
- are you completely unable to travel unless special arrangements are made? 1

3. Can you go shopping for groceries
- without help, 3
- with some help, or 2
- are you completely unable to do any shopping? 1

4. Can you prepare your own meals
- without help, 3
- with some help, or 2
- are you completely unable to prepare any meals? 1

5. Can you do your own housework
- without help, 3
- with some help, or 2
- are you completely unable to do any housework? 1

6. Can you do your own handyman work
- without help, 3
- with some help, or 2
- are you completely unable to do any handyman work? 1

7. Can you do your own laundry
- without help, 3
- with some help, or 2
- are you completely unable to do any laundry at all? 1

8a. Do you take medicines or use any medications?
- Yes (If yes, answer Question 8b.) 1
- No (If no, answer Question 8c.) 2

8b. Do you take your own medicine
- without help (in the right doses at the right time), 3
- with some help (if someone prepares it for you and/or reminds you to take it), or 2
- you are completely unable to take your own medicine? 1

8c. If you had to take medicine, could you do it without
- help (in the right doses at the right time), 1
- with some help (if someone prepared it for you and/or reminded you to take it), or 2
- would you be completely unable to take your own medicine? 3

9. Can you manage your own money
- without help, 3
- with some help, or 2
- are you completely unable to manage money? 1

The IADL Scale evaluates more sophisticated functions than the ADL Index (see Figure 12.2). Patients or caregivers can complete the form in a few minutes. The first answer in each case—except for 8a—indicates independence; the second, capability with assistance; and the third, dependence. In this version the maximum score is 29, although scores have meaning only for a particular patient, as when declining scores over time reveal deterioration. Questions 4–7 tend to be gender-specific: Modify them as you see fit.

Source: Adapted with permission from M. Powell Lawton, Ph.D. Director of Research, Philadelphia Geriatric Center, Philadelphia, from *Older Americans Resource and Assessment Multidimensional Functional Assessment Questionnaire.*

TABLE 12.2

Prevalence of selected reported chronic conditions by age and sex, 1990

Chronic condition	Male 65–74	Male 75+	Female 65–74	Female 75+
Arthritis	37.3	37.7	47.2	62.9
Cataracts	8.1	12.9	13.7	27.1
Other uncorrected visual impairment	7.3	11.0	3.4	10.5
Hearing impairments	35.0	48.0	19.5	37.0
Heart conditions	27.5	40.5	24.3	29.3
Hypertension	28.5	30.4	41.0	44.4

Adapted from: US Census Bureau, Statistical Abstract of the United States, 113th edition. Table 206, p. 135. Washington, DC.

disability into a shorter period of time at the very end of the life span. This means that as the old become very-old, the massive drain on the economy to care for a growing population of frail, disabled older people that some people predict and fear, will not happen.

> *"As a result of ...demographic [changes] and work-force trends, the long-term care industry has boomed over the past few decades, from just over 500,000 nursing home beds in 1963 to 1.7 million today."*
>
> Mary H. Cooper, 1998

LIVING ARRANGEMENTS AND MARITAL STATUS

Only a small percentage of the oldest-old are institutionalized. Of the oldest-old, those age 85 and over, more than 50 percent still live at home. More than 35 percent live alone at home; in fact, about 75 percent of those 85 and over are widowed. An estimated 25 percent of the oldest-old live in the household of an adult child or other person (usually a relative), and another 21 percent reside in nursing homes.

For the oldest-old, the most critical need in the future will be for programs and policies that reduce the risk of dependence and promote self-determination. If housing were more affordable and home help services more available, more people could live in their own homes. Most people live in their own homes. Not until elders reach age 90 are there more than 50 percent who cannot live independently.

However, much of the needed help is not covered by Medicare. For example, if a medical diagnosis is osteoarthritis of the knees, the primary problem is trouble with walking. Although the problem is medical, and some help involves pain medication (to control but not cure), major assistance is needed with shopping and self-maintenance. Such categories of help are not "treatments" and, therefore, are not covered by Medicare.

The marital status of men and women at the upper age levels affords a dramatic comparison, with the oldest-old women much more likely to be widowed, and the oldest-old men, married. From Table 12.3, one can compare the percentage of single, married, widowed, and divorced men and women under 75 and 75 and over. The number of widowed men more than doubled (from 10 percent to 24 percent). For women in both age groups, the percent of widows is dramatically higher than the men. Nearly 36 percent of women aged 65 to 74 are widowed. The majority of women 75 and over are widowed (65 percent), whereas the majority of men (70 percent, in fact) in the same age group are married. Widowhood is the predominant lifestyle for women 75 and over.

INFORMAL CAREGIVING

Among those elders requiring assistance in living, a great number receive in-home care from relatives. Although the numbers vary depending on definitions, at least 17 percent of all noninstitu-

TABLE 12.3

Marital status for two age groups: 1992

Sex and Age	Percent Distribution				Percent Total
Male	Single	Married	Widowed	Divorced	
65–74	4.6	79.1	10.2	6.1	100%
75 and over	3.5	70.2	23.7	2.6	100%
Female					
65–74	4.4	53.0	35.9	6.7	100%
75 and over	5.4	25.6	65.0	4.0	100%

Source: Adapted from U.S. Census Bureau, *Statistical Abstract of the United States,* 113th ed. (Washington, DC.: U.S. Government Printing Office, 1993), p. 54, table 61.

tionalized elders are in need of help. This percentage more than doubles for those age 85 and over. For every disabled person who resides in a nursing home, two or more equally impaired aged live with and are cared for by their families (Brody, 1990). An even larger number of people provide help to old people who do not share their households.

There is a myth that the extended family, especially the three-generation family, was common in the 1700s and 1800s. In fact, the three-generation family is more common in the 1900s than it was then. The primary reason for this is longevity: More elders are alive today, and they live longer. Five percent of U.S. children today live with their grandparents or other relatives. In a third of these homes neither parent is present (Minkler et al., 1993). In 1993, 19 percent of all women 70 and over lived with someone other than their spouse, as did just under 7 percent of all men. Of those, just over 12 percent of women and 4 percent of men lived with a child or children (Soldo et al., 1997). The preferred living arrangement of elders, however, is independently from adult children. The trend over the last several decades has been to encourage such independence, with more care being provided in the homes of elders, not in the homes of the adult children.

Informal caregiving is caregiving that comes from relationships existing naturally in a person's environment, such as family, friends, church, and organizations that are not professional or financed by the government (members of a garden club, for example). The care is given by "lay" members of society, while formal care is provided by "professionals" (Pickens, 1998). **Formal caregiving** includes health care professionals, hospitals, and day care centers and nursing homes. Staffs are professionals or paraprofessionals and are paid for their caregiving.

The stress of caring for a frail, disabled person is very costly in human terms among both formal and informal caregivers, but particularly for informal family caregivers, whose psychological relationship with the care recipient is generally intense and complex. It is not uncommon for an elderly caregiving spouse to die, leaving the "frail" spouse behind. Informal caregiving is most commonly carried out by a spouse, and when no spouse is available, by a daughter.

From a statistical perspective, the typical caregiver is a 46-year-old working woman who spends 18 hours a week caring for her 77-year-old, chronically ill mother who lives nearby. Forty-one percent of caregivers also care for their own children under the age of 18 (Cooper, 1998). Most caregivers get help—usually from a son,

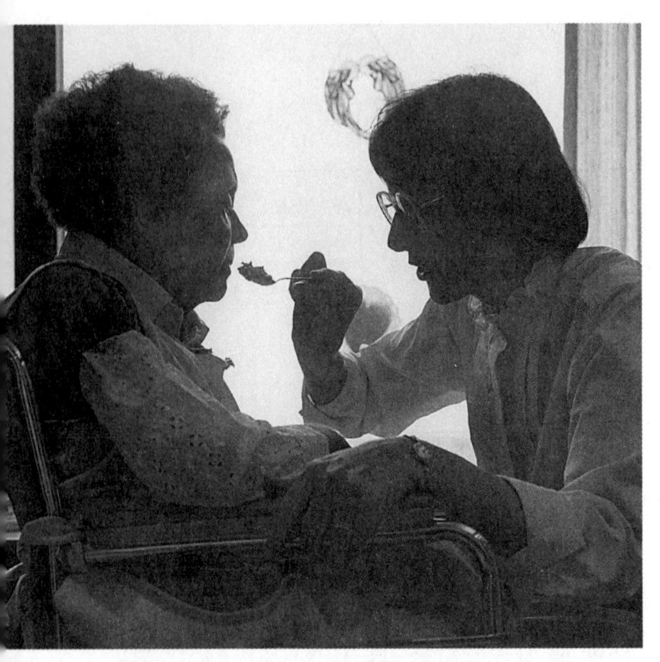

Contrary to popular belief, Americans feel a tremendous responsibility for their frail and aging parents. The tasks of caregiving can be enormous for people with responsibilities for their own children and with careers.

daughter, or other relative—in providing services such as transportation, grocery shopping, and household chores for their relative (Adams, 1998). Despite the myth of the nonfunctional nuclear family, research has found that families generally work hard together to provide care for a frail member. That care adds a heavy toll on family caregivers, but it occurs nevertheless.

OBLIGATIONS OF ADULT CHILDREN TO PARENTS

The **modified nuclear family** concept describes the typical American situation. There is a great deal of family interaction, for example visiting and exchanges of gifts and services, but no extended family household. Most elders live in separate households, but they are not cut off from their families. The standard indicators used to measure family interaction do not measure emotional closeness; nor do they measure how responsible the family feels for frail, older parents. The intensity and prevalence of intergenerational caregiving is thereby underreported and often underacknowledged.

"It's just really, really hard. It was a year and a half of unbelievable sandwich-generation problems. With the best will in the world you aren't necessarily doing the best thing because you don't know what that is. What worked yesterday won't work today, but how you're supposed to figure it out, I don't know."

ADULT CHILD CAREGIVER, REPORTED IN COOPER, 1998

Gerontologists observe that there are no clear cultural guidelines, no specific norms for behavior, in the area of intergenerational relationships between elderly parents and adult children. Some older parents expect that (1) married children should live close to parents; (2) children should take care of sick parents; (3) if children live nearby, they should visit their parents often; and (4) children who live at a distance should write or call their parents often. Indeed, that is why the phrase "modified extended family" has been used—it describes families that keep close ties even though they do not share households. These norms or expectations of close relationships are adhered to in the typical American family.

He doesn't know us anymore. But every time I go to say goodbye it kills me. I'm so sick of saying goodbye... One time when the doctors told us he wouldn't make it through the night, my mother and I actually made funeral arrangements... It was so hard. I grieved. I mourned. He didn't die—and I actually got angry. I was like—when is this going to end? Of course I felt guilty.

DAUGHTER, QUOTED IN MCCARTY, 1996.

FIGURE 12.4

Vignettes to elicit sense of responsibility of adult children for dependent parents

Vignette 1

A 64-year-old woman had a major stroke 8 months ago causing paralysis of her right side. Because of this weakness, she is unable to get out of bed and into her wheelchair or onto the toilet without physical assistance. Her 71-year-old husband, who has some minor health problems, finds it very difficult to do this for her and is only just managing. Also, he is obviously having trouble coping emotionally with seeing his wife in such a weak condition.

Their only source of income is the government old-age pension, so they are unable to afford private help.

Vignette 2

A 76-year-old man has had Alzheimer's disease for the last 4 years. He presently lives with his wife in an apartment where a community nurse visits him every week. Besides poor memory, his major problem is that he has no understanding of his illness. He gets quite upset, and at times aggressive, when anyone tries to get him to do something against his will. He tends to get more agitated at night and has trouble sleeping. He has reached the stage where he requires supervision for most activities and so cannot safely be left alone for any length of time.

His wife, who is 72 years old, is in reasonable physical health but is becoming exhausted with having to take care of her husband. She is unable to get a good night's sleep and cannot rest during the day because she is afraid her husband will get into trouble.

They are living on their old-age pension supplemented by a small amount of savings.

Vignette 3

An 82-year-old widower lives alone in a small second-floor apartment with no elevator. He has quite bad arthritis causing pain in his knees and deformity in his hands. He can get about his apartment safely with specially designed canes but is unable to get outside without help. Even though he has few visitors he claims not to be lonely, but the visiting social worker thinks that he must be.

Two years ago he had an operation to remove a cancer from his bowel. Unfortunately, he required a permanent colostomy, which means that he has to wear a plastic bag on the side of the abdomen to collect his stool. Because of the arthritis in his fingers he needs help to empty and maintain the bag.

He receives the old-age pension along with a small pension from his former employer.

Source: C. Wolfson et al., "Adult Children's Perceptions of Their Responsibility to Provide Care for Dependent Elderly Parents," *Gerontologist* (June 1993): 318.

Extreme financial or physical dependence of aged family members tests the limits of adult children's sense of responsibility. In seeking to determine whether there is a solid moral underpinning for filial responsibility, Canadian researchers used the vignettes in Figure 12.4 to elicit adult children's sense of responsibility for physically ill or disabled parents (Wolfson et al., 1993).

Respondents in the Canadian study were first asked what levels of assistance adult children *should* provide in each case. Second, adult children were asked to imagine that it was their own parents described in the vignettes. They were asked what levels of financial assistance, emotional support, and physical assistance that they *could* provide if the elders in the vignettes were their own parents.

The overwhelming majority of people interviewed (almost all) felt that emotional support *should* be provided by adult children in general and *could* be provided by them for their parents. Not quite as many, but still a substantial majority, believed adult children *should* provide physical assistance; a somewhat lower percentage *could* provide physical assistance. And a majority believed adult children *should* help out financially. The lowest figure in the study was the degree to which adult children *could* help financially, and even these scores were reasonably high. The researchers concluded that adult children feel a strong moral obligation to provide care for their disabled parents.

Another study in a similar vein asked respondents to agree or disagree with statements such as the following (Mangen & Westbrook, 1988):

> *If an old man has a medical bill of $1,000 that he cannot pay, his son or daughter is morally obligated to pay the debt.*

The purpose of the study was to reach a deeper understanding of **intergenerational norms,** which are the standard, expected behaviors of one generation towards another. Interestingly, on the preceding item, older generations were more likely to disagree than younger generations. Among Americans, the strong value of independence may well prevent older parents from expecting their adult children to take on any economic responsibility for them. In contrast, the majority of adult children agreed with the above statement.

Not all studies show similar expectations of aid to older parents from adult children. Intergenerational conflict was revealed in a classic study of three generations of women, using a hypothetical story about a widowed mother to ask each generation what adult children *should* do for an elderly parent (Brody et al., 1984). Respondents from each generation recommended in general that adult children not share a household with the mother. (The youngest group of women was most in favor of sharing the household, a feeling the researchers interpreted as a youthfully idealistic view of the caregiver role.)

Older parents judged female family members as acceptable to provide personal care such as meal preparation, housework, and grocery shopping, whereas male family members were judged unacceptable. Middle-aged daughters, reluctant to change family schedules or give up jobs outside of the home, were somewhat reluctant to become caregivers, yet the oldest mothers in the study were the most likely to expect caregiving from their middle-aged daughters.

A study recently released by Stanford University Medical Center found that the physical cost to those middle-aged daughters for caring for a frail parent can be actually greater than the physical cost to the spouse of the person requiring care. Daughters experienced a significantly greater increase in heart rates and blood pressure than did wives during social interactions with the ailing loved one, and recorded significantly more distress in interpersonal interactions (Evans, 1998). Divided energies, divided loyalties, and feelings of guilt for being unable to meet all of the demands of caregiving exact a heavy toll.

Did You Know . . .
The number of extended family households in the U.S. steadily decreased from the turn of the 20th century until the 1980s, when the downward trend reversed. This shift resulted from increases in horizontally extended households among immigrants—primarily Mexican, Guatemalan, and Salvadoran. It is related to young, single adults living with relatives, and in increases in poverty rates among immigrants from these countries which precludes independent living among the newest immigrants.

JENNIFER E. GLICK ET AL., 1997

WEAKENED FAMILY SUPPORT SYSTEMS

In 1977 Treas accurately predicted that the family would be more and more strained by caring for its oldest members. She cited three factors that contribute to the **weakened family support system,** which remain relevant at the turn of the century: (1) demography, (2) women's changing roles, and (3) changing intergenerational relationships.

DEMOGRAPHY

Long-run trends in morality and birthrates have startling consequences for the kin network. At the millenium, the aging parent, having raised fewer children, will have fewer offspring to call upon for assistance than did his or her own parents. Middle-aged children without siblings to share the care of the elderly parents will feel increased strain, and those adult children will themselves enter old age along side their own parents, who will then be in the oldest-old category.

Kin networks offer fewer options and resources when the younger generations have fewer members. Generally speaking, an aging couple will fare better when several children can contribute to their support. Having a number of grown children increases an aging widow's odds that at least one will be able to accommodate her.

With more living into their eighties and beyond, a greater proportion of the old will be frail elderly. The burden of their physical, financial, and emotional support may be considerable, especially for the young-old children of old-old parents, children whose own energy, health, and finances may be declining.

WOMEN'S CHANGING ROLES

Traditionally, providing older parents with companionship and services has produced a sexual division of labor. The major burden for physical care and social activity has traditionally fallen on female relatives' shoulders, while the burden for instrumental care such as tax completion, medical bookkeeping and the like, has become the responsibility of male relatives. In a study of the division of caregiving responsibility among siblings, Wolf and associates (1997) found that the presence of siblings does reduce the workload on any one adult child; however, it is far less than a one-for-one basis. They further found that the primary predictor of parent-care hours is the presence of sisters; when one's siblings include sisters, the workload on any of the siblings is less.

CHANGING INTERGENERATIONAL RELATIONSHIPS

In the past, children have been expected to tend to their aging parents in return for inheriting the family farm or business. This exchange created a pattern of economic interdependence. Parents had greater certainty of care in their later life through their ownership of the greatest family asset.

Children are now less likely to take over their parents' farm or business. They are freer to take jobs elsewhere or establish careers independent of their parents. Emotional ties, however, remain strong in the American family. Affection, gratitude, guilt, or a desire for parental approval still motivate adult children to care for their aging parents. Thus, the basis for helping is now less for economic and more for psychological reasons.

We may view these changes either as positive or negative. On one hand, the power of elders to ensure family support is reduced. On the other hand, Social Security and other governmental programs have also reduced the dependence of the old on family-support systems. As we experience the postindustrial society and the welfare state, both grown children and aged parents have been liberated from complete economic dependence on one another.

It seems that society is so enamored with the notion of "the family," that we overlook the fact that parenting can be a very painful experience. Too often, we deprive our older people of the chance to express the guilt, grief, uncertainty, fear, and uneasiness that are tied to their concern that they have not been effective parents.

ROBERT BUTLER, 1977

Changes in the family, demographic shifts, and changes in the economic structure have necessitated greater levels of governmental and formal intervention in the care of older people. Programs like day care centers, hot meals, and housekeeping services are essential to help relieve overburdened family-support systems. However, these programs still suffer from high cost and limited availability.

Spousal Caregiving

Spouses provide a large percentage of caregiving, with wives more likely to be caregivers than husbands. About 40 percent of all caregiving is provided by spouses, 14 percent by husbands, and 26 percent by wives (Harris, 1993). Living to very old age as a married couple represents a biological and social achievement. Nevertheless, the consequence of marriage in late life is not always blissful. If illness and chronic impairments loom large, heightened anxiety, interpersonal difficulties, and economic strains may result. Older married women often become part-time nurses for their husbands, who tend to be older and in worse health than themselves. Among noninstitutionalized elders in the community, some are homebound, and of those, a portion is bedridden. A husband or wife, if available, is most often the primary caregiver, and if the couple is lucky, paid helpers and children provide additional assistance.

In addition to family structure, both gender and race differences shape the caregiving experience. A recent study comparing male and female Anglo and African American caregivers showed that men of either race are less likely to refer to caregiving in terms of emotional work, and men and African American women caregivers are less likely to acknowledge a difference in the caregiving role between males and females (Miller & Kaufman, 1996).

Sometimes the caretaking role is assumed for years and years. In the following example the husband has Alzheimer's disease:

> *For nearly a decade, Hildegarde Rebenack, 69, has watched her 78-year-old husband, Robert, deteriorate from Alzheimer's disease. Robert was a bank examiner, a man proud of rising above his eighth grade education. Now, he spends his days staring at a collection of stuffed animals in their Louisiana home. . . . Robert was diagnosed in 1982. By 1984, he could no longer be left alone, and, two years later, Hildegarde had to put him into a nursing home. . . . Last March, the latest price hike forced her to bring him home. "We had 37 good years together," says Hildegarde, her voice breaking. "But the last six years have been hell"* (Beck et al., 1990).

For the spouse of an impaired person, decline challenges long-established patterns of interaction, goals, and behavior. The loss of functional capacity in one partner has reciprocal emotional effects on both partners, and those effects are highly variable, depending on the couple (Ade-Ridder & Kaplan, 1993). Spouses meet with circumstances that bring up the most intense emotional issues—life and its meaning, freedom, isolation, and death. Different styles of caregiving bring different problems and issues. Some women feel "burned out" by giving too much of themselves over the years, both before their husbands' health began to fail and after. Both men and women sometimes have the need to redefine their roles as spouse, and they may require assistance in establishing an identity as an individual as well as someone who is part of a marriage, as the marital role changes with the changing health of the frail partner. In a study of husbands who were caregivers, Harris named four types (1993). They are described as follows:

1. The worker: He models his role after the work role. He plans his work schedule every day. He reads everything he can about Alzheimer's disease and has a desk to organize the insurance papers and other materials.
2. Labor of love: He provides caretaking out of deep feelings of love. He often holds his wife's hand and embraces her. Caring is out of devotion, not duty.

A spouse is generally the primary caregiver when one's life partner becomes frail and requires caregiving.

3. Sense of duty: Caregiving stems from commitment, duty, and responsibility. He says, "She would have done the same for me. I will never abandon her."
4. At the crossroads: This is typical of a new caregiver who hasn't oriented to the role. He is floundering and in crisis.

Harris concluded with a variety of support recommendations: (1) educational groups led by a male caretaker and nurse clinicians; (2) support groups limited to men, because men often are not comfortable discussing personal matters in predominantly female groups; (3) computer networking programs for men who would not join groups; and (4) more quality and affordable in-home respite services.

These conclusions are consistent with a second study that provided a comprehensive psychosocial intervention program available to all family members, male and female, over the entire course of an aged family member's disease (Mittleman et al., 1995). By providing options for helping interventions, spouse caregivers were able to use services most suited to their unique situation and relationship with their spouse and their larger family. The results showed significantly lower rates of depression among the treatment group than among those in the control group. Supportive intervention can work to help ease the tremendous emotional and physical burden of caring.

ADULT CHILDREN AS CAREGIVERS

Now is the first time in history that American couples have more parents than children. The number of years of caregiving a married person with children might plan for is now around 17 years for children, and 18 years for elderly parents (Stone et al., 1994). These numbers are particularly dramatic for women. Nearly 30 percent of aging persons who need home care receive it from adult daughters; 23 percent from wives; and 20 percent more distant female relatives or female nonrelatives, compared with 10 percent of home care from adult sons (Stoller, 1990; Older Women's League, 1989).

The greatest strain seems to be on "women in the middle" —middle-aged women who have children and jobs, and who also are responsible for the home care of parents. The demands of multiple roles on the caregiver can be profoundly stressful. That stress is mediated by the history of the relationship with the parent, by the extent of social support the caregiver has, by her coping skills, and by her self-image (McCarty, 1996; Adams, 1996). Some adult child caregivers, for example, have long histories of conflict with the very parent for whom they now feel responsible, and these histories shape the caregiving experience for both the caregiver and the care recipient. One care-providing daughter (reported in Brackley, 1994) wrote:

> *...When I was young my mother manipulated me until I could get away from her. To have to take responsibility for her now is quite distressing. Everyone thinks she's "cute," or "quite a character," but don't understand that these qualities are not endearing on a lifetime basis. In fact, they are outright distressing when they seem to take over your life. I am trapped in a circle of anger and guilt, guilt and anger, with a smattering of denial and grief... (p. 15).*

Unmarried adult children who share a household with the ailing parent provide the most care. Being married and being employed decreases the amount of help given. Living apart further reduces the amount of help elders receive. Adult children caregivers most commonly offer help with the following activities: getting out of bed and going to the bathroom, shopping for food, traveling, doing laundry, preparing meals, doing housework, bathing, taking medicine, dressing, getting around the house, and providing personal, supportive communication.

Family size, socioeconomic level, and ethnicity are all determinants of family caregiving patterns. In one study of middle- and upper-socioeconomic neighborhoods, non-Hispanic whites with no children were more likely than Mexican Americans to report other family or nonfamily as their available caregiver. Among those with five or more children, however, non-Hispanic whites were *less* likely than Mexican Americans to report nonfamily as their caregiver (Talamantes et al., 1996). These findings imply that Mexican Americans have access to a more extensive support system, especially informal support, than do non-Hispanic whites and highlight the need for services and policy to address ethnic differences.

Parent care involves a constant tension between attachment and loss, pleasing and caring, seeking to preserve an older person's dignity and exerting unaccustomed authority, overcoming resistance to care and fulfilling extravagant demands, reviving a relationship and transforming it.

ABEL, 1991

Unlike caregiving for children, who become more independent with age, caregiving for the severely impaired requires more effort as the years go by. Coping skills and management strategies become stretched to the limit. Clearly, providing care for a frail parent might promote compassion and personal growth or it might become overwhelming with a negative outcome for both the caregiving child and the parent.

An early study of 30 women caring for a chronically ill parent or parent-in-law along with the person receiving care, observed two kinds of parent-caring roles: (1) care provision and (2) care management (Archbold, 1983). A care-provider was one who personally performed the services an older parent needed, whereas a care-manager was one who identified and obtained needed services, then supervised their provision by others.

The care-providing individuals were generally more strained; had lower income and less knowledge of available resources; were more involved in the heavy physical work of daily care; and were less likely to provide stimulating activities and entertainment in their caregiving role. In contrast, though the care-managers did not totally avoid strain and stress, they experienced less than the care-provider. The expenses care-managers incurred were greater, but financial expenses were high for care-providers as well.

We might note here that the Tax Reform Act of 1986 entitles anyone who works and who pays for the care of a dependent to a federal tax credit. However, care must be for a child or other relative for whom the taxpayer provides *more than half* the needed support, and the maximum credit allowance is only 30 percent of care expenses per dependent. Therefore, the act provides very little actual relief.

CHILDLESSNESS

Children were once described as one's "old-age insurance." Today, however, 20 percent of the population over age 65 have no children, and this trend will accelerate with increased longevity among the Baby Boom generation, who experienced decreased fertility rates and increased divorce rates (Choi, 1994). Most studies on childlessness have addressed psychological and emotional health rather than care provision. The general profile of the childless elder, compared with the elderly parent, emerges as someone who is more financially secure and in better health; more reliant on siblings, nieces and nephews, and on hired care providers; and experiencing no greater loneliness, isolation, or unhappiness than their counterparts with children (Choi, 1994; Rempel, 1985; Cicirelli, 1981). Patterns of help seem to be shaped more by marital status than by parental status (Keith, 1983).

Childless elders follow the "principle of substitution" by turning to extended kin for help, but these sources are less available than are children. Childless married couples tend to rely primarily on each other and to remain otherwise independent from extended kin. Unmarried elders, having established lifetime patterns for seeking assistance, seem to be more resourceful in using a variety of people and social resources to meet their needs. The childless elderly require more highly available substitute supports (Chappell, 1991).

Elder Caregiving to Adult Children and Grandchildren

The number of older parents who care for dependent adult children and grandchildren is increasing. Census figures estimate the number of children being cared for by grandparents in the United States at just over three million and project that number to steadily increase in the wake of AIDS and increased drug abuse in some population sectors (Saluter, 1992). Reduced mortality in the second half of the century among children with mental and physical disabilities has placed many older parents in the role of being a care-provider throughout their lives. It is no longer unusual for an 85-year-old parent in good health to be caring for a 65-year-old offspring with developmental disabilities or a grandchild who has been abandoned by parents.

Sometimes older parents assume the caregiver role because no one else is available to care for their dependent children or grandchildren. Support groups for elderly parents have become more available in recent years to help them with their caregiving in times of stress and crisis. The impact of later-life caregiving on 105 mothers of adult children with mental illness and 208 mothers of developmentally disabled adult children was assessed to determine their experienced levels of stress (Greenberg et al., 1993). It was found that elderly mothers had the most problems with mentally ill adult children. The mentally ill children posed greater behavior problems and were less likely to have day care outside the home or be employed. The mothers' social network of friends and relatives was smaller than that of mothers of developmentally disabled adult children.

The emotional cost of caring for a disabled child is high. Strawbridge and colleagues (1997) found differences in mental health, but not in physical health, between elderly people caring for an ailing spouse and those caring for an adult child. Grandparent caregivers in that study experienced decreases in physical health as well as mental health.

Solving Caregiving Problems

The stresses and strains of caregiving have drawn considerable attention over the last decade. The discussion that follows summarizes some of the solutions that have been offered.

STRESS AND STRESS MANAGEMENT

A fierce tangle of emotions comes with parenting one's parents: anguish, frustration, inadequacy, guilt, devotion, and love. Stress comes not only from these emotions but also from work overload. **Caregiver distress** indicates the negative stresses of caretaking, including role strain, subjective burden, depression, anxiety, hostility, and other troublesome emotions. Scales such as the Zarit Burden Interview (ZBI) have been developed to measure degrees of caregiver distress (Knight et al., 1993).

One specific emotion that has been widely studied is depression. Gerontologists seek to understand how much of the depression precedes the caregiving distress and how much is solely the result of the new added role. Those who are not initially depressed cope better than those who are. Personality factors have been examined, using personality inventories, for their role in the ability to cope (Hooker et al., 1994).

Coping is a response to the demands of specific stressful current situations. Coping techniques and abilities vary from person to person. These variations in ability need attention and explanation so that those with poor skills can be helped.

Problems in caregiving come from (1) the strain of responsibility for direct personal care of the elder, (2) the caregivers' own current personal and health problems, (3) role strain from the demands of other work and the need for leisure, (4) intersibling problems and other strained family relationships, and (5) arranging outside help and coping with bureaucratic mix-ups. A social support network is very important to caregivers. Additionally, caregivers experience an intense process of grieving.

Although helping parents can be rewarding for many adult children, it can be accompanied with enormous burdens, both financial and emotional. The principal caregiving adult children are "women in the middle," pulled in many directions from competing demands on their time and energy. Brody (1990) reports that three-fourths of daughter caregivers said that they felt they were not doing enough for their mothers. Adult children often express feelings of guilt as caregivers because of a deep commitment to "repay" their parent for care given in their childhood and infancy. This is impossible, and guilt is the result.

Ellen McCarty's intensive interviews with seventeen adult child caregivers (1996) found that stress experienced by daughters could be modified by specific changes in attitude and behavior. A daughter was less likely to experience stress, for example, if she could restructure her parents' former identities and her own prior filial relationship—in other words, give up old patterns and accept the parent in the present. Daughters who sought management strategies such as taking time for themselves, taking it "day by day," receiving support from siblings, using humor to diffuse stressful situations, feeling that they had support from formal caregivers, and "having someone to talk to" all reported less stress. Daughters with less stress were more likely to seek support from professional caregivers, and to grieve the losses they experienced in their parent and in themselves.

In McCarty's study, the daughters who fared best under the stress of parent caregiving had the ability to positively restructure important aspects of the relationship with their parent in the reality of the parent's changing circumstance. That is not an easy task. Giving up old patterns in relationships is difficult enough under the best of circumstances. It is small wonder that caregiver stress is so profound. The physical tasks of caregiving, though enormous, pale in comparison with the psychological tasks.

PSYCHOLOGICAL INTERVENTIONS AND RESPITE CARE FOR CAREGIVERS

The burdens of caregiving have been documented again and again, and gerontologists still study what kind of help is most useful. Possibly the only controlled study of psychosocial interventions (psychological help from paid professionals) and respite programs (programs that allow the caregiver time off) showed those two sources of help to be generally effective in easing the pressures on family member caregivers (Knight et al., 1993). The types of **psychosocial interventions** for the caretakers were varied: individual counseling, family counseling, support groups, educational groups, problem-solving groups for the caretaker and patient, social worker visits, and family consultants.

Support groups are typically available in larger communities at mental health clinics, and also from individual counselors. They usually meet once a week for eight weeks or so, in which individuals share problems and help each other with emotional support, friendship, and ideas. A paid professional leads the group. We should keep in mind that group interventions such as these work for some, but not for everyone. Counseling, either individual or family, can also be helpful if families can afford it; although for some families suffering from poor relationships, no amount of professional help can "fix" the problem. In this case, emotional distancing may be the only stress-management technique that would alleviate guilt and despair. Organizations are available in most communities to offer services to caregivers or to refer them to individuals who do.

In the study cited earlier by Knight and associates (1993), respite care was somewhat more effective than psychosocial interventions. **Respite care** can mean placement of the dependent elder in a nursing home for two weeks or so, or it may involve bringing a hired home care worker into the home for one to two weeks or more while the caregiver goes on a vacation. Time off for the caregiver is very important in relieving distress. Intervention and respite care should not measure its success by the alleviation of caregiver distress only. Other important outcomes have been found: improved functioning of the dependent elder, reduced use of hospital days for the elder, and improvements in patient mortality.

In the future, research must direct attention to how much and what kind of intervention is necessary to achieve the desired effect of stress reduction. If interventions and respite care work, which they often do, the next step is to determine what works best in which amounts, with which kinds of caregivers for elders with which kinds of impairments. A broad range of ethnic differences in real and perceived family support and in coping styles exist, and social service programs must identify and address these cultural differences to adequately support the provision of family-based care (Talamantes et al., 1996; Strom et al., 1997).

THE HOME CARE CRISIS

The percentage of elders is increasing, and more family members work outside the home. Is a crisis emerging? Who will care for the very old in our society? Many gerontologists believe that a trained paraprofessional labor force for long term care of the aged and disabled must be a national priority. Others believe the next cohort of elders will be more healthy and less disabled than their parents were, and that medical and lifestyle advances will compress their morbidity and morality into the very end of their lives, as opposed to living for decades with disabling diseases. Regardless of which scenario plays out in the next century, the number of Americans needing long term care is expected to reach nine million by 2000 and mushroom to 24 million by 2060 (Cooper, 1998). Home health care personnel are now the fastest growing segment of the long term care industry, and the demand for their services will continue.

Home care workers are generally poorly paid, overworked, and poorly trained. They are disproportionately middle-aged ethnic minority women (Feldman, 1993). Wages, job conditions, and opportunities for caregiving work have typically been at the lower end of the employment scale, with no chance for advancement. Outstanding **paraprofessional caregivers** in such job categories as nurse's aid, home health aide, personal care attendant, chore worker, and homemaker receive prospects for increased responsibility and advancement. Poorly paid **paraprofessional home care workers,** on the other hand, are a transient work group with a high turnover rate.

Paraprofessionals at present have little training. In some states they must undergo about 75 hours of training and pass a competency test. In many states, however, the requirements include fewer hours of training and no test. In the face of easy entry into the field, one might expect a large labor pool, but this is not the case. Many states report having trouble delivering state-funded home care services because of worker shortages and high turnover. Increased wages and better working conditions will reduce caregiver turnover and continuity of care will be improved.

The private sector has a stake in care for elders. The cumulative growth of the population 85 years and over from 1995 to 2050 is projected to be over 400 percent. This group should make up nearly 5 percent of the population that today is 1.4 percent (Siegel, 1996). The need for formalized caregiving services will increase proportionally, even after adjusting for lower disability rates in the future brought about by changes in lifestyles. This provides an opportunity for the private sector to respond in many different ways, from developing caregiving services to providing assistance to employees with caregiving needs for aging parents.

Businesses are run better if caregiving adult workers receive outside help in caring for aged parents. To date, only a few U.S. companies have policies that assist employees who care for the elderly; but many more are considering such programs. Such programs need to develop, and quickly, for the growth in the labor force in the 1990s and beyond will come primarily from women aged 35 to 54, those "women in the middle."

Options for care provision in later life must be developed now, before the tidal wave of the Boomer generation requires care. In some families, home care with occasional paraprofessional assistance works to provide the best care for the elder. In others, broad ranges of outside assistance are necessary, and the needs of elders in other families will be best met by living in assisted-living housing or long term care facilities. Some companies, such as IBM, Stride Rite, and Travelers Insurance Company, have eldercare programs. They offer flexible work schedules to allow employees time to care for older relatives and further, pay for leave up to 26 weeks for elder care. Adult day care costs can be lower than bringing in home health care aides, depending on how much care is needed. The elderly are a very diverse group with widely diverse needs. Services must address those needs.

Evaluation of Life

Americans continue to share only vague notions of age-appropriate behavior. At some point between 80 and 90 years of age, individuals become willing to describe themselves as "old" (Bould et al., 1989; Settersten & Hagestad, 1996). There is a definite awareness that the spirit is willing, but the body is unable to cooperate. Malcolm Cowley (1980), who wrote of his personal experience with aging in *The View from Eighty*, describes this reality:

> *Everything takes longer to do—bathing, shaving, getting dressed or undressed*
> *Travel becomes more difficult and you think twice before taking out the car . . .*
> *Many of your friends have vanished . . .*
> *There are more and more little bottles in the medicine cabinet . . .*
> *(You hesitate) on the landing before walking down a flight of stairs*
> *(You spend) more time looking for things misplaced than using them . . .*
> *It becomes an achievement to do thoughtfully, step-by-step, what (you) once did instinctively.*

Evaluations of reality vary with one's age and life view. To people age 85 and over who are in good health, living at home, and still driving, the absence of limitations keeps them feeling lucky in life. A study of 12 centenarians found a sense of comparison to be an important part of the evaluation of life. I'm "doing pretty good for my age" was commonly said (Pascucci & Loving, 1997). **Life satisfaction** is the sense of well-being experienced and identified by the individual, not something recorded by measures external to the individual. To a certain extent, satisfaction in later life seems to depend on an elder's sense of self-efficacy—the extent to which a person is able to master the environment effectively and feel a sense of control in life (Jacob & Guarnaccia, 1997).

Most life satisfaction studies have focused on the young-old and show that life satisfaction does not particularly change over time for an individual. This implies that life satisfaction is more a personal way of seeing the world than it is something affected by current circumstances. Measuring life satisfaction, however, is difficult to do—some researchers believe that self-report measures of life satisfaction are superficial and do not actually measure an individual's subjective experience of well-being (Euler, 1992; Hogan & Nicholson, 1988). Gerontologists generally believe that phenomenological methods (interviews in which the subject's own words are used to define well-being) are more useful in studying quality of life and life satisfaction among older people.

A greater number of longitudinal studies of the old-old would help us to better understand this age group. Life may or may not be different as one progresses from age 75 to 85 to 95 to 100. Among the "one hundred over 100" (Heynen, 1990) interviewed for a book about centenarians, full and meaningful lives were the norm. No single factor predicted who would live to be over 100—some were smokers, worrywarts, or non-exercisers. Some were homebodies, others travelers; some were religious fanatics, others skeptics. Old people are as varied a group as are younger people—there are just fewer of them, and because of physical limitations their activities and their interests are generally more limited.

Studies of the very old continue to identify themes of good health, good coping patterns, and a strong sense of well-being throughout life (Poon, 1992; Pascucci & Loving, 1997; Kratch et al., 1996; Aquino et al., 1996; Wallis, 1995) These qualities do *not* imply the jolly, twinkly-eyed old person of popular stereotype, however. Common qualities of the very old also include being completely willing to voice an opposing opinion if need be, and being an assertive voice for self-care. The very old are a group of people who have survived because of the combination of (1) their genetic makeup; (2) the lifestyles they have both chosen and been blessed with throughout their lives; and (3) personality characteristics having to do with taking care of themselves physically, psychologically, socially, and spiritually. They are generally people who are able to experience joy in surviving and appreciation for what is available to them.

Chapter Summary

This chapter extends information in the chapter on social bonds, providing an emphasis on the oldest-old and on caregiving. Norms governing intergenerational relationships are not clear-cut, which leaves room for elders to feel disappointed when adult children do not live close by and act in a supportive manner. Aged women far outnumber aged men, especially at advanced ages. The existing studies show the oldest-old to be healthier and more active than stereotypes would have us believe. Most manage to live outside nursing homes, either in their own homes or with adult children. Chronic conditions are common, but most people are not totally disabled by them. Caregiving by adult children is becoming more and more common as more elders live into their 80s, 90s, and 100s. The largest percentage of caregiving is provided by older wives and middle-aged daughters. A smaller but substantial percentage of caregivers are older husbands and sons. Caregiving places a great deal of stress on families because more women are employed outside the home and families have fewer children than they once did. In spite of the burdens, the family in the United States remains strong and a major source of aid to its members. More paraprofessionals are needed in the home care field to offer quality care at a reasonable price to the oldest-old.

Key Terms

caregiver distress
coping
formal caregiving
functional ability
informal caregiving
instrumental activities of daily living
intergenerational norms
life satisfaction
modified nuclear family
oldest-old
paraprofessional caregiver
paraprofessional home care worker
personal activities of daily living
psychosocial interventions
respite care
robust aging
weakened family support system

Questions for Discussion

1. Assuming that you have or plan to have children of your own, what role do you expect them to play should you require caregiving?
2. What kind of life do you hope to live when you are one of the oldest-old?
3. Based on your relationship with your parents now, what will your relationship be like if and when they become very old and need care?
4. What satisfactions could one enjoy from serving in capacities such as nurse's aide, home health aide, personal care attendant, chore worker, or homemaker?

Fieldwork Suggestions

1. Interview five people, using the vignettes listed in Figure 12.4. What were the similar responses? What were the unique responses? What conclusions can you draw from the experience of this small study?
2. Contrast the daily life of a very old person who is frail and ill with one who is active and fit. Describe the two people physically and in terms of attitude and personality. What conclusions might you draw from your observations?

Online Activities

1. Beginning with the home page for AHEAD (Asset and Health Dynamics Among the Oldest Old) locate current information on health factors among the oldest old in the U.S. What ethnic differences are evident? (Use www.umich.edu/~hrswww/index.html for your initial address in this search.)
2. Locate three of the following resource home pages on the Internet, and prepare an outline highlighting the resources that each makes available to the consumer:

- American Association of Homes for the Aging
- American Association of Retired Persons
- American Heath Care Association
- Assisted Living Facilities Association of America
- Health Care Financing Administration
- National Citizens' Coalition for Nursing Home Reform and
- National Council on the Aging

13

Suicide

Crimes Against Persons

Fraud

Drug Abuse

Promoting Consumer Education

Special Problems

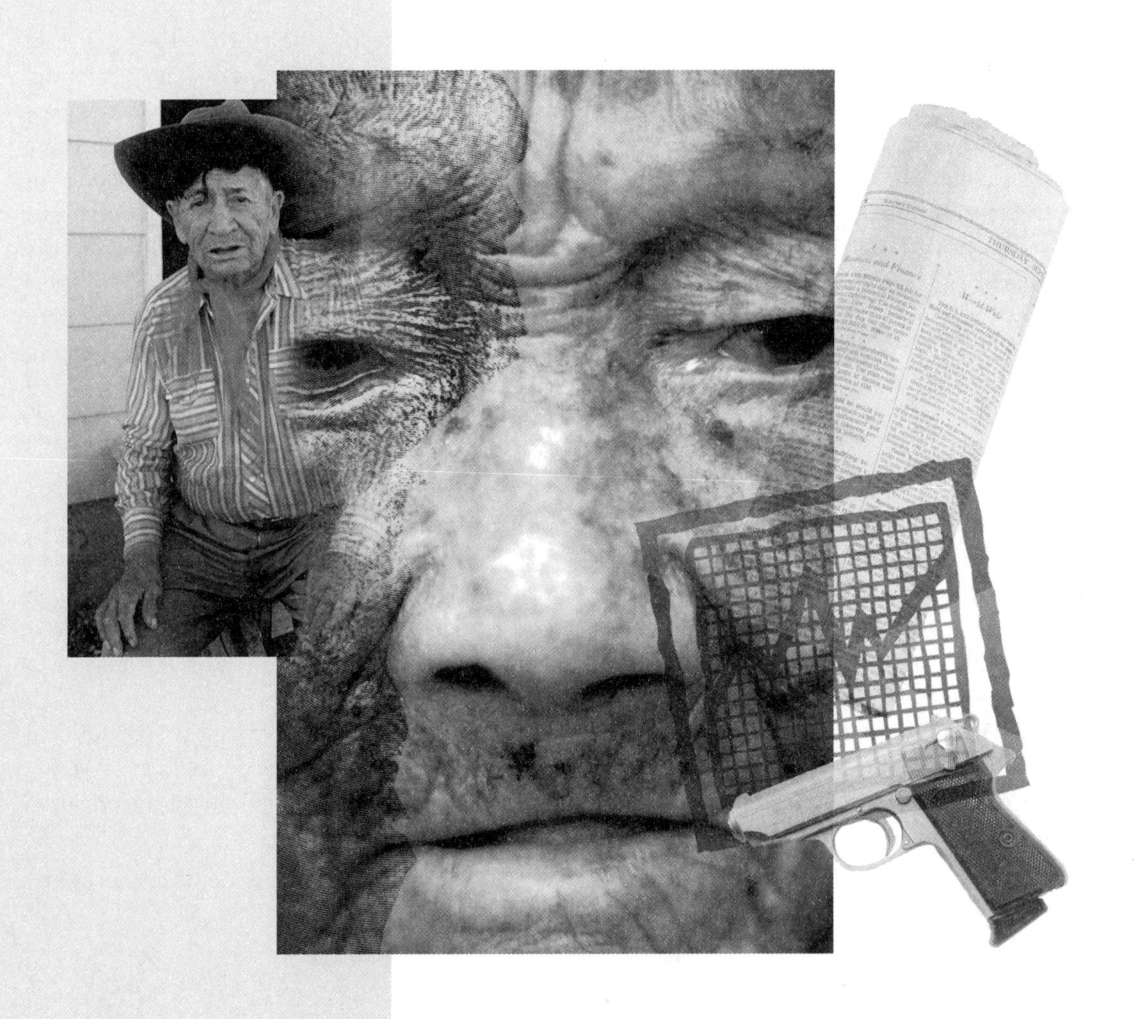

Facing Up to Elder Abuse

Charlie LeDuff

Anne DeBraw lives in fear. On a dark night not long ago, she heard the footsteps of a prowler on her roof. There was a tormented moment of silence before the intruder came crashing through the skylight.

"I felt so scared, so alone at that moment," said Mrs. DeBraw, 71, the memories tumbling out in tears. The man had been there before, but there was little she was willing to do. "He is my son and I didn't want to hurt him."

Mrs. DeBraw's is a common story, but one not often told. Many elderly parents like Mrs. DeBraw live in silent fear of their children. Quieted by shame, Mrs. DeBraw was battered and browbeaten for a decade.

People like Mrs. DeBraw, who have been abused by their children, may soon have a refuge of their own. By next spring, a Long Island City-based organization hopes to open a 20-bed emergency facility that will offer shelter, counseling and medical assistance to victims of elder abuse and their families.

"Elder abuse is New York's dirty little secret," said the Rev. Coleman Costello, founder and director of Walk the Walk, the group that plans to build the shelter. "Many of our old people are isolated and dependent on those who hurt them. Nobody wants to report that they're suffering at the hands of their children.

With $350,000 in grant money, Father Costello and his organization expect to close this week on a piece of property in Glendale, Queens, where the shelter is to be built. Father Costello, a Catholic priest, assisted Mrs. DeBraw after the court system was unable to stop her son's uninvited visits to her home.

Father Costello believes that the shelter in Glendale may be the first in the country just for victims of elder abuse. According to statistics provided by the National Center on Elder Abuse, more than 5 percent of New York City's 1.3 million people over the age of 60 are the victims of domestic mistreatment. Usually the abuse comes at the hands of an adult child and it can include physical or emotional duress, financial exploitation or abandonment. As the Baby Boomers age, those numbers will skyrocket, particularly in Queens and Brooklyn, where the majority of New York's elderly live.

"This is a disgrace that is not perceived of as a problem because nobody wants to talk about it," said Herbert W. Stupp, Commissioner of the New York City Department of the Aging. Although abused elderly people can take refuge in shelters for battered people, they often leave after only a few days, Mr. Stupp said.

"They have different physical and emotional needs," he said. "As difficult as it is, a young woman can start another life while a senior citizen is coming to the end of hers."

Right at this moment, an older person is being robbed or mugged. Right at this moment, an elder is being abused by caretakers, cheated of his or her savings, or victimized by medical quackery. Some abuses against elders are committed by street thugs; others are perpetrated by presumably reputable business people and professionals. Still others are committed by adult children or by paid caretakers. And some of the abuse is self-inflicted. Every 83 minutes an elderly American commits suicide (McIntosh, 1992).

With regard to crime, the actual commission of it is only one aspect of the problem; the fear of crime brings its own set of problems. Law enforcement and social agencies now recognize the crime patterns most likely to affect elders. Older people themselves are devising ways to fight back, and they are taking initiative, both as individuals and as a group, to protect and defend themselves.

As we develop our understanding of what it means to be old in our society, we must understand that it brings a vulnerability due to ageism and, for some, further vulnerability due to physical and financial limitations. Here we discuss some special problems that, if not unique, occur in high frequency within the aged population. And let us not forget that older persons are not always victims; they can also be perpetrators. This topic will be covered briefly.

Suicide

Suicide is the ultimate reaction to hopelessness—the acting out of a belief that there is no promise to the future and no reason to live in it. It is inextricably linked with depression and is one of the 10 leading causes of death in the United States. The reported annual national **suicide rate** is about 12 persons per 100,000 (National Center for Health Statistics, 1995). Elder suicide is particularly understudied, even though suicide rates among the elderly are the highest for the general population—perhaps double—and white men over age 85 are the most at risk. One of every five suicides in the United States is now someone over the age of 65 (Centers for Disease Control, 1996).

For four decades, the suicide rates among older Americans declined, but from 1980 to 1992 they climbed by almost 9 percent. During this time, men—predominantly white men—completed 81 percent of those suicides (Centers for Disease Control, 1996). In 1933, the first year the National Center for Health Statistics kept suicide statistics, the suicide rate among elders was an alarming 45.3 per 100,000 compared with a national average of 15.9. Between 1950 and 1980—years in which Medicare, housing, and other social programs targeting elders were initiated—suicide among elders declined by 40 percent (Marrone, 1997). By 1981 the rates had dropped to 17.1, compared with a national average of 12 per 100,000 people. Since 1981, however, elder suicide has increased to 22 people per 100,000, compared with a national average of 12 per 100,000, and this trend continues.

DIFFERENCES BY GENDER AND AGE

Suicide in old age is *statistically* a man's issue—particularly older white men. Women of any color 65 years and older, although reporting higher depression rates, have a disproportionately lower rate of suicide. The rates in old age for white and black women combined were about 6.5 per 100,000 people in 1986, compared with 61 suicides per 100,000 that year of white men over 85 years of age. On the other hand, the risk of suicide for men in the United States begins in the teen years and continues to increase with age, making an alarming increase in very old age. The proportion of **successful suicides** to **attempted suicides** is far greater in old age than in younger age. Older people express and demonstrate a firm determination to complete suicide (Silverman et al., 1995).

TABLE 13.1

Suicide rates of older population by sex, race, and age group, 1991

		Male		Female	
Age	Total	White	Black	White	Black
55–64	16	27.5	10.8	8/0	2.6
65–74	17	34.2	14.7	7.2	2.6
75–84	24.9	60.2	14.4	6.7	Unknown
85+	22.2	70.3	Unknown	5.4	Unknown

Adapted from: U.S. Bureau of the Census (1993). *Statistical Abstract of the United States.* 113th edition. Washington, DC: U.S. Government Printing Office.

Table 13.1 shows the suicide rates for the older population in the United States. Notice the dramatically high suicide rates for older white males. The high rate among aged American men is not a universal pattern; in some countries suicide peaks in middle age (Lester & Savlid, 1997). World Health Organization (1991) statistics, however, indicate that suicide rates throughout the world are generally higher for people over 65 years of age—often by two or three times that of the national average. The highest international rates were in Hungary, Sri Lanka, Denmark, and Finland, and the lowest rates were in Columbia, Ecuador, Greece, and Venezuela. Rates for elder suicide in the United States fit somewhere in the middle (Schaie & Willis, 1996). International gender differences in suicide also exist. In Japan, for example, suicide rates for older women have risen steadily over the past three decades—possibly as a reflection of the progressive loss of the traditional importance of older women in that culture (Shimizu, 1992).

Examining numbers and proportions of suicides by themselves can be misleading. For example, women outnumber men in unsuccessful attempts at suicide by about three or four to one (Schaie & Willis, 1996). Men's attempts to kill themselves are simply more successful; if *suicidal intent* is considered, older women outnumber older men. Men are more likely to kill themselves by violent and more certain means—guns were chosen by 74 percent of men who killed themselves in 1994, compared with 31 percent of women. Women are more likely to overdose with medications or poisons, which are clearly less effective (Marrone, 1997). Among young adults, more people attempt suicide than actually succeed. By about the age of 50, that trend reverses itself and the suicide completion ratio grows larger. Even considering the ratio of suicide attempts to completion by women, when compared to younger adults older adults are more likely to kill themselves when they attempt to do so.

Notice on Table 13.1 the comparatively low rates of suicide for older black men and women. The reasons for these low rates are not entirely clear, but they are thought to be related to more positive views of aging, a developed tolerance for suffering, strong religious and cultural prohibitions against suicide, and the lack of a giant step downward in status that white males experience in retirement.

TABLE 13.2

Risk factors associated with suicide in later life

Risk factor	Description
Interiority	A turning in toward ourselves in search of personal meaning; has both healthy and unhealthy aspects: can promote self-knowledge, spirituality and increased satisfaction with life; or result in unhealthy self-absorption and increased social isolation.
Chronic illness	Organic and psychological decline along with chronic illness and pain contribute to depression. Seventy percent of older suicides visited a physician within 1 month of their death.
Multiple losses	Job loss, death of friends, death of a spouse, the divorce of a child, loss of health and social status—all are cumulative experiences, and can occur so rapidly that resolution of the inherent grief of loss does not happen; associated depression of recurring losses can become chronic depression.
Alcoholism	More important among males 35 to 64 than any other age group; alcohol abuse enhances depression and exacerbates negative live events. Bereaved adults report significant increase in alcohol consumption, psychological distress, and decline in physical health.

Adapted from: Robert Marrone (1997). *Death, Mourning, and Caring.* © 1997 West Publishing Co. by permission of Brooks/Cole Publishing Co.

Did You Know . . .
A study in the early 1970s subjected dogs to minor but discomforting electrical shocks that they could not escape. The animals became apathetic, seemed sad, and were unable to think or move quickly. This behavior led psychologist Martin Seligman to the concept of learned helplessness *as a source of human depression. After a series of inescapable losses, if people feel they have no mastery or control of their environment they develop a feeling of futility, even toward events they can control. The resulting emotional state is apathy, hopelessness, and depression.*

SELIGMAN, 1975

CAUSES OF SUICIDE

Some experts speculate that medical technology has introduced a quality of life that elders cannot accept. These advances give people longer lives, but not necessarily a *better* long life—there is greater *quantity* in terms of longevity, but the *quality* of life suffers.

Did You Know . . .
Suicide notes among the elderly, more than among any other age group, often include references to loneliness, isolation, and to pain.

DARBONNE, 1969

Suffering and loss are factors known to be related to depression and suicide, and take place on psychological, physical, and social levels. Table 13.2 outlines some risk factors related to suicide, including the psychological risk inherent in the process of interiority; physiologically-mediated risks of chronic illness and pain; the social risks of isolation through repeated loss; and the behavioral risk of alcoholism—an outcome of a behavior promoting denial (Marrone, 1997). The most significant factor, summarized in the table under "multiple losses," is the loss of loved ones by separation or death. When children

After decades of inadequate funding for mental health programs, many old people have lived a lifetime of marginal existence. For some, hopelessness is a way of life.

leave home, when friends and relatives die, and especially when a spouse dies, the survivor is often beset with the desperate feeling that there is no reason to continue living. Social isolation has been associated with suicide—and elders are all too often isolated both socially and psychologically through society's attitudes and practices of ageism.

". . . Existential philosopher Soren Kierkegaard (1843) argues that the price we pay for not coming to terms with our own death is despair. . . In not coming to terms with death, the person in despair avoids the insights that life is precious, that existence is delicate, that a life filled with vibrancy, choices, and risks is the truest antidote to loneliness and despair, and that the dignity with which you live your life is the dignity with which you die."

MARRONE, 1997

Perhaps most importantly, physical illness, pain, or disability can prompt suicide. Aversion to the bodily changes that illness brings and worry over medical bills, coupled with the possibility of becoming a burden to one's family or to society, are typical reasons for older persons to take their own lives. Fully 70 percent of elders who commit suicide have seen a doctor the previous month. Physical illness as a cause of depression may be a common precipitating factor in completed suicides. More than 60 percent of older suicide victims have extreme medical problems (Devons, 1996).

CHOICES

The Hemlock Society was founded by Derek Humphry in 1980 to help people make choices about how they would deal with terminal illness. The motto of the society is "Good life, good death through control and choice." Humphry gained international fame after writing *Jean's Way,* the personal account of how he helped his terminally ill wife kill herself in 1975.

Until recently, most Hemlock Society members were older people. With the advent of the AIDS epidemic, however, many younger people have joined the organization. Humphry's books *Let Me Die Before I Wake* (1985) and the more recent *Final Exit* (1991) describe specific methods to use to ensure a gentle, painless death. Both the 1985 book and *Final Exit* have become national best-sellers, reflecting the public interest in the topic of planned suicide. The Hemlock Society does not believe that suicides are necessarily the result of poor mental health, but can be the result of a sound decision based on good mental health in what is called **rational suicide.** Thus, the relationship between suicide and mental health is not as clear-cut to some as it is to others.

Therapeutic intervention by skilled professionals is always recommended for a suicidal person. Depression can be treatable; suicide is not. Many communities have established suicide-prevention centers that maintain 24-hour crisis lines for helping persons in distress. The National Center for Studies of Suicide Prevention has assigned a high priority to the problem of suicide among those 65 and older. There is, however, a shortage of skilled therapists to treat self-destructive elders, and of all calls to suicide hot lines, those over 65 make only 3 percent of them—even though suicide is more common in the elderly than in other age group, it is still a relatively rare event.

Why some people can cope with stress and loss and others cannot is not fully understood, nor is the line between "rational suicide" and that emerging from hopelessness and depression very clear (Lester & Savlid, 1997). Barbara Haight (1996) found that elders being relocated to nursing homes who expressed suicidal ideation reported a strong sense of self-esteem, and described suicide as a way to retain control of their lives. We do not sufficiently understand the mixed picture of the hardy survivorship qualities of old people and the isolating effect of relentless loss of peers (Kastenbaum, 1992). All in all, the viability and allegiance to life of elders in general should not be underestimated.

SELF-DESTRUCTIVE BEHAVIOR

The approximate 6,500 suicides per year of people 65 and over leaves a large number of survivors who grieve and mourn. The solitary act of suicide has a ripple effect, affecting the lives of many. In some instances, couples who fear leaving or being left by their partner conduct **double suicides.** The most common pattern of double suicides is the mercy killing of a frail and dying wife, followed by the husband's suicide.

Elders in nursing homes are especially vulnerable to suicidal behavior. Although the rate is only 16 per 100,000, the attempted rate is 63 per 100,000. The rate of death from indirect self-destructive behavior is 79 for every 100,000 people, and the rate of nonlethal, indirect self-destructive behavior is 228 per 100,000 (Osgood, 1991). Methods included self-mutilation, ingestion of foreign substances, the refusal to eat or drink, or any repetitive act bringing physical harm or tissue damage.

FUTURE TRENDS

Suicide is twice as prevalent in western states as in the East and Midwest. Older persons in the West are more likely to have moved away from friends and family, and the divorce rate is higher in western states. Although no direct relationship has been found between suicide and divorce or mobility, the trends are important (Parker et al., 1997). The trends imply that meaningful social interaction might be more difficult to come by in the West, and meaningful personal relationships are the most potent antisuicide remedies—failures and losses are burdens easier to bear in the context of close family and friends.

Health experts anticipate an even higher rate of suicide as the Baby Boomers reach age 65. Baby Boomers have had higher rates of mental illness than their predecessors; after age 65, this group may suffer a tragically high suicide rate. The implications of this projection for mental health professionals are awesome regarding programs and services for a very diverse and large emerging portion of the population.

Crimes Against Persons

Though attacks on elders have drawn increasing media attention in recent years, national surveys show that they are less likely to be victimized than younger adults. When one considers **crimes against persons,** such as robbery, rape, and assault, only one specific area shows elders victimized as frequently as younger adults—the personal larceny of purse and wallet snatchings and pocket picking (U.S. Census Bureau, 1993). Despite the relatively low rates, the elderly express the greatest fear of crime of all age groups (Bureau of Justice Statistics, 1992). This fear has serious psychological, physical, and financial consequences for the elderly. Fear of crime appears to be independent of environmental variables such as trust of neighbors, years of residence, or type of housing (Bazargan, 1994). It is a psychological state based on a sense of vulnerability, and among many elders it results in fear or avoidance of leaving home (Joseph, 1997).

Gerontologists are aware of the wide variations in victimization rates. A majority of violent victimizations of older people occur in or near their homes. The converse applies to younger adults, who are more likely to be attacked when away from their homes. Unlike younger adults, elders tend to avoid places of danger and to restrict their use of public streets. But, in spite of precautions and their tendency to stay home more, some elders still are victimized.

Their particular vulnerability may well be a reason for attacks on older individuals. Many are poor, living on fixed incomes, and dependent on public transportation. They may live in neighborhoods with relatively high crime rates, or in changing neighborhoods where unemployed youths prey on them. Often, they are not physically strong enough to defend themselves against their assailants. Further, they are often unable to identify attackers, or may be unwilling to report crimes or press charges for fear of reprisal. Crimes against the elderly are often called **crib jobs,** because robbing an old person is supposedly like taking candy from a baby.

A 33-year-old woman decided to experience victimization by "becoming old" herself. Donning a gray wig, wearing semiopaque glasses, and putting splints and bandages on her legs, she created, at various times, three characters: a shopping bag lady, a middle-income woman, and an affluent woman. She traveled through 116 big cities and small towns across the United States, walking the streets, eating at restaurants, and living in motels. While some people were kind to her, she was overwhelmed at the abusive and neglectful attitudes of others, and by the constraints she suffered because of transportation systems inadequate for those who have difficulty walking or seeing. She was mugged twice in New York City. Today she lectures to designers and gerontologists on the needs of elders (Ryan, 1993).

Some elders defy the stereotype of being weak and easily threatened. A 73-year-old woman in New York City battled an intruder and foiled a rape attempt in her apartment (Woman, 73, Battles Intruder, 1991). In an elder housing project, tenants got involved when gang members had been arrested and charged with attacking 12 older women over a three-week time period, choking them from behind, punching them, and stealing their money. Older tenants got involved in helping police set up a stakeout, and in being witnesses to identify those arrested. Anger won out over fear as the residents who "didn't want to take this" came forward (Hevesi, 1994).

These examples are not meant to advocate fighting back in every circumstance. It is not widely recommended that anyone fight an armed assailant. These accounts merely remind us that not all old people are easily intimidated. If this fact were more widely known, the number of attempted attacks might decrease.

The damage an attack can do to an older person is hard to measure. Crime can destroy one's possessions, body, and emotional well-being. Attacks against persons can shatter pride and self-esteem. They can change one's view of the world from trust and security to bitterness and paranoia and can change one's concept of humanity from good to bad. The memory of an attack can disturb sleep and rest and cause continuous anxiety during waking hours. Recouping financial losses because of crime can be difficult or impossible for the older victim. And, although a bodily attack may be fatal to anyone, the danger of serious injury is even greater for frail oldsters, whose bones break more easily and for whom the shock of assault may trigger heart or respiratory failure. Sensory acuity diminished by age may be completely lost by a blow to the head.

Fear often accompanies frailty because being frail means having less personal control over life's events. Being frail, alone, and frightened is the bleak circumstance that some elders experience.

FEAR OF ATTACK

The National Opinion Research Center (NORC) has conducted national surveys on the **fear of crime.** When asked, "Is there any area right around here (your home) that is within a mile where you would be afraid to walk alone at night?" more than 50 percent of those over age 65 answered yes. The image of frightened, older persons barricaded behind locked doors, however, is overplayed in the media. A study in Dade County (Miami) Florida found that the elderly did not have a statistically higher fear of crime than did younger adults (McCoy et al., 1996). This suggests that fearfulness might be less evident in relatively age-homogeneous neighborhoods, or that older people are capable of making context-based judgments of community safety. The Florida study found that dissatisfaction with neighborhood and physical vulnerability were important correlates of fear of crime, but that actual victimization experience is not the main determinant of fear.

Most literature and research finds, however, that older persons are more fearful than younger persons. The literature consistently reports that (1) women are more fearful than men; (2) African Americans are more fearful than whites; (3) those with less money are more afraid of crime than those with more money; and (4) residents of large cities are more fearful than people in smaller towns and rural areas.

The manner in which fear of crime should affect social policy is not entirely clear. On the surface, it would appear that one way to reduce fear of crime among elders would be to segregate them in walled and guarded retirement communities. But age segregation in our society could have undesirable consequences. Studies generally show that the more integrated one is in community activities the less one fears crime. Related to this is the finding that one feels less threatened by crime if one knows and trusts one's neighbors. The social implications are that developing cohesive, close-knit communities reduces fear of crime. These two alternatives are opposites, but either may be needed depending on the possibility of developing a close-knit, friendly neighborhood.

A consistent finding over the years has been that although older women fear crime more than older men, they are less likely to be victims. And though older people are more fearful than younger people, they are less likely to be victims. One explanation for this paradox may be that women and elders, considering themselves to be more vulnerable, do not as often expose themselves to risk. An additional explanation may be that they associate more minor offenses with more serious ones. For example, an older person, thinking that begging is a pretext for mugging, might be more afraid of a beggar than a younger person is. A woman might fear burglary more than a man because of the threat of rape in addition to theft. Thus, the possible consequences of the criminal act can be as frightening as the fear of victimization itself.

FIGHTING BACK

In many cities, new programs aimed at preventing crime against the elderly, helping those older persons who have become victims, and teaching them what they can do to help themselves are receiving priority. For example, one common approach is the use of police units trained in the problems particular to older people. Such units tip off the elderly to the latest trends in crime, help them to be on the alert for suspicious activity, and instruct them how to be effective witnesses against criminals caught in the act. Programs like **Neighborhood Watch,** which emphasizes crime awareness in residents of all ages, have resulted in crimes being spotted while in progress.

In many cities "granny squads" of older people patrol neighborhood blocks and give lectures on how to avoid being raped, robbed, and burglarized. Granny squads, organized under titles such as Heaven's Angels and Gray Squads, recommend such precautions as the following:

- Report all suspicious persons and all crimes to the police.
- Use automatic timers to turn on radios and lamps when you are away from home.
- Do not carry a purse. Make a band to wear inside clothing to carry money.
- Have Social Security and pension checks mailed directly to the bank.
- Join a Neighborhood Blockwatch, in which neighbors in a block meet each other and watch out for one another's person and property.

Some cities provide escort services to older people when they are the most vulnerable to attack—such as on trips to stores and banks. For example, one Chicago police district supplies a bus and driver on the day that Social Security and relief checks arrive to pick up people from two housing projects, take them to a bank and a grocery store, and then return them safely home. New York City police, hoping to bridge the gap between young and old, use teenage volunteers to provide escort services for elderly persons. In Milwaukee, Wisconsin, neighborhood security aides patrol the streets in high-crime areas that house many older residents, walking in pairs to offer safety in numbers. Although they have no power to arrest, they carry cell telephones to call police or firefighters if they encounter suspicious persons.

Efforts to protect elders from crime exist at the state level as well. Many states offer reimbursement programs for crime victims, and some of these programs give priority to older persons.

A New York State law makes a prison sentence mandatory for anyone, including a juvenile, who commits a violent crime against the elderly. Many states have extended child-abuse laws to include elders. Other states are currently considering legislation that does not allow probation for those who commit crimes against older persons.

AGING CRIMINALS

Although studies find that younger adults are at least 10 times more likely than elders to commit crimes, elderly crime is very much a reality. Most crimes committed by elders are misdemeanors—petty theft, sleeping on the sidewalk, alcohol violations, and traffic violations. Shoplifting is a frequent misdemeanor charge, and most shoplifters are white females. But felonies occur as well, most frequently in the form of grand theft and narcotic charges.

There is not necessarily a relationship between economic hardship and crime. Typically, older people are caught stealing lipstick, perfume, night creams, even cigars. They are not necessarily stealing to eat. Shoplifting among elders represents the combined influence of stress, age, and merchandising. Fear of the future may compel some to shoplift in order to conserve money for anticipated expenses. Some steal to ease fear; others do it to get attention. Only a minority of elder shoplifters has been engaged in criminal activity throughout their lives.

In general, the older perpetrator accounts for only a minority of all crimes committed. The average age for incarceration is 30.7 for men and 32.1 for females, with only about 6.6 percent of the U.S. prison population above the age of 50 (Camp & Camp, 1996). The proportion, however, is expected to increase, and by 2005 the population of inmates 50 and over in federal prisons is projected to be between 11.7 percent and 16 percent (Smyer et al., 1997). Their number more than doubled between 1981 and 1990 (Morton, 1992). The criminal activities most likely to be engaged in by older inmates are (1) violence against a family member; (2) white-collar crimes such as fraud; (3) drug sales; and (4) alcohol-related crimes such as vehicular manslaughter.

OLDER PROFESSIONAL CRIMINALS

Professional criminals tend to remain active because crime represents their life's work. The longevity of some professional thieves is incredible. Joseph (Yellow Kid) Weil, a prototype for Paul Newman's role in *The Sting,* lived to be over 100 years old and was last arrested at age 72. Willie Sutton, professional bank robber, was into his eighties and still on parole when he died (Newman et al., 1984). Most leaders of organized crime are in the upper registers of the age scale. Organized crime is age-stratified, and the heads of "families" tend to be well over 50. Vito Genovese died in prison at age 71, still commanding his organization from his cell. Older offenders also play an important role in white-collar crime. And, as the percentage of elders increases in the total population, their percentage of criminal arrests will probably increase as well.

GROWING OLD BEHIND BARS

More people are being sent to prison and receiving longer sentences, increasing the number of older prisoners. In California, for example, the number of inmates over 50 increased to 6,735 (4.8 percent of the total) from 3,874 (4 percent of the total) in 1996 (Anderson, 1997). Older convicts are (1) chronic offenders who have grown old in a steady series of prison terms; (2) those sentenced to long mandatory terms who have grown old in prison; or (3) first-time offenders in their old age.

The routine of prison life starkly separates the old from the young and middle-aged. The young men tend to be muscled and heavily tattooed, have an "in-your-face" attitude, and form groups, even gangs, for friendship and safety. The old men tend to stay to themselves trying to find quiet. The gang tensions, the chaos, the constant chatter, the televisions going from early morning until late at night take their toll over the years. There is virtually nothing in the construction of prison life that acknowledges the needs of older prisoners.

The greater threat, beyond illness or victimization, is despair. Many prisoners... "put their lives on hold." As they age, they begin to face the fact that they may never get out. "The dream of getting out, you equate with heaven. Dying in prison, you equate with hell."

PRISON INMATE, QUOTED IN ANDERSON, 1997

Taxpayers have reason to be alarmed by the increasing numbers of old prisoners, as do prison officials and humanitarians. Prison inmates are not eligible for Medicare or Medicaid. Age and illness are associated more strongly behind bars, given a life of chronic stress, idleness, cigarettes, and heavy food. Prison costs for eyeglasses, dentures, heart surgery, emphysema, prostate problems, strokes and other age-related needs are rapidly growing and will continue to do so. The average annual maintenance with medical costs for inmates 55 and older in California was estimated to be $69,000 in 1997—triple that of younger prisoners (Smyer et al., 1997). An Iowa study of 119 male inmates 50 and older found increased rates of incontinence, sensory impairment, plus 40 percent with hypertension, 97 percent with missing teeth; 42 percent with gross physical impairment, and 70 percent smokers (Colsher et al., 1992).

Tish Smyer and associates (1997), on reviewing the mental and physical health of elderly prison inmates, concluded that new models of incarceration are emerging, and changes must continue to be made:

> *The use of medical parole/release, community placement (secure skilled nursing facilities...), and growing use of prison hospice programs are being implemented as an alternative to placement of the chronically ill or elderly inmate in the general prison population. Those with functional disabilities who require help with activities of daily living may require more intensive contact with skilled professionals and counselors. Their dependent status merely intensifies the meaning of violence and powerlessness to these elderly inmates within the prison environment (p. 16).*

ELDER ABUSE

Most abuse of elders is done by the person with whom he or she lives. Often an adult child is the abuser. Though we are familiar with the "battered baby syndrome," evidence increasingly indicates a corresponding syndrome at the other end of the age scale—**battered parent syndrome**—in which parents are attacked and abused, sometimes fatally, by their own children. Factors that increase the risk of a caregiver becoming an abuser include alcohol and drug abuse, cognitive impairment, economic stress, caregiver inexperience, a history of family violence, a blaming personality, unrealistic expectations, and economic dependence on the elder (Allan, 1998).

Among community dwelling elders in the United States and other Western countries, it is estimated that between 3 and 6 percent of individuals over the age of 65 report having experienced abuse, usually at the hands of family members (Lachs et al., 1997; Ogg & Bennett, 1992; Podkieks, 1992).

Abuse can be intentional (e.g., willfully withholding food or medications), or it might be unintentional, resulting from ignorance or the genuine inability to provide the necessary care (Allan, 1998). On a national level, neglect is by far the most common form of abuse, followed by physical abuse, then financial and material exploitation (Lachs et al., 1997). Several measures of abuse have been identified:

1. *Physical abuse* is the willful infliction of pain or injury and may include beating, choking, burning, inappropriate medication, tying or locking up, and sexual assault.
2. *Psychological abuse* includes threats, intimidation, and verbal abuse.

TABLE 13.3

Theoretical explanations of elder abuse

Theory	Description
Psychological model	Relationship of violent behavior to aggressive personality traits; at the most severe end of physical aggression, large proportions of elder abusers have histories of mental illness and/or substance abuse. Intervention is individual, focused on the caregiver.
Situational model	Abuse as a problem of caregiving; high levels of stress and burden of caregiving increase mistreatment and neglect of the frail elder. Intervention is on stress reduction of the care-provider.
Symbolic interaction model	Each person approaches in interaction with personal definitions and expectations; if behaviors match the roles expected, the interaction continues, otherwise conflict arises. The caregiver's subjective sense of stress related to the dependency tasks creates stress, not the tasks themselves. Assessment of the caring situation by caregivers is necessary for abuse prevention.
Social exchange theory	When each individual contributes equally, a fair exchange results; when one party is unable to reciprocate, the exchange is seen as being unfair. Unequal distribution of power in caregiving situations can result in abuse. In this model, intervention should focus on the abuser.
Feminist theory	Identifies violence as a tactic of entitlement and power that is deeply gendered, rather than a conflict tactic that is personal and gender neutral. This model has been more successful in explaining wife abuse than child or elder abuse.
Ecological model	Focuses on behavior within the social context and on the accommodation between the person and the environment. According to this model, mobilization of the community is the intervention strategy.
Political economy model	Elder abuse arises from the way older people are marginalized in society. These experiences are a product of the division of labor and structure of inequality in society, rather than a product of relationship and aging. Intervention focuses on change in social policy.

Adapted from: Rosalie S. Wolf (1997). Elder Abuse and Neglect: Causes and Consequences. *Journal of Geriatric Psychiatry, 30* (1), 153–174.

3. *Financial/material abuse* means taking financial advantage of frail or ill elderly. It is the misuse of an elder's money or property: theft, deception, diverting income, or mismanagement of funds.
4. *Violation of rights.* Old people have the right to vote and the right to due process. A conservator, for example, may take away all the rights of an older person.
5. *Neglect* occurs when a caregiver's failure to provide adequate food, shelter, clothing, and medical or dental care results in significant danger to the physical or mental health of an older person in his or her care.
6. *Self-abuse and neglect.* Some old people do not adequately care for themselves. Sometimes it is intentional; other times they simply cannot adequately provide for themselves.

The abuse of elders, despite the meanness of the crime, is not a well-studied topic; therefore, systematic ways to address the problem have not been developed in social policy. Table 13.3 presents a summary of existing theories of elder abuse developed by Dr. Rosalie S. Wolf, President of the National Committee for the Prevention of Elder Abuse. The table shows that resolution of the problem of elder abuse depends on the theoretical perspective taken: Psychological models address caregiver personality and relationships in the family setting; other models look to the community and to the larger society (Wolf, 1997).

The primary policy implication for the issue of elder abuse is that strained families must have more help available to them—help from social services, home care services, protective services, personal-care homes, and family counseling.

The profile of the "typical" abused elder has traditionally pointed to the frail, widowed female who is cognitively impaired and chronically ill. Subsequent studies, however, show wider variation in the at-risk older adult. In one nine-year study of more than 2,800 elders linked to abusive victimization through adult protective service records, the predictors of mistreatment were poverty, race, functional and cognitive impairment, worsening cognitive impairment, and living with someone (Lachs et al., 1997). Gender did not emerge as a profile in this study.

A common predictor of abusive behavior is economic dependence. In one case, an older woman lived with her son and supported him while he drank all the time and abused her. In another case, an older mother cared for her epileptic daughter who stole money from her. In some cases, wives were abused by the severely disabled husbands they were caring for. Abusers are rarely stable individuals, brought to the brink by the excessive demands of an elderly dependent. Rather, these caretakers suffer emotionally and are barely able to meet their own needs, much less the needs of another person. The older person who stays in an abusive situation can see no better alternative. Under the social exchange theory, the abuser's lack of power is a factor in the abuse. The caretaker's dependency, especially his or her financial dependency, rather than the dependency of the victim, correlates most strongly with abuse.

Abuse can and does take place in nursing homes by staff. Older persons are more at risk in institutions than in their own homes because of their exceptional frailty and danger of retaliation by caretakers. Abuse in institutions is not necessarily reported or reflected in national statistics. A survey revealed that 36 percent of the staff at several nursing homes had observed other staff psychologically abusing patients and had witnessed physical abuse that included employing excessive restraints; pushing, grabbing, kicking, or shoving patients; or throwing things at them. Over 70 percent of the psychological abuse included yelling and swearing at patients; this abuse also included isolating patients, threatening them, and denying them food and/or privileges (Pillemer & Moore, 1989).

Despite existing regulations monitoring the treatment of institutionalized elders, the need for vigilance remains. Penalties have been stiffened, county and state agencies are receiving more power to investigate and prosecute, and people are being encouraged to report suspicious happenings. Signs of abuse include abrupt negative changes in physical appearance; inappropriate behavior, such as extreme fear, asking to die, or extreme anger; a bad attitude on the part of the caregiver; and deteriorated or isolated living quarters. As more people live to extreme old age and, thus, to the point of becoming physically dependent on someone else— adequate social service programming for elder care is critical.

Fraud

Any person with money is a potential victim of the huckster and the con artist. Although victims of confidence schemes and consumer frauds who file crime reports are not normally required to give their age, accounts of fraud state that the elders, who constitute approximately 13 percent of the population, represent approximately 30 percent of those who are swindled. Many elders have accumulated a nest egg over the years or have recently come into a large lump-sum pension or life insurance benefit. Some may be seeking investments they can make with relative ease. For some, low returns on passbook savings accounts motivate the search for new investments

(Bekey, 1991). Additionally, older people are more likely to be at home when a con artist calls. The following descriptions summarize some of the major kinds of fraud.

SOCIAL REFERRAL

Some dating and marriage services seek out the lonely and the widowed to lure them into paying big fees for introductions to new friends or possible mates. A victim may pay hundreds of dollars for a video to be shown to prospective dates (and then it is never shown) or for a computerized dating service that never generates any dates. Religious cults also have targeted elders and even entire retirement communities as recruitment areas for new members (Collins & Frantz, 1994).

LAND AND HOME EQUITY FRAUD

In one type of **land fraud,** real-estate developers may offer lots for sale in a still-to-be-built retirement community, promising all kinds of facilities, such as swimming pools and golf courses, and describing the site in glowing phrases. None of the descriptions and promises may be accurate.

Home-equity fraud has left some elders homeless (Wallace, 1992). Swindlers pose as financial experts who offer help in refinancing a home. The swindler ends up with the cash from the home-equity loan or actually gets the owner to unwittingly sign papers transferring title.

FRAUD THROUGH MAIL ORDER AND TELEVISION

Mail-order catalogs and television advertising can be misleading and result in **mail-order fraud.** Current ads that may be hoaxes or wild exaggerations tout nutritional miracles, breast developers, and weight-reducing and exercise devices. Mail ordering and phone ordering from television ads are particularly attractive for those who no longer have transportation. Although many firms are honest, the mail-order and television industries have yet to eliminate the racketeers in their midst.

Mail-order health insurance has, in the past, proved to be worth little. Fraudulent hospitalization policies can be filled with small-print exceptions—ifs, ands, and buts—that will eliminate the policyholder when a claim is made. Coverage for the person may not exist at the very time of failing health and hospitalization.

In 1986, a national consumers' group filed a complaint charging 19 insurance companies with trying to sell extra health insurance to elders using deceptive mailings that bore official-sounding names and Washington, D.C., addresses. These companies sent out hundreds of letters warning people about Medicare cutbacks. Those who returned a response card, thinking they were dealing with a concerned government group, were solicited by insurance agents. The companies were given cease-and-desist orders (Reich & Morrison, 1986). In a similar case, U.S. attorneys are conducting mail fraud investigations on a direct-mail kingpin of the political right who exploits the fears of elders by telling them their Social Security benefits are being taken away (Stone, 1993).

The "contest winner" fraud is ever present in our mail system. In some, the "winner" of a vacation, car, stereo, or other prize must either send money for postage or registration or pay to make a long-distance telephone call for more information. Twice in four months, an 88-year-old man flew, confirmation letter in hand, to Florida to collect his $11 million "winnings." The letter read, "Final results are in, and they're official. You're our newest $11 million winner." The fine print, however, fully informed the "winner" that a specific winning number was required. In a statement to Ann Landers, the attorney general of Florida was quoted as saying, "In their zeal to sell magazines, American Family Publishers and their high-profile pitchmen have misled millions of consumers. They have clearly stepped over the line from advertising hype to unlawful deception" (Ann Landers, 1998).

TELEPHONE FRAUD

Telephone fraud is also a problem. For some elders, telephone contact is their primary source of interaction with other people. In New York, an 80-year-old woman reported that she had lost thousands of dollars to telemarketers because "I've been a widow for 19 years. It's very lonely. They were nice on the phone. They became my friends." Said a 77-year-old man, "I wasn't a victim—I was a sucker. I lost $200,000" (New York Times, 1997). The typical story is that the elder has won a wonderful prize—a vacation in Hawaii, a new car, or substantial cash. They then are asked to send a check by overnight mail to cover taxes, postage, and handling of the winnings. The same victims often fall prey to more than one scheme.

Telephones are now the vehicle of choice for committing fraud. Telemarketing fraud accounts for $10 billion in investor losses annually, and southern California alone has as many as 300 **boiler rooms** (offices from which the telephone calls are made) functioning at any one time. The telephone vacation scam has lured many retirees. Callers tout fantastic-sounding Hawaiian packages for an unbelievably low price—$179 for two people for a week, for example. The "lucky traveler" need only provide their credit card number for reservations. But the trip is either postponed indefinitely or uses sleazy hotels with untold extra charges.

A Tennessee criminal fraud investigation team recommended to elders: (1) beware of requests for money to prepay taxes; (2) beware of requests to send a check by overnight delivery; (3) beware of requests for credit card numbers to show eligibility; (4) beware of a rush for action; and (5) to fight back, just hang up (New York Times, 1997).

DOOR-TO-DOOR SALES

Peddlers of various kinds of merchandise often target the homebound because their loneliness makes them eager for conversation. Some salespeople are honest; others sell shoddy goods or offer useless services. For example, a salesperson might scare a person into contracting for unnecessary home repairs, and then flee with the down payment. Or one salesperson may make a pitch while the other robs the house (Cronk, 1998).

Life Alert, a company whose television ads used the memorable line "Help! I've Fallen and I Can't Get Up!" has been sued for deceptive advertising. The lawsuit contends that the company uses high-pressure sales tactics (including sales presentations that last up to six hours!) and misleading ads to bully old people into buying the product. It also alleges that salespeople lied to senior citizens and disabled persons during sales pitches and refused to leave until a sale—the system's cost ranged from $1,700 to $5,000—was made. Misrepresentations included the claim of an emergency hotline more reliable than the public 911 system (Holding, 1991).

Investment Fraud

There are many "get-rich" schemes used to fleece older people. Older people eager to invest their savings as a hedge against inflation may become victims of numerous investment frauds involving bogus inventions or phony businesses. One California scam artist was convicted of stealing close to $700,000 from mostly older investors invited by mail to investment seminars (Brignolo, 1998).

ESTATE RIPOFFS

Some scam artists contact elders to offer services in preparing living trusts. They charge high fees, make phony pledges, and make off with money, and no living trust is provided (Crenshaw, 1992). Court-selected guardians or conservators assigned to look after older persons are in a position to steal from them, and some do. To preserve an inheritance, children will sometimes force adult parents to live in inferior dwellings. Individual cases can become complicated, when the line between generosity and friendship and fraudulent taking-advantage becomes blurred. In a California case, a savings and loan manager conserva-

Because some elders experience loneliness and isolation or reduced judgment, they are a group targeted by unethical businesses. Companionship, advocacy, and legal vigilance can help protect the more vulnerable of the country's elders.

tor, as well as the corporation for which he works, are being sued for $10 million on behalf of family members of a woman with Alzheimer's disease, whose friendship with the thrift manager clearly preceded her mental deterioration (Mintz, 1998). Some authorities are urging the government and the courts to more closely audit estates, so that abuse can be discovered. They also suggest a limit on the yearly fees that conservators can charge.

A study of guardianship revealed the following:

- Elderly in guardianship courts are often afforded fewer rights than criminal defendants.
- The overburdened court systems puts elders' lives in the hands of others without enough evidence that such placement is necessary.
- The more than 300,000 persons 65 and over who live under guardianship are "unpersons" in that they can no longer receive money or pay bills, marry, or choose where they will live or what medical treatment they receive.

Though most appointed guardians are dedicated, caring people, there are not enough safeguards against the minority who are corrupt and greedy (Associated Press, 1987).

MEDICARE AND MEDICAID FRAUD

One kind of medical hoax involves outrageous abuses of the federal Medicare and state Medicaid programs. The violators are licensed physicians and registered pharmacists who file exaggerated claims for reimbursement.

Despite an elaborate system of safeguards, some experts say that the Medicare program is being bilked of millions of dollars a year. Vague regulations, overworked investigators, swamped claims processors, and gullible consumers all play a part. Typical frauds identified by federal fraud investigation teams include (1) a 20-minute procedure being billed as a 24-hour procedure; (2) unnecessary surgery; (3) billing for multiple procedures when a single procedure was used; (4) the submission of bills for patients who are no longer living; and (5) sale of outrageously overpriced medical equipment for which Medicare pays 80 percent.

United States Health and Human Services Department has paid out nearly $2 million to recruit and train retired professionals to fight against fraud, waste, and abuse in Medicare and Medicaid. Twelve projects have been funded to develop demonstrations to train people in uncovering federal insurance fraud. The Administration on Aging estimates that as much as 14 percent of Medicare claims ($23.2 billion) were overpaid in 1996 because of improper fee-for-service billings (Bellandi, 1997). The program trains volunteers to work with people in their communities to help them understand their benefits and look for overbilling and unnecessary care. In California, more than 500 volunteers work in 24 Health Insurance Counseling and Advocacy Programs (HICAP) to help seniors and Social Security offices navigate Medicare's explanation of benefits (Bellandi, 1997).

CONFIDENCE GAMES

Con artists use various tactics. In a **confidence game,** the victim is tricked into giving up money voluntarily. Several games are common. Some examples are (1) the "block hustle," in which the con artist sells the victim a worthless item that he or she claims is both stolen and valuable; (2) the "pigeon drop," in which the victim is persuaded to put up money on the promise of making much more; and (3) the "lottery swindle," in which the victim pays cash for counterfeit lottery tickets. In one case a man was arrested for bilking older tenants by dunning them with fake water bills (James, 1994).

MEDICAL QUACKERY

Though **medical quackery,** the misrepresentation of either health or cosmetic benefits through devices or drugs that are presumably therapeutic, can victimize both young and old, older people tend to be more prone to this kind of victimization. For one thing, older persons often have more ailments than younger persons; for another, the "youth culture" in the United States sometimes leads older persons on a medical quest for more youthful looks.

Many who offer medical goods and services are honest. Some are not, however; and the elderly are often cheated. Americans spend about $27 billion a year on quack products or treatments. The following are the top five health frauds in the United States, according to the FDA: (1) ineffective arthritis products; (2) spurious cancer clinics (many of which are located in Mexico); (3) bogus AIDS cures (offered at underground clinics in the United States, the Caribbean, and Europe); (4) instant weight-loss schemes; and (5) fraudulent sexual aids (The Top Ten Health Frauds, 1990).

We will cover four topics here: medical devices, youth restorers and **miracle drugs,** cancer cures, and arthritis cures. It might be added that although no new numbers are currently available for sexual aid fraud, the advent of the impotence drug Viagra on the marketplace will undoubtedly spur creative new forms of fraud in this category.

MEDICAL DEVICES

According to the Federal Trade Commission, many older Americans who need such medical devices as eyeglasses, hearing aids, and dentures frequently are victims of overpricing, misrepresentation, and high-pressure sales tactics. Because Medicare does not cover the cost of eyeglasses, hearing aids, or dentures, many persons cannot pay for devices and must do without them. Some problems include (1) 200 to 300 percent variation in the cost of identical eyeglasses, dentures, hearing aids; and (2) outrageous profits for lifesaving devices such as heart pacemakers, which may sell for four times the manufacturing cost.

YOUTH RESTORERS AND MIRACLE DRUGS

Elders are likely targets for products that promise to restore the appearance of youth—cosmetics, skin treatments, hair restorers, male potency pills, wrinkle and "age spot" removers, and the like. In a society like ours, which glamorizes youth, the desire to remain young is strong.

Like the medicine shows that once traveled from town to town offering miracle tonics and multipurpose cures, those who today provide cosmetic surgery and breast implants are enjoying a booming business. Unfortunately, the cosmetic surgery field contains many quacks. Poorly trained "surgeons" have mutilated faces and bodies and endangered lives.

Even ads for beauty products promising to restore wrinkled skin border on quackery. But even though the Federal Drug Administration (FDA) believes that many claims by the cosmetic industry are misleading if not absolutely false, the interpretation of the law is fuzzy, and there's not much that can be done.

The skin-care market has grown into a huge money-making industry. Dermatologists say that despite the claims of all the antiaging creams and lotions, there is no substance that can alter the structure or functioning of your living skin. The only thing that any product can hope to do is add some moisture to the top layer of skin. Nevertheless, advertisers are having a heyday because the FDA spends its time regulating more harmful substances.

Even products that have been FDA-approved tend to be advertised with exaggerated claims. A product called Retin A (generic name: tretinoin), originally used to treat acne, is now touted as a miraculous cure for wrinkles. Actually it is not a permanent cure. Further, use of the product, like use of any chemical product, carries some risks and side effects. The FDA-approved antibaldness medication minoxidil, under the brand name Rogaine, may not produce a perfect head of hair and does not work for everybody.

CANCER AND AIDS CURES

Cancer victims have been offered "cures" ranging from seawater at $3 per pint to irradiated grape juice to machines alleged to cure cancer. Scientific studies have not shown Laetrile, a substance extracted from apricot pits, to have value in treating cancer. The FDA's disapproval of Laetrile has caused many states to ban it. Yet, many cancer sufferers claim to have been helped by the drug.

Many factors account for the popularity of proven "cures" like Laetrile. Because hundreds of thousands of new cancer cases are diagnosed each year and because two out of three victims will ultimately die of it, people are rightfully afraid of cancer. Conventional treatment is neither simple nor pleasant—surgery is often extensive, radiation can burn, chemotherapy can cause hair loss and vomiting. Laetrile, for example, offers a far more easy treatment. It comes in tablets to be taken with large doses of vitamin C on a low-sugar diet that avoids all foods containing additives.

Fraudulent cancer "cures" rob the sick not only of their money. Cancer quacks also rob their victims of the most precious thing they have: time for proper treatment.

AIDS patients who can perceive no cure in the traditional medical establishment are especially willing to try unconventional treatments. In desperate efforts to prolong their lives, AIDS patients are prime targets for medical quackery. Some have spent thousands of dollars on worthless cures.

ARTHRITIS CURES

Arthritis is the most common chronic condition of elders. An inflammation that makes joints stiff and painful to move, arthritis appears in a hundred or so forms, the most severe and crippling of which is rheumatoid arthritis. Some forms of arthritis are painless; others cause severe pain.

Because no one knows exactly what causes arthritis, doctors can do little more than prescribe pain relievers. This lack of certainty leaves the field wide open for all kinds of fake cures. Copper bracelets have been sold to cure arthritis. Wearing two kinds of metal in each shoe purportedly sets up "chemical impulses" that ward off pain. Various diets, cod-liver oil, brown vinegar with honey, "immune" milk, alfalfa tablets, megavitamins, and snake or bee venom have all been sold to "cure" arthritis.

Drug Abuse

Elders can be victims of drug abuse. Our society offers drugs—both legal and illegal— as a solution to a host of problems. The abuses discussed here are not those involving illegal drugs, such as heroin and cocaine, but those that involve legal drugs: prescription drugs, over-the-counter drugs, and alcohol.

PRESCRIPTION DRUGS

Though persons of all ages need prescription drugs for various health problems, elders need them in much greater proportions, because they are more likely to suffer from chronic illnesses or pain. The elderly, who comprise 13 percent of the population, consume 30 percent of all prescribed drugs (Blazer, 1990). More than 30 percent of all prescriptions for Seconal and Valium, two potent and potentially addictive sedatives, are written for persons over age 60.

With high drug usage, a more significant chance exists for adverse drug reactions and drug abuse. Health professionals are responsible for some of the drug abuse suffered by the older population. Their errors can be of two types: (1) not prescribing a drug correctly, or (2) prescribing less or more drugs than necessary. A study from Harvard University found that almost one-fourth of seniors are prescribed drugs that by themselves or in combination are dangerous or wrong (Stolberg, 1994). But such errors can sometimes seem intentional. Health professionals in nursing homes, for example, may over prescribe drugs so that patients become calm and easier to manage. When overused, drugs can stupefy, injure, and kill. Educational intervention is advised, not only for older drug consumers, but for practicing physicians and pharmacists as well.

The nearly two million nursing-home residents are perhaps the nation's most medicated people, often suffering depression and disorientation from receiving too high a dosage of drugs such as Valium, Calpa, and Elavil, or a combination of such drugs. Elderly patients both in and out of nursing homes may get prescriptions from several doctors and have reactions from their combined ingestion. Friends may exchange prescription drugs without regard to side effects or combination (synergistic) reactions with other medications. They also may mix prescription and over-the-counter drugs without realizing that the interactions can be harmful, or they may take the wrong amounts of their own medications. Adverse drug reactions occur more frequently in old age, and multiple drug use should be closely monitored.

Stereotypes and the negative portrayal of older people have a considerable impact on a physician's prescribing habits. In ads in physicians' magazines, such as *Geriatrics*, elders tend to be pictured as inactive and described in negative terms: aimless, apathetic, disruptive, insecure, out of control, and temperamental. Drug advertising influences the medical professional to offer drugs as a first solution to emotionally disturbed elders. Viewing old people in this manner may result in a physician giving increased prescriptions.

OVER-THE-COUNTER DRUGS

Although over-the-counter (OTC) drugs may seem harmless, they are overused and consequently abused. One can either blame the drug companies, who push their products through advertising, or the poorly informed consumer.

Aspirin is the most widely used OTC drug. Many old people use very high doses of aspirin for arthritis, even though aspirin is a stomach irritant and can deplete the body of essential nutrients. (Some doctors use a milder drug, suprofen, rather than aspirin, to treat arthritis; but suprofen is not available over the counter.)

Laxatives have been advertised as "nature's way," however nothing is further from the truth. Prolonged laxative use can impair normal bowel function. Nature's way is plenty of water and fiber in the diet; many people, however, get "addicted" to laxatives, thinking they are making the best choice.

The same is true of those who take sleeping pills, which must be taken in escalating doses to be effective. Consequently, they can cause rather than cure insomnia (Kolata, 1992). Because people need less sleep as they get older, many are better off to accept this fact rather than to try to force themselves to sleep eight or more hours a night. Hemorrhoid medication ads exaggerate the effectiveness of their products, and mouthwash does little more than add to the complaints of dry mouth.

Antacids such as Alka-Seltzer contain sodium bicarbonate, which may harm kidney function. Also, excess ibuprofen can cause liver damage. These OTC drugs can be a waste of money, cause bodily harm, and/or delay proper treatment of potentially serious ailments.

ALCOHOLISM

Alcoholism as a problem for elders has been largely ignored until recent years. If, after retirement, older persons lead much less visible lives, alcoholism can remain well concealed, becoming a self-generating cycle of abuse. Diminished contacts and a sense of loss may trigger drinking that goes unrecognized.

Alcoholism: ". . . a primary, chronic disease with genetic, psychosocial and environmental factors influencing its development and manifestations. The disease is often progressive and fatal. It is characterized by impaired control over drinking, preoccupation with the drug alcohol, use of alcohol despite adverse consequences, and distortions in thinking, most notably denial."

NATIONAL COUNCIL ON ALCOHOLISM AND DRUG DEPENDENCE AND THE AMERICAN SOCIETY OF ADDICTION MEDICINE [REPORTED IN MORSE & FLAVIN, 1992]

Elders *do not* have higher rates of alcoholism than younger adults, however. One review of the literature concluded that alcohol consumption goes down with age, plus there are fewer alcohol-related problems among heavy drinkers who were elderly than among those who were not (Liberto et al., 1992). Among those with problems, however, the strain of alcoholism on the body is profound.

Some older alcoholics began their drinking early in life. Between half and two-thirds of older alcoholics are estimated to have begun early in life (Council on Scientific Affairs, 1996). "Early onset" alcoholics have had alcohol-related problems for years and are more identifiable because of earlier dysfunctional behavior that brought them to the attention of the medical or helping establishment.

In contrast, the "late-life onset" alcoholic, who begins abusive drinking in his or her fifties or sixties, is often viewed as a reactive drinker, one whose problem began after traumatic events such as the death of a spouse, retirement, or moving from an original home. He or she will have fewer chronic health problems and is likely to drink alone at home. In cases where alcoholism first occurs in old age, the alcoholic will often respond readily to intervention—help for depression or loneliness, for example, may reduce the need for alcohol. Treatment focuses on rebuilding a social support network and overcoming negative emotional states. Long-term alcoholics are more difficult, but not impossible, to help.

Psychiatric hospital and outpatient clinic records show that admission for alcoholism peaks in the 35-to-40-age group. Some researchers believe that alcoholism may be a self-limiting disease; that is, the decrease in alcoholism in the older age groups results not from treatment but from a spontaneous recovery with age due to factors such as a lowered social pressure to achieve. Others think that alcoholism kills many of its victims before they reach old age. Still, about 10 percent of elders manifest symptoms related to excessive use of alcohol. Older men are more at risk than older women. And two-thirds of older alcoholics are severe chronic alcoholics whose symptoms tend to be obvious and profound (Council on Scientific Affairs, 1996).

Risk factors for alcoholism in later life include: (1) family history of alcoholism; (2) personal history of excessive alcohol consumption; (3) discretionary time, money, and/or opportunity to drink; (4) age-related volume of alcohol distribution in the body; (5) increased central nervous system sensitivity to alcohol; (6) pain or insomnia secondary to chronic medical disorders; and (7) other psychiatric disorders, such as schizophrenia and depression (Goldstein et al., 1996).

Alcoholics Anonymous (AA) and other groups can be instrumental in stopping heavy drinking. Countless people have benefited from AA. Addiction can touch even the powerful and the famous. Former First Lady Betty Ford described her cross-addiction to alcohol and painkillers as "insidious." She went public about her multiple drug abuse and eventually founded the Betty Ford Rehabilitation Center.

Promoting Consumer Education

Consumer education is vital in helping individuals to avoid fraud, medical quackery, and drug abuse. Adult education programs are one way of reaching the public. Videotape systems now provide advice on a variety of topics, such as how to buy a used car without being swindled, how to handle the estate of a deceased relative, or how to recognize and avoid con artists. Books and magazines offer consumer information aimed at the older population, covering topics such as prescription drugs and their side effects, as well as the use and abuse of over-the-counter drugs and alcohol. Consumer action groups are available for persons of all ages who want to support the creation of stricter consumer-protection laws and the enforcement of existing laws.

Chapter Summary

Suicide continues to be a significant problem among those 65 and over. The suicide *attempt* rate for older women is much higher than for older men, yet older men (white males, that is) have the highest rate of *actual* suicides of any age group. Many factors may be involved, especially dependency, depression, physical illness, and social isolation.

The dimensions of the problem of crime against the elderly are being studied by law-enforcement and social-service agencies. National surveys show that elders are less likely to be victimized than younger adults, except in the area of personal larceny (e.g., purse and wallet snatchings), where attacks on elders are considerable. Over half of the violent victimizations occur in or near one's home. Fear of crime is widespread among elders and exists in a greater degree than the actual crime rate against them would suggest. It is the metropolitan elderly for whom fear of crime takes its greatest toll. Elders, themselves, can also be the victimizers. Older criminals come from two groups: (1) those who started at a young age engaging in illegal activities, and (2) those who committed offenses for the first time in their later years. The older prison population is growing, but adequate medical care is lacking in jails and prisons.

Elders are potential victims of the huckster and con artist. Land fraud, mail-order fraud, mail-order health insurance, and confidence games are used to deceive and cheat people out of money. Medical quackery often entices the sick and ailing. Medical devices, youth restorers, and cancer and arthritis cures have robbed many of their money. Elders are sometimes victims of drug abuse—both prescription and nonprescription drugs.

Education, self-help groups, and professional help should be available to assist elders with their special problems. Consumer education is useful in learning to detect frauds and gaining knowledge about over-the-counter and prescription drugs.

Key Terms

attempted suicide
battered parent syndrome
boiler room
confidence games
credit card fraud
crib job
crimes against persons
double suicide
fear of crime
granny dumping
home-equity fraud
land fraud
mail-order fraud
medical quackery
miracle drugs
Neighborhood Watch
rational suicide
successful suicide
suicide rate

Discussion Questions

1. How does fear of crime affect one's behavior?
2. Imagine that you are an old person and that your adult offspring is taking advantage of you in some way. How would you handle the situation?
3. Why might some elders be susceptible to con artists?
4. Imagine that you have just been cheated of $1,000 by a con artist who has promised that your money will be quadrupled in four days. What would you do?

Fieldwork Suggestions

Clip articles from magazines and newspapers that advertise goods and health insurance that are probably fraudulent. Find other evidence of fraud, such as letters from funeral homes, which border on the unethical.

Online Activities

1. Locate a grief forum on the Internet. What themes do you find? What ages do you guess are represented among the correspondents? Can you find a source of Internet discussion about depression, death, and suicide that reflects the perspectives of older adults?
2. Write a content analysis of the Hemlock Society's Internet home page. What resources are linked? Why? How would you characterize the "tone" of the information presented?
3. Search a Web site that would provide useful and appropriate information for a family member concerned about alcohol consumption of an elderly person in the family. Hint: Try the American Medical Association and Alcoholics Anonymous home pages.

14

Women and Ethnic Groups

Maya Angelou Offers the Grace of Good Advice

Paul Craig

The scope of Maya Angelou's life is breathtaking.

She has been during her 65 years an actress, dancer, journalist, educator, author, screenwriter and TV and movie director-producer. She also has served on federal commissions and, at the inauguration of President Clinton, delivered her poem, "On the Pulse of Morning."

Angelou's book, *Wouldn't Take Nothing for My Journey Now*, offers some of her thoughts on what the years have taught. From her comparatively tranquil vantage point as a professor at Wake Forest University in Winston-Salem, N.C., Angelou (pronounced AngeLOW) comments on everything from the status of women to tired phrases she hates.

Above all, Angelou issues a plea for honoring diversity as the country grows into a more varied mixture of peoples and creeds: "It is a time for the preachers, the rabbis, the priests and pundits and the professors to believe in the awesome wonder of diversity so that they can teach those who follow them. It is a time for parents to teach young people early on that in diversity there is beauty and there is strength."

Angelou admits she ponders death "with alarming frequency" but fears the loss of others more than her eventual demise, recommends forgiveness but no patience with fools and heartily recommends taking a day off now and then just for fun. She even suggests a paranoia can have its valid uses.

On the less serious side, Angelou, always a woman who dresses in cheerful colors she says make her happy, writes of fashion's intimidation of those who "are imprisoned by powerful dictates on what is right and proper to wear. Those decisions made by others and sometimes at their convenience are not truly meant to make life better or finer or more graceful or more gracious. Many times they stem from greed, insensitivity and the need for control."

She also warns the whiners of the world, "Whining is not only graceless, but can be dangerous. It can alert a brute that a victim is in the neighborhood."

Some of her accomplishments?

She toured Europe with the cast of *Porgy and Bess* in 1952; has been an editor and writer in Cairo and in Ghana's capital, Accra; was northern coordinator of Martin Luther King Jr.'s Southern Christian Leadership Conference at the start of the 1960s; worked on commissions under Presidents Ford and Carter; acted in TV's *Roots*; and has seen her autobiographical works, such as *I Know Why the Caged Bird Sings*, adapted for television.

Additionally, she appeared in such plays as *Mother Courage* and *The Blacks*, was nominated for a Tony Award for her stage role in *Look Away*, and received a Pulitzer nomination for her book *Just Give Me a Cool Drink of Water 'Fore I Diiie*. (Yes, "i" three times is how she wanted to spell it.

Her career in education has included teaching in Italy, Ghana and Israel, as well as in American universities, including an appearance as distinguished visiting professor at California State University, Sacramento. And she has clear-cut evidence of her welcome at Wake Forest—the professorship is for life.

Her thoughtful work soars far above most "what I have learned" books. Angelou has things to say and says them gracefully. Her book is an excellent learning investment for any reader.

Author's Note: Born in 1928 as Marguerite Johnson, Maya Angelou was raised in rural Arkansas. She married a South African freedom fighter and lived for 5 years in Cairo, Egypt. During that time she became the editor of *The Arab Observer*, the only English-language news weekly in the Middle East; she taught in Ghana; and she was the feature editor of *The African Review*. In the 1960s she remarked that being black, female, non-Muslim, non-Arab, six feet tall, and American made for some interesting experiences in Africa! In addition to her profile talents in the English language, Dr. Angelou speaks French, Spanish, Italian, and West African Fanti.

Multiculturalism has become a central focus of the social sciences. This focus corrects a past tendency to ignore the diversity and richness that ethnic groups have added to American life and to assume that Americans' experiences are relatively similar, despite their roots of origin and cultural traditions. Until recently the study of aging America was a study of the older white Americans who made up nearly 90 percent of America's elderly population, while the many ethnic groups were ignored. Generalizing from the larger population to all subcultures of elders is misleading, incorrect, and insensitive. Being old and a member of a minority group, or to be an old white woman, is to experience the political economy—the context of aging—in ways strikingly different than that experienced by older white males in America.

By 2030 there will be about 70 million people over 65 in this country—more than two times their number in 1996. Of this number, 25 percent will be minority populations by 2030, and by 2050 minorities will constitute 33 percent of the older population (Administration on Aging, 1997). Thus, with every passing year the ethnic aged become a larger proportion of aging America. The bars in Figure 14.1 illustrate the proportional shift of elderly minorities from 1990 to the middle of the 21st century.

The non-Hispanic white elder population is projected to increase by 91 percent from 1990 to 2030. The proportion of all elders who are

FIGURE 14.1

Percent elderly by race and Hispanic origin, 1990 and 2050

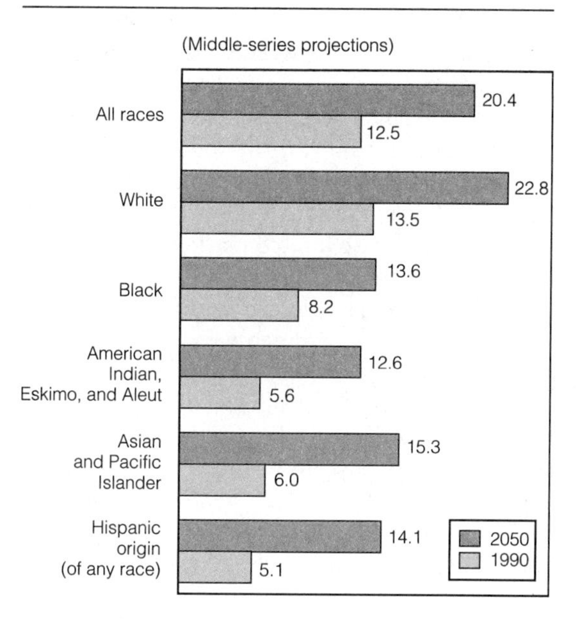

Source: US Bureau of the Census (1990). *U.S. population estimates by age, sex, race, and Hispanic origin: 1980-1991.* Current population reports, Washington, DC: U.S. Government Printing Office.

African American will increase by 159 percent. The Native American, Eskimo, and Aleut populations will increase by 249 percent. Finally, Asians and Pacific Islander elders will increase by 643 percent from 1990; and the elder Hispanic population will increase by 570 percent. Increases in all the groups are related to past fertility patterns, immigration patterns, and to increasing life expectancy (National Institute on Aging, 1993).

The categorization of minorities, however useful it might be for bureaucratic purposes, often flies in the face of group identification. Koreans, for example, identify strongly as Koreans, and most certainly do not identify with, say, the Japanese. Both groups, however, are considered to be "Asian" under U.S. government standards.

Ethnicity involves (1) a culture and an internalized heritage not shared by outsiders, (2) social status, and (3) the composition and function of support systems (Hooyman & Kiyak, 1996). Discrimination is not necessarily associated with ethnicity. Some German, Scandinavian, Eastern Bloc, and southern European immigrants have retained close cultural ties with their ethnic backgrounds, but do not necessarily hold minority status. **Minorities** in this context are ethnic elders identified by language, physical, or cultural characteristics, and, based on those characteristics, have experienced unequal treatment in certain segments of society.

A particular challenge to American society at the turn of the century will be that its aged population is homogeneous, but its younger population is quite heterogeneous—the diverse population of younger adults will be responsible for developing national policy that affects a homogeneous older age group. It will not be until around 2020 that the elderly population will begin to reflect the diversity of the larger population. By 2050, elder diversity will be established: around 30 percent of the elderly will be African American, 36 percent will be elderly Hispanics, and whites will constitute around 40 percent of the population of elders (Hobbs & Damon, 1996).

Acknowledging the limitations of the "ethnic" concept and the vagaries of group identification, we consider here five groups: women of any ethnicity, African Americans, Hispanics, Asians, and Native Americans. Women, although not an ethnic minority group, hold a lower status in our culture than men. Therefore, women have been judged a minority group not in terms of numbers, but in terms of status. Older women are considered first in this chapter and the section on ethnic minority elders follows.

Women

The minority status of women is based on the sexism that pervades U.S. society. For older women sexism is compounded by ageism. Older women have trouble finding acceptance and equality in the work world, in politics, and in romance. Women are making progress in these areas; however, hundreds of years of established patterns cannot be changed overnight.

One advantage for women is their willingness to reach out and get help—from each other, from books and seminars, and from various counseling services in the community and at universities and colleges. Self-help and self-understanding books abound, ranging from books about relationships of daughters and mothers (see for example *From Daughters to Mothers,* Warloe, 1997) through numerous books on physical and mental health (for example, *Women's Bodies, Women's Wisdom,* Northrup, 1998).

The range of popular books suggests that the present generation of older women is receiving more attention and validation than previous generations. Roles for older women, which formerly have been narrowly constructed in the United States, are broadening. Even the topic of menopause, previously considered to be an individual, silent process, is out of the closet as women begin to view menopause not as a marker to the end, but as a bridge to a new stage of adulthood. Increasingly, older women have more options to experience a rewarding and fulfilling later life. Two areas of struggle for older women are discussed in this section of the text: finances and the double standard of aging.

POVERTY AMONG WOMEN

Poverty among elderly people is very unevenly distributed, with women being among the most poor in the United States. Poverty among married women is fairly low; poverty among unmarried women is three to four times higher than that of their married counterparts, reflecting their work and marital histories (Burkhauser et al., 1994; Sandell & Iams, 1997). Some have called the high percentage of women and their children among the poor the "feminization of poverty." Of all individuals poor enough to receive Supplemental Security Income (SSI), two-thirds are women.

MIDDLE-AGED DISPLACED HOMEMAKERS

Financial problems for women frequently originate in middle age, or even earlier. A typical displaced homemaker is middle-aged and has been a homemaker for most of her adult life, dependent on her husband for her income and security. She finds herself suddenly alone with little or no income and with limited marketable skills. In 1993, 30 percent of all women in the 45 to 64 age category were single, widowed, or divorced.

The middle-aged woman who can save some money (or at least pay into Social Security) improves her chances for a fulfilling old age. Though middle-aged women are now in the workforce in large numbers, a pay gap persists for these women and for older women. They tend to be in low-paying "women's jobs," working as secretaries, salesclerks, waitresses, nurses, or teachers.

SINGLE, WIDOWED, AND DIVORCED OLDER WOMEN

Single Women

More than 25 percent of women 65 and older who live alone or with nonrelatives live below the poverty level (U.S. Bureau of the Census, 1993). This percentage would almost double if the Federal Poverty Index were updated as experts recommend. In contrast, 8 percent of those living with their husbands are poor. Those married and living with their husbands have the benefits of another income. Those single women receiving Social Security receive lower pensions than men do because the earnings on which they contributed to the program tend to be lower than the earnings of men of their generation. Women who are 65 years old today are still paying for the wage and social discrimination they suffered in their earlier working years.

Among unmarried women who are currently old, spotty and lowpaying work histories have resulted in negligible pensions. Many unmarried female elders have no source of income other than welfare.

Widows

Widows constitute nearly one-half of all women 65 and over. Of women 65 and over who live alone, 85 percent are widows. Some widowed women depended on their husbands' incomes, and, when retired, on their husbands' private pension plans or Social Security. More often than not, private pension plans fall sharply when a retired spouse dies. The death of a spouse also lowers the amount of Social Security benefits. If this is the case, widows' low incomes expose them to greater social and economic risks than other segments of the elder population. Data from a national sample of widows of all ages found that widowhood decreased living standards by 18 percent and pushed into poverty 10 percent of women whose prewidowhood incomes were above the poverty line. The problem is so great that some laws have been passed to protect women during times of marital transition. This includes the Consolidated Omnibus Budget Reconciliation Act (COBRA) that allows women to keep their health insurance coverage under their husbands' plans, at their own expense, for up to three years after divorce, separation, or widowhood.

The opportunity for older widows to remarry is quite limited, due to the relatively small number of eligible males in their age group. Older females who are eligible for marriage outnumber eligible males by a ratio of three to one. In addition, males who marry after age 65 tend to marry women from younger age groups.

Divorced Women

The socioeconomic well-being of divorced women is significantly below that of married or even widowed women. Given current statistics and expected trends in marriage, divorce, and widowhood, the numbers of married and widowed older women will decline, but the proportion of divorced older women will dramatically increase. Included in the increasing divorce rate are divorces involving women over age 40. Although 7 percent of women over age 60 are divorced (and not remarried), this statistic is increasing. In 1993, 1.5 percent of all married women over 65 divorced their spouse (Lanza, 1996). Each year, at least 50,000 persons older than 60 dissolve marriages of 30- to 40-years' duration.

For women, the probability of remarriage after divorce declines steeply with age and is quite low after age 45. In 1990, for example, fewer than five out of every 100 divorced women between the ages of 45 and 64 remarried within the year. If current rates persist, few women who enter midlife divorced, or who divorce after midlife, will ever remarry. Remarriage rates have fallen dramatically since 1965; they have fallen by half for women between the ages of 45 and 64.

According to rough projections, by 2025 no more than 37 percent of women between the ages of 65 and 69 will be in their first marriage. Half will not be in any marriage; this figure could be considerably higher if the divorce rate after age 40 continues to increase and the remarriage rate continues to decline (Uhlenberg, 1996). There is good reason for public concern over these statistics. Older women living outside marriage, especially those who are divorced, have much lower standards of living than married women. The high divorce rates of adult children can compound the strain on family resources, as well, as their needs and the needs of grandchildren are often addressed from a family, not an individual, perspective.

UPGRADING THE FINANCIAL STATUS OF OLDER WOMEN

In our society, in spite of positive steps toward equality, women in the workforce and in politics remain in inferior positions. Their lower incomes reflect this fact. Inequalities in income for older women will not totally disappear until women achieve equality in the workplace from the beginning of their careers.

If women are homemakers or caretakers of children or elder parents during their working years, they suffer financially in old age. Being removed from the paid labor market reduces their Social Security benefits (Devlin & Arye, 1997). They could be compensated in a number of ways. One way would be for women to receive full credit for their nonmarket labor in pension plans, including Social Security (Quadagno & Meyer, 1993). Another plan suggests combining the wage earner's 100 percent benefits with the dependent homemaker's 50 percent benefits. The wage earner and the homemaker could then divide the resulting 150 percent into equal shares of 75 percent that they would receive regardless of gender or family earning roles. They could place the equal shares in separate accounts under their own names and Social Security numbers. The funds would thus remain unaffected by possible divorce or separation.

Some centers provide job counseling, training, placement services, legal counseling, and outreach and information services to middle-aged and older women. Policies that encourage work and insure adequate survivor benefits improve the financial status of older retired women.

DOUBLE STANDARD OF AGING

In 1972, Susan Sontag coined the term **double standard of aging.** By implication, the standard of aging for a woman progressively destroys her sense of beauty and self-worth, whereas the standard of aging for a man is much less wounding. More recent literature questions the belief that changes in body self-concept are more difficult for women than for men, but opinion is unified around the issue of intense social standards for women's appearance (Wilcox, 1997; Harris, 1994; Cohen & Adler, 1992).

"Like wolves, women are sometimes discussed as though only a certain temperament, only a certain restrained appetite, is acceptable. And too often added to that is an attribution of moral goodness or badness according whether a woman's size, height, gait, and shape conform to a singular or exclusionary ideal. When women are relegated to moods, mannerisms, and contours that conform to a single ideal of beauty and behavior, they are captured in both body and soul, and are no longer free."

PINKOLA ESTES, WOMEN WHO RUN WITH THE WOLVES, 1992

Society trains women from an early age to care about their physical beauty. As a result, women spend a tremendous amount of time and money on their appearance. Women are very concerned about being "fat" or "ugly"—indeed, dieting and eating disorders are far more a woman's issue than a man's (Abbott et al., 1998). Cosmetic and plastic surgery and face-lifts are performed more often on women than on men. Many women's exercise programs emphasize appearance rather than strength or endurance. In the self-help section at any local video store, note the number of cassettes that promise shapelier breasts, thighs, or buttocks. Or attend an aerobics class at a local health club and note the female clients' concerns about their exercise clothing.

Not all women can confront their aging so directly and honestly. They buy into the idea that they must stay young and beautiful in appearance forever, and when physiological and health changes occur to alter that image, healthy adjustment to aging becomes difficult. Self-neglect in old age is thought to come about because of the negative self-concept that results in part from comparing one's physical condition and personal competence to a standard that is unattainable (Karpinski, 1997; Rathbone-McCuan, 1996).

The successful exploitation of women's fears of growing older has been called **age terrorism.** Pearlman (1993) speaks of **late midlife astonishment**—a developmental crisis in which women aged 50 to 60 work through society's devaluation of their physical appearance. Women suffer a loss of self-esteem, depression, and feelings of shame and self-consciousness. Feminist therapists believe that body image disturbances are not limited to eating-disordered clients and occur to women of all ages.

One dangerous outcome of negative shifts in self-image can be self-neglect. Women's fear of age-related physical change can take on a pathological flavor, since personal changes can cause a woman to doubt her social capability, which leads to low self-assessment, leading to low self-esteem, leading to self-neglect (Watson, 1997; Rathbone-McCuan, 1996). Self-concept itself, however, does not seem to undergo age-related change. The key to successful aging appears to be that women develop adequate strategies to maintain their self-identities even as key aspects of their bodies, their minds, and their health change (Matthews, 1979; Kaufman, 1986; Barusch, 1997).

"Our nation is moving toward two societies, one Black, one White—separate and unequal; discrimination and segregation have long permeated much of American life; they now threaten the future of every American."

US Riot Commission report, 1967

African Americans

African Americans constitute the largest minority group in the United States, totaling 30 million in 1990 (U.S. Bureau of the Census, 1993). About 2.5 million of these African Americans are 65 or over. They are a diverse group, yet some overall pictures do emerge. A majority of elder African Americans (53 percent) live in the South. There are fewer males than females. Older men tend to be married; women tend to be divorced or widowed. African American elders are less likely to be married than any other ethnic group, but all ethnic elderly, including African Americans, are more likely to live with other family members (not counting the spouse) than whites.

African Americans as a group differ widely in socioeconomic factors. As a result of the civil-rights movement, African Americans have gained a large middle class, a class having grown so greatly that it now outnumbers the African American poor. As comparatively well-off African Americans move to better neighborhoods, they leave behind an African American "underclass"—chronic welfare recipients, the unemployed, high-school dropouts, and single-parent families. Although many moved into the upper middle class in the 1980s, one-third remained locked in deprivation. As a result, there now exists a deep class division among African Americans. Elders in inner cities are often left to cope with deteriorating neighborhoods, high crime rates, and the threat of violence; or they are left in rural areas to struggle with poverty and lack of medical and social services.

INCOME AND HOUSING

Compared with Caucasian elders, **African American elders** have less adequate income, and poorer quality housing. This constitutes a serious social problem because the elderly cannot easily move elsewhere due to those limited incomes and because they face a stronger likelihood of housing discrimination (Golant & LaGreca, 1994). Although the income level for older African Americans has improved over the past 25 years, the improvement rate has not been as rapid as that for older whites. In 1959, 62.5 percent of African American elders were living in poverty, double the percentage for whites. In 1992, 24.9 percent of African Americans aged 65 and over were living below the poverty level, a figure more than *triple* that of whites. Unemployment rates for African Americans of all ages are far higher than those for whites and have been for many years.

A small percentage of retired African Americans are from the upper class, having owned large businesses or real estate, headed large corporations, or worked in the highest levels of industry. Other retired African Americans are middle class, having been schoolteachers, owners of small businesses, or government employees. Still others are retired from manual labor or domestic service jobs. Overall, however, older black Americans suffer appalling levels of poverty, having not paid as much into Social Security as whites, and having worked predominantly in jobs with no pensions. Older African Americans will be eligible for less in old age than older white Americans.

African American elders are slightly more likely to be looking for work after age 65, due to inadequate retirement income. Older African American men have higher unemployment rates than older white men. Elders in the lower socioeconomic groups, regardless of race, have a different understanding of retirement. Health permitting, they often must work at lower-paying jobs well beyond retirement age in order to meet basic expenses for food, medical care, and housing. Studies of work patterns among African Americans revealed a large group of "unretired retirees" aged 55 and over who need jobs but cannot find them. They do find occasional work well into old age, but this work is usually part-time and temporary. Those under age 62 are not eligible for Social Security or other pension programs and, therefore, without work, are more financially needy than those eligible for pensions.

Studies of African American retirees aged 65 and over show that those who receive Social Security have relatively high morale—higher, in fact, than that of their counterparts who are still working. This finding is reversed for whites. One explanation for the high morale of retired African Americans is the undesirable work they often face should they remain employed (Gibson, 1993).

Older African Americans are more likely than older whites to reside within decaying central cities and to live in substandard housing. They are also more likely than whites to live in public housing. Those who work with minority elders must be able to advise them accurately on low-cost public housing, low-interest housing loans, and other forms of available property relief.

Older African Americans are admitted to nursing homes at between one-half and three-quarters of the rate of whites. Although black elders' physical health has at least the same proportion of chronic physical illnesses as white elders' health, low use of long term care cannot be explained only with the statement that African Americans prefer to care for elders within their families. Having the economic option to make long term care a choice is not available to many black American families.

HEALTH CARE AND LIFE EXPECTANCY

Low-income African American elders have health care problems. Many poor elders have lacked the resources for adequate health care throughout their lives, which has resulted in a life expectancy rate that is much lower than that for whites. The average life expectancy of African American males in the 1990s was approximately 62 years (U.S. Bureau of the Census, 1996). The lower life expectancy of males compared with African American females (approximately 74 years) reflects diseases such as hypertension, diabetes, and stroke that occur at a rate two or three times greater than European men, and a teenage mortality rate that is six times greater in African American males than in African American women (Morgan & Kunkel, 1998). Given retirement ages of about 65, the average African American male cannot realistically expect to live long enough to collect Social Security and Medicare benefits.

The differences in life expectancy between African and white Americans fade away if a number of social variables are held constant, including marital status, income, education, and family size. (Marriage, high income and education, and small family size are correlated with longevity.) Table 14.1 contrasts some key social and economic variables in the African American population with the white American population. Upon examination of the differences in education, income, and poverty rate, it becomes apparent that longevity is probably more socially than racially determined

Between 1986 and 1991, life expectancy for African Americans actually *dropped.* Though African Americans had been sharing in life expectancy increases over the decades, the trend reversed in the late 1980s. Several factors combine to create this finding: (1) the high number of African American babies who die in their first year; (2) the tragic rate of loss of life among young male blacks through violence; and (3) the far greater incidence of fatal and life-shortening illnesses than among whites. Some of these include: appendicitis, pneumonia, hypertension, cervical cancer, tuberculosis, and influenza.

The experience of profound, personally-directed racial discrimination is a lifelong experience for almost every older African American. Assuming that low social status generates re-

TABLE 14.1

Social and economic characteristics of white and African American population, 1992

	Percent	
Characteristic	**White**	**Black**
Age 65 and over	13.0	8.3
Homeowner	67.5	42.3
College, 4 years or more	22.1	11.9
Income of $50,000 and over	34.1	14.9
Unemployed	4.3	8.9
Living below poverty level	10.3	33.8

Source: U.S. Bureau of the Census (1993). *Statistical Abstract of the United States, 1993.* Washington, DC: Bureau of the Census.

pressed negative emotions and inner tensions, some gerontologists believe the high incidence of hypertension among black Americans reflects the pressures of low social status. Both physical and mental illnesses can result from the chronic stress of prejudicial attitudes and behavior of others. Combined with the possibility of genetic predisposition for hypertension, the health of older African Americans is precarious for tragically unjust reasons.

Whatever the cause, the incidence of high blood pressure among African Americans is nearly two-and-a-half times that of whites, and the mortality rate from high blood pressure is higher for African Americans than for whites (U.S. Bureau of the Census, 1993). Though yoga, aerobics, and biofeedback programs to reduce blood pressure have in the past typically been attended by white, middle-class persons, African Americans are now joining these programs.

FAMILY AND SOCIAL RELATIONSHIPS

More than 40 percent of African American women 65 and over live in poverty. Some groups urge African American women to become politically active and to lobby for equality on behalf of themselves and their mothers, aunts, and sisters. Organizations such as the National Association for the Advancement of Colored People (NAACP) and the National Black Women's Political Caucus can speak and work on behalf of issues most salient to black Americans.

Despite racism and economic woes, African Americans possess a resolve to persevere. The solid family ties, which are one source of this strength, are indicated in the concept of **familism**—a notion of family extending beyond the immediate household. Family network roles are flexible and interchangeable. A young mother, an aunt, a grandfather, or an older couple may head a family. Grandmothers often help raise children while their parents work. The high divorce rate has encouraged reliance on older relatives. Families tend to value their elder members because they have survived in the face of hardship and because they play important roles within the family (Choi, 1996; Mullen, 1996).

Religion has also been a resource of support in the African American family (Nye, 1993; Walls & Zarit, 1991). The black American church traditionally has been a source of strength for coping with racial oppression and has played a vital role in the survival and advancement of African Americans. The church has provided a place of importance and belonging. Within the church, elders receive recognition as members, choir vocalists, deacons, and treasurers.

A spirit of survival has seen older African Americans through hard times. Thankful to have survived, they are more likely to appreciate aging; thus, they accept it more easily than those who have not experienced such hardship.

FUTURE OUTLOOK

Though data on the lives of African American elders are becoming more available, our knowledge is still far from adequate. We are gaining knowledge about their lifestyles, roles, and adaptations to living environments, but the information on whites that pertains to these topics still far exceeds that about minorities.

Studies of *fear* of crime and victimization show much higher rates of fear for African Americans than for whites; and, in fact, their rates of victimization are significantly higher than those for white Americans. The major reason is thought to be geographic locations. More of them live in high-crime areas such as the inner city and in or near public housing compared with white American elders. Because feelings of alienation and mistrust of police may have existed from their youth, many black elders are less likely than their white counterparts to reach out for help. Social policy experts suggest neighborhood watch programs to unite residents and also recommend age-segregated housing with more safety features (Barazan, 1994).

Despite the progress made through affirmative action in the United States, the economic outlook for large numbers of older African Americans is bleak. African Americans and other minorities are still disproportionately clustered in peripheral industries that pay lower wages, such as agriculture, retail trade, nonunionized small businesses, and low-profit companies that pay minimum wage. In contrast, white Americans are still clustered in better-paying "core" industries, such as the automobile industry, construction, and other high-profit, unionized industries. Although some improvement can be expected by the 21st century, it will be small. Between 1982 and 1992, the ratio of African American family income to white family income actually declined. In 1996, the average income of whites was $29,470 a year; the African American average was $21,068 (Administration on Aging, 1997). If young and middle-aged working African Americans cannot fare as well as whites, they will not compare much better in old age. Only through major economic changes that promote the hiring of minorities in major businesses and industries will they begin to achieve economic parity in middle and old age.

Hispanic Americans

Older Hispanics, the *ancianos*, are not a homogeneous group. Researchers are often unprepared for the cultural and socioeconomic diversity of the Hispanic community. One of the many obstacles preventing **Hispanic elders** from being understood and served is the lack of a clear-cut definition of who they are. Census counting often uses two inclusive terms that increase the problem: Spanish heritage (having Spanish blood or antecedents) and Spanish origin (having been born in a Spanish-speaking country or having antecedents who were). Theoretically, then, a person could be of Spanish origin but not of Spanish heritage and vice versa. The term *Hispanic* will be used here to mean Spanish people in a broad sense including either term.

DEMOGRAPHICS

In 1990, more than 22 million people in the United States were of Hispanic origin. Of these, 5.5 percent were aged 65 or older, and far less than 1 percent (131,000) were 85 or older. By the year 2050, it is expected that over 14 percent of the over-65 population in the country will be of Hispanic origin, including more than 3 percent of those who are 85 years old and greater (Siegel, 1996). Mexican Americans are the largest Hispanic group in the United States, as illustrated in Figure 14.2.

The Hispanic population, one of the fastest-growing ethnic groups, is expected to be the largest U.S. minority group after the year 2000. Under Census Bureau projections, the elderly Hispanic population will more than double from 1990 to 2010, and will be 11 times greater by 2050. In 1990 the Hispanic elderly numbered less than half the black elderly population; however, in 2030, the number of Hispanic elderly (7.6 million) will be larger than the elderly African American population of 6.8 million (Hobbs & Damon, 1996).

FIGURE 14.2

Hispanic population by nation of origin

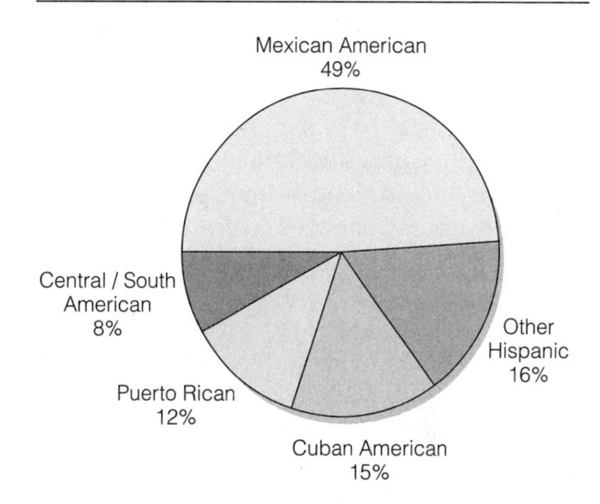

Source: Data for circle graph from national Institute on Aging, *Profiles of America's Elderly* (1993) Washington, DC: U.S. Department of Health and Human Services.

Minority Status

Several social factors indicate the minority status of Hispanic elders: (1) high percentage that live below the poverty level; (2) inadequate health care; (3) high illiteracy rates (second only to those of Native American elders); and (4) low occupational levels such as operatives, artisans, unskilled laborers, and farm workers. These job categories have few benefits, including retirement and pension benefits. Some Mexican-American elders are unlikely to seek social services support because they entered the country illegally or are uncertain about their legal status and fear detection and expulsion.

MIGRATION PATTERNS

The two largest Hispanic subgroups are Mexican and Puerto Rican, whose portion totals 76 percent of all Hispanics. The majority of Mexican American elders were born in this country; other Hispanic elders are more likely to be foreign born. Foreign-born Hispanics are not as acculturated as native-born citizens. They need more help to understand and utilize services. Further, programs developed for them must acknowledge the traditions and values they have retained.

Differing patterns of migration have brought Hispanics to various locations in the United States. Hispanic-American immigrants tend to live in urban areas. Immigrants from 6 of the 12 Hispanic nations identified in the 1990 census have more than 80 percent of their populations in the nation's 20 largest cities (New York, Los Angeles, Chicago, Miami, Washington, D.C., Boston, Philadelphia, and San Diego, for example). Three others have between 70 percent and 79 percent in the 20 largest cities. Because so many Mexican Americans are born in the United States, they are not as extensively urbanized as other Hispanics. Some became citizens when the rural Mexican territory in the Southwest was incorporated into the United States. It is still very rural and heavily populated with Mexican Americans.

Generally, Hispanics who immigrate (including Mexican immigrants) tend to locate in urban areas. In Texas, for example, the older urban immigrants outnumber their rural counterparts by a ratio of five to one. San Antonio, Houston, and Dallas have large numbers of Mexican Americans who are foreign born. Puerto Rican and Cuban elders are almost exclusively city dwellers. The Hispanic populations of Florida and the Northeast are more urbanized than those in the Southwest.

THE AMERICAN EXPERIENCE

Hispanic elders today are an ethnic composite that has suffered major linguistic and cultural barriers to assimilation and has occupied a low socioeconomic status. Forty-five percent of Hispanic elders are not proficient in English (Seelye, 1997). In 1992, 16.3 percent of persons of Hispanic origin aged 65 and over lived below the poverty level. A major reason for the financial disadvantages of older Hispanics is the lack of pension plan coverage during their working lives. Their coverage rates are lower than those for whites or African Americans. Health problems such as diabetes and obesity are more common among Hispanic elders than in the aged population as a whole.

UTILIZATION OF SERVICES

Hispanic elders are generally somewhat suspicious of governmental institutions and of service workers and researchers not of their culture. Their suspicion, along with a lack of education and money, results in isolation and nonutilization of available services. This underutilization tends to conceal their very real need. Further, because the census undercounts minorities, underutilization is even greater than is generally recognized. One example is in nursing home care, where Hispanic elders are greatly underrepresented (Mui & Burnette, 1994).

Social program providers need to develop greater sensitivity to and communication skills with Hispanic seniors. Popular beliefs characterize Mexican Americans as living in extended families and, in fact, Hispanic families do tend to be larger than white families in the United States. But that does not mean that the extended family system runs smoothly. Both cultural values and economic need dictate these close family ties, and the patterns of intergenerational assistance are strong compared to white Americans, for example. However, older parents have expressed dismay at the shift in filial responsibility of their adult children.

Asian Americans

Asian American refers in the broadest sense to persons of Chinese, Korean, Japanese, Filipino, East Indian, Thai, Vietnamese, Burmese, Indonesian, Laotian, Malayan, and Cambodian descent who live in the United States. Most **Asian-**

American elders are concentrated in California, Hawaii, New York, Illinois, Washington, and Massachusetts. The total U.S. population of Asians and Pacific Islanders was 7.5 million in 1991 (U.S. Bureau of the Census, 1993). Of this number, 6.3 percent are aged 65 and over, or nearly 500,000 persons. Of the Asian elders in 1990, about 30 percent were Chinese, 24 percent Japanese, 24 percent Filipino, 8 percent Korean, and 14 percent other Asians and Pacific Islanders.

A single description cannot encompass the Asian communities in the United States. Differences of culture, language, and religion make each group unique (see Table 14.2). Asians are alike, however, in the sense that they all have encountered language barriers and racism.

American laws have discriminated against Asians for some time. The Chinese Exclusion Act of 1882, passed during high unemployment by fearful whites, made all Chinese immigration illegal. It was amended twice to allow immigration under certain circumstances, then in 1924 became totally exclusionary again. It was not repealed until 1943, when China became a U.S. ally in World War II. The legislative history is not an honorable one, and has important social implications, as outlined by Hooyman and Kiyak (1996):

> *Laws discriminating against Asians are numerous, ranging from...the Japanese Alien Land Law of 1913, the Executive Order of 1942 for the internment of 110,000 persons of Japanese ancestry, denial of citizenship to first-generation Asians in 1922, the anti-miscegenation statue of 1935, and more recently Public Law 95-507 excluding Asians as a protected minority under the definition of "socially and economically disadvantaged" (US Commission on Civil Rights, 1979). Such legislation, combined with a history of prejudice and discrimination, has contributed to feelings of mistrust, injustice, powerlessness, and fear of government among many Pacific Asian elders, and thus a reluctance to utilize services (p. 455).*

TABLE 14.2

Asian-American diversity

- Asian
  - Chinese
  - Filipino
  - Japanese
  - Asian Indian
  - Korean
  - Vietnamese
  - Lao
  - Thai
  - Cambodian
  - Pakistani
  - Indonesian
  - Hmong
- Other Asians
- Pacific Islanders
  - Polynesian
    - Hawiian
    - Samoan
    - Tongan
  - Micronesian
    - Guamanian
  - Melanesian
- Other Pacific Islanders

The current generation of Asian Americans, conditioned to traditional American social and cultural folkways and mores, may be just as likely to regard their elders as an unwelcome burden, just as many middle-class white Americans seem to do. According to traditional culture in China, Japan, and Korea, the eldest son assumes responsibility of his elder parents. **Filial piety** is a traditional custom demanding that family members respect and care for elders. Japanese-American families have preserved to some extent the norm of ***enryo***, a pattern of deference and modesty, as well as ***amaeru***, the value of dependency that encourages special dependent relationships (Johnson, 1996).

These patterns are carried into respectful attitudes toward elders; however, they contrast markedly with dominant American values. As children and grandchildren become more enculturated, intergenerational tensions are bound to result. This becomes a moral "generation gap" between young Asian Americans and their elders. Older family members hold on to traditions, especially those concerning moral propriety, while the young move away from them.

Because health and welfare agencies have few bilingual staff members, and because they therefore have difficulty publicizing their available services to the Asian community, outreach programs to Asian-American seniors have been limited in their success. These deficits, in addition to their socially conditioned reluctance to seek aid from their adopted land, result in neglect of Asian-American elders.

JAPANESE AMERICANS

Most of the Japanese who first came to the United States were single men, oftentimes younger sons who did not inherit any family wealth. The bulk of the Japanese immigration, which took place between 1870 and 1924, were men who wanted to have traditional families. Many waited until they could afford a wife, and then paid for one to come from Japan. This pattern reinforced traditional values of high status for men and elders. The survivors of that earliest immigration period, called *issei,* are now mostly women, because the men, being much older, have died.

The first generation worked primarily on farms or as unskilled laborers or service workers. However, within 25 years of entering the United States, they showed great economic mobility. Though their internment during World War II was economically as well as morally devastating, Japanese Americans as a group rebounded remarkably. First-generation Japanese, the *issei,* learned to live socially segregated from American culture. The children of the *issei,* the *nissei,* generally born between 1910 and 1940, are more likely to be integrated into the American mainstream. Most *nissei* are now over 65 and doing well economically and socially.

Japanese-American elders, on the whole, have adequate savings or family support in their retirement years. Through the normative values of *amaeru, filial piety*, and other Confucian moral principles, Japanese Americans have largely replicated the traditional pattern of family care for elders; 46 percent live with an adult child in addition to, or in lieu of, a spouse. In traditional Japanese society, when retirement occurred, the retiree joined the ranks of elders and assumed religious duties in the community. This particular tradition is lacking in the United States (Markides & Mindel, 1987).

CHINESE AMERICANS

Because past restrictive immigration laws denied entry to wives or children, a disproportionate share of Chinese- and Filipino-American elders are men. Male immigrants have outnumbered females by at least three to one in census counts. These Asian men were valuable as cheap labor in U.S. mines, canneries, farms, and railroads, but their wives and children were neither needed nor wanted. Though we cannot fully assess the damage to the family life of the elderly Chinese American, such damage has no doubt been extensive, traumatic, and demoralizing.

The immigration law of 1924, which halted Asian immigration, forbade males of Chinese descent from bringing their foreign-born wives to the United States. As a result, many Chinese men in the United States could not marry. Although the men who originally came in the early 1900s are a rapidly vanishing group, a few are still around, typically living in poverty and without close family ties, because they never married and lived out their lives in preparation to return to their home country.

Chinese Americans retain a tradition of respect for elders based on Confucian ethics. Traditionally, the Chinese family was embedded in a larger system of extended family and clans than was the Japanese family. Older family members held wealth and power, not only in their immediate family, but also all the way up the family hierarchy to the encompassing clan. Though this traditional structure has never been reproduced in the United States, respect for elders persists. The Chinese American pattern is for adult children to bring a widowed parent into their household.

Increasing proportions of Chinese elders are second generation. This generally means that they are more educated, more acculturated, and have a more comfortable financial situation. There is a vast difference between the lifestyles of those who are foreign born and who have never learned English and those who were born in the United States. The second generation is retiring with pensions and savings, reaping the harvest of their hard work in this country. Despite discrimination, Chinese Americans have achieved a high rate of occupational mobility; many have gone from restaurant and laundry businesses to educating children who have entered professional and technical occupations.

SOUTHEAST ASIAN AMERICANS

The settlement of Vietnamese, Cambodians, and Laotians in the United States has included a small percentage of elders, who enter a world alien in all facets of life, from language, dress, and eating habits to religious beliefs. Family ties are strong for most of these people. Traditionally, extended families are standard. Southeast Asians have a special respect for their elders, especially for fathers and grandfathers.

The role of elders in the Southeastern Asian family has changed. In Laos, the elders acted as counselors for adult children experiencing marital difficulties. In the United States, in contrast, they are more out of touch with young couples' marital problems; and they rarely act as advisers and mediators. The older women try to help with child care, but the men don't have much to do. Many would like a farm and animals to tend. Elderly Southeastern Asians have experienced loss of function, loss of mobility, loss of religious customs, and loss of status. Some are very depressed. Studies of Southeast Asian refugees find that, because of the language barrier and lack of communication with the larger society, displacement is more difficult for the elderly than for their young.

Native Americans

Measured by numbers alone, **Native American elders** constitute a small percentage of American society: Of the total elderly population in 1994, about 29.8 million were white, and about 137,000 were American Indian, Eskimo, and Aleut (Hobbs & Damon, 1996). By any social or economic indicator of living conditions, however, Native American elders are possibly the *most* deprived of all ethnic groups in the United States.

Many of the problems of Native American elders are due to minority status rather than to age. American Indians on reservations and in rural areas experience extremely high unemployment rates. Few jobs exist on the reservations, and those who leave in search of work pay the high price of losing touch with family, lifestyle, and culture. Many houses on reservations are substandard, and, despite substantial improvements in health, disparities still exist, especially in sanitation and nutrition. More than 140 years of federal programs have done little to improve the lives of Native Americans.

CULTURAL UNIFORMITY AND DIVERSITY

Family structure, values, and norms among Native American tribes are diverse. Generally speaking, Native Americans have close family ties. Though many family structures are patriarchal, a wide variety of descent systems exist. The largest tribe, the Navajo, follows a matrilineal structure. The position of the elderly varies from tribe to tribe, as does emphasis on peace versus war and many other values. And, although some tribes are rivals, there exists today an extensive pan-Indian network that promotes intertribal networking, visiting, and cooperation. Marriage between members of different tribes is also more common (Kitano, 1991). The United States has approximately 278 federally recognized reservations, more than 300 recognized tribes, and around 100 nonrecognized tribes (John, 1991a). This includes Eskimo and Aleut populations.

POPULATION DATA

For many years, despite rapid growth in the population of the country as a whole, the Native American population declined. At the time of the first European settlement in what is now the United States, the number of Indians is estimated to have been between 1 and 10 million. By 1800, the native population had declined to approximately 600,000; by 1850, it had shrunk to 250,000. This mortifying decrease, the result of malnutrition, disease, and an all-out military assault on Native Americans, was a unique occurrence in our national history. However, the population eventually stabilized and is now increasing (Kitano, 1991). Because of early childbearing, it is common for Native Americans to become grandparents in their mid- to late thirties. By comparison, grandparenthood usually comes to whites in their midfifties (John, 1991b).

Many older Native Americans live on reservations, tending to stay behind while the young seek work in the city. Young or old, those who go to the city often expect to return to rural reservations to retire. Although the American population as a whole is more urban than rural, the reverse is largely true for the Native American population. Native Americans are the most rural of any ethnic group in the country, 53 percent live in nonmetropolitan areas (Schick & Schick, 1994).

Life expectancy among Native Americans is substantially lower than that for whites. The Native American population is largely young; in 1991 nearly 50 percent were under the age of 25 (Hobbs & Damon, 1996). Elders constitute slightly more than 6 percent of the total Native American population; by comparison, they represent 12 percent of the total U.S. population. As in the white population, Native American women live longer than Native American men.

EDUCATION, EMPLOYMENT, AND INCOME

The educational attainment of Native Americans today is behind that of whites. Among Native American youths, the school dropout rate is twice the national average. Because education has been a traditional means of social advancement in the United States, these data suggest that future generations of Native American elders may continue to suffer from functional illiteracy.

Unemployment is a tremendous problem in the Native American community. An extremely high percentage of the Native American workforce is unemployed, and most of those who work hold menial jobs with low pay and few, if any, fringe benefits. Because they have often paid only small amounts into Social Security, retirement for Native Americans is a great hardship. White Americans often associate major difficulties of growing old with retirement from the workforce. Native Americans usually have no work from which to retire. For most over 65, old age merely continues a state of poverty and joblessness that has lasted a lifetime.

HEALTH CHARACTERISTICS

Native American elders are more likely to suffer from chronic illnesses and disabilities than any other ethnic aged group, and they have the lowest life expectancy. Native Americans are more likely than the general population to die from diabetes, alcoholism, influenza, pneumonia, suicide, and homicide (Hobbs & Damon, 1996).

Lack of income leads to poor nutrition and health care and is associated with lower education levels, which compound other variables. The Native American accident rate, for example, is high. Native Americans are more likely than the general population to be killed in motor-vehicle accidents, and death from other types of accidents is also more likely.

Native Americans suffer disproportionately from alcoholism and alcohol-related diseases. American Indians are generally disposed genetically to have a low alcohol tolerance; however, the abuse rate of alcohol in the Native American population is probably related to the stressors of minority status and poverty. Health problems are compounded by the alien nature of the dominant health care system to the traditional culture of Native Americans.

Older Native Americans remain an enormously needy group. Today, Native Americans suffer both from dependency on the federal government and from the impact of conflicting federal policies. They are sometimes denied assistance from various government agencies under the excuse that the Bureau of Indian Affairs (BIA) is responsible for providing the denied service. The BIA has 12 area offices in the United States, so that the distance between the service provider, the work site, and the reservation (place of residence) compounds the difficulties of eligibility and availability of assistance.

In the next century minority women will represent a far larger proportion of elders than in the past. This shift to greater diversity in later life will impact social policy.

Improving the Status of Ethnic Elders

A large number of minority elders spend the last years of their lives with inadequate income and housing, poor medical care, and few necessary services. Aging accentuates the factors that have contributed to a lifetime of social, economic, and psychological struggle. Rather than achieving comfort and respect with age, minority persons may get pushed further aside.

Upgrading the status of ethnic elders in the short term requires, first, recognition of the various factors that prevent them from utilizing services and, second, outreach programs designed to overcome those factors. The object should be to expand present programs, to develop more self-help programs, to increase the **bilingual** abilities of social service staffs, and to recruit staff members from the ethnic groups they serve.

With these goals in mind, the Administration of Aging (AOA) has funded four national organizations to improve the well-being of minority elders.

1. The National Caucus and Center on Black Aged (NCCBA) in Washington, D.C.
2. The National Indian Council on Aging (NICOA) in Albuquerque, New Mexico
3. *Asociación Nacional Pro Personas Mayores* (National Association for Hispanic Elderly) in Los Angeles, California
4. National Pacific/Asian Resource Center on Aging (NP/ARCA) in Seattle, Washington

These centers educate the general public and advocate for their groups.

Ultimately, though, spending a bit of extra money and adding a few services will not solve the real problem. The disadvantages tend to derive from economic marginality that has lasted a lifetime. One's work history is a central factor in how one fares in later life. A work history that allows for a good pension or maximum Social Security benefits is a big step toward economic security in old age. Also, those who have made good salaries have had a chance to save money for their retirement years—a safety net not possible for low wage earners. Until members of minority groups are from birth accorded full participation in the goods and services our society offers, they will continue to suffer throughout their lives. The critical perspective in sociology calls for addressing these basic inequalities and taking major steps toward making all citizens equal.

Chapter Summary

Women, including older ones, are in a minority status in the United States. They do not participate equally in the political and economic structures. Older women are victims of the double standard of aging—a standard that judges them more harshly as they age. A large percentage of elders in poverty are female.

Ethnic elders suffer from inequality in the United States. Older blacks are poorer than older whites and have a lower life expectancy, poorer health, more inferior housing, and less material comforts. Although some older African Americans are well-to-do, others are impoverished. Family ties, religion, and a resolve to persevere are special strengths.

Hispanic elders are not a homogeneous group. About half of all Hispanic elders are Mexican Americans; others come from Cuba, Puerto Rico, and various Central and South American countries. Hispanic elders have suffered major linguistic and cultural barriers to assimilation and have occupied low socioeconomic status.

Asian-American elders come from many countries, also. They, too, have encountered racial hatred, language barriers, and discrimination. Native American elders are a small group. But by any social or economic indicator, they are, possibly, the most deprived group in the United States. More efforts need to be directed at correcting inequities for ethnic minorities and women.

Key Terms

African American elders
age terrorism
amaeru
Asian-American elders
bilingual
double standard of aging
enryo
ethnic group
ethnicity
familism
filial piety
Hispanic elders
late midlife astonishment
minority
minority elder
Native American elders

Questions for Discussion

1. What special problems do older women experience? Older African Americans? Hispanics? Asian Americans? Native Americans? White Americans? In what ways are older women's issues unique to their ethnic or cultural background, and in what ways are their issues ones shared by all older women?
2. What are the primary gender-gap issues that arise between generations in each of the five cultural/racial groups above? Describe some *particular* cultural values that are held by the older generation but not shared as deeply by the next generation for different cultural groups.

Fieldwork Suggestion

Interview an older person from a racial minority. Note carefully the person's lifestyle and outlook on life. What past and present discrimination has he or she experienced?

Online Activities

1. Locate the AARP home page, and search for information on retired women's issues. Now search for information on minority issues. What levels of analysis do you find? Are the issues of retired women and minorities well addressed, or are they addressed as being "other" to the dominant (white male) population of retired persons?
2. Go to the U.S. Government Bureau of the Census home page and search out the number of children living with grandparents in the country. Can you locate this information by race and ethnicity? Does your home state have parallel information? Where else might you search for data on ethnicity and family household structure?
3. Seek out Internet information on minority elder status, other than U.S. Census data. Maintain a log of your Internet "travels." How easy or hard was it for you to locate the information? Who is the intended audience of the information you have?

15

Death and Dying

A Death Doctor's Strange Obsessions

James Risen

He was a bright young doctor at a time when the United States was just beginning its post-World War II ascent, and Jack Kevorkian, University of Michigan Medical School Class of 1952, could have—should have—had it all.

But he had this nagging, inexplicable fascination with the dying and the dead, a personal obsession, really, one that was all the more peculiar because it first appeared during an optimistic era of limitless possibilities and unquestioning faith in the resiliency of American life.

Perhaps it was reinforced during his brief time as a U.S. Army doctor in Korea; certainly it was there during his residency at the University of Michigan Medical Center in the mid-1950s. . . .

"I don't like to watch someone die," he insists. "It is a traumatic, wrenching experience. . . ."

Over the years, Kevorkian's obsession would cost him dearly. On the fringes of medicine, he would become permanently unemployed in his mid-50s—rejected even for a job as a paramedic.

His last patients were acquaintances who would stop him in the street to ask his advice on minor ailments. He would complain that American medical journals refused to publish his ideas. By the onset of the 1990s, Kevorkian had retreated into a private world. . . .

And so when Janet Adkins came to him eager to end her life, eager to stop the suffering of Alzheimer's disease before she became mentally incompetent, Kevorkian was ready.

He already had traveled the slippery ethical slope that leads from medicine to euthanasia. In his own mind, he was no longer a practicing pathologist.

Instead, he printed up new business cards. On them, he called himself an "obitiatrist," with its root in the word "obituary"; a doctor of death. "The world's first," he says.

On June 4, 1990, Adkins, a 54-year-old mother of three from Portland, Oregon, climbed into the back of Kevorkian's rusting old Volkswagen van in a rural Michigan park not far from Pontiac and allowed Kevorkian to connect her to his homemade "suicide machine."

She then pushed a button three times to ensure the machine's death-inducing drugs would course through her veins. According to Kevorkian, "Thank you, thank you," were her last words.

Author's Note: This was Kevorkian's first physician-assisted suicide widely publicized by the media. In March 1998, the Kevorkian-assisted suicide of a 66-year old man with lung cancer marked the 100th suicide assist of Jack Kevorkian (age 69), his lawyer Geoffrey Fieger stated publicly. Kevorkian, who lost his license to practice medicine in Michigan in 1991, has been acquitted in three trials in Michigan, the last one in 1997. In that trial, Fieger provided a video of Kevorkian's latest subjects begging to be allowed to die, and stated that "Government has no business telling you what to do." The controversy surrounding Kevorkian continues because he helps people die who are not necessarily in extreme pain nor in the final months of terminal illness, the two major criteria in Holland for physician-assisted suicides.

Source: James Risen, "Death Doctor's Strange Obsession," *San Francisco Chronicle* (26 June 1990): A8.

Adapted from: New York Times, 1998 Associated Press. "Kevorkian Deaths Total 100," *New York Times*, March 15, 1998 v 147, p14(N), p 18(L).

Death is one of the few certainties of life. This statement is neither pessimistic nor morbid. Despite our wildest fantasies about immortality, no one has yet escaped death permanently. Despite its universality, however, death is not easily discussed in American society. People tend to be sensitive and shy about discussing the topic openly.

Facing death, dealing with the fact of death in a rational way, and exerting control over the manner of one's dying are all difficult situations in a society that denies death. Just because one is old does not mean that one does not fear death or that one welcomes dying. In this chapter, we will examine the ability of the older individual to experience a "good" death to the extent that our society permits it.

Life itself is a sexually-transmitted, terminal condition.

A Death-Denying Society?

Our words, attitudes, and practices suggest that ours is a **death-denying society.** Have you ever used the word *died* and had the uncomfortable feeling that those with whom you were talking considered the word too direct and in bad taste? "Passed away" might be the preferred phrase, or "passed on"—but not "dead." There are dozens of euphemisms for the process of dying. Funerals, presenting an embalmed and painted body, try to project an illusion of life. There even exists a sort of prescribed script that mourners follow: "She looks just like she did yesterday when I was talking to her" or "He looks so natural." Those selling cemetery plots advise us not to buy a grave but to invest in a "preneed memorial estate." The funeral industry in the United States is enormous, now offering services in addition to burial, from funeral planning to bereavement counseling.

Watching death on television or killing after violent killing in the movies is not facing death. Violent deaths portrayed in cartoons and action films do not evoke the human emotions—the deep sorrow, anger, and guilt—that the actual death of a loved one would. "Sensitive" television dramas that depict the death of a family member tend to be just as unrealistic.

At the end of the 19th century, dying and death were household events that encompassed not only elders, but the young and middle-aged as well. At the end of the 20th century, death is characterized by life-extending medical procedures, hospital and insurance bureaucracies, and secularism. As chronic diseases and increased technology keep people in a prolonged state of dying, bureaucracy makes the setting impersonal, and a secular society robs a person of the religious significance of dying. These three trends promote the impersonalization of the process through which the dying individual must go. Small wonder that death is perceived as such a fearful, lonely experience.

Did You Know . . .
According to Barbara Barzansky, director of the AMA's Department of Medical School Services, only 6 of the nation's 125 medical

schools have a separate course on death and dying.

WORSNOP, 1997

Death avoidance is not unique to modern times, however. Dealing with the unknowable, whatever its outcome, is anxiety producing for humans, whose driving desire is toward *understanding*. The French philosopher Montaigne (1533-1592) argued in the 16th century that to become free of death's grip we must immerse ourselves in all the aspects and nuances of death (Montaigne, quoted in Marrone, 1997):

> *We come and we go and we trot and we dance, ...and never a word about death. All well and good. Yet when death does come—to them, their wives, their children, their friends—catching them unawares and unprepared, then what storms of passion overwhelm them, what cries, what fury, what despair! ...To begin depriving death of its greatest advantage over us, let us adopt a way clean contrary to that common one; let us deprive death of its strangeness, let us frequent it, let us get used to it; let us have nothing more often in mind than death...We do not know where death awaits us: so let us wait for it everywhere. To practice death is to practice freedom. [One] who has learned how to die has unlearned how to be a slave (p. 328).*

Denial of death is possible on a grand scale now not because we choose to deny it more than our ancestors did, but because we have greater institutional resources for helping us to avoid its reality.

About 85 percent of American deaths occur in hospital rooms and convalescent hospitals (Marrone, 1997). The final moments of life are seldom observed, even by family. Health professionals and paraprofessionals are the predominant care providers for the dying, but health professionals are seldom trained in the process of death. They are trained to extend life, and death is a failure of the promise of that training. Death is often as hard a reality to health professionals as it is to everyone else.

Despite social customs that decrease the interaction of the living with death and dying, interest in the topic has escalated in the last decade or so. College courses on death and dying, seminars instructing health professionals and clergy in understanding the dying person, and many books on the subject have become available.

Fear of Death

Fear of death is a normal human condition—we struggle for life, and for the lives of others, and we desperately desire to avoid unknowns. But are people more fearful, or less fearful, at different ages?

Old people are commonly stereotyped as waiting fearlessly for death. And, though any given individual may be an exception to the rule, elders as a group do seem less fearful than younger persons. Thanatologist Richard Kalish (1987) attributed this difference to three things: (1) many elders feel they have completed the most important tasks of life; (2) they are more likely to be in pain or to be suffering from chronic diseases and view death as an escape from that pain; and (3) they have lost many friends and relatives. Those losses have made death more a reality.

Some people who work with elders, however, believe that old people may fear death *more* because they are closer to it. There is less time available to complete important life tasks, to make amends, to say goodbye. Other observers say that fear is the greatest in late middle age, when midlife brings a heightened awareness of aging and death. Once that transitory phase passes, however, fears usually decline. Most observers and philosophers agree that fear of death is innate in all individuals, regardless of age, and that it provides direction for life's activities. Understanding that we will die may be a precondition for a fuller and deeper understanding of life.

> *"There are two ways of not thinking about death: The way of our technological civilization, which denies death and refuses to talk about it; and the way of traditional civilization, which is not a denial but a recognition of the impossibility of thinking about it directly or for very long because death is too close and too much a part of daily life."*
>
> ARIES, 1994

Given painful experiences and the power of storytelling and imagination, people have many reasons to fear death itself or to have **fears about dying.** People fear a long, painful death; illness, such as cancer; senility; the unknown; judgment in the afterlife; the fate of one's body. They fear dying alone or, conversely, of being watched; fear dying in a hospital or nursing home; and fear the loss of bodily control. Some of the fears are of death itself; others are fears about the process of dying, such as the imagined pain, helplessness, and dependence. Fear of the *condition* of death—of being dead, as well as fear of the *process* of dying are important to understand if we are to help people who are dying, and to help ourselves in our own deaths.

Some fears seem normal, that is, justified and within reason. Others seem to be exaggerated. The term **fear of death** is usually used when such apprehension has a specific, identifiable source. In comparison, **death anxiety** describes feelings of apprehension and discomfort that lack an identifiable source. **Death competency,** on the other hand, is our capability and skill in dealing with death. But how fearful, anxious, or competent are people? Does an individual's fear of death, or overriding anxiety about death impact their process of grieving, or shape their own deaths? If we knew more about which aspects of death were most problematic for a given person, could that person be better assisted through a "good" death, or with grief and mourning over the death of someone beloved?

Several measures of death fear have been developed in an attempt to understand more about the fears and anxieties surrounding death for groups of people, and to provide a better understanding about a particular person. The questions generally cover a range of fears, such as fear of dependency, fear of pain, fear of indignity, fear of isolation or loneliness, fears related to an afterlife, fear of leaving people we love, and fear of the fate of the body (Lemming & Dickinson, 1994; Neiman, 1994). Findings from more general research provide a road map for understanding individual issues with death and dying.

Though the experience of death will be different for every person, in general, our fears about the suffering of death may be at least somewhat unfounded. Most people die relatively painless deaths. In most cases, an individual's health does not deteriorate until very close to death. Most people are in good or excellent health until a year before they die, and many are in good health

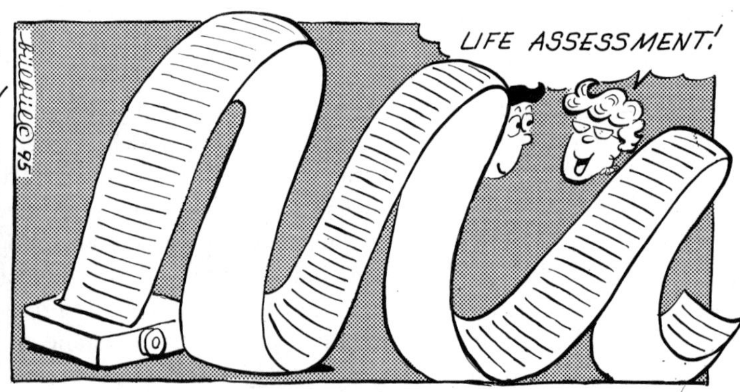

up to the week of their death. It is the haunting stories of lingering, painful, lonely death that many people carry in their heads when they think of death that feeds our innate fears. In reality, the more we know and understand about death, the less fearful it will seem.

Elders' fears and concerns about dying must be dealt with as openly as possible, as difficult as that might be. Because of their own anxieties about death, adult children often will not allow parents or grandparents to fully express their views on the subject. Older people often attempt a discussion about their own death, and/or what the family will do after (or just before) the elder dies, only to be told in many different ways, "Oh, you don't have to think about this yet! You have a lot of time for that." Yet this "death talk" can be realistic, practical, and therapeutic. Family members would be wise to listen.

Living Fully until Death

The marginal status of elders in our society affects their ability to live fully until death. Richard Kalish (1985) discovered that although the death of an elder is less disturbing than the death of a younger person in our American culture, this attitude is not universal. He told this story:

> *I once asked a group of about two dozen Cambodian students in their mid-twenties whether, given the necessity for choice, they would save the life of their mother, their wife or their daughter. All responded immediately that they would save their mother, and their tone implied that only an immoral or ignorant person would even ask such a question (p.116).*

Although we all hope to live fully from the moment of birth until death, for some elders, living fully until death may not be possible. Some spend their final years confined to nursing homes or other caretaking institutions. Oddly, researchers have generally found a more positive attitude toward death among institutionalized elderly than among those living in their own homes. Upon closer examination, this positive attitude may not represent an acceptance of dying as much as it represents a desire not to continue living. Elders living in nursing homes are generally more frail and less physically competent than elders living at home. Death for some elders, rather than being a point of acceptance, is one simply of resignation in a life that is no longer meaningful.

During her pioneering work in hospitals with death and the dying, Elisabeth Kubler-Ross invited dying patients to share their wants, anxieties, and fears with professionals involved in their care. Though talking about death was off-limits for doctors, it was definitely not so for the dying patients:

> *With few exceptions, the patients were surprised, amazed, and grateful. Some were plain curious and others expressed their disbelief that a...doctor would sit with a dying old woman and really care to know what it is like. In the majority of cases the initial outcome was [like] opening floodgates... The patients responded with great relief to sharing some of their last concerns, expressing their feelings without fear of repercussions (Kubler-Ross, 1969, pp. 157-158).*

Kubler-Ross' work provided the foundation for modern thanatology—she moved dying out of the medical closet, in which it had lived throughout the 20th century.

The following section summarizes Kubler-Ross' theory of the process of dying. Although articulated as stages, Kubler-Ross found that a person might be in any stage or in several **stages of dying** simultaneously, and the "stages" are not necessarily sequential. People might move back and forth, in and out of the categorizations, or skip some altogether. The Kubler-Ross stage model provided the most fundamental groundwork for developing a greater understanding of the process of dying. It also provides a good framework to understand the process of grief and bereavement, which might, indeed, be what the dying person experiences.

Telling the story of one's life is a way of confirming values, recognizing the growth and development that has occurred over time, and of connecting with other people.

Stage 1: Denial and shock. Of the more than 300 dying patients interviewed by Kubler-Ross, most reported first reacting to the awareness of a terminal illness with statements such as, "No, not me, it can't be true." The reactions of denial and shock are necessary to give us time to come to terms with the reality of the impending death.

Stage 2: Anger. Following the initial shock, a new reaction sets in: anger, or resentment of those whose lives will continue. "Why me? I have [young children]... [finally found love in life]... [responsibilities to family]...[not yet done something important]..." or a myriad of other realities that give our lives meaning. This anger often becomes displaced to the doctors, who are no good; the nurses, who do everything wrong; the family, which is not sympathetic; and the world, which is a mess. I'm not dead yet–so pay attention to me! Do not abandon me with my fears. The anger serves to give emotion to feelings of helplessness, despair, frustration—it can be a very important process to help the dying person move vague anxieties to a psychological point at which he or she can deal more openly with the experience of dying. Understanding that anger has a function for the dying person can help the people around him or her to cope with those expressions of dissatisfaction or rage.

Stage 3: Bargaining. Bargaining is an attempt to postpone the inevitable. If life can only be extended until they can do the one thing they have always wanted to do, or until they can make amends for something they have regretted, or until they can see someone again, they promise to accept death. Some pledge their life to God or to service in the church in exchange for additional time. Others might promise to give their bodies to science, if only life could be extended. Bargaining is a compromise stage that follows the realization that death cannot be denied or escaped and functions to help the individual cope with the reality of the approaching death.

Stage 4: Depression. When terminally ill patients can no longer deny an illness because of its advancing symptoms, a profound sense of loss is experienced. The loss may be of physical parts of the body removed by surgery, of money that is being spent on treatment, of functions that no longer can be performed, or of relationships with family and friends. A deep sorrow generally accompanies the recognition that death is undeniable. The depression might be **reactive** (the reaction to loss) or **preparatory** (preparation for one's impending loss of life; such preparation facilitates a state of acceptance), but it comes with the profound recognition that there is nothing that can be done about the approaching death.

Stage 5: Acceptance. Most people ultimately move into a weak, quiet state of submission to that which fate has to offer. Kubler-Ross referred to this as acceptance, but it is apparently a time devoid of emotion—it is a twilight for the dying person, who is often sleepy or half-conscious, but no longer depressed or angry. "The struggle for survival is over," and the dying person seems to be taking "a final rest before the long journey," said one of Kubler-Ross' patients (Kubler-Ross, 1969, p. 19). The individual's vital capacity has ebbed and interaction seems unimportant.

At this time, the dying person often wants to be with only one particular, special person. Despite the disinclination to engage at this time, Kubler-Ross emphasized the profound importance for the dying person to be touched and spoken to, as a loving reminder of the context of their life.

Facing death is a difficult task upon which age, status, and experience have little bearing, if any. Young children, old people, and those in between seem to experience a similar process. We die as we have lived, the saying goes. If we are angry, or energetic fighters, or philosophers—those will be the characteristics we bring with us to the process of our death. People do have choice in the way they die, however. Lynne Lofland (1979) proposed that four dimensions of choice shape the role of a dying person. They are: (1) how much "life space" to devote to the dying role—the degree of activity to give over to dying; (2) whether to surround oneself with others who are dying; (3) whether to share information about the facts and feelings of one's death with others; and (4) the sort of personal philosophy one wishes to express in the dying role.

Making decisions about the way in which one will die might be the final act of self-determination the dying person can make. Understanding the process makes the possibility of addressing it and making choices about it far more possible.

THE LIFE REVIEW

Since the early 1970s gerontologists and psychologists have tried to provide insight into the factors most likely to affect the life satisfaction of older people. According to Erikson (1982) and Butler (1981), **reminiscence** provides a source for life satisfaction for the elderly. It allows for the integration of past experiences (who I was then) with the present (who I am now), to make reasonable projections about the future (who will I be...what will happen to me?).

During reminiscence, a person progressively remembers more of past experiences and reexamines and reintegrates unresolved conflicts with the present. This process can bring new significance and meaning to life, reduce anxiety, and prepare one for death. It may well occur in all individuals in the final days of their lives. Though a life review can occur at a younger age, the drive to put one's life in order seems strongest in old age—and it seems to be a necessary process in order to make sense of the life as lived.

According to Butler and Lewis (1991), at some point in late life, the individual develops a particularly vivid imagination and memory for the past and can recall with sudden and remarkable clarity events of early life, seemingly moving thoughts from their subconscious to their conscious mind. This process allows people to grapple with their vulnerability and mortality as they reassess the meaning of life.

The **life review** that results from this process may be told to other people, or it may be preserved as private reflection. Finding the process of expression therapeutic, some older people will tell their life history to anyone who will listen; others share their thoughts with no one. Those who cannot resolve the issues their life review uncovers may become anxious or depressed, or even enter a state of terror or panic. Those who cannot face or accept the resolution of their life conflicts may become deeply depressed, or even commit suicide. Others gain a sense of satisfaction, a sense of tranquillity, a capacity to enjoy to the utmost the remainder of their life. Counselors are advised to be attentive and ready to question and to listen about life and about dying with patients. By creating the opportunity for a dying elder to talk about his or her life in terms of the integration of past, present, and future, the listener helps them to deal more effectively with stress (Puentes, 1998).

Although it may seem that older people, whether close to death or not, are wasting time by talking of the past and dwelling on details that have little meaning to younger listeners, these elders may be engaging in life review. Bernice Neugarten (1986) coined the term "interiority" to refer to a process common in mid- and later-life of becoming more focused on internal messages and stories, and less focused on outside, social issues. This disengagement from the social may accurately describe what happens just prior to death: People turn inward, mentally evaluate their lives, and gradually reduce connections with the larger social world. In contrast, seeking to remain actively, externally connected may potentially damage the self-concept of the dying person by discouraging this reflection, reevaluation, and resolution.

Older residents in nursing homes who belong to reminiscing groups seem to have higher rates of life satisfaction than do residents who do not engage in reminiscing (Cook, 1997). In the early 1980s, a sense of closeness to death among nursing home residents was examined. Researchers named this "awareness of finitude," and found that this awareness was a better predictor of disengagement than was chronological age. The residents who gave a shorter estimate had altered their behavior by constricting their life space and had already become more introverted (Still, 1980).

Did You Know . . .
Deng Ziaoping, China's former leader, died on February 19, 1997, just after the Chinese New Year. The timing of his death, just following the biggest holiday of the year for the Chinese, is a predictable phenomenon. People who are near death often postpone dying until after an event of personal importance. Deaths in New York, a city with a large Jewish population, are lower just before the Jewish Day of Atonement. Death rates drop precipitously among Chinese Americans just before the Harvest Moon Festival (Chinese equivalent of Thanksgiving).

American Demographics, 1997

Care of the Dying in Hospitals

Medical anthropologist Sharon Kaufman identifies a conflict between the **medicalization paradigm** (belief in scientific answers to health), and the paradigm of **individualism and autonomy** (belief in noninterference in personal choice). She suggests it is this conflict that is the source of the "problem" of frailty in old age in American society (Kaufman, 1994), and by extension, the "problem" of dying in a hospital.

In their pioneer study of patient-staff interactions in a number of hospitals, sociologists Barney Glazer and Anselm Strauss (1966) created a typology of awareness contexts of dying for terminally ill patients: (1) closed awareness, (2) suspicion awareness, (3) the ritual drama of mutual pretense, (4) open awareness, and (5) disconnection.

Closed Awareness

The patient does not yet know that he or she is going to die. The physician in charge decides to keep the patient from knowing or even suspecting the actual diagnosis, and the rest of the staff do all they can to maintain the patient's lack of knowledge. The physician gains the patient's trust and at the same time avoids revealing the fact of his or her impending death.

Suspicion Awareness

The patient suspects the truth, but no one will confirm his or her suspicions. Because the patient is afraid to ask outright questions, he or she therefore receives no clear answers. Still, the patient, who wants evidence, tries to interpret what the staff says and does. Peeking at medical charts, eavesdropping on medical conversations, and watching listeners' reactions after declaring, "I think I'm dying," are typical behaviors.

Ritual Drama of Mutual Pretense

This is the third type of awareness. Both patient and staff now know that death is impending, but both choose to act as if it is not. The patient tries to project a healthy, well-groomed appearance and behaves as if he or she will be leaving the hospital soon; the staff makes comments such as "You're looking well today"; and both follow the script as if acting out a drama. Blatant events that expose the mutual pretense are ignored.

Open Awareness

This may or may not extend to the time of death and mode of dying, but both patient and staff openly acknowledge that the patient is dying. Game playing is eliminated.

Disconnection

Doctors and nurses for whom daily encounters with dying patients produce painful and bewildering emotions can be distant and tense with dying people. To face a dying person is a reminder in the health care context of the "failure" at keeping that person alive and vigorous, as well as a reminder of one's own mortality and the finality of death. Some hospital staff members react to the dying person by withdrawing emotionally at a time when the patient most needs their support.

RESPONSE OF THE HEALTH CARE SYSTEM

Fortunately, in no small part because of hospice and chaplaincy services, the health care system is showing an increased sensitivity to issues about death and dying. If health professionals can face their own mortality, they can more easily face mortality in others and are less likely to transmit their fear, shock, or horror to the dying person. Generally, the goal for hospital staff is to maintain an open awareness context, as appropriate to the patient. Sometimes other contexts are called for; closed awareness, for example, may be appropriate if the patient indicates a strong desire not to know any details about his or her condition and clearly denies his or her own illness.

How much hope to offer the dying patient is another task health care professionals must face. Some degree of hope can be helpful to the terminally ill. A glimpse of hope can maintain a person through tests, surgery, and suffering. Patients show the greatest confidence in doctors who offer hope without lying, who share with them the hope that some unforeseen development will change the course of events. Hope does not particularly mean that people who understand they are dying, believe they will live. It means they have something to live for a little while longer.

The "Dying Person's Bill of Rights," drawn up by those who nurse cancer patients, includes this statement about hope: "I have the right to be cared for by those who can maintain a sense of hopefulness, however changing this might be."

For two decades, the National Cancer Institute has offered a seminar to physicians planning to specialize in the care of cancer patients. The physicians meet to come to grips with their own anxieties about death and to better understand their interactions with dying patients and their families. Doctors and nurses often feel an involuntary anger at the dying patient, who comes to represent their own sense of failure and helplessness. "When you've exhausted everything you can do for a patient medically, it becomes difficult to walk into the room every day and talk to that patient." The seminar seems to relieve stress on the cancer ward's nurses, who used to regularly ask for transfers to other wards. It also teaches the staff to be more comfortable in discussing death and other potentially sensitive topics with the patient.

Courses in death and dying are now available at Harvard, Tufts, and other medical schools. Nine of 10 medical schools in the country have at least one or two lectures for students on the topic, but only six medical schools offer an entire course on death and dying. In only half of the schools with such a course is it required; in the other half it is an elective. Personal involvement of students with dying patients was minimal in almost every course at every medical school. One exception is the Yale School of Medicine, which developed a course enabling medical students to interact with very sick patients. The course tries to help students develop and demonstrate their compassion, without being afraid.

A MATTER OF CHOICE

Individuals who face the prospect of imminent death increasingly seek to expand their rights in determining the manner of their dying. Deciding to die at home or to not prolong life by artificial means are becoming two areas of choice for terminally ill patients. In addition, suicide and funeral plans, which also involve the matter of choice, have special implications for elders.

Did You Know . . .
Searching the medical literature for articles on "death" will yield more articles on cell death than on human death.

HORGAN, 1997

PALLIATIVE CARE

Palliative care—pain control—is the core of the practice, in which an individual's death is neither hastened nor prolonged. It provides, in the words of Christine Cassel (1996), "aggressive comfort care." Tremendous advances in the management of pain have occurred in the final decade of the 20th century: Drugs can be delivered through skin patches, through topical creams, and by intravenous pumps. Some new drugs and delivery systems have helped to minimize the side effects of many painkillers, such as grogginess, nausea, and reduced mental clarity (Horgan, 1997).

Social attitudes that have limited prescriptions of analgesics—opiates such as morphine, particularly—have shifted somewhat in recent years. The Pain and Policy Studies Group at the University of Wisconsin has conducted some outstanding research on attitudes of the public and of physicians about painkillers, and find changing perceptions on the use of "addicting" drugs for pain control (Horgan, 1997). It is striking to note that medical research in the field of pain control has not been directed by humanitarian philosophy, but by the market potential brought about by longevity and by governmental funding through Medicare for palliative care.

The Hospice Movement

Hospice was virtually unheard of in this country until the mid-1970s. It received a tremendous boost in 1982 when Medicare payments were authorized to cover care for terminally ill patients. In 1989, a federal law raised disbursement rates for hospice services by 20 percent, and another surge of interest occurred (Worsnop, 1996). In 1996 the Hospice Association of America reported that over 2,100 Medicare-certified hospice programs were in operation across the country, compared with 158 in 1985.

The hospice model, which stresses effective pain relief for terminal cancer patients, is designed to care for the dying person—the whole person, not the disease. The term **hospice** can be any organization that provides support services to dying patients and their loved ones in the place where that care is given, whether it is in the home, in a hospital, or in a nursing home (Worsnop, 1997).

The first hospice program in the United States, Hospice of Connecticut, in New Haven, offers a model of care for the dying. The New Haven hospice began as a home care program. Outreach workers visited and counseled patients, and they also provided home nursing to the dying. Family members could receive individual or group counseling throughout the dying process to get support from others experiencing the same shock and grief. The program later developed a residential hospice, in which families and friends could be with the dying person, away from the home.

Hospice works with an interdisciplinary team of workers, including nurses, health aides, counselors, physical therapists, nutritionists, chaplains, volunteer visitors, doctors, and long term care administrators. Volunteers provide care so family members can get out of the house, or feel

Dr. Jack Kevorkian is a controversial advocate for doctor assisted suicide. His aggressive public style on behalf of his cause has effectively forced a public debate.

comfortable leaving the bedside. Volunteers also might do light housekeeping, laundry, meal preparations, and run errands for the family or the ill person.

Some hospitals run hospice programs, and programs are becoming available at nursing homes as well. These programs offer an integrated approach to death in which medical and nursing staffs, chaplains and visiting clergy, and social service staff members work together to meet the physical, spiritual, and psychological needs of the dying.

Hospice care in the 1990s has focused a great deal of attention on AIDS patients. Nursing homes that, until recently, have cared mostly for elders now provide facilities for young adult AIDS patients. Hospice care, though stretching to meet the needs of all clients, is, nevertheless, overburdened in areas where the numbers of AIDS patients are high. Additionally, they have become far more bureaucratized and regulated, especially where Medicaid and Medicare reimbursements apply (Magno, 1990). The AIDS epidemic, with no cure in sight, has underscored the need for the hospice orientation, an approach that emphasizes care when there is no cure. Hospice care promotes the philosophy that comfort and quality of life are, in and of themselves, worthwhile and essential goals to the end of one's life.

Although most people, when asked, express a desire to die at home, only a small percentage actually do. Not everyone should die at home. For a patient who has an unhappy or unstable family, or who needs complicated nursing care, a hospital or nursing home may be a better option. Parents and grandparents sometimes choose to die in hospitals to avoid traumatizing young children. However, some psychiatrists believe that the very fact of a death occurring at home can ward off psychological damage to the family. The child who is involved throughout the dying process does not have to face the sudden, unexplained disappearance of a parent or grandparent. In contrast, children who are not involved may believe, for example, that they are somehow responsible for the death. Keeping a dying family member at home can both make it easier for relatives to accept the death and prevent the patient from being alone in the dying process.

Reframing the Craft of Dying

Lynne Lofland (1979) refers to the hospice movement and a number of other groups that work toward improving attitudes and conditions surrounding death as the "happy death movement."

This movement opposes the conventional view that the dying person be stoic, strong, and silent. It began, she says, in academia and filtered out to ordinary citizens who are embracing the "happy death" concept (in Hoefler, 1994). Lofland notes that although the new movement has helped some people to freely express their fears, others still refuse to express their concerns.

The new movement has advocated the view that dying can be a learning, growing, and positive experience. Lofland observes that this emphasis, in itself, may pressure dying people to assume a certain way of thinking. Those who will not or cannot share their thoughts and feelings, or who do not develop positive attitudes, may feel like failures. She believes that alternative ideologies are critical to provide dying people a maximum choice in their mental preparation for death.

In a similar vein, some who work in the field of death and dying have criticized the phrase "death with dignity" as placing too much emphasis on being proper or accepting (Nuland, 1994). *Dignity* has a Latin root, *dignitas*, meaning "worthiness" (Meyer, 1995). A potential exists that "death with dignity" might place a burden of particular behavior on the dying individual, rather than emphasize its meaning to create an environment in which the dying person is helped to be aware of his or her worthiness.

Did You Know . . .
In 1937 a nationwide Gallup Poll reported that 46 percent of Americans interviewed favored "mercy deaths under government supervision for hopeless individuals."

WORSNOP, 1996

THE RIGHT TO DIE

We have grappled with the **right-to-die issue** for many decades. The first bill to legalize doctor-assisted suicide was introduced in 1906 in the state of Ohio, which proposed that a doctor could ask a terminally ill person in the presence of three witnesses whether he or she wished to die. If the answer was yes, and three other physicians agreed that the patient's condition was hopeless, they could assist in his suicide. Opponents feared a lack of safeguards, and the measure was defeated. This issue has continued to be discussed and debated over the past nine decades.

The Oath of Hippocrates
I swear by Apollo the physician, and by Aesculapius [god of medicine], Hygeia [goddess of health], and Panacea [goddess of healing], and all the gods and goddesses, that, to the best of my ability and judgment, I will keep this oath and agreement: to regard my teacher in this art as equal to my own parents; to share my living with him and provide for him in need; to treat his children as my own and teach them this art if they wish to learn it, without payment or obligation; to give guidance, explanations, and every other kind of instruction to my own children and those of my teacher, and to students who subscribe to the Physician's Oath, but to nobody else.

I will prescribe treatment to the best of my ability and judgment for the benefit of my patients and will abstain from whatever is harmful or pernicious. I will give no poisonous or deadly medicine, even if asked to, nor make any suggestion; neither will I give any woman a pessary to produce an abortion. I will both live and work in purity and holiness. I will not operate, not even on patients suffering from the stone, but will leave this to specialists who are skilled in this work. Into whatever houses I enter, I will make the patient's good my principal aim and will avoid all deliberate harm or corruption, especially from sexual relations with women or men, bond or free. Whatever I see or hear about people, whether in the course of my practice or outside it, if it should not be made public, I will keep it to myself and treat it as an inviolable secret.

While I abide by this oath and never violate it, may all people hold me in esteem for all time on account of my life and work; but if I break this oath, let the reverse be my fate.

The issue slowly grew in public acceptance, fermenting until the liberation of the Nazi death camps in 1945 at the end of World War II. The full horror of medically assisted death—systematic termination of life—suddenly became so abhorrent a concept, that assisted suicide ceased to be a public topic (Worsley, 1996).

In the 1970s, the parents of Karen Quinlan, a 21-year-old woman in a permanent vegetative state, initiated a court battle in the state of New Jersey for the right to disconnect the life-support machines to which Karen was attached. Though a trial judge initially ruled against them, in 1976 after taking the case to the New Jersey Supreme Court, the Quinlans were allowed to have the machines removed. Karen lived in a comatose state another nine years.

A second case that galvanized the public's awareness was that of *Cruzan v. Missouri Department of Health*. Following an auto accident rendering her in a vegetative state, Nancy Cruzan had been kept alive for seven years by a feeding tube. In a suit filed in 1988, her parents, acting on her behalf, requested that her food and fluids be stopped. A lengthy and extraordinarily expensive process ensued for the Cruzans. In a summary of the case in the *Congressional Quarterly*, Richard Worsnop reported (1996):

> *The Missouri Department of Health appealed the decision to the State Supreme Court, which reversed it. As a result, the Cruzans appealed to the US Supreme Court, which held on June 25, 1990, that a person whose wishes were clearly known had a constitutional right to refuse life-sustaining medical treatment. At the same time, however, it ruled that states could require that comatose patients be kept alive unless there was "clear and convincing evidence" that they would not want to live under such conditions. Such evidence, said the court, was lacking in the* Cruzan *case.*
>
> *Instead of giving up, the Cruzans returned to Jasper County Circuit Court. Three of Nancy's former co-workers now testified that she had told them years earlier she would not want to live out her days in a coma. ...[The court ruled that] this disclosure amounted to clear and convincing evidence. ...The Cruzans had the right to order the removal of their daughter's feeding tube (p. 780).*

Nancy died 12 days following removal of the feeding tube. Her death came two months after a U.S. law was passed requiring hospitals and other health care facilities receiving Medicare or Medicaid payments to inform patients of their right to execute living wills or other advance directives (Worsnop, 1996).

Families are still fighting similar court battles today. Doctors traditionally have felt they must prolong life as long as possible without questioning the circumstances, an idea that constitutes an intrinsic part of the Hippocratic oath. However, values and laws traditionally lag behind technological advancements; and the value system doctors have followed for centuries is now in a state of flux. The right to die is but one of many issues confronting **medical ethics** in the new century.

In the following sections, we will discuss that issue and several others. The issues are complex: At what point should the decision not to prolong life be made, who should make the decision, and does an individual have the right to choose death when life could be extended in some fashion? Some of the right-to-die issues can be stated as specific questions:

1. What is the difference between killing and allowing a person to die?
2. What is the difference between stopping treatment and not beginning it?
3. Are there reasonable and unreasonable treatments?

The answers to these questions, which cannot be easily answered, vary on both moral and legal grounds.

"In an odd way, the right-to-die movement has improved the quality of care of the dying in America. After Measure 16 passed [in Oregon] in 1994, the health profession started sponsoring seminars and lectures on pain control and set up task forces on end-of-life care. Now people reckon Oregon is the finest place to die in America. Doctors and nurses here will do their very best for you so that you don't ask for assisted dying."

DEREK HUMPHRY, HEMLOCK SOCIETY FOUNDER, 1997

ADVANCE DIRECTIVES

Margaret Jones's 88-year-old mother was in terminal stages with brain cancer. When Margaret arrived to visit, she found her mother unconscious on the bathroom floor. Margaret telephoned 911; when the paramedics arrived, they resuscitated the elder Mrs. Jones, as required by law. The painful intubation procedure and a portable ventilator kept the Mrs. Jones alive for the remainder of the month, when she finally died. She had no advance directives. In trying to be sensitive to Mrs. Jones' sense of hope, Margaret probably did her mother a great disservice.

Though nearly 90 percent of all Americans will have a "managed death" in a hospital or skilled nursing facility that can lengthen life for up to several years through medical and nursing interventions, only about 15 percent of patients have advance directives (Haynor, 1998). Figure 15.1 is an example of a **Living Will,** one form of advance directive.

Two terms are important to a discussion of the right to die: (1) **passive euthanasia,** or the process of allowing persons to die without using "extraordinary means" to save their lives; and (2) **active euthanasia,** or performing a deliberate act to end a person's life, such as administering a fatal injection. There are acts between active and passive euthanasia that are difficult to categorize. Not treating a person for pneumonia is one example. Is the intentional lack of action in itself "active"?

THE PATIENT SELF-DETERMINATION ACT (PSDA)

The **Patient Self-Determination Act** (PSDA) of 1991 requires all health care facilities receiving Medicare and Medicaid funding to recognize the living will and durable power of attorney for health care (health care proxy) as advance directives. It further requires "all hospitals, nursing homes, health maintenance organizations, hospices, and health care companies that participate in Medicare or Medicaid to provide patients with written information on their rights concerning advance directives under state and federal law" (Duffield & Podzamsky, 1996). The PSDA created no new rights for patients, but it reaffirmed the common-law right of self-determination as guaranteed in the 14th Amendment (Haynor, 1998).

"The decision to commit suicide with the assistance of another may be just as personal and profound as the decision to refuse unwanted medical treatment, but it has never enjoyed similar legal protection. Indeed, the two acts are widely and reasonably regarded as quite distinct. ...First, when a patient refuses life-sustaining medical treatment, he dies from an underlying fatal disease or pathology; but if a patient ingests lethal medication prescribed by a physician, he is killed by that medication."

SUPREME COURT CHIEF JUSTICE REHNQUIST, 1997

PHYSICIAN-ASSISTED SUICIDE

Adults of all ages support the right to die by refusing treatment, as reflected in living will legislation in all 50 states. When it comes to actively hastening death, or physician-**assisted suicide,**

FIGURE 15.1

Example of living will

The following document is only a guide. It should not replace necessary consultation with a qualified legal professional regarding your state's regulations regarding a living will's length of effectiveness, requirements for witnesses, or other factors.

LIVING WILL OF **[fill in your name]**

To my physician, attorney, family, friends, and any medical facility or health care professional whose care I may come under or happen to be under and all others who may be responsible for decision making with respect to my health or well-being:

On this **[fill in ordinal number, e.g., first, second]** day of **[fill in month], [fill in year]**, I, **[fill in first name, middle name, and last name]**, born **[fill in birth date]**, being of sound mind, willfully and voluntarily direct that my dying and death shall not be artificially prolonged under the circumstances set forth in this declaration:

If, at any time:

1. I should be in a coma or persistent vegetative state and, in the opinion of two physicians who have personally examined me, one of whom shall be my attending physician, have no known hope of regaining awareness and higher mental functions no matter what is done; or

2. I should have an incurable injury, disease, or illness certified to be a terminal condition by two physicians who have personally examined me, one of whom shall be my attending physician, and the physicians have determined that my death will occur as a result of such incurable injury, disease or illness, whether or not life-sustaining procedures are utilized, and where the application of such procedures would serve only to prolong artificially a hopeless illness or the dying process, I direct that life-sustaining or -prolonging treatments or procedures (including the artificial administration of food and water, whether intravenously, by gastric tube, or by any other similar means) shall not be used and I do not desire any such treatment to be provided and/or continued.

3. I would like to live out my last days at home rather than in a hospital, long-term care facility, nursing home, or other health care facility if it does not jeopardize the chance of my recovery to a meaningful life and does not put undue hardship on my family or significant other.

4. I direct that I be permitted to die naturally, with only the administration of medication and/or the performance of any medical procedure deemed necessary to provide me with comfort and/or to alleviate pain. In the absence of my ability to give directions regarding the use of such life-sustaining procedures, it is my intention that this document and my wishes with respect to dying shall be honored by my family and physicians as a definitive expression of my legal right to refuse medical or surgical treatment and to accept the consequences from such refusal.

As a consequence of the foregoing instructions, I hereby direct my Personal Representative, my Trustee, the beneficiaries under my Will, and my heirs that none of them may or shall maintain or cause to be maintained any legal or administrative action that has as its foundation or as one of its claims or causes of action the failure of a physician, nurse, hospital, clinic, or any other natural or legal person or entity whatsoever to prolong my life while, because of an incurable injury, disease, or illness certified to be a terminal condition, under the procedures described above.

(*continued*)

FIGURE 15.1

Example of living will—continued

This statement is made after careful consideration and is in accordance with my strong convictions and beliefs. I want the wishes and directions here expressed carried out to the full extent permitted by law. Those concerned with my health and well-being are asked to take whatever action is needed (including legal) to realize my preferences, wishes, and instructions. Insofar as they are not legally enforceable, let those to whom this is addressed regard themselves morally bound by these provisions.

I am an adult of sound mind and otherwise legally competent to make this Declaration, and I understand its full import.

Signed by: **[print your full name and address]**

Signature of the above:
Date: **[fill in date]**

Under penalty of perjury, we state that this Declaration was signed by **[name of individual signing]** in the presence of the undersigned, who, at the Declarant's request, in the Declarant's presence, and in the presence of each other, have hereunto signed our names as witnesses this **[fill in ordinal number, e.g., first, second]** day in the month of **[fill in month],** in the year of **[fill in year].**

Each of us individually states that: The Declarant is personally known to me, and I believe the Declarant to be of sound mind. I did not sign the Declarant's signature to this Living Will Declaration.

Based upon information and belief, I am not related to the Declarant by blood or marriage, a creditor of he Declarant, entitled to any portion of the estate of the Declarant under any existing testamentary instrument of the Declarant, financially or other wise responsible for the Declarant's medical care, or an employee of any such person or institution.

Name: **[fill in name]** Name: **[fill in name[**
Address: **[fill in address]** Address: **[fill in address]**
Date: **[fill in day, month, year]** Date: **[fill in day, month, year]**

Copies of this Living Will have been distributed to:

Name: **[fill in name]** Name: **[fill in name]**
Address: **[fill in address]** Address: **[fill in address]**

The original Living Will is located in **[fill in]** at **[fill in address].**

people are less certain. Between 40 percent and 50 percent of physicians believe that physician-assisted suicide may be an ethically permissible practice, and around 66 percent of the general public favors its legalization (Koenig et al., 1996). Polls, however, have included only a small proportion of older adults (a proportionally representative sample).

In November 1997, Oregon voters overwhelmingly—by 60 percent—reaffirmed their support for the nation's only law allowing physician-assisted suicide. The legislation was originally passed in 1994, and was brought to a second vote in 1997 by political referendum. The law includes a 15-day waiting period after a terminally ill person has requested physician assistance with suicide. At least two doctors must agree that the patient's condition is terminal, and the patient must request the drugs in writing and administer the drugs to him or herself.

When elderly patients are asked about their attitudes toward physician-assisted suicide and the types of assistance that should be provided, interesting attitude differences emerge. In two separate studies, elderly patients were found to be less likely than their relatives to support physician-assisted suicide. Those patients who oppose the practice represent a particularly vulnerable portion of society: women, African Americans, the poor, and people with lower educational achievement (Koenig et al., 1996; Duffield & Podzamsky, 1996). This implies that special protection might be necessary for some groups of individuals who by tradition have less "voice" in the system.

About half the states have laws that make assisted suicide an actual felony. In other states, the assistant might be prosecuted under a general charge of manslaughter; in still others, the law is unclear and not vigorously pursued. The issue has created intense public debate, and split the health care community. A review by John Horgan (1997) summarizes:

> *The American Medical Association (AMA), the American Nursing Association, the National Hospice Organization and dozens of other groups have filed briefs with the Supreme Court opposing physician-assisted suicide. Supporters of legalization include the American Medical Student Association, the Coalition of Hospice Professionals, and Marcia Angell, editor of the New England Journal of Medicine.*
>
> *Nonetheless, the dispute masks a deep consensus among health care experts that much can and should be done to improve the care of the dying (p. 100).*

The arguments both in support and against assisted suicide touch upon powerful issues of ethics and American values. On the one hand is fear that laws allowing for physician-assisted suicide will introduce a "slippery slope" toward involuntary euthanasia. Ethicists worry that the power to decide who should live and who should die will get into the hands of the wrong person. The ability to make a decision as powerful as this might move to the "next step" of making the determination for a "medically defective" person, or someone who is "too old" or "too poor" to warrant expensive medical care.

On the other hand is the belief that self-determination by competent individuals is an inviolable right and essential to the maintenance of human dignity. Validation for this perspective comes in part from teaching hospitals, which report that 40 percent of terminally ill patients experience severe pain "most of the time" (Horgan, 1997). The perspective also emerges from a greater sensitivity of cultural diversity. The Japanese, for example, have a more casual attitude toward suicide. It is seen as a "sad but not morally ambiguous response to human relational struggles" (Matzo, 1997).

Those in the center of the argument believe the stage is set for an assisted suicide if doctor and patient have thoroughly explored all options, and if the patient is not depressed. If the patient is terminally ill, is near death, and cannot face either the pain of the disease or the agonizing efforts of more useless treatments, then a physician-assisted suicide is acceptable from this position.

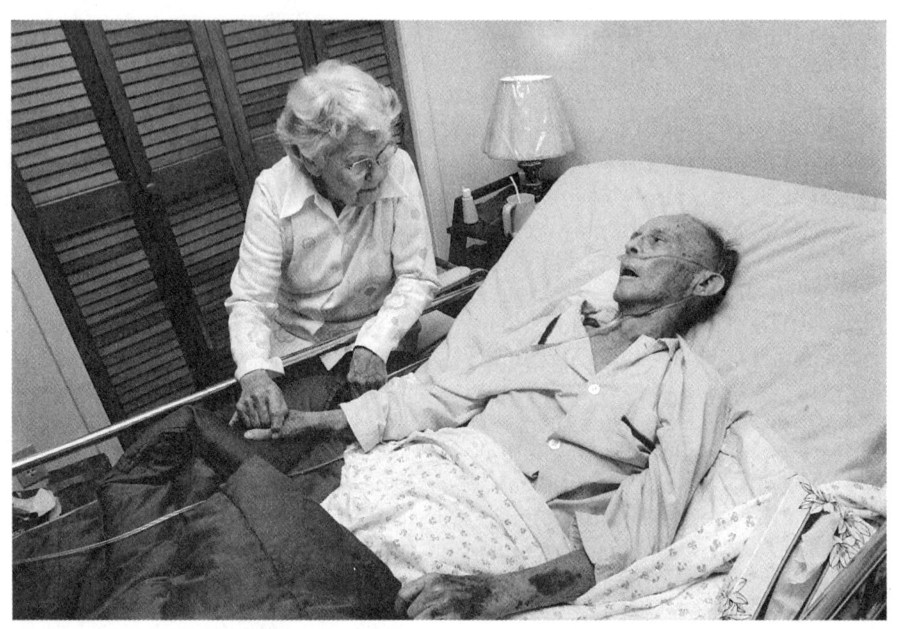

Perhaps the most precious gift to be given is to be with someone else on their journey into death. To help someone with their dying, one's own death must have been squarely addressed.

> *"Even in the very shadow of death, one's living experience can give rise to accomplishment. Dying is just a time of living. It's a particularly difficult time of living that has a propensity for problems and suffering.... People are dignified even in their dying, even in their physical dependency, if they're treated in a dignified manner."*
>
> IRA BYOCK, DYING WELL, 1996

Yet another approach is to sidestep the issues of ethics and morality and address the need for pain control. The capability exists to control pain far better than it is often controlled. It simply is not made available in all cases (Matzo, 1997). The seriously ill may become trapped in a cycle of intensifying distress in which chronic pain becomes more severe over time, leading to psychological distress, making the pain more difficult to endure. Even with the advances in pain medications and their delivery, pain is not adequately addressed by health care services (Beresford, 1997). Too little, too late creates too much suffering.

Dr. Jack Kevorkian

Suicides such as these pose this question: Do people have a right to choose death by suicide? Several groups, such as the Hemlock Society, advocate control over one's dying, which includes committing suicide, if necessary, to escape profound pain or great bodily deterioration. AIDS advocates, for example, often argue for the right to commit suicide, if that is the choice of the suffering person. But no one has received as much publicity in terms of assisted suicide as Dr. Jack Kevorkian—"Doctor Death."

By 1998, Dr. Kevorkian had helped one hundred people commit suicide. All of his suicide patients have been in terminal stages of disease, generally accompanied by excruciating pain. Kevorkian refers to assisted suicide as "**patholysis**" (Greek for freedom from suffering) and has dedicated his life and career to bringing to public awareness the need, in his perspective, for the legalization of assisted suicide.

Patients of Dr. Kevorkian who request assistance with their suicide are interviewed at length by him and his associates, usually for several weeks before actually meeting with him. His agreement to provide assistance is based on his assessment of the mental competence and the physical condition of the person, among other factors. If he agrees to provide assistance, the patient meets with Kevorkian and his attorney for personal interviews and to review the case. Documents assuring the patient's competence and desire to commit suicide are signed. Those people who are willing to do so make a videotaped personal statement, often in interview format with Kevorkian and/or his attorney.

Examples of people whose deaths were assisted by Kevorkian are a 72-year-old woman, a double-amputee in severe pain from rheumatoid arthritis and advanced osteoporosis. Another person with multiple sclerosis was assisted, who was unable to sit or lie down because of excruciating pain. People who complete their suicide with Kevorkian's assistance leave a note directing family and/or police to the location of their body; generally the note includes a personal statement including the person's choice in the matter. A 78-year-old Canadian emigrant from India with severe Parkinson's disease left a note including the statement, "I am grateful to the merciful hands of Dr. Kevorkian ...to bring about a happy deliverance—Maha Samadhi—a final embrace with the divine" (US News Bulletins, 1997).

Jack Kevorkian and his associates, including an attorney, an assistant, and a psychiatrist, are attempting to challenge the legal system into making a definitive ruling on the legal status of physician-assisted suicide. His objectives are to make it an accepted medical practice. "It's time to clear the air," said Kevorkian in a news interview. "I admit I assisted in the [deaths of 100 people]. If there was a crime committed, charge me. If there isn't, don't bother me" (US News Bulletins, 1998).

In 1996, a Michigan jury acquitted Jack Kevorakian of charges that he assisted in two suicides. In the same time period, California and New York struck down state prohibitions against physician-assisted suicide, however there is no legislation in either state to specifically support the concept (Horgan, 1997).

Informed Consent to Treatment

Norms have radically changed in acceptable medical practice in the final decade of the 20th century. Issues of autonomy, self-determination, and quality of life now impact the way in which medicine is delivered. Approximately 85 percent of deaths in the United States occur in institutions, and 70 percent of those involve elective withholding of life-sustaining treatment (Matzo, 1997).

A couple of short decades previously, doctors felt comfortable making all informed decisions for their patients, certain that their judgment, though imperfect, was the best judgment available. Nurses acquiesced without question to doctor's judgments—they were considered technicians whose job it was to do the physician's bidding. This is no longer the case. Patients have the right to accept or reject any treatment or prescription that their physician may offer them, and they have the right to be informed of their choices. Those suffering a serious or life-threatening illness for which several treatment plans are possible or optional now are in the difficult position of needing to select what they believe to be the best plan, under the informed guidance of their physician.

In terms of cancer, for example, surgery, radiation, chemotherapy, and special diets are all available as treatment options. Patients have an obligation to inform themselves of both the options and risks involved with each option, and then base their consent to treatment on three principles:

1. They are competent to give general consent.
2. They give consent freely (e.g., are not coerced by economic situation or relatives).
3. They have a full understanding of the meaning of the options (DeSpelder & Strickland, 1991).

Informed consent means that patients share in their health care decision making by becoming informed and by basing their choice, acceptance, or rejection of treatment on the information available to them.

MORE ETHICS IN AGING

Other ethical issues have arisen now that medical technology has the capacity to prolong life almost indefinitely, and disease control keeps more people alive into advanced age. Here are some of those issues:

1. What is the appropriate level of direction family members and the health care system should provide when dealing with a person who is losing competency? For example, is the person with early Alzheimer's allowed self-determination in deciding whether to drive a car? With more advanced Alzheimer's, how is a "wanderer" restrained and who makes the decision? (Moody, 1992)
2. With regard to the ethics of nursing home placement and ethical dilemmas in the nursing home, how much self-determination and autonomy is allowed the older person to make decisions and act for himself or herself?
3. Should we ration health care on the grounds of age? Using formulas of cost and age, who decides when the cost gets too high and when the very old are not saved?
4. What kind of research can legally and morally be conducted on older subjects? Effects of various drugs and therapeutic procedures are constantly under study. Yet ethical guidelines for research with aged patients is not discussed nearly as much as with younger patients (Wicclair, 1993).
5. What obligations do adult children have for the financial, physical, and emotional support of frail elderly parents?

Funerals and Burial

Dying in institutions is depersonalized for the dying individual, and dissociates society from the process of dying. The person dies, usually alone. The body is sent to a funeral parlor, where it is prepared for burial by strangers, who never knew the living person. Preparation includes washing the body; it often includes injecting preservatives; dressing it for burial in whatever garment the family or caretaker chooses; applying flesh-colored makeup to whatever skin is exposed after dressing; arranging the hair; and arranging the facial expression to give the impression of peaceful slumber. It is often *after* this point that family members spend time with the body, to say goodbye to the person who has died.

The majority of Americans who die are buried, but cremations are more frequently chosen now than in the past. Between 1990 and 1996, cremations increased from 17 percent to 21 percent, and the number of people who plan a cremation for themselves increased from 37 to 42 percent (Cassel, 1996). Both burial and cremation, however, allow for a funeral or memorial service at which the bereaving friends and family can commemorate the life of the person they loved. These rituals serve as a way that families or groups can share their identity and reestablish their collective presence in the absence of the person who has died.

Old and young alike can be victims of coercion when arranging funerals for themselves or for their loved ones. Commercialization, unnecessary extravagance, and deception are criticisms leveled at the modern funeral industry. An individual, vulnerable after the death of a spouse or relative and wanting to do the very best for the deceased person, is easily persuaded to spare no expense for a funeral.

Some funeral directors play on the emotions of the bereaved. They may, for example, persuade a grief-stricken relative to buy an expensive casket to show how much he or she loved the deceased. The cost of the casket can be one financial trap; embalming can be another. Funeral directors are hesitant to mention that no law requires embalming or that no casket is required for cremation.

The cost of cemetery plots also can be high. Charges for limousines, burial clothes, use of the viewing room, and a headstone are not necessarily devious. In this culture, mortuaries are a necessary business, operating for profit. However, consumers should not be pressured into spending thousands of dollars on a funeral that will create financial hardship.

Some organizations help to provide simple, dignified funerals for their members. Cremation, which involves about one-eighth the cost of a conventional funeral, is becoming more common, appealing especially to those who believe that cemeteries are a needless waste of land. Individuals should be aware that they do have choices in these matters.

Because of complaints about the funeral industry, the Federal Trade Commission (FTC) ruled in 1984 that funeral directors must provide itemized lists of goods and services and their prices. This may keep prices from varying depending on a client's vulnerability, and it shows clearly that a price range exists. The FTC also ruled that misrepresentation of state laws concerning embalming and cremation is against the law. In addition, funeral parlors must itemize on a funeral bill every charge—the cost of flowers, death notices in newspapers, the provision of hearses and limousines, guest registers, and other related services (Aiken, 1994).

Consumer groups still need to educate the public about the laws governing the funeral industry and to inform individuals about their rights and choices. An individual needs to know about the itemized price list, for example, to ensure that he or she asks for and receives one. The average cost of a funeral is now more than $7,000. But no one has to spend that much. For example, inexpensive caskets are available; but family members of the deceased may not know this. Sometimes family members feel guilty if they purchase a casket made of, say, particleboard rather than wood, not realizing that a particleboard casket can be just as beautiful as a wooden one. It's helpful to family members if these matters can be discussed before death occurs.

Some people buy their plots and tombstones long before they are near death. In good health with a clear mind is the best condition in which to discuss funeral decisions with one's family. If a person can give specific instructions about the kind of funeral and burial he or she wants, a surviving spouse and children are less likely to be led into agonizing and/or expensive choices they will regret.

Facing and Preparing for Death

Realizing that death is the ultimate destiny for each of us, we need to understand, regardless of our age, the importance of preparing for it. Facing death, or at least easing personal anxiety about it, can improve the quality of an individual's life. Whether you have thought about or have already answered any of the following questions tells something about your degree of preparation for dying.

1. Do you have a will?
2. Do you have life insurance?
3. Did you prepare advance directives?
4. Are you willing to have an autopsy done on your body?
5. Are you willing to donate the organs of your body for use after you die?
6. Do you know how you want your body disposed of (burial, cremation, donated to a medical school)?

7. What kind of last rites do you desire (funeral, memorial services, a party)?

When we reduce our own fears of death and dying, we can offer others, including the terminally ill, better care and help them cope. If our thoughts of death elicit thoughts of satisfaction with a life well-lived, we have reached what psychologist Erik Erikson means by integrity, his final stage of psychosocial development. In the later years of life, those with a sense of integrity reflect on their past with satisfaction; those filled with despair dwell on missed opportunities and missed directions. With luck and understanding, the path each person takes will prepare them for death, which Kubler-Ross calls "the final stage of growth."

BEREAVEMENT

The loss of a loved one is generally the most tragic event an individual experiences in a lifetime. It is an experience that occurs some time or another in nearly everyone's life. In old age, these events occur with increasing frequency, as friends and family members die. Social scientists believe that their goal, after empathizing with another person's suffering, is to step aside from the maze of emotion and sensation and to make sense of it—what is the function of suffering to the human condition? A folk wisdom states, "Pain is inevitable. Suffering is not." Is that so? If we can understand more about bereavement, we can understand more about supporting those who are bereaved.

Bereavement theory and research is expanding into unknown areas, such as why some bereaved people themselves die soon after their loved one. Though there are vast individual differences, bereaved persons tend to recover within a two-year period, yet a smaller high-risk group of people simply cannot make a recovery.

Complicated mourning is a cognitive disorganization and emotional chaos that can lead some people into profound depressions that do not move toward resolution (Rando, 1995). Types of complicated mourning reactions include chronic grief reactions, masked grief reactions, exaggerated grief reactions, and chronic depression (Aiken, 1994; Marrone, 1996).

Chronic grief reactions involve reactions to death that are of long duration and do not lead to resolution. The survivor feels sorrow for years after the loss.

Masked grief reactions are the complete absence of grief reactions accompanied with substitute psychosomatic complaints (headaches, insomnia, pain). The broken heart syndrome, referring to findings that a widow or widower is more likely to die within the first two years following the death of his or her spouse, may be connected to this type of grief reaction (Stroebe et al., 1993).

Exaggerated grief reactions are repressed reactions to former grief-causing situations that erupt in response to a current loss. Old losses that were covered up erupt as phobias, psychosomatic symptoms, psychiatric disorders, and so forth (Marrone, 1996).

Clinical depression is the profound sadness and depression experienced in mourning; however, its effects are more powerful and it lasts longer. Clinical depression is considered to be a mood disorder that includes sadness, helplessness, guilt, and a pervasive sense of suffering. The inability to concentrate and general apathy accompany clinical depression.

Complicated grief reactions occur based on personality characteristics of the bereaved individual, the degree of support available to him or her in the grief process, and the relationship of the deceased person with the bereaved individual. Feelings of ambivalence toward the deceased person can bring about a complicated grief reaction, as can the circumstances of the death.

Mourning is a profoundly individual matter. Bereavement is a state of loss—to bereave, in fact, means "to take away from, to rob, to dispossess" (Kalish, 1985). The ways in which we respond to that loss will be as different as are our personalities and our life experiences.

Chapter Summary

Death is one of the few certainties of life, yet denial of death is common. We have euphemisms for the word *death*; we protect children from hearing about it; and death on TV is not real. Instead, death is disassociated with everyday events by typically occurring in a hospital setting. Elders, just as any other age group, may have fears about dying. The phases that a terminally-ill person goes through include: (1) denial and isolation, (2) anger, (3) bargaining, (4) depression, and (5) acceptance. Efforts must be made so terminally ill patients are given care, concern, and support. Elders are being given more choices in dying, but suicide is still not socially accepted. Yet changes are slowly taking place to broaden choices for the dying.

Physician-assisted suicide has become a topic of wide debate and has been legalized in Oregon. The hospice movement has supported people in their choice to die at home and to refuse life-extending measures that bring pain and discomfort. Medical ethics are challenging the assumption that lives should be extended at any cost. Patients are being informed of their rights, especially the right to refuse treatment. The "right-to-die" movement has gained momentum. Social scientists are now seriously exploring the issue of near-death experiences. It is important for elders to face death and prepare for it.

Key Terms

active euthanasia
assisted suicide
awareness contexts of dying
bereavement
chronic grief reactions
clinical depression
complicated mourning
death anxiety
death competency
death-denying society
exaggerated grief reactions
fear of death
fears about dying
hospice
individualism and autonomy
informed consent
life review
Living Will
masked grief reactions
medical ethics
medicalization
palliative care
passive euthanasia
patholysis
Patient Self-Determination Act
reactive
reminiscence
right-to-die issue
stages of dying

Questions for Discussion

1. Why do death and dying evoke fear? Why might a person fear death?
2. What is the function of the life review?
3. What are the arguments for and against euthanasia?
4. Imagine being told that you have six months to live. What would be your reaction? Explain in depth. What would you think? Where would you go? What would you do?

Fieldwork Suggestions

1. Go to a cemetery, walk around, and examine your own feelings about death and dying.
2. Talk with three people about their attitudes toward physician-assisted suicide. What do they think about Dr. Kevorkian? Did you find anyone who is not familiar with his name?
3. Ask five people about their fear of death. How do people go about talking about their fears (or lack of fears)—that is, what *themes* do you hear?

Online Activities

1. Locate the Web site for Batesville Casket Company (http://www.batesville.com). What products and services are offered through this corporation? To whom is the marketing addressed? What is your assessment of this Web site? Can you think of ways in which it might be improved or otherwise changed?
2. Find information on cremation and other online resources for burial and body disposal. (Hint: http://www.twoscan.com/2s...erals/

cremation.html) What did you locate? How difficult was it to find this information? Who do you think uses this site, and for what purpose?

3. Find information on estate and funeral planning; on living wills, legal assistance, and directories concerning other advance directives. How difficult was it to locate this information? To whom is it directed? If you were in the terminal stages of a disease, would the information you have found be useful for you in developing a living will or other advance directive?

16

Aging in Other Cultures

The Invisible People: The Sebastopol Pomos

Jeff Elliott

The oldest name for Mr. Young's property—and all of the city of Sebastopol—is Batikletcawi, which roughly means "The Village Where Elderberries Grow." The blood ties of the Sebastopol Pomos to this place are deep, hallowed by the graves of their dead. Last spring, when the Sebastopol City Council again denied the landowners permission to build an upscale subdivision on the site, Grant Smith (an 88 year old Pomo) spoke at the public hearing. "This whole Laguna was the Indian's; our babies died here," he told the hushed council and audience. "Their bodies are buried on the shore of this Laguna. What will they find when they build this? They will find the bodies of our children."

At issue in Sebastopol is a Pomo identity with homeland, a place to show their children where ancestors lived and died. Becerra [A Native American child-welfare activist] is clear that taking this step has nothing to do with building casinos, what has recently become the most contentious issue with Indians in Sonoma County and elsewhere. "Gaming is an economic development, and that is completely different from the spiritual sense of connecting with the land," she says.

It is a subtlety lost on bureaucrats and developers, to whom land is merely property. But listen to Grant Smith and a single message comes loudly through: this area is his home, and part of his very being. Not the modern-day town of Sebastopol, not the county of Sonoma, but right here: the "shore of this Laguna."

. . . Not until 1908 did the United States attempt to identify and count native people in California; by that time, much was lost. Within a few short years of California's 1850 statehood, the American engine of genocide was at full throttle.

"The Americans were the worst," says Grant Smith firmly. "They drove my grandmother up north."

The people call it the Death March. Starting around 1857, horse-riding whites with bullwhips—either local militia or vigilantes, there being at the time only a breath of difference between the two—forced the people to walk some 120 miles north to the newly established reservation at Round Valley, near Covelo. Says Smith, "They herded them like cattle, like animals. Old people couldn't make it, couldn't keep up, and died on the road. [When I was a boy] they talked about it, they would talk about what happened on the road and they would cry, go all to pieces. It was misery, it was hardship. It was death."

When Round Valley began in 1856, there was no veneral disease among the people; two years later, 20 percent were afflicted. Also common was kidnapping of their children; Pomo children were highly esteemed as house servants, fetching $50 for a child who could cook, and up to $100 for a "likely young girl," according to an 1861 news clip.

Not surprisingly, the people began to escape. Grant Smith continues: "They were there in Covelo and they began to die off, sick. My great-grandfather brought the people together, said we're going home. They went up, walked along the tops of the ridges, traveled all night, but they got back home." Asked where "home" was, Smith explains, "Anywhere around here. Our people came down; they suffered to come home."

Once home, they faced a devil's choice of options. Some Indians sought refuge in the wild; Grant Smith's niece remembers her great-grandmother forever talking about "hiding," and how anxious she was when in public. Many resigned themselves to work on ranches or in the orchards that were being planted around Sebastopol.

Young and the Ghilottis have sued Sebastopol after the City Council turned down the fourth construction project in 13 years on this site. An attempt to mediate the dispute is planned. Sebastopol already has a hefty legal bill from a just-concluded suit brought by another thwarted developer. A citizen's group has offered to contribute $60,000 toward acquiring the land for open space.

"I remember when old folks would get together in camps and cry and cry," says Grant Smith. "These pictures I'll carry with me until I die: I see the people on the riverbanks and their fires, so many things.

Meanwhile, the last remnant of Batikleteawi lies quiet.

People everywhere tend to believe that the way they live is the "right" way to live and should be typical of the whole world. In other words, they tend to be **ethnocentric**. As Americans, we fall too easily into the habit of thinking that our ways are the only ways. We can learn a great deal about ourselves as a culture and the value we assign to old age by looking at value systems, families, and cultures around the world.

The Cross-Cultural Approach

Anthropologists using the **cross-cultural approach** study values and norms affecting elders in other cultures. A cultural **value** is a widely held belief that a quality is good or bad, right or wrong. A culture may value privacy, financial success, nudity, certain animals, close mother-daughter relationships, or selected sports. Values reflect the importance of various activities, relationships, feelings, or goals, and are deeply rooted. They form the description of a culture and even the nature of its reality.

Value systems vary from culture to culture, affecting every aspect of the culture, including the society's expectations for the older person. In turn, these expectations shape the self-perceptions of elders. There is always an interplay between the individual and society, each influencing the other. Some cultures foster views of old age that are conducive to happy, contented later years. Other cultures foster feelings of worthlessness, despondency, and futility.

Values can be continuous or discontinuous throughout the life cycle. Where there are **continuous values,** the transitions from childhood to adulthood to old age are smooth, natural, and comfortable. In a society where **discontinuous values** exist, sharp or abrupt changes in the life cycle can subject individuals and family units to severe trauma and strain. Consider our own society, where the onset of adolescence causes an upheaval in behavior. We are expected to suddenly become an adult at the age of 21, and from 21 on we are expected to assume varying adult roles until we reach age 65. At that time, we are con-

Physical aging and cultural values interact to create the experience of being old, which varies in different cultures. This Inuit elder, a respected hunter, is a valued and central part of his family and community.

sidered old and encouraged to retire. Our society offers little preparation for these life changes.

Cultures vary in the extent to which they emphasize individual achievement and self-reliance. The more these values are emphasized, the lower the **status of elders** who are dependent or incapacitated. In societies that stress the work role, striving, and competition, older individuals eventually lose ground.

Cultures also vary in the way they define old age. Some societies use **functional age:** One is old when he or she is unable to perform certain physical functions—when the body no longer possesses either the strength or the mobility required to do adult work. Other societies use **formal age:** Old age depends on some external symbolic event. The entrance to old age might be the birth of a first grandchild. In such a culture, a person might therefore be old at age 40, at age 70, or never. The definition of old age in the United States is formal rather than functional. **Chronological age** is the determining factor, not one's ability to function; and the arbitrary mark of old age in the United States is still circa age 65. Our society uses this purely chronological fact to classify many able-bodied, well-functioning people as old.

Cultural values vary from familial to religious, from economic to political. We can estimate a culture's ageism by the extent to which its values work against the self-esteem and social status of elders. Examining the phenomenon of aging in other cultures allows comparisons of ageism. How many cultures are ageist? By comparison, how widespread is ageism in the United States? What causes ageism? How can it be avoided?

Nonindustrialized societies usually have proportionately fewer elders in their populations because the birthrate is higher and more people die at earlier ages. In many ways, however, elders are more prized because of the knowledge and skills they have accumulated—skills and knowledge that are still relevant in a more slowly changing culture and economy.

The Graying of the Planet

The world's older population is growing faster than the total population. All regions of the globe will be confronted with population aging by the 21st century

Among the 50 facts selected by the World Health Organization as having the greatest impact on the world's population in the next century, were the following (World Health Organization, 1997):

- The world population reached 5.8 billion in mid-1996, an increase of more than 80 million over the previous 12 months; in 1990 the increase was 87 million.
- Between 1980 and 1995, life expectancy at birth has increased globally by 4.6 years; 4.4 years for males and 4.9 years for females.
- There are 380 million people aged 65 years and above. By the year 2020, the over-65

population is projected to increase globally by 82 percent, to more than 690 million.

- For every baby born today in an industrialized country, there are 10 people aged 65 or over. By the year 2020 there will be 15 such elderly persons for each newborn. In developing countries, the ratio today is two people over 65 for every newborn, and four for every newborn by 2020.
- Life expectancy at birth was 48 years in 1955; 59 years in 1975; and 65 years in 1995.
- In 1960, most deaths were among people under 50. Today, most are among the over-50.
- By 2025, more than 60 percent of all deaths will be among the over-65s, and more than 40 percent among over-75s.

Having large extended families is essential for the well-being of elders in some cultures. This grandmother helps support herself by selling mushrooms at the city market in Oaxaca in Mexico.

In developing countries, the annual growth rate of people over 65 was 3.2 percent in 1994; in the developed world, it was 2.3 percent, compared with an average annual rate for the total world population of 1.6 percent. These percentages mean that the world's elderly population increased by 1,000 people every hour from 1993 to 1994, and of that increase, 63 percent occurred in developing countries. This growth is predicted to continue far into the 21st century (Hobbs & Damon, 1996). In 1994, 30 nations had elderly populations of at least 2 million; by 2020, there will be 55 nations with this number of elders.

Sweden is the "oldest" country in the world (see Figure 16.1), with 18 percent of the population age 65 and over (about the same proportion as the state of Florida), and 5 percent of its citizens 80 and over. The Caribbean is the oldest of the major developing regions, with 7 percent of its population 65 and over in 1994. By the year 2020, many European countries will have elderly populations of from one-fifth to nearly one-fourth of the population. Germany, for example, is expected to have a 23 percent elderly population, with 22 percent for Italy, Finland, Belgium, Croatia, Denmark, and Greece (Hobbs & Damon, 1996). Japan's elderly population is expected to make dramatic growth, from 14 percent of the population in 1994, to 17 percent at the century change, and on to 26 percent by the year 2020. Their population of elders 80 and older is expected to increase substantially, also, from 3 percent in 1994 to 7 percent in 2020 (Hobbs & Damon, 1996).

The social implications of the shifts in a population's age are profound. Japan is already reducing retirement benefits and adjusting a medical system for a rapidly aging society—as should all other countries with similar population patterns. The implications for human well-being are also staggering. A newly developed measure, used by public health programs and the World Health Organization, is **health expectancy**, defined as life expectancy in good health. It is the average number of years an individual can expect to live in a favorable state—disability-free life expectancy (Murray, 1997; World Health Organization, 1997). This measure addresses the issue of *quantity* of life as opposed to *quality* of life.

FIGURE 16.1

Life expectancy and percentage of population 65 and over: Selected developed and developing countries (*), 1993

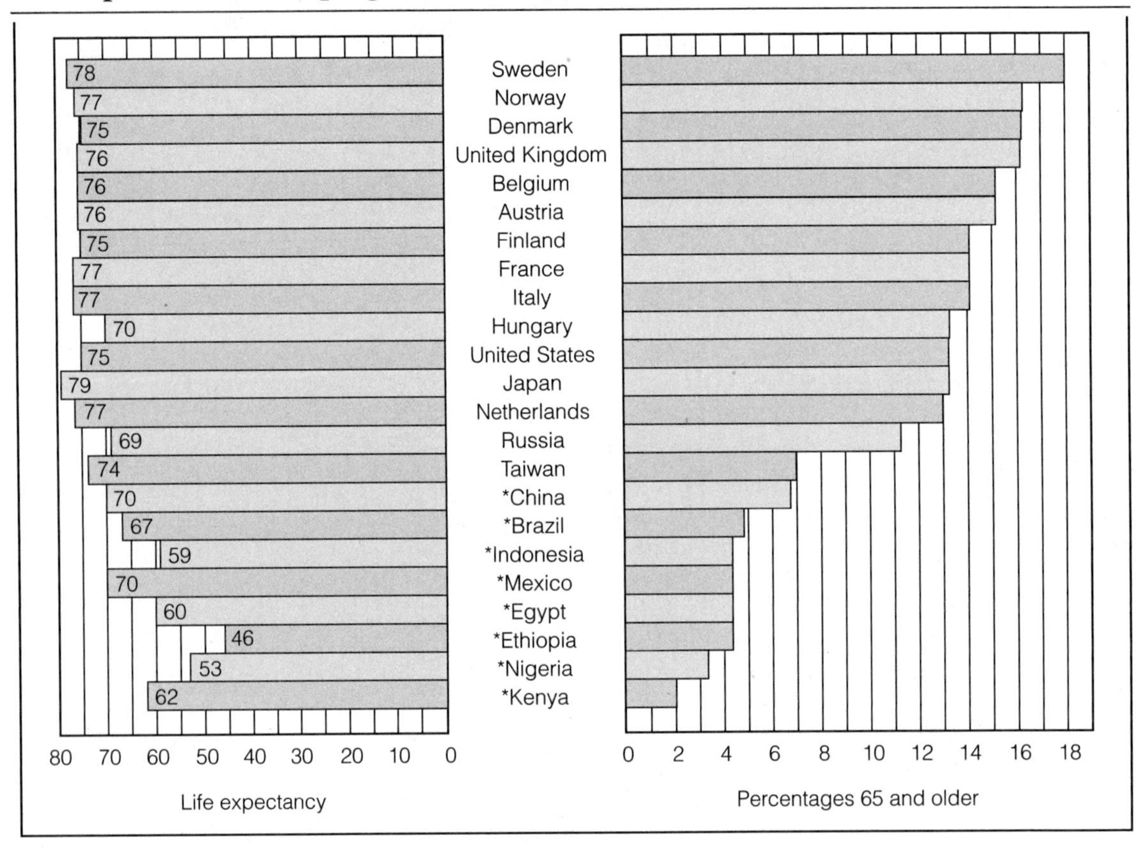

Source: Adapted from: World Population Data Sheet of the Population Reference Bureau, Inc. Prepared by demographers Carl Haub and Yanagishito Machiko. Washington, D.C., 1993

Until recent years, the biggest factor contributing to population aging around the world has been a drop in fertility. This reduces the number of births and therefore increases the ratio of old to young. Only in the last several decades has the fall in mortality significantly increased in the developing nations. (It has been a fact in the United States, a developed nation, since the beginning of the century.) The lower mortality rate means that more people survive to old age, a major contributing factor to "aging" a country. As one gerontologist said, "Mass longevity is a gift of industrialization" (Kinoshita & Kiefer, 1992). But the "gift" comes with strings attached.

In celebrating our extra years, we must recognize that increased longevity without quality of life is an empty prize, that is, that health

FIGURE 16.2

An aging population: Population aged 65 and above, 1996

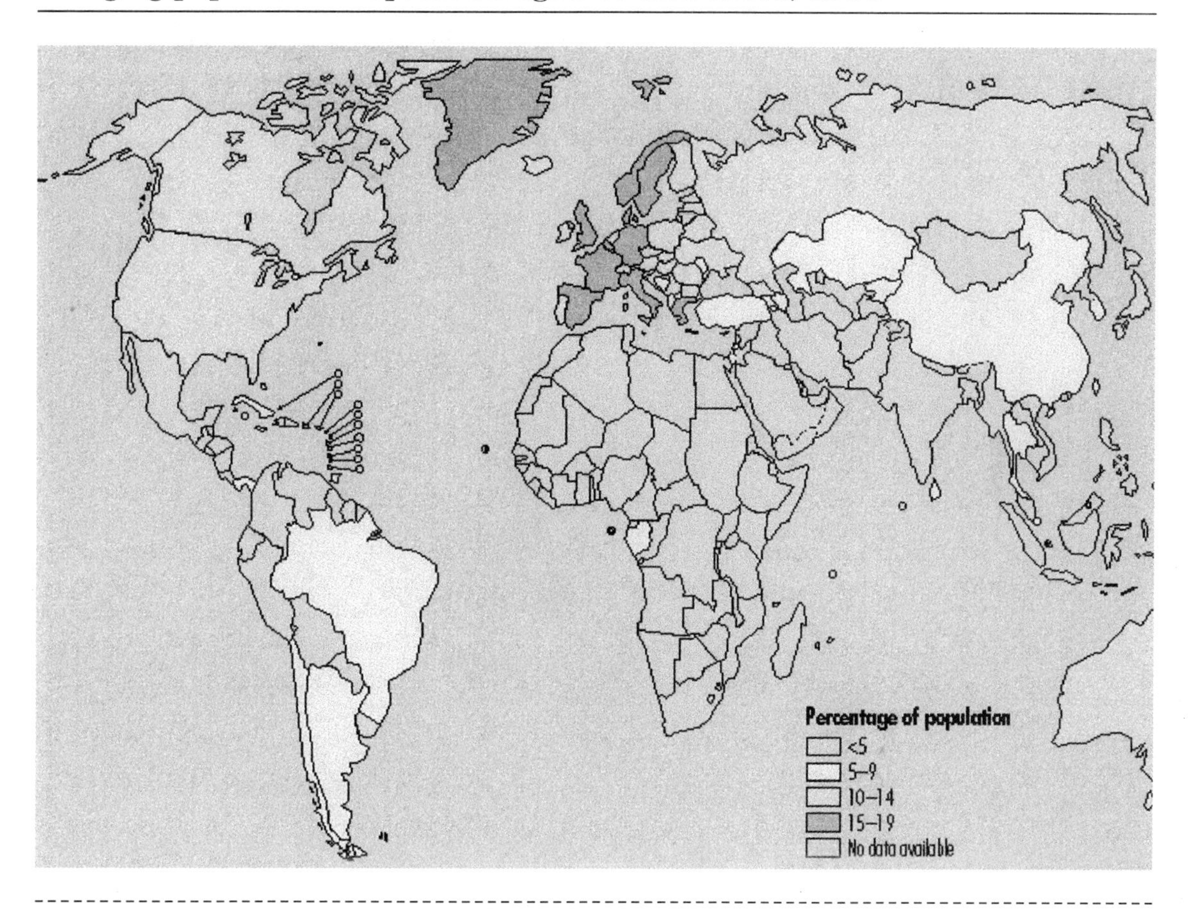

expectancy is more important than life *expectancy.*

World Health Report, 1997, Executive Summary, Dr. Nakajima

The European countries took 150 years from the time they entered the "demographic transition," which accompanies industrialization, to reach an older population of 12 percent. The developing countries as a whole are expected to reach it in 75 years. In countries such as China, where fertility has fallen dramatically, this percentage will be reached in less than 50 years, sometime between 2005 and 2010. Fifty-seven percent of all older people in 1991 lived in the developing world. This percentage will increase to 69 percent by the year 2020 because fertility and mortality rates are continuing to decline in developing countries. Figures 16.2 and 16.3 show current and projected percentages of world populations age 65 and above.

The developed nations, too, will continue to increase their percentage of elders, especially the

FIGURE 16.3

An aging population: Population aged 65 and above, 2020

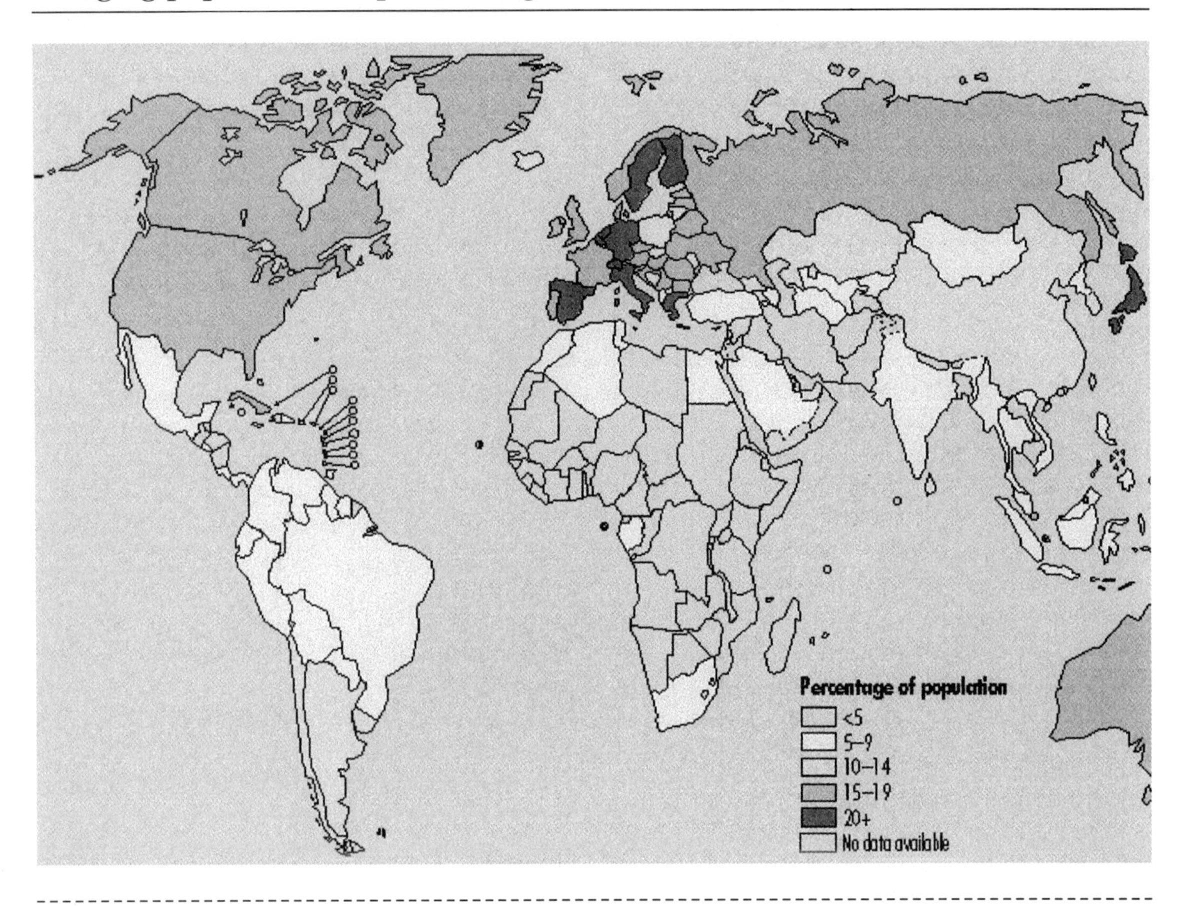

very old. However, their rates will not be as great because their birthrates are stable rather than declining. (Only their mortality rates are still showing decline.) Developing countries have scant resources with which to face up to the problems of old age; some developed countries, like the United States, have chosen to provide limited social resources for the task. The explosion of numbers represents a tremendous global challenge and the concomitant need for the reexamination of social policy priorities.

Social Modernization and Elder Status

In their classic study, Cowgill and Holmes (1972) developed a formal theory of aging from a cross-cultural perspective. Their **theory of social modernization** holds two tenets: (1) the status of elders in the community declines as the society's degree of modernization increases, and (2) their status goes down in proportion to the rate of social change. These statements suggest that the more modernized a society is and the more rapidly modernization has come about, the lower the status of the elderly.

Additional tenets to their theory explain why lower status accompanies **modernization. Non-industrial societies** tend to emphasize tradition and ceremony, and the elders within such societies know the most about these customs. Therefore, especially in preliterate societies, their status is high. Older people function as historians, genealogists, vocational instructors, researchers, and often as doctors and priests. According to Cowgill and Holmes, the status of the elders is always higher in societies where they continue to perform useful and valued functions. In most agrarian societies, for example, old men and women continue their accustomed economic roles as long as they are physically able. Retirement is a modern invention found only in industrialized, high-productivity societies.

Societies that embrace the extended family system offer their older members a stronger familial role and, therefore, higher status. Old people are not as central in the nuclear family of industrial societies, which often relegate care of the dependent aged to the state or other outside agencies. Cowgill and Holmes hypothesize that "modernization tends to decrease the relative status of the aged and to undermine their security within the social system." Numerous studies have supported their modernization theory. One example is employment studies that indicate lower economic status for older members as the shift occurs from agriculture to industry.

Did You Know . . .

The role of social policy to aging and longevity is most striking in Russia and Eastern Europe. Since the demise of the former Soviet Union, life expectancy has declined—*a trend unprecedented in modern history. The life expectancy for Russian males in 1960 was 63.5 years, and for females, 72.7 years. By 1994, males could expect to live 57.5 years, and females, 71.1. The increased mortality seems due not to infectious diseases, but to social behavior—heart disease and unhealthy lifestyles, stress, smoking, alcohol abuse, and accidents.*

COCKERHAM, 1997; AND VELKOVA ET AL., 1997

VARIATION IN NONINDUSTRIALIZED SOCIETIES

The status and role of elders in industrially undeveloped cultures vary widely. The diversity of social and economic roles for older people in societies around the world makes generalization difficult. Broadly speaking, Cowgill and Holmes's modernization theory helps explain elders' status in nonindustrial societies, but high status may be related to other factors as well. Modernization theory cannot explain the low status of elders in some nonindustrial societies.

The role of the aged in technologically primitive societies depends partially on resources. Scarcity or abundance of resources can determine the position of elders in hunting-and-gathering societies, in agrarian societies, or in any nonindustrial society. With abundance, societies can afford to indulge their dependent, nonproductive members. With scarcity, societies cannot afford to be so generous and must, at times, make difficult choices.

Anthropologist and historian Cox (1990) believes that **nomadic societies** in general have the lowest esteem for their senior members. Such societies have the fewest material resources and are usually located in harsh environments, which favor youth and vigor. Because of the high geographic mobility nomadic life requires, individual autonomy is a primary value. There is no reason for younger members to secure the favor of parents and grandparents.

Societies that settled permanently in one place and established property rights gave elders economic power through ownership and control of land. In addition, elders had the power to arrange marriages, thereby discouraging individualism. In such traditional societies, older people

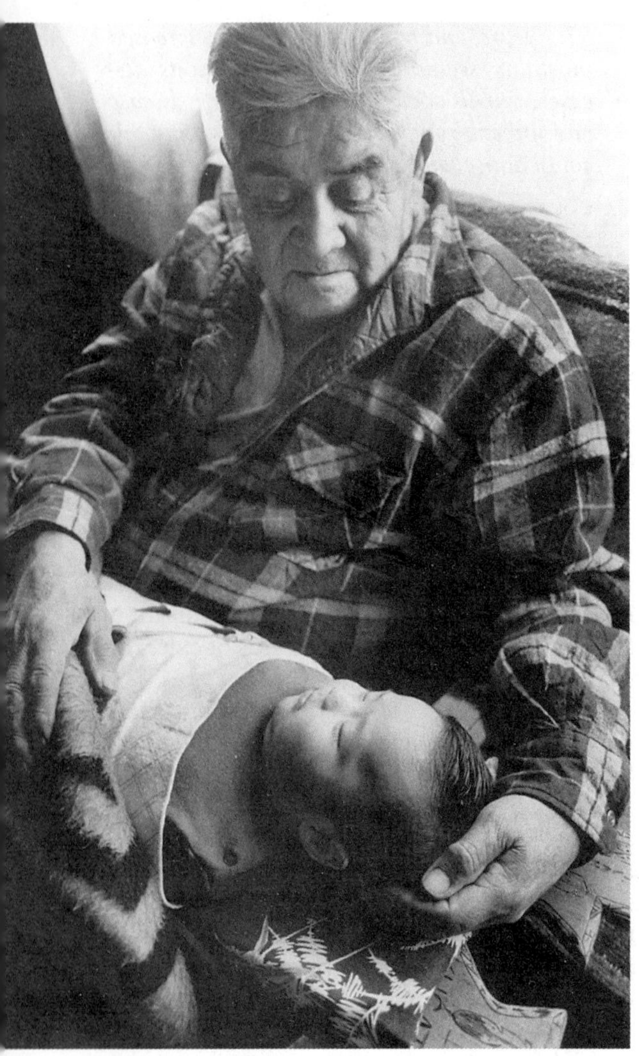

The value of elders in any culture depends to a great extent to the degree the older generation is able to pass on important cultural information to a younger generation.

pass on legends, myths, and ethical principles. The Aleuts in northern Russia are an example:

> *...every village had one or two old men at least, who considered in their special business to educate the children, thereupon, in the morning or evening when all were home these aged teachers would have the young folks surround them and listen (Elliott, 1987, quoted in Cox, 1990, 60).*

The printing press destroyed the strong need for this type of teaching and, consequently, undermined the status of elders where the oral tradition was used.

THIRD WORLD COUNTRIES: A TEST OF MODERNIZATION THEORY

Third World is a term used to designate countries in the early stages of modernization. Such nations, also called developing or **less-developed countries (LDCs)**, are not yet as industrially advanced as the United States, Western Europe, and other technology-oriented areas, which are considered to be **developed countries.** Though the proportion of those 65 and over is increasing in Third World countries, we have as yet, few studies of aging from these areas. According to Cowgill and Holmes's modernization theory, within the agrarian LDCs that have not undergone modernization, the status of elders should be high. But this may or may not be the case.

In Turkey, a study of the status of older men affirmed the modernization theory. Old men headed households in villages with low levels of urbanization and industrialization. Further, their labor force participation was higher in these villages than in cities. This provides strong support for the major tenets of modernization theory (Gilleard & Gurkan, 1987).

Older Hindus in Katmandu, Nepal, were still living in extended families in the 1980s, but were suffering from changes caused by urbanization and industrialization (Goldstein, 1983). Unemployment and inflation were widespread. The sons' salaries were insufficient to support their extended families, and financial choices were made in favor of children rather than parents. The extended family structure was intact yet modernization altered family relationships, creating stress.

The Igbo of Nigeria provide another example of modernization theory. They have extended families with great respect for the authority of the aged. Their culture did not reject the aged or disengage them from society (Shelton, 1972). But recent changes such as mass migration to towns and cities have reduced the authority of elders and lessened the value of traditional ritual. As the young receive formal education, the spiritual power of the elders has been eroded (Ohuche & Littrell, 1989).

In China, 82 percent of the elders lived with adult children in 1987, the first time such a survey was even conducted. Fifty-three percent lived in households with three or more generations, but these figures are expected to gradually decline with time. The traditional role of grandparents is to supervise grandchildren in return for board and care. But recent social changes that have created more jobs, wealth, and mobility are leading to changes in the extended family. As adult children move to the city for jobs, grandparents lose their important family roles of watching grandchildren and other household tasks.

These changes, as well as current population policy, believed to be essential to China's goal of modernization, have modified the traditional cultural patterns of family solidarity and mutual responsibility. Will Chinese elders fall between the cultural cracks, before new patterns emerge to replace the old? The immediate answer seems to be a more extensive pension program for elders, but currently only 10 percent of retired workers, largely in cities, now get a pension.

As a socialist country, China's intent is to care for all who need it, but only a small proportion actually get help. Widows and widowers get special care from local and state government programs. In rural areas 80 percent of elders are still cared for by family. In urban areas the figure is somewhat lower and on a gradual decline throughout the country (Kwong & Guoxuan, 1992). Limited health and social services are provided by the government. Entertainment for elders is a required service of all state-run organizations, but China's annual budget allocation for its older population is small.

A major problem in developing nations where traditional family support systems are breaking down is that pension systems are difficult to initiate. Older workers may not have been part of a work-based economy and may not earn enough to make payroll contributions. Governments are often unstable, and inflation is a typical problem. Studies of many different countries, including China, Kerala, Mexico, Nigeria, Laos, Turkey, and the Philippines, describe a cultural inconsistency between the industrial social welfare programs and traditional values of filial piety, family reciprocity systems, and religious beliefs (Tracy, 1991; Apt, 1995; Aday & Kano, 1997; Dai & Dimond, 1998). Every country is unique, however, and cultural traditions must be made an integral part of whatever social security models are developed. The aged are the "transition generation" in developing countries; they *live* the decline in family support and changes in status values (Hugo, 1992).

Despite vast economic and cultural changes, women's caregiving patterns remain strong in virtually all cultures, and traditional values of filial piety survive. Daughters and wives in Chinese and Filipino families continue with "paying respect" for their elders through their patterns of care (Jones, 1995; Guyotte, 1997); and filial piety shows evidence of remaining strong among those cultures for which it is traditionally meaningful (Dai & Dimond, 1998; Sung, 1994). An outstanding case study for observing modernizing change in a multicultural society is that of Singapore. In an artful phenomenological study of changing cultural values, Kalyana Mehta (1997) found among the aged and the middle-aged generations that the meaning of respect has shifted from obedience to courteous behavior; and the degree of respect accorded to elders has decreased in the decade of the 1990s. The study concluded:

> *... Status and respect cannot be presumed to be synonymous although there is some degree of overlap. Status as a concept appears to be closely linked with roles and functions whereas respect has a personalized dimension which explains why people in authority often do not draw respect... Whether the Asian value of respect for elders continues to be transmitted will depend on whether the*

present adult generation takes the effort and time to instill this in the next generation. Even then, it seems that elders in future will need to give respect to younger generations in order to receive it (p. 217-218).

In contrast, a few studies show that modernization does not affect the status of the aged. A study of aging in American Samoa (an island territory of the United States since 1900) shows that rapid and extensive social changes have not eroded their status. Historically, Samoa has given its elderly strong respect and prestige, and they report being very happy (Rhodes, 1984). The explanations seem to be that the traditional family system continues to function and that traditional values continue to thrive. Further, the Samoans accept the idea of dependency in old age because they are taught throughout their lives to rely on the group, especially the kin-group, rather than on the individual.

In reality, the traditional family care of elders is much more cost effective than the modern system of pensions and nursing homes. Social gerontologists encourage policies that support the traditional family system, even if the inevitable modernization is rolling forward (Nugent, 1990).

Both modernization itself and the economic failure of modernization can threaten the traditions of a culture. Hardship and poverty are typically a way of life in poorer nations. Countries in which the family structure and value system has been kept intact are the lucky exceptions. Even there, we can ask, "For how long?" We need to find ways to assist families in less-developed countries as their traditional way of life changes to new patterns, unfamiliar and strange to the elders.

Case Study of an Industrialized Nation: Japan

Many of us in the West think of Japan as a country that grants its elder members high status. Nevertheless, reality reveals a changing Japan in which elder status may be declining. The stereotypes surrounding aging in Japan concern love, honor, and respect. The Confucian teaching from *The Book of Rites* and *The Book of Filial Piety* (Confucious, translated 1982) describes the importance of **filial piety,** which dictates that children respect and care for their parents; protect and glorify their parents; and worship deceased parents and ancestors. Filial piety today means being responsible for one's parents and one's family honor, encouraging family harmony, making sacrifices for one's parents and one's family honor. In societies that practice filial piety, older people are revered and valued by virtue of being a family elder. But the ideal value has always been just that: an *ideal*, as opposed to a reality. Confucius said,

Today when people call a man filial, they mean that he is supporting his parents. But he does as much for his dogs and horses! If he does not show respect for his parents, how is he differentiating them from the animals? (quoted in Mehta, 1997).

Gerontologist Erdman Palmore (1975) wrote that the Japanese are the only exception to the theory that the status of the elderly declines with industrialization. Since the 1970s it has become apparent that, indeed, industrialization does change family relationships and therefore cultural patterns, even in a strongly traditional culture such as Japan.

Even in premodern Japan, a belief that elders who become burdensome have an obligation to leave this world countered the Confucian ideal of filial piety. And, in modern Japan, many older men, for example, are rudely labeled *sodaigomi*, or "unwieldy refuse" (Berger, 1987). A similar translation of the word is "big trash," which describes retired men who are overly dependent on their wives and who expect to be waited on. The term has by far more negative connotations than the American term *couch potato* (Martin, 1989).

The Japanese concept of filial piety has an economic basis. Traditionally, the eldest son cares for his aging parents in return for inheriting their land and possessions. This arrangement is much more pragmatic than the Confucian philosophy of filial piety would suggest. Nevertheless, a tension between the pragmatic and the ideal, between affectionate care and formal obligation, pervades Japanese culture.

HISTORY

World War II brought many changes to Japan. The old social establishment and traditional value system were overthrown in much the same way that nonindustrialized or Third World cultures are undergoing change. Japan's reform of the Civil Code in 1948 changed the father–eldest son arrangement by providing equal inheritance to all siblings. By breaking the legal foundations for the eldest son's sole inheritance, the code fundamentally altered the age-old care system.

Because the accompanying social change has been gradual, the role of the eldest son is not yet clear, however. If anything, a generation gap seems to be developing, with tradition-minded elders on one side and younger, nontraditional family members on the other. A 1988 survey indicated that although 47 percent of those 60 and older thought it an eldest son's duty to look after his parents, only 32 percent of those younger than 60 thought so (Martin, 1989).

Modernization favored the younger generation, particularly after 1960, by making jobs abundant in cities. It affected the older population negatively, especially in rural areas, where elders were left behind to work the land alone. Although those in the rural areas had to cope with a changing and disintegrating lifestyle, older people who moved to the city with their children had problems adapting to a new life in the city. Such rapid change in ways and values has had a significant and sometimes devastating impact on the mental health of the Japanese people, especially the older population.

However, for Japan, modernization has had positive effects as well. Industrialization has dramatically increased the life expectancy at birth, raising it from 50 to 79 years. In 1997, the average life expectancy was 77 years for Japanese

The Japanese culture has a long tradition of respect for elders. In post WWII-Japan, however, cultural changes have altered the status of elders, whose position of high status is less certain at the turn of the century in this highly industrialized country.

males and 82 for females—the highest life expectancy in the world. Fourteen percent of the Japanese are 65 or over, and demographers predict that, by 2020, 26 percent of the Japanese population will be composed of elders, half of whom will be over age 75 (Hobbs & Damon, 1996). The numbers of the very old are a staggering 40 percent of the aged population now. They present an increasingly huge proportion of health care dollars and an overwhelming problem to caretakers (Sasaki et al., 1997).

Did You Know . . .
A new health monitor for the quality of life among the elderly is dementia-free life expectancy. This is the average number of years

an individual is expected to live without dementia, based on incidence and prevalence of dementia and on mortality. In 1997, calculations were available for France, three places in the United Kingdom, Australia, Belgium, and Japan. In Japan in 1997, at 65 years, the dementia-free life expectancy was 89 percent of the total life expectancy for males, and 79 percent for females. Life-years with dementia are longer among females, attributable to higher incidence of dementia and lower mortality.

SAUVAGET ET AL., 1997

PROBLEMS OF MODERNIZATION

Business and marketing agents are trying to find ways of cashing in on the growing number of elders in Japan. For instance, though old people usually are called *rojin,* businesses have created a catchier phrase, *jitsunen* (age of fruition), to advertise private retirement residences, day care centers, medical equipment, drugs, travel, education, social clubs, and even a "love hotel" for those who want a rendezvous (Berger, 1987). The term *silver selling* has been used to describe these attempts to target the older market (The Silvering of Japan, 1989).

Even though some Japanese workers are mandatorily retired as early as age 55, most pension payments do not begin until age 60. A considerable percentage of Japan's companies release workers at age 55; a smaller percentage between the ages of 56 and 59; and the largest percentage at age 60 (over 50 percent); only 5 percent of Japanese companies allow employees to work past the age of 60. However, in spite of these mandatory retirement policies, Japanese elders are more than twice as likely to keep working as elders in any other developed country. Those Japanese who continue to work often hold occupations in agriculture, forestry, and fisheries. Many who are mandatorily retired from high-paying jobs in large firms accept work in these lower-paying industries. Some sociologists believe that the strong work ethic in Japan does not allow men to enjoy retirement; thus they continue working because it provides them with identity and meaning in life.

Not all of Japan's elder workforce is automatically barred from big business. A number of Japan's large firms have systems for extending employment. The aging employee, however, usually must agree to a pay cut, a loss of title, and no guarantee of continued employment. Unemployment is a troublesome fact of life for older Japanese men. Some who would like to work simply cannot find it, even in the lower-paying industries. However, in spite of the difficulty of finding employment, Japanese elders tend to have large savings, a high rate of home ownership, and economic well-being.

A key question facing all industrialized nations is how much national income to spend on health care, public pensions, and other benefits for elders. In 1994, Japan's public medical insurers spend 23.8 trillion yen (approximately 238 billion U.S. dollars) on that country's rapidly aging population (Sasaki, 1997). Japan currently spends approximately 41 percent of its national income to fund its universal health insurance and pension systems, more than half of which goes to those over 65. By the year 2020, Japan plans to spend 50 percent of its national income on such systems, with two-thirds going to programs for the elderly. (Although this sounds like a great deal of money, welfare states such as Norway and Sweden currently spend 60 percent of their national revenues to fund such programs.) However, private Japanese economists project that the percentage of national income spent on health care and welfare could soar to 60 percent or higher if present benefit systems, such as pensions beginning at age 60 and virtually free health care for those 40 and older, continue. The government is already planning to have older people absorb some of the increasing costs by increasing the fees they pay for health care.

The government is also hoping that families will continue to be highly involved in care of the aged, but these hopes are in question. Although more than 60 percent of Japan's aged live with their children or extended families (compared with 10 percent in the United States), this represents a decrease from 77 percent in 1970. The percentage will continue to fall as more women work outside the home and as the declining birthrate produces fewer adult children to care for aging parents.

Even though fewer elders are living in three-generation households, 60 percent is a high figure compared with 10 percent in the United States. The custom persists, and the tendency to live with the oldest son is strong. In that case, the financial responsibility rests with the son and the caretaker responsibility with the daughter-in-law. The life of Japanese elders is still intricately tied to their children. One gerontologist (Hashimoto, 1992) states:

> *Given the rapid social change that has occurred in Japan over the past decades, it is remarkable that the solutions to the problem of old age are still largely found within tradition (p. 41).*

Major reasons for this reliance on tradition are (1) small pensions, (2) lack of affordable and acceptable housing, (3) ethics of filial piety legitimate and entitle the aged to family care, and (4) the Japanese culture promotes family orientation and interdependence over autonomy and independence (Dai & Dimond, 1998).

A lower birthrate also means increased government costs for elder care. As in the United States, the number of retirees in Japan is growing faster than the number of laborers in the workforce. Japan's Baby Boomers (the eight million babies born between 1947 and 1949) provided the country with a vast, cheap, young workforce in the 1960s and 1970s—one reason for Japan's phenomenal economic growth. But the tables will turn around by the year 2010, when these Baby Boomers start to receive their pensions. The birthrate in Japan has declined considerably since the postwar years, and there will be a shortage of workers and a corresponding abundance of retirees after the year 2000. To save costs, the government is working to raise the age of eligibility for public pensions from 60 to 65. But many businesses, who fear being saddled with costly older workers, are opposed. This sounds remarkably like the ageism in American business (Schultz et al., 1991).

Despite these somewhat stalemated efforts to control costs, Japan has done reasonably well so far in providing medical care and social education for elders, but government costs are increasing rapidly. Free physical examinations are offered annually to everyone over age 65. Public health insurance programs cover most medical expenses, and local governments are beginning to pay for the remainder. Thousands of senior citizen centers have developed across the nation, offering educational and recreational programs at little cost. Many of the severely impaired—those who are completely bedridden or totally incontinent—are cared for at home. The sheer number of impaired elders and the lack of family to care for them dictate the need for more outside help. Although Japanese custom still declares that children must provide support for aging parents, more and more adult children are seeking home help or retirement homes for their dependent elders.

To maintain tradition as well as to save money, Japanese government policy supports the concepts of family care for older members. Caretakers may receive the following assistance:

- Tax deduction or exemption. (Income tax credit is given to all taxpayers who are supporting a family member aged 70 or older. If the older person is functionally impaired, the caretaker is eligible for additional tax credits.)
- Loans to build or remodel a home in which an older parent is to live.
- Provisions of special equipment, such as special beds, bathtubs, and telephones.
- Short-term stay service at a nursing home when a caretaker becomes ill or must leave home.
- Community care centers.

The government has adopted a 10-year Gold Plan for the Aged that adds more geriatric rehabilitation centers and training for 60,000 "home helpers," a kind of housekeeping assistant or nurse's aid who visits several times a week (Baba,

1993). But even in Japan these low-paying jobs are considered "3-D"—dirty, demanding, or dangerous. Although the government plans to build many more nursing homes, at present nursing home demand is so high that some have a two-year waiting period. On the positive side, hundreds of social programs have been initiated to meet the leisure, social, and educational needs of elders in Japan (Campbell, 1992).

The "welfare" retirement centers are much needed, but at the same time, resisted. Most Japanese still believe that family care is the most desirable arrangement for the well-being of the aged and that it is basically wrong to segregate old people. The Japanese are far less accepting of retirement communities and homes for the aged than are Americans. Retirement communities have not been popular, especially low-income welfare housing called *yūryō* homes. It is shameful to be there with no family and little money, although the image and status of such homes is gradually improving.

An ethnographic study of such a community revealed some positives and some negatives for the residents (Kinoshita & Kiefer, 1992). Interaction among men was limited and formal. Their vocabulary indicated the highest level of politeness and formality. Two norms were "don't cause trouble to others" and "exchange respect." The women were a bit more friendly with each other in terms of talking casually, but few close friendships formed. Health and economic needs were met, but the residents did not have norms or expectations for intimate relationships. Participation in adult day care was found to have a positive relationship with quality of life indicators for female participants, but not for male participants (Hashizume & Kanagawa, 1996). The researchers concluded that self-esteem among elderly Japanese men needed to be better understood in order to develop programs of greater benefit to them.

There are thousands of community centers and old people's clubs throughout Japan. In 1990 there were more than 130,000 old-age clubs with over 8 million members—more than 40 percent of those 60 and over in all of Japan. The healthy retired Japanese are expected to keep quietly busy with household activities. Their favorite activities are watching television, traveling, and gardening. In

A CROSS CULTURAL DELEGATION IS HERE TO SHARE THEIR CULTURAL DIVERSITY

the centers and clubs elders are offered training in the arts of *haiku* (a 17-syllable poem), *tanka* (lyric poem of 31 syllables), bonsai gardening, *haiga* (philosophical painting), *shingin* (poem recitation), *shodō* (calligraphy), sado (tea ceremony), and Japanese classical dancing. These activities can be done alone, and they bring deep satisfaction (Maeda, 1993; Mehta, 1997).

The answer to the question "Is aging really better in Japan?" is mixed. Health and longevity have dramatically improved. Income adequacy and government care has improved. Elders receive somewhat more respect than in the United States. But industrialization gradually continues to take its toll on the traditional family relationships. And the very old population is growing faster than the ability of the society to accommodate them.

To summarize, the increasing percentage of frail elderly, combined with the decreasing capability of families to care for older parents, is placing increasing strain on Japan. The government is struggling to meet the escalating financial demand while remaining, economically, a leading world power. The older Japanese themselves, showing many parallels to their counterparts in the United States, are organizing to seek more privileges and rights.

Aging in Scandinavia

Aging in the Scandinavian countries is of special interest because Denmark, Sweden, and Norway have very large aged populations. In 1991, for example, 18 percent of Sweden's population was 65 or over. The number of people aged 90 and older will nearly double in the next 30 years (Hedin, 1993). In addition, these countries are more welfare oriented, imposing higher tax rates to provide social services and financial support to those who need it. Are older individuals better off in Scandinavia in terms of medical care and finances? Are attitudes toward elders improved as a result? Is ageism, therefore, reduced?

The Scandanavian countries of Norway, Sweden, and Denmark have histories of people living into late old age. The socialist governments in these countries provide health care, housing, and long term care for their elders.

The Scandinavian countries, like the United States, are highly industrialized. Per capita real incomes are high, and the standard of living in Scandinavia is higher than in most other countries. The Scandinavian countries, like Japan, are world leaders in the proportion of citizens over age 65 and in life expectancy in general.

Though the basic pension, or social security, rate in Denmark is very modest, the retiree may add pensions from a former employer and special housing or rent supplements. Some who compare the financial situations of the elderly in Denmark with those in the United States conclude that Danish are better off. In Denmark, the difference between rich and poor is not as great, and elders have incomes more equal to those of younger groups. On the basis of income, Scandinavian elders are not affluent; at the same time, neither do they suffer economic deprivation or live in poverty. Slums do not exist in the Scandinavian countries. Elderly people are neither homeless nor destitute. Their welfare system works very well in this regard.

Both Norway and Sweden have experimented credibly with flexible retirement plans. In Sweden, the practice of partial retirement is widespread. The Norwegian system opposes mandatory retirement and other work barriers. Many elders there, however, choose a partial retirement system. Public policy formation in the United States would benefit through examination of these systems.

Sweden implemented its flexible retirement system in 1976, and the system has been working reasonably well ever since. Under Swedish law, persons between the ages of 60 and 64 may reduce their work hours and receive partial compensation for their loss in earnings from a national pension fund. The law stipulates that partial retirees must work at least 17 hours per week and reduce their average weekly hours by at least five. This provides a fair amount of leeway for those who find full-time work too demanding or otherwise undesirable. For example, under this system a 60-year-old could work half-time, or perhaps a four-day week. The average reduction in workload is 13 to 14 hours per week. Under this flexible plan, older workers can retain valued employment with the same company; they do not have to turn to self-employment or part-time employment in an undervalued job (Wise, 1990).

Medical care in Scandinavia is provided by the government. In Denmark, for example, 95 percent of the population receives medical care through health insurance societies established by local and state governments. Membership, which is free to elders living on pensions, provides life-saving drugs and medical and hospital treatment at no cost. The elderly receive free physiotherapy, pedicures, and dental and eye care. The state even pays for funeral expenses. In Sweden, pensioners are reimbursed for most of their doctors' fees and for travel to and from medical facilities. Health care is comprehensive and offered at virtually no cost to older individuals.

All the Scandinavian countries provide extensive services that enable elders to maintain themselves in their own homes. Family members in Sweden and Norway, for example, receive government pay for helping aging relatives at home. A home helper (a trained worker paid by the government) may visit regularly to clean, shop, cook, and to offer assistance with personal activities such as letter writing or bathing. In some cases, hot meals are delivered daily.

For the municipal governments, which also provide home nursing for the sick who do not require hospitalization, a major goal is to prevent the financial hardship or physical deterioration that forces seniors into institutions. National policies offer workers up to 30 days of paid leave to care for ailing elder relatives. The Scandinavian countries had extensive family leave policies long before the United States enacted its limited family leave policy.

In addition to providing health care, many Scandinavian countries encourage and sponsor fitness programs and holidays for seniors. Sweden, for example, annually sponsors the *Vasa* Race, a cross-country ski race in which many older people compete. The *RiksKommitten*, a Swedish local community agency, supervises and encourages fitness programs for all ages. Every year, Swedish elderly enjoy two pensioners' holidays and two special pensioners' weeks (one in spring and one in the fall) during which senior citizens receive public recognition and attend special functions.

In addition to health care and other public programs, Scandinavia also offers its elder population a variety of housing options, ranging from "sheltered villages" for the elderly to integrated housing for both young and old. In Sweden, for example, it is not uncommon for an old-age home to be next to a youth hostel. There, old and young share a common cafeteria. In comparing Scandinavia to the United States, a journalist wrote:

> *My instant impression was that there are fewer old people in Scandinavia who just stare vacantly into space as they await death.*

There are more elderly who walk, talk, and smile. (Szulc, 1988)

In Stockholm, Copenhagen, and Helsinki, daytime community centers for elders are open to all who care to walk in from their homes in the neighborhood. Such centers offer classes in dance, English, French, weaving, and other skills, in addition to providing care tables, books, magazines, and inexpensive meals.

Government officials are dedicated to eradicating the institutionalizing of frail elders. A half hour from downtown Stockholm is the *Hagstrata*, an integrated housing project where more than 1,000 older people, averaging 85 years old, rent apartments alongside young families with children. *Hagstrata* has a social center that houses a library, a wood and textiles workshop, and a photography lab, as well as a school, hospital, hockey rink, tennis court, gym, and sauna. This complex gives older inhabitants a sense of connection with the larger world and allows them to live, in the words of Mauno Koivisto, president of Finland, "active, self-reliant, and free" lives (Szulc, 1988).

The elder care system in Sweden has a guiding principle of independent living and freedom of choice. Large institutions are being phased out; small-scale housing such as group dwellings are being developed. It usually means a small housing collective for six to eight persons, in which each resident has his or her own room, shares communal areas, and has 24-hour-a-day access to staff.

A study of one **group home** showed a very calm, homey environment. Residents' rooms were filled with their furniture and memorabilia. Staff satisfaction was high and resident turnover low. The familiar atmosphere of home was a great positive for those with senile dementia. The group home concept is a great success in Sweden (Malmberg & Zarit, 1993).

Group homes actually cost less per resident than large-scale institutions. These homes are most common for persons with senile dementia, but are used for older and younger persons with other physical and mental disabilities. In 1992 there were 5,300 residents of group homes and plans to develop facilities for another 6,400 people. In Scandinavian countries, aging parents do not typically live with adult children, but they do remain in close contact. A survey of persons aged 60 and over found that only 4 percent of Danes and 3 percent of Americans thought it best for older and younger generations to live together as compared with 58 percent of the Japanese surveyed (Martin, 1989). Studies of family relationships in Scandinavian countries have found that, in general, elders have frequent contact with their children. However, Danish elders involve themselves relatively less in the daily lives of their children and have greater independence. Sociologist H. Johansen (1987) found limited help and support between the generations in Denmark. Family relations in Denmark are fairly formal; spontaneous gatherings at the home of an older parent, for example, are rare. Adult children are not traditionally responsible for supporting their parents financially or housing them in their own homes. Denmark's extensive system of support developed partly because care of aging parents was not considered a family obligation.

Despite such comprehensive public programs, life for Scandinavian elders still has its negative aspects. Social mobility has separated younger and older family members, and the stressful lifestyle of the middle class has left less time to help older family members. The Norwegian term *gammel,* which means "old," is associated with negative traits; old people prefer the word *eldre,* which means elderly. Loneliness, isolation, and a feeling of uselessness are serious problems for Scandinavians just as for Americans.

In Sweden, a study of adults and their aging parents revealed a high degree of contact between aging parents and their adult children who have remained in the same social class and who live nearby (Sundstrom, 1986). However, a recurrent theme in Swedish fiction—that "socially arrived" children tend to sacrifice their parents and their cultural heritage—was borne out in the study. Middle-class adult children of working-class parents tend to move away from home and to have a lower degree of contact with their parents, whereas adult children who remain in the working class live closer to their parents and maintain more contact.

The future for Sweden's system is that resources for elder services will become less available. There have already been some cutbacks in home-help services. There is almost universal support for the concept of the state as primary provider of care for the aged, but new, more cost-effective means of care may need to be sought. A social scientist visiting Sweden said, "I was told that requiring family members to perform caregiving tasks is illegal at present, but at some point in the near future, this may be reevaluated" (Boise, 1991). The language and tone of this statement does not sound as though it would dare be uttered in the Asian countries. Even the thought of mandating family care of elders would probably be an insult. Some individuals think that the strong state support of the aged has undermined family support. Others think that Sweden has the best care of the aged in the world.

Applying the Findings

Though we are learning about elders in other cultures, more research is needed. In addition to an overall lack of research, much of the work done by researchers in other cultures has not been translated into English. Journalists are filling some of the gaps, but their work needs corroboration through a scientific approach that gerontologists, anthropologists, and sociologists must provide.

Findings from other cultures have many uses. For example, we can use them to test our theories of aging, which may be culturally biased. In the United States, gerontologists have developed the disengagement theory, which proposes that old people inherently and gradually disengage from society and that society, in turn, disengages from them. Yet, studies of peasant societies offer little support for the universality of this theory: their members never disengage.

Sometimes in cultures other than our own we can see new ways to improve the status of elders in our own country. In socialistic countries such as Scandinavia, health care is essentially provided to one and all through government-subsidized national health insurance, and the Scandinavian health care system is generally more innovative and progressive than our own. Extensive homemaker services, such as those available in Sweden, are also lacking in the United States. We have also been slow to offer many integrated hospice services for the dying. And several European countries provide more comprehensive social security than the United States does.

We can look beyond our society for other patterns of improvement. The British pension system, for instance, issues a standard payment, regardless of previous earnings. Germans receive social security benefits at age 65 even if they are working full time. In countries with the best coverage, the government usually contributes to social security through its general tax revenues. The U.S. government at present does not, although it may do so in the future. In some other countries, pension deductions from wages are proportionately higher than in the United States. If Americans want comprehensive social security coverage equal to that of many European nations, they can find ways to accomplish that goal. But these ways will generally involve more taxes. What kind of commitment do we have?

In addition to providing seniors with better care, what might we do to increase their status? Integrating—or reintegrating—them into the mainstream of society by providing more job opportunities is an important first step. Palmore, in *Honorable Elders Revisited* (1985), suggested a national annual Senior Citizen Day similar to Japan's Annual Respect for the Elders Day. They recommend a special celebration of the 65th birthday and gestures of social respect such as reserving special seats on buses and trains for elders.

In closing, we should consider the viewpoint of Margaret Mead, the noted anthropologist who traveled the world observing the process of aging in many cultures. Mead questioned the great emphasis we place on the independence of elders in our society. Our preoccupation with independence compels our elderly to live apart from their families and from the younger generation. Mead observed:

> *The young need to know about their past before they can understand the present and plot the future. Young people also need reassurance that change does not mean an end to the world, but merely an end to the world as they first saw it (Mead, 1972).*

Integrating older people into the mainstream of our lives, rather than excluding them, allows them to be valuable role models, and lets them share their experience for the benefit of youth.

Chapter Summary

The cross-cultural approach compares value systems and social structures across cultures. Value systems and social structures reflect on the status of elders and vary widely from culture to culture. In some countries, the elders have a central place in the social structure and are held in high esteem. Social scientists are testing the hypothesis that modernization decreases the status of the elderly. Undeveloped, developing, and developed countries offer a test of the hypothesis, which generally speaking, is supported. However, one can overgeneralize on this subject because exceptions do exist.

We think of Japan as a country honoring elders, yet industrialization and other socioeconomic changes have eroded the concept of filial piety. Aging in Scandinavia seems to have advantages over other countries in the comprehensiveness of its health care. Scandinavian countries are more socialistic and have more tax dollars to spend on programs that tend to be progressive and enlightened.

Key Terms

chronological age
continuous values
cross-cultural approach
developed countries
discontinuous values
ethnocentric
filial piety
formal age
functional age
group home
health expectancy
less-developed countries (LDCs)
modernization
nomadic society
nonindustrial society
status of elders
theory of social modernization
value

Discussion Questions

1. What cultural factors are possibly involved in longevity?
2. What aspects of modernization affect the elderly adversely? What aspects of modern life affect the status of the elderly today?
3. How does growing old in nonindustrialized countries compare with growing old in America?
4. How does growing old in Japan and Sweden compare with growing old in America?
5. Describe the ideal culture in which to grow old. Describe yourself living in this ideal culture and your attitudes toward aging and toward life in general.

Fieldwork Suggestions

1. Interview the oldest living member of your family. Was anyone born outside the United States? Find out about their childhood and their experiences growing up.
2. In the library, find descriptions of the status of the elderly in nonindustrial or developing nations. Is this status high or low? Why?

3. Interview an older person born in another country. Ask him or her to compare old-age experiences in his or her birth country with those of the United States.

Online Activities

1. Locate the home page for the World Health Organization. What comparisons can you make between the three or four countries with the largest population of elders and those three or four with the largest birthrates? What relationships can you find between aging demographics in a country and health statistics?
2. Begin with the United Nations site, and follow the population trajectory of an industrialized country and of a developing country.
3. Locate the home page for an international organization that deals with quality of life issues for people of all ages (suggestions: Greenpeace, UNISEF or another United Nations committee, WHO). What are the information links at this site? For whom has this Internet site been designed? What commercial, educational, and personal uses might be made of information found through this site?

17

Senior Power: Politics, Policies, and Programs

Mandela's Journey Perhaps Unsurpassed in History of Human Spirit

Rener Tyson

On trial for sabotage at Pretoria's Palace of Justice, Nelson Mandela knew he faced the gallows. But he would have his say even if it cost him his life.

That was April 20, 1961. Mandela was 45 years old. The charge against him, which carried the death sentence, was sabotage with intent to overthrow the white government. It was a charge he readily admitted.

Thirty years later, Mandela used the exact words he spoke to the judge during that 1961 trial as he campaigned for the presidency of South Africa.

"During my lifetime I have dedicated myself to this struggle of the African people," Mandela told the Pretoria court. "I have fought against white domination, and I have fought against black domination.

"I have cherished the ideal of a democratic and free society in which all persons live together in harmony and with equal opportunities. It is an ideal which I hope to live for and to achieve. But if it needs be, it is an ideal for which I am prepared to die."

Mandela lived to achieve that ideal. At the age of 75, he became South Africa's first black president—the victor in the country's first all-races election that sounded the death knell of apartheid.

Born into African aristocracy (July 18, 1918), Mandela was groomed to rule from childhood.

When Mandela was 12, his father died. The youngster was placed under the care and instruction of his guardian uncle, Chief Jonquintaba, at the nearby village of Maekezweni.

"In my youth in the Tranaei, I listened to the elders of my tribe telling stories of the old days," Mandela told the Pretoria court back in 1961.

Eager to learn and always a good student, Mandela enrolled at the University of Fort Mars in South Africa's eastern Cape Province, where he met a reserved but highly intelligent student named Oliver Tambo. Their friendship was to prove a powerful force in the struggle for freedom. Later they opened South Africa's first black law firm in Johannesburg.

But after two years at Fort Mars, both Mandela and Tambo were expelled for protesting poor food and living conditions.

In Soweta, a sprawling black township on the southwestern edge of Johannesburg, Mandela took refuge in the modest home of real estate agent Walter Sisulu. It was a move that shaped his life forever.

Sisulu encouraged Mandela to attend law school in Johannesburg. Mandela, Sisulu, along with Tambo and other young turks, took over direction of the moribund ANC (African National Congress—the major native African political organization) through its youth league. At that time the Afrikaner-dominated National Party had just come to power and began imposing apartheid.

Tall, handsome, an amateur boxer, Mandela, now a lawyer, quickly emerged as the liberation movement's main man.

He led the passive resistance Defiance Campaign of 1952, which aimed at getting white officials to hear black grievances about discrimination. White officials banned him from public activities. A court convicted him under the Suppression of Communism Act, but gave him a suspended sentence. He was tried and acquitted for treason.

In 1960, the government of Prime Minister Henrik Varwoard, apartheid's architect, declared the ANC unlawful and banned it. The ANC went underground. . . .

Mandela was captured near the Natal town of Howick. Last year, Mandela made a visit to Howick and remarked how after his arrest, "I went on a long holiday."

On July 12, 1961, Mandela, Sisulu and six other leaders were sentenced to life in prison. Mandela's powerful and emotional speech in court probably saved his life and the lives of his compatriots.

In prison, Mandela excited the passions of human rights activists around the world. Even though he was behind bars, he gained stature year by year as a symbol of the fight against apartheid.

On February 11, 1990, President F. W. de Klerk, who was to share the Nobel Peace Prize in 1993 with the former political prisoner, released Mandela from prison to make the walk to freedom and into the presidency, completing a journey perhaps unsurpassed in the history of the human spirit.

Political Voice and Power

To judge strength by size alone, the older population of the United States is stronger than ever before. Numbers command political power at the voting booth and in lobbying efforts. Yet, because of fiscally conservative federal policies in the 1980s and harsh economic turns in the 1990s, the United States has a general political environment increasingly hostile to the aged or for that matter, to any group that makes a request of local, state, or federal budgets. Though elders have made significant strides over the last 50 years in gaining the wherewithal to maintain healthy and meaningful lives, their progress, like that of our society in general, depends primarily on the condition of the U.S. economic system.

At the turn of the century, the nation approaches a demographic evolution of revolutionary proportion. Whereas proactive social policy is necessary if we are to adequately meet the changing needs of our citizens, it takes specific, targeted, cause-based organizational dedication to make that social policy happen.

The threat of cutbacks in government programs exists in most of the nations of Europe and will grow larger in the next 20 years as the global Boomers of the World War II era reach age 65. The Netherlands provides a clear example of threatened cutbacks; their social welfare policies provide substantial benefits to elders that they have come to take for granted. A conservative political environment has now challenged these policies. In a country of 11 million, some 15,000 Dutch senior citizens marched into a soccer stadium to rally, shouting to opposing political parties, "Keep your hands off our pensions" (Drozdiak, 1994). In that country the General Old People's Union, along with another senior citizens' party, won six seats in parliament. The political awakening of the elderly is gathering momentum. The cost of social welfare in Holland has gone off the charts. The Dutch spend over $100 billion a year on health and social security costs, about 10 times what they pay for their military defense. The older population fears a decrease in their standard of living as cost-cutting measures become inevitable, and they support political candidates who do not advocate the reduction of their entitlements.

We begin this chapter by briefly reviewing periods during which elder political activism in the United States flourished. Today's political climate can then be examined in the light of these earlier decades of struggle and progress.

Early Political Movements

Political movements are the combined result of social, economic, and historical events. Circumstances develop that make political action imperative. Those who are affected respond by joining forces and asserting their need to improve their situation. This happened in the early 1900s, when a large proportion of older people was living in poverty. Although retirement had become increasingly mandatory, pensions were not yet generally available, which often left the elderly with neither work nor money.

In 1921 a limited pension system was established for federal employees, but the vast majority of elders still had no pensions at all. In 1928, 65 percent of those over 65 were receiving assistance of some sort from children. The Depression had wiped out the pensions and savings of millions, leaving elders in the most desperate poverty of any age group. Described in *Endangered Dreams* by Kevin Starr (1996):

> *With 12 million people out of work by 1933, voluntary assistance to parents plummeted along with the rest of the economy. To whom could the elderly now turn? Not to government. American culture had no discernible tradition of old-age pensions from government. Only 6 American states had any form of old-age assistance program. By 1934 a mere 180,000 elderly, out of a total population of 15 million-plus senior citizens, were receiving any form of legally mandated assistance. Yet fully 50 percent of the elderly in America were in need of some form of outside aid if they were to make it through the slump (p. 134).*

Their plight created the social environment for the nation's first elderly uprising, which took political form as the **Townsend plan.** Named after the retired physician, Francis E. Townsend, who headed the program, the Townsend plan was organized through local clubs. By 1935 a half million Americans had joined Townsend Clubs, and by the end of 1936, about 2.2 million people belonged (Starr, 1996). The Townsend plan proposed placing $200 of government funds per month in the hands of persons aged 60 and older, with the requirements that the recipients be retired and spend the money within 30 days. The plan was to end the economic problems of elders and solve unemployment, plus introduce new spending to stimulate the economy. It would not increase the deficit, because it was funded by a multiple sales tax.

While popular with older people, the plan was resoundingly criticized. The political Left argued that the transactions tax was regressive; the political Right feared the tax would cut profits and the spending would undermine the incentive to work (Amenta et al., 1992). Scholars and policy experts felt the tax implied higher levies on finished goods, and believed it would not work to register farmers for the tax. Ultimately, following internal conflict among Townsend plan leaders over charges of graft, plus vigorous opposition from the Roosevelt administration, less than 4 percent of the national electorate approved the Townsend plan (Starr, 1996). The plan was not a utopian scheme, however. It provided for the aged to have a national pension, the size of which would be determined by an earmarked tax (Amenta et al., 1992). It provided the model for old-age assistance to come.

The Social Security Act adopted one of Townsend's main interests—a pension for elders. However, the Social Security Act was a more conservative measure. Rather than "giving" pensions to the retired, it paid pensions out of sums collected from workers; and the amount of each pension was determined by each individual's employment record. Those who did not work were not eligible for benefits. In the decades that followed, amendments to the Social Security Act added coverage for more kinds of workers and their dependents.

> *"Few Californians could be found in the inner circle of President Roosevelt or at the helm of New Deal agencies. While eager for a myth of individualism and self-improvement, Californians seemed incapable, the majority of them, of moving to an expression of such ambitions beyond the instant solution of an old-age pension plan. The affluence and altered attitudes of the 1950s and 1960s would reverse this orientation and make of California, briefly, the very model of the social democratic experiment" (p. 222).*
>
> KEVIN STARR, 1966

Other political movements, many of which originated in California, attempted to help the elderly during this era. Even before the Townsend plan, there had been EPIC (End Poverty in California). The EPIC movement was based on campaign promises of Upton Sinclair's gubernatorial campaign in California in 1934. His platform of sweeping social reform was energized by utopianism, which had popular support in California at the same time. The movement's slogan was decidedly socialist in orientation: Production for use, not profit.

Also from California, the California Pension Plan Association, popularly known as **Ham and Eggs,** proposed that the government issue $30 in warrants every Thursday to all unemployed Californians over 50. The script would expire, thus the elderly pensioners who received it would spend it promptly and stimulate the economy. Despite strong popular support, in 1938 Ham and Eggs was narrowly defeated, by 3,671 of 2.3 million votes.

A significant characteristic of the various movements in the 1930s and 1940s, including McLain's, was that they extracted great sums of money from the elderly themselves. Indeed, although the movements set a precedent for political organization, they also demonstrated how vulnerable elders could be to corrupt leaders who preyed on their trust:

> *Certainly old-age power was helped to grow because of them; however, the secretiveness, greed, and paranoia with which the advocates held power stymied grassroot growth" (Kleyman, 1974, p. 70).*

Although the civil-rights movement began in the 1950s, this decade is arguably one of the most politically conservative and socially apathetic decades in American history. It was an era of general economic prosperity characterized by inattention to needy groups. The early 1960s brought more fervor to the civil-rights movement, and President Lyndon B. Johnson declared the War on Poverty. The high incidence of poverty among some groups—racial minorities, the rural, and elders—began to attract public attention. With the advent of the antiwar movement and the hippie lifestyle, the 1960s also saw increasing political activism among students and other adults. Gay liberation and the women's movement evolved in the 1970s as civil libertarian ideals gathered support. The women's movement in particular dealt with the issue of aging by attacking job discrimination against middle-aged and older women. The National Organization for Women (NOW) established an energetic task force of older women to identify issues and organize political action.

The 1970s also ushered in the advocacy of rights for the disabled. These humanistic movements created an environment in which one movement could combine forces with another. In this sense, all of the social movements of the 1960s and 1970s contributed to the social movement of **senior power.** A number of pro-senior interest groups and programs materialized in the 1960s; their chief accomplishments were the passage of the Older Americans Act (1965) and Medicare (1966).

The early 1970s brought forth a more visible and vital seniors movement. For the first time since the Great Depression, older people, with cries of "gray power" and slogans such as "Don't Agonize—Organize," showed evidence of considerable political activism. Demonstrations, sit-ins, and sleep-ins by oldsters wearing "Senior Power" buttons made the headlines. The new militancy of old-age groups such as the Gray Panthers presented a surprising and exciting image for those who had once been stereotyped as powerless, dependent, slow, and unenthusiastic. The name "Gray Panthers" captured the new consciousness of the elderly. It suggested strength, power, and radical—if not revolutionary—political and social behavior.

The political activism of elders often targets issues that are at national and international levels. This woman is an AIDS activisit, providing leaflets to shoppers in New York City.

Political Power Today

VOTING

When enough older people turn out to vote on a given issue and vote as a bloc, they wield considerable power. Approximately 90 percent of Americans over age 50 are registered to vote, compared with an overall national figure of less than 75 percent. In all recent elections; older people are more likely to vote than younger ones (Hooyman & Kiyak, 1996). Citizens in their eighties are more likely to vote than those in their early twenties. Older voter turnout (those 65 and over) is generally double the voter turnout of young adults under 25 years of age. Thus, the voting power of older people is greater than their actual numbers in the population would indicate, even though disability and lack of transportation keep a few elders from the polls. Voting patterns do not change much over time: Those who vote in their younger years continue to vote for as long as they are able. Only one subgroup of older voters shows low turnout—homemakers, virtually all of whom are women.

Despite generally large voter turnout among elders, there is no old-age voting bloc—not even on old-age issues. In national politics, people of similar social classes are more likely to vote alike than are people of similar age groups. The wealthy older person, for example, might not support welfare measures for older people living in poverty; neither would the wealthy younger voter. Political organization and mobilization would be necessary to encourage elders to use their potential power by voting as a bloc.

Older people are neither more nor less conservative than younger people, unlike the common stereotype that people grow more conservative with age. The elderly are spread fairly equally balanced between the Republican and Democratic parties, and they have good voting records. The 75-plus age group has been more likely to vote in the last five presidential elections than those voters under 35. When older voter turnout is low, factors such as gender, ethnic minority, and education are more important than age: Only 51.5 percent of African American elders voted in the 1988 presidential election, and less than

50 percent of the older Hispanic voters regularly vote (Hooyman & Kiyak, 1996).

OFFICE HOLDING

Another measure of political power is the ability to be elected or appointed to public office. Only two U.S. presidents have entered office after the age of 65: William Henry Harrison (age 68) and Ronald Reagan (age 69). Many more have turned 65 while in office. Because life expectancy has increased greatly since George Washington's time, one might guess that presidents have entered office at increasingly older ages. However, this has not happened. Though the first four presidents were 57 or older, in the following years, the nation has seen some very young presidents. The youngest was Theodore Roosevelt (age 42), followed by John F. Kennedy, who was 43 years old at his inauguration in 1961. President Bill Clinton was aged 47 at his inauguration in 1993.

Children, believe me: Things were not better in the old days... I remember black people riding in the back of the bus. I remember summer being a season of fear because summer was when polio stalked the neighborhood, crippling and killing. I remember cars being cranked by hand and seeing men with arms broken from cranking carelessly. I remember headlines about gangsters spraying crowded streets with Tommy guns, remember hoboes at kitchen doors begging for sandwiches....Just like right now, back then was chock full of meanness.

RUSSELL BAKER, 1996

Members of Congress, because they are elected officials, are not subject to mandatory retirement laws. Some members have served into their eighties and, occasionally, into their nineties. Since 1974, the average age has risen to over 50; in 1996, many congressional members were over age 65. The seniority system in Congress allows older members who have served many years to wield the most power, often as heads of important committees.

Cabinet members and ambassadors tend to be older, perhaps because they are appointed by the president rather than elected. These positions, which imply years of experience, are often filled by men and women who, in any other area of work, might have been forced by age alone to retire. Supreme Court justices also tend to be older. There is no mandatory retirement for them, and they generally serve as long as their health allows. In 1991, the controversial appointment of Clarence Thomas, age 43, made him the youngest justice to serve on the Court. In 1998, four justices were over age 65: Paul Stevens, 77, and Chief Justice William Rehnquist, 74 are the two oldest members. Sandra Day O'Connor was 68 in 1998, and Ruth Bader Ginsberg, 65 years of age.

Despite the representation of elders in elected and appointed positions, we do not seem to be headed toward a **gerontocracy**—rule by the old. Both young and old are involved in the political arena. Although it has long been acceptable for members of Congress to be middle-aged or older, a political youthful image has been favorable since the time of Teddy Roosevelt. In addition, even among old politicians, age does not appear to be a major variable affecting their position on political issues. A presidential candidate or Congress member does not support old-age measures simply because he or she is near age 65. The support that members of Congress give to issues ideally reflects not only their political ideology but also the wishes of their constituents.

Political Associations

Interest groups representing older Americans have increased in number and political effectiveness over the past several decades.

One type of specialized interest group is the **trade association**. Trade associations represent specific concerns and lobby to achieve their purposes and goals. Some examples are the American Association of Homes for the Aging, the American Nursing Home Association, the National Council of Health Care Services, and the National Association of State Units on the Aging. There are also **professional associations**, such as the Gerontological Society, the Association for Gerontology in Higher Education, and the American Society of Aging, composed primarily of academicians in the field of aging. States and regions also have professional associations, such as the California Coalition for Gerontology and Geriatrics. **Interest groups**, such as the National Association of Retired Federal Employees (NARFE) and the National Retired Teachers Association (NRTA), are composed of retired persons.

A few organizations representing older persons have enjoyed special growth, success, and media attention. Here we consider six of them: the American Association of Retired Persons, the National Committee to Preserve Social Security and Medicare, the National Council of Senior Citizens, the National Council on the Aging, the National Caucus and Center on the Black Aged, and the Gray Panthers.

AMERICAN ASSOCIATION OF RETIRED PERSONS (AARP)

The current premier lobbyist for elder causes in the United States is the **American Association of Retired Persons (AARP)**, with 32 million members over 50, two-thirds of whom are over 65 (Morris, 1994). Although the goals of some groups have always been to exert political influence, the primary goals of AARP have only recently become political.

The group's founder, Ethel Percy Andrus, was an educator—the first woman in California to become a high school principal. She founded the National Retired Teachers Association (NRTA) in 1947 when she was forced to retire from her position after reaching the age of 65. She was 76 in 1958 when she created AARP as a parallel organization to bring benefits of the NRTA to elders who had not been teachers. The organization's cofounder was Leonard Davis, a young insurance agent who developed the group health insurance plan for NRTA members. It has been suggested that Davis financed the creation of AARP to expand his own mail-order health insurance market. Until being forced out in the early 1980s, Davis was in control of AARP, "operating as a sales network to hawk very high-priced insurance and a host of other...products to old people " (Morris, 1996, p. 10). He left the organization as a very wealthy man.

In 1994 the organization's operating budget was $382 million, plus $86 million in federal grants to operate programs for seniors (Morris, 1996). Services available through AARP now include, in addition to health insurance, travel packages, special prescription rates, an auto club, education, income tax counseling, and training services. The AARP's array of services, financed primarily by federal grant dollars, ranges from widows' counseling to driver reeducation.

Membership makes the AARP one of the largest voluntary organizations represented in Washington and one of the nation's largest lobbying groups. The group, which tries to remain nonpartisan, has directed its political efforts at improving pensions, opposing mandatory retirement, and improving Social Security benefits, widely shared goals that unite the association's members. Their congressional lobbyists support causes for poor elders, and their magazine *Modern Maturity* stresses an image of well-to-do, healthy aging.

THE NATIONAL COMMITTEE TO PRESERVE SOCIAL SECURITY AND MEDICARE

Founded by James Roosevelt (son of President Franklin Roosevelt) in 1983, the **National Committee to Preserve Social Security and Medicare** is concerned about the solvency of the Social Security Trust Funds. Now boasting 5 million members, it is a nonprofit organization funded entirely by membership fees and donations. Its

Nineteen-sixties style, hit-the-streets protesting is the model of choice for some advocacy groups. The Gray Panthers has a tradition of speaking out with noise on local and national-level issues needing the immediate attention of voters.

59-member staff works to protect and improve Social Security and Medicare benefits. Many of the staff are full-time lobbyists.

NATIONAL COUNCIL OF SENIOR CITIZENS (NCSC)

The **National Council of Senior Citizens** (NCSC) originated in 1961 as a pressure group to support the enactment of Medicare legislation. Its leadership has always come from labor unions, mainly the AFL-CIO and other industrial unions. From a small, highly specialized group, the NCSC has grown to include a general membership of about one million in 1994. It is now an organization of autonomous senior citizens clubs, associations, councils, and other groups. Their aims are to support Medicare, increases in Social Security, reductions in health costs, and increased social programs for seniors.

The organization's stated goals are broad and straightforward: "We work with, persuade, push, convince, testify, petition, and urge Congress, the Administration, and government agencies to get things done on behalf of the aged." The council, located in Washington, D.C., lobbies for Social Security revision, a national health insurance program, higher health and safety standards in nursing homes, and adequate housing and jobs for elders. The membership base is composed primarily of labor union retirees, but membership is open to anyone aged 55 or older.

NATIONAL COUNCIL ON THE AGING

Founded in 1950, the **National Council on the Aging,** a confederation of social welfare agencies and professionals in the field of aging, has been at the forefront of advocacy, policy, and program development on all issues affecting the quality of life for older Americans. The organization, which has its headquarters in Washington, D.C., has regional offices in New York and California. The council publishes books, articles, and journals on aging, sponsors seminars and conferences, and funds eight special-interest groups.

National Association of Older Worker Employment Services (NAOWES)

National Center on Rural Aging (NCRA)

National Institute on Adult Day Care (NIAD)

National Institute on Community-Based Long Term Care (NICLC)

National Institute of Senior Centers (NISC)

National Institute of Senior Housing (NISH)

National Voluntary Organizations for Independent Living for the Aging (NVOILA)

The Health Promotion Institute (HPI)

THE NATIONAL CAUCUS AND CENTER ON BLACK AGED (NCCBA)

Formed in 1980 when two groups—the National Caucus on Black Aged and the National Center on Black Aged—joined, the **National Caucus and Center on Black Aged** attempts to improve the quality and length of life for senior African Americans. The NCCBA, which believes that problems can be resolved through effective and concentrated political action on behalf of and by older African Americans, was initially formed as an ad hoc group of African-American and white professionals who shared a concern for older African Americans. NCCBA activities have been largely national, focusing on such areas as income, health, and housing. An annual conference is held every May. The National Center on Black Aged in Washington, D.C., established by the NCCBA through federal funding, is the location for various activities: training, research, legislative development, and assistance to black elders.

The five groups discussed so far are neither revolutionary nor radical. Rather than advocating a redistribution of wealth, they work to improve the status of the elders by ensuring that more federal money is channeled to them. For example, they have successfully lobbied the Department of Health and Human Services, the Department of Education, the Office of Economic Opportunity, the Administration on Aging, and other government agencies to increase resources for the older population.

THE GRAY PANTHERS

One pro-age political group that identifies itself as radical nonviolent is the Gray Panthers, a loosely organized group that includes young people as well as old ("age and youth in action") to fight ageism in U.S. society. It received a great deal of media attention when it was formed in the 1970s.

The late Maggie Kuhn, a dynamic woman who was unwillingly retired at age 65, founded the movement in her search for new ways to constructively use her energies. She and the group's other members describe themselves as a consciousness-raising activist group. Drawn together by deeply felt concerns for human liberation and social change, the Gray Panthers operate out of an office in a West Philadelphia church. From that office, a small staff and a group of volunteers maintain a center for the entire organization—thousands of concerned persons in several hundred chapters in cities and towns across the nation. Their goals are to bring dignity to old age, to eliminate poverty and mandatory retirement, to reform pension systems, and to develop a new public consciousness of the aging person's potential.

Describing themselves as a movement rather than an organization, the Gray Panthers have no formal membership requirements and collect no membership dues. They have opposed the national budget deficit, the nuclear arms race, and cuts in Social Security. Currently, the group advocates a national health insurance program. These views are similar to those who espouse the critical perspective in sociology.

In a newsletter called Network, the Gray Panthers espouse their views. Writes one member:

> *We stand firm in our commitment to oppose all forms of discrimination and to challenge harmful prejudiced attitudes and values. Now, we reaffirm our pledge to help create a world that is fair to* all *people regardless of their gender, race, ethnicity, nationality, sexual orientation, religion, income, physical or mental abilities, or age (Kerr-Layton, 1993).*

Gray Panthers also defend the rights of gays, lesbians, and AIDS victims and their friends. They are opposed to violence and abuse of any kind and draw special attention to the presence of hate crimes in our society. They also sponsor jointly with other organizations an international "People's Summit for Peace" and work for world peace in any way they can.

Researchers offer divergent views on the political impact of the "gray lobby." In some areas they are organized and strong. The AARP, along with the other organizations, has been effective in staving off large cuts in Medicare (Morris, 1996). Reductions in Social Security benefits proposed by the Clinton administration were abandoned as politically dangerous because of the "gray lobby" groups (Heyser, 1996). And because of senior power, higher taxes on Social Security benefits are also viewed as a politically risky move by politicians (Heyser, 1996). On the other hand, the state of the economy (the national debt, the trade imbalance, worldwide recession), and the growing number of elders, along with the shrinking workforce are not factors the "gray lobby" can control.

Assessing the impact of the senior movement is difficult because it is so complex—representing, as it does, the vast diversity of that collection of Americans who happen to be 65 years old or older.

The Older Americans Act and Other Programs

The **Older Americans Act** (OAA) attempts to alter state and local priorities to ensure that older people's needs are represented in social services allocations. It was created to form a national network for comprehensive planning and delivery of aging services. Funding for the Older Americans Act comes up for Congressional renewal every four years, therefore the U.S. political and economic climate is a major determinant of OAAs level of funding.

The OAA was adopted by Congress in 1965, a period very favorable to programs for the aging. (Medicare, for example, was enacted during the same general time period.) Whereas the 1960s and 1970s saw budget increases and expanded programs under the OAA, the 1980s brought decreases in funding, and the 1990s experienced more of the same. Since participation

NOTICE THE CONGRESSMAN EATING HIS SUBSIDIZED LUNCH... HE VOTED TO CUT THE ELDERS FOOD PROGRAM

Some political movements are not targeted solely to older Americans. The Feminism movement, including the National Organization of Woman and Older Women's League, has been enriched by the voices of America's oldest women, whose lifelong experiences have provided grist for changes in public policy to address women's issues.

rates in many OAA services have been highest among middle-income older persons, cuts in funding alongside proposals for cost-sharing have been introduced in Congress. The major portion of OAA funds is devoted to congregate meals, senior centers, and transportation programs.

The Older Americans Act contains six major sections, or titles, which outline the intentions and objectives of the act. Title II establishes the Administration on Aging (AOA) in Washington, D.C., the organization that administers the programs and services that the act mandates. Title III provides for the distribution of money to establish state and community agencies—Area Agencies on Aging, or AAAs. These agencies disseminate information about available social services and are responsible for planning and coordinating such services for the elderly in local settings. A local community that has a council or center on aging is probably receiving federal funds through Title III. Title IV, its funding slashed in the 1980s, and not increased in the 1990s, provides funds for training people to work in the field of aging as well as for research and education on aging. Other titles provide funds for multipurpose senior centers to serve as community focal points for the development and delivery of social services.

The specific titles of the act are intended to achieve the following objectives for older citizens, as spelled out in Title I: (1) adequate income; (2) good physical and mental health; (3) suitable housing at reasonable cost; (4) full restorative services for those who require institutional care;

(5) equal employment opportunities; (6) retirement with dignity; (7) a meaningful existence; (8) efficient, coordinated community services; (9) benefits of knowledge from research; and (10) freedom, independence, and individual initiative in the planning and management of one's life.

The act's major programs are developed to address these goals at local levels, with guidance from state units and the federal Administration on Aging. Funding comes partially from the federal government and partially from state and local governments and charity organizations. Some of the programs funded and administered through this system are discussed below.

MEALS AND NUTRITION

The success of pilot projects in the 1960s resulted in federal funding for home-delivered meals and, in 1972, funding for congregate, or group, dining projects. Under the Older Americans Act, funds are available to all states to deliver meals to the homebound elderly or to serve meals in congregate sites. Meals on Wheels, for example, delivers meals to the homebound at a minimal charge. Congregate dining is aimed at getting the elderly out of their homes and into a friendly environment where they can socialize with other people as well as enjoy a hot meal.

Meals and activities take place in churches, schools, restaurants, or senior centers. Besides serving hot meals, some agencies provide transportation to and from the dining site, information and referral services, nutrition education, health and welfare counseling, shopping assistance, and recreational activities. The act establishing the congregate dining program specifies that participants not be asked their income; they may make a contribution if they wish, but there is no set charge.

FRIENDLY VISITING AND TELEPHONE REASSURANCE

The OAA provides limited funding for volunteer community services such as friendly visitor and telephone reassurance programs. Because of decreasing funds, however, local staffs have had to become increasingly adept at fund-raising to keep programs afloat.

The Friendly Visitor Program has improved the quality of life for many people. Visitors are volunteers of all ages who have an interest in developing a friendly relationship with older persons. They are matched with elderly persons in their community on the basis of such things as common interests or location. In some cases, the Friendly Visitor has proved to be a lifeline. The program has a small paid staff that organizes and instructs volunteers.

Telephone reassurance programs have staff, either paid or volunteer, to check on older persons daily by phone at a given time. For the homebound, this call may be an uplifting and meaningful part of the day. If the phone is not answered, a staff member immediately goes in person to check on the elder's welfare.

EMPLOYMENT

The Title V employment program is small but is one of the most politically popular programs. The major program, the Senior Community Service Employment Program (SCSEP), which provides community service work opportunities for unemployed low-income persons aged 55 and over, employs 62,500 older applicants in part-time minimum-wage community service jobs throughout the United States.

A related program is Green Thumb. Men and women aged 55 and older who live in rural areas may work up to 20 hours per week at minimum wage in public projects that include landscaping, horticulture, and highway maintenance.

ADULT DAY CENTERS

The Older Americans Act partially funds multipurpose day programs to provide services on an outpatient basis to the many older people who need services on a daily or weekly basis but do not need 24-hour institutional care. Older people may come to such centers for health care, meals, social activities, physical exercise, or rehabilitation. Practitioners from the centers may, on occasion, deliver home services. These centers allow people to enjoy the advantages of both institutional care and home living.

OTHER SERVICES

Local agencies on aging may offer legal services to low-income elders for civil matters such as landlord disputes; other agencies may offer home health services as well. Still others may offer housing services such as counseling regarding housing options, home equity conversion information, and assistance in locating affordable housing. Information and referral is a hallmark of agencies on aging.

Considering the budget constraints within which the AOA must work, fulfilling all the goals of the OAA is largely impossible. In 1994, for example, Social Security and Medicare payments to older persons totaled between $300 and $400 billion, vastly more than the $15 billion OAA appropriation. Nevertheless, the OAA provides an excellent outreach structure for elders across the United States. Vast numbers have enjoyed and appreciated the services the act offers. Though the limited funds cannot reach far enough to include those above the poverty line as well as those below it, many elders living in modest if not meager circumstances do meet eligibility requirements.

Grassroots Programs

Certainly not all successful programs for older people have been funded by the Older Americans Act. Some have sprung up locally and are funded by local tax dollars. Others are funded by private donations or charity organizations, or sponsored by churches or various federal or state government agencies separate from the Administration on Aging. The following are two examples of these programs: Elderhostel, made available through a combination of state colleges and universities and private pay; and Foster Grandparents, a grassroots organization that grew to national association proportions.

ELDERHOSTEL

Offering special one-week or summer residential academic programs for citizens age 60 and over, the very successful Elderhostel program is designed to meet some of the educational interests of older people. From its Boston headquarters, the program, inspired by the youth hostels and folk schools of Europe, directs a network of several thousand high schools, universities, national parks, environmental education centers, and many other educational institutions throughout the United States, Canada, and more than 100 overseas locations. Hostelers can go to school (a different school every week, if desired) as many weeks as they wish and take up to three courses per week. Noncredit courses with no exams, no grades, and no required homework are offered in multitudinous subjects; no-cost extracurricular activities are also provided. Scholarships are available, and students are charged a reasonable flat fee for class, room, and board. Elderhostel offers personal assistance with overseas travel arrangements. The program has been enormously popular among older "students of life."

THE FOSTER GRANDPARENT PROGRAM

Funded through participating states and ACTION (the principal federal agency that administers volunteer service programs), the Foster Grandparent Program (FGP) allows low-income citizens of age 60 or older to use their time and talents to provide much needed love, care, and attention to disadvantaged youngsters. Begun in 1965, FGP was the first federally sponsored program to offer challenging activity to retirees. The FGP provides opportunities for close relationships to two different groups: low-income elders who want to feel needed and who want to participate in and contribute to the lives of institutionalized children and/or children with special or exceptional needs.

Foster grandparents exist in every state. Participating elders receive 40 hours of orientation in the specific area of their choice. In most cases, they work four hours a day, five days a week, assisting youngsters in physical or speech therapy or with their homework. Their main task is to provide for the emotional, mental, and physical well-being of children by affording them intimate and continuing relations through uncomplicated activities such as going for a walk or reading stories, or within family intervention structures. Foster grandparents receive a nontaxable stipend of an amount per hour that is approximately minimum wage, transportation if needed, a meal each day that they work, accident and liability insurance coverage, and an annual physical exam. Sometimes, nonstipended volunteers may enroll in the program under certain conditions. Many seniors work in this program for years both because they need the extra income and, more importantly, because their "grandchildren" love them.

Activism and Advocacy

Activism connotes more than simply voting or joining an organization. The term *political activist* brings to mind an individual who is politically committed to a cause and who uses a variety of means to push for social change.

Elders and those interested in their causes participate in community activities by serving on boards of trustees, advisory councils, and committees in all kinds of social service agencies. Interested persons may get involved in police/community relations, join voluntary organizations, and enter local politics as either campaign workers or as candidates. They may lobby to maintain or increase funding for federal programs, including those of the Older Americans Act. Legal activity is another area for activism. Class-action lawsuits can be brought against organizations and institutions that discriminate against or do not properly serve elders. Voter registration drives are important. They ensure that older persons can support those who support Social Security, Medicaid, home-delivered meals, public housing, employment programs, improved transportation, health benefits, and dozens of other programs for the elderly. Grievance procedures can be initiated to aid complaints against Social Security or welfare departments. Collective activity is a good tactic for the activist who joins with others in membership drives, marches, and demonstrations. That activism can be high profile, such as a Gray Panthers-sponsored march, or it can be on a far smaller scale. In either case, it is taking the responsibility to put values into action, and the result can be profoundly validating.

An example of a political and social action group on a smaller scale is **Seniors for Justice.** This association was started by a recreational therapist in a nursing home of 550 residents. The group advocates for improvements in long term care, and in the process, enhances residents' sense of control and self-identity (Hubbard et al., 1992). They address a range of issues and use a range of tactics, from a petition drive supporting legal abortion to letter-writing campaigns to support a senior program. They have organized food drives to help local hungry children, and got the nursing home to start a recycling program.

Resistance activity can be an effective form of social activity. It includes boycotts, rent strikes, wheelchair sit-ins, and voting against bond issues. Designated individuals may act as watchdogs on agencies that serve the elderly. In any type of organized activity, the media can provide an important tool in airing the interests and concerns of elders.

Advocacy is a term widely used in the field of aging, perhaps because of numerous individuals and organizations doing just that. Advocacy involves using one's resources and power for the benefit of a special-interest group, such as the elderly. Stereotypes of the 1950s and 1960s portrayed elders as dependent and passive, in need of someone to advocate for them. The 1970s and 1980s changed that idea. The Gray Panthers were in the forefront of creating a stronger, more forceful image for elders. It is becoming quite clear that

The physical health and social well-being of American elders is strong and getting stronger as we enter a new century.

older persons are capable of advocating for themselves; nonetheless, they do appreciate all the help they can get. In the 1990s, advocacy will, ideally, combine the efforts of individuals, regardless of age, who desire to promote a more satisfying later life for all U.S. citizens.

The Equity Issue

Generational equity is a controversial issue that was first popularized by the media in the mid-1980s. Critics of elder programs, who fear that the older generation is advancing at the expense of the younger one, have described older people as selfishly demanding programs targeting their age group only, at the expense of children and children's programs. An example of the argument in action is the criticism of a politician who supports Meals-on-Wheels programs for elders, but votes to cut federal nutrition programs for school lunches. The reason? "The elderly vote, and children don't" goes the slogan. Perhaps so, perhaps not. The issue of social programs for special-needs groups is far too complex to be dealt with simplistically. From a national policy perspective, decisions on programmatic support must be made in the context of the total net of services available, as well as the need for those services. Sloganism brought to the public by a media searching for the 20-second sound bite does not provide reasoning adequate to make decisions that will affect millions of American citizens, whatever their ages.

Those who advocate generational equity believe that younger generations will suffer because of the older population's unprecedented size and affluence. Around the country, suburbs include a growing number of older residents. Older residents have no direct stake in the public school systems, and the constituency for supporting schools and other youth services is shrinking proportionally as the nation ages.

The idea, however, that increased numbers of elders leads to decreased support for children is unsound. The improved financial status of elders is due largely to better Social Security coverage. Although dramatically reducing poverty rates among seniors, small cost-of-living increases in Social Security benefits are not the reason for poverty among children and other younger generations. Nor is the increased cost of medical care for elders. If, as some suggest, Medicare premiums tripled in cost for the well-to-do and expensive surgeries were rationed for the very old, women and children would still be poor in this country. The growing number of older people is hardly the major reason for spiraling health care costs. It is one contributing factor in a complex economic system. The basic reason for the poverty of children is their parents' unemployment or underemployment and the increasing number of female-headed families with low incomes. To protect children, our economic house must be in order.

Economic prosperity and public support for education are strongly associated. American industry must have workers capable of making informed decisions, learning new tasks, and following complex instructions. A system of public education in the United States has provided such competent workers in the past, and must be strong enough to do so for the future. Blaming either Medicare and Social Security, or blaming poor parents does not address issues necessary for national-level, workable, effective policy for caring for America's citizens.

In 1950 Social Security was amended to establish a program of aid to permanently and totally disabled persons, and to broaden aid to dependent children to include a relative with whom the child lives. Social Security actually provides benefits to many different age groups, and every worker can rest easier knowing that, despite recent doubts about the program's continued solvency, he or she will likely be covered in retirement. A working father or mother who has paid in to Social Security can know that, should he or she die, their children will be provided for to some extent by Social Security. Social Security is a retirement *and disability* program—in reality, an intergenerational safety net to reduce poverty.

Public policy based on the competition to "get" limited resources will ultimately be unworkable because it will not meet the needs of those who require assistance, and it flies in the face of the deeply held value of interdependence across generations. Rather than competing for human services dollars—dividing the piece of pie into yet smaller sections—politicians and citizens need to be reformulating the way in which the pie is sliced.

The costs of providing services to an aging nation are mighty, however. The retirement and disability programs today are financed by a payroll tax that exceeds 12 percent of covered wages and salaries (Feldstein, 1998). This is a bigger tax burden on most households than personal income tax. Additionally, Medicare plus the means-tested Medicaid benefits that is for the aged costs as much as the Social Security pensions. Together these programs cost about 10 percent of the Gross Domestic Product. This is around 25 percent more than the entire revenue from personal income tax (Feldstein, 1998).

What must a nation do to address the dramatic shifts in the age of its population? With advances in medical science and improvements in lifestyles, it is possible that people will live even longer than current projections predict. The "contract between generations" is the relationship of expectations between older and younger age groups, in a context of changing resources and values. The relationship goes beyond parents and children, to that of generations in a nation: who owes what to whom and how, and when is it transferred. The exchanges, or **intergenerational transfers**, are based on the question, "To what extent do we hold older generations accountable for the effect of current policies on future generations?" At the cusp of the 21st century, we might take a lesson from ancient Native American philosophy: The consequences of all actions must be considered through the seventh generation. In what ways do my actions (my political perspective) affect those generations surrounding me, as well as future generations?

Epilogue: A New Generation of Older Adults

What does the future hold for older individuals? In some respects, the future looks bright. Elders are living longer and healthier lives, and they are becoming more visible not only in numbers but also in political activism. They have required, and to some degree have received, a bigger slice of that pie than did their parents, who were not as long-lived. As a result of dollars put into health, education, nutrition, and socialization for elders, the quality of life for the average older person has dramatically improved over that of several decades past.

On the other hand, the future is uncertain. The line between paying for programs for the well-being of elders and seeing thousands of elders live in poverty, as many elders once did, is a fine one. The nation is faced with a stark, "no-fault" reality: People are not growing old because they are mean-hearted or self-centered. Longevity has increased so suddenly in terms of human history that those who are currently living into very old age are at the cutting edge. They have few role models, and they did not "plan" to live to be 80, 90, and older. The questions are of the nation itself: Where do national values lie *vis a vis* the responsibility to provide for the country's elders now and in the future? What services should be provided; who should be targeted to receive those services; and what cost, if any, should participants pay for those services?

The 1997 reauthorization of the Older Americans Act provided an opportunity (and requirement) for advocates and policymakers to debate the role and future of OAA—essentially, to develop a plan for the future of services to elders (Wacker et al., 1998). Two options are to target services and to introduce cost sharing.

Targeting services to low-income individuals by developing financial eligibility standards is energetically endorsed by many policymakers, particularly those with budget as the bottom-line criterion (Wacker et al., 1998). Using income eligibility standards, however, might undermine the "social insurance" principle that has provided broad public support for Social Security and Medicare. Including the middle class along with the lower class provides a very broad base of programmatic support that otherwise might not be there.

Implementing a format of **cost sharing** is another option being discussed and is supported by many elder advocates. This plan would provide for an income-based sliding scale of shared cost responsibility similar to the theoretical income tax. Low-income individuals would have services paid for; and higher-income individuals would burden a proportion of the cost, depending on income. In this way, continued popular support for programs could be maintained. The image of a large administrative overhead looms for many people in this proposal, however. The choices are not easy, the task is enormous, and the outcomes are monumental for the shaping of the lives of elders in the 21st century.

The most exciting part of the future, however, is that the turn of the century brings with it a new generation of elders. Foremost, their parent generation will have given them the experience of extended longevity. They will know so much more about living to be 90, and more of them will *expect* to do so, than did their parents. They will have made plans, even if those plans are psychological and not practical. The gift of the previous generation is an understanding that the *possible* is likely to be the *probable*. The new generation of elders will have a better understanding of the relationship between lifestyle and health, and they will have lived in greater affluence than did their parents and have had greater opportunity to make lifestyle choices. They will bring with them the ability to redefine the timing of life course transactions. They just might choose to work (or introduce the *possibility*) until they are 55, then work for five years, take two years off, and repeat the cycle until they become completely unable to do so. They will bring with them different attitudes toward marriage, responsibility to the community, and responsibility for personal growth.

The future is a very exciting place. The present responsibility is to understand the ways in which an aging nation and globe will shape that future, economics will shape that future, and both will combine to shape the cultural environment of the nation.

Chapter Summary

Judging by numbers, the political power of elders is stronger than ever before. However, numbers do not tell the whole story. The political environment for elders in the 1990s is rather harsh because of the recession and budget deficits.

In earlier times, there have been examples of social movements by and for elders. The Townsend plan and Ham and Eggs movement in the 1930s are two examples. The activism of the 1970s symbolized by the Gray Panthers is a third example.

Today there are a number of indicators that older people have reasonable political clout. They vote in larger numbers than do younger persons. We have recently seen two presidents (Reagan and Bush) over 65, and the seniority system in Congress insures power to elder members. A number of political associations are strong—the leading one being the American Association of Retired Persons. The Older Americans Act of 1965 authorizes taxpayer spending on elders. However, funding is *not* increasing in the 1990s. The major funding goes to congregate meals, senior centers, and transportation programs. Only if there is effective advocacy and activism can these programs remain in place.

The question of generational equity will continue to raise its head as the percentage and number of elders continues to increase while funding for social programs decreases. It is unfortunate when old are posited against young. People of all ages should unite to improve the quality of life for everyone.

Key Terms

advocacy
aging network
American Association of Retired Persons
cost sharing
Elderhostel
Foster Grandparents Program
generational equity
Generations United
gerontocracy
Gray Panthers
Ham and Eggs movement
interest groups
intergenerational transfers
National Caucus and Center on Black Aged
National Committee to Preserve Social Security and Medicare
National Council of Senior Citizens
National Council on the Aging
Older Americans Act
professional associations
resistance activity
senior power
Seniors for Justice
targeting services
Townsend plan
trade association

Discussion Questions

1. What do you predict will be the future social movements for seniors? Why? How politically active do you expect these seniors to be?
2. Do you think ageism will be reversed in the future? Why or why not?
3. Do you expect to be politically active as an elder? Is so, why? Why not?
4. What organization(s) will you join? What measures do you support? Do you see yourself as being an activist when you are 60, 70, 80, 90? Explain.

Fieldwork Suggestions

1. Interview the head of the AARP in your area. How politically active is this person? Do you think that the AARP will represent your best interests when you are eligible to join? If you are eligible to join, why or why not are you a member? How well informed are the people you know about the AARP?
2. Locate the nearest chapter of the Gray Panthers. Write for information on their activities. What activities are they focused upon? Who is attracted as a member to this group?
3. Interview an old person who considers himself or herself to be an activist or radical, or to have been one at an earlier point in their life. What were the issues that brought them into activism? What are the issues they have addressed since?

Online Activities

1. Multidisciplinary resource centers of gerontology are funded by the Administration on Aging, and they include the Institute of Gerontology, University of Michigan; Wayne State University; Andrus Gerontology at University of Southern California; and the Center for Aging and Human Development at Duke University. Updates on the status of the centers are posted on the *Community Resources for Older Adults* Web page. Locate this page and develop a summary of the current status of resource centers supported by AOA funding. (http://www.hhs.unco.edu/geron.htm)
2. Locate the AARP (American Association of Retired Persons) home page and create a list of resources available from that Web site.
3. Using the resource list at the back of the text, locate an appropriate agency or interest group and write an analysis of (1) the description and content of the site, and (2) your evaluation of its intent and purpose.

Internet Information Resources

(AARP) American Association of Retired Persons
http://www.aarp.og/cyber/guide/1.htm
Guide to Internet Resources; includes alphabetical index.

Administration on Aging
Home page
http://www.aoa.dhhs.gov
Extensive links to other national organizations and programs.

Administration on Aging
Family Caregiver Options
http://aoa.dhhs.gov/aoa/webres
Good place for information about respite and caregiver support services. Updated frequently.

Administration on Aging
Links to Senior Centers
http://www.aoa.dhhs.gov
Selected links to various senior centers around the country. As more senior centers create their own Web pages, this site will grow.

Administration on Aging
Elder Law and Elder Abuse and Safety Page
http://wwwaoa.dhhs.gov/aoa/webres/
Legal resources for older adults.

Aging Network Services
www.ageis.com
Older adult assessment and recommendations for appropriate services.

Alliance of Information and Referral Systems (AIRS)
www.ir-net.com/airs
Access to info regarding professional development opportunities, information resources library, calendar of events.

Alzheimer's Association
www.alz.org
Home page

Alzheimer's Disease
www.biostat.wustl.edu/alzheimer
Information and discussion on AD and related dementias; Links.

Alzheimer's Disease Review
www.coa.uky.edu/ADReview
Latest research on AD.

American Association of Homes and Services for the Aging
www.seniorsites.com/aahsa
Free information on long-term care and housing for older adults.

Benefits Link
www.benefitslink.com
Free nationwide link

Canada Pension Plan
www.mb.hrdc-drhe.gc.ca/isp/retire.htm
Compare Canada's retirement pension program with the U.S. Social Security program.

Caregiver's Handbook
www.ascu.buffalo.edu/drstall/hndbkO.html
Complete caregiver's handbook; also guide to choosing a residential facility.

Community Resources for Older Adults
www.hhs.unco.edu/geron.htm
Updated changes in the OAA.

Demographics
www.intellectualcapital.com
Charts & graphs of population projections from 1995 to 2050.

East Bay (California)Elder Abuse Prevention
www.aimnet.com/oaktree/elder
Definition, recognition, who must report, and where to report. Interesting links.

ELDERWEB
www.elderweb.com
Information for caregivers and older adults. Interesting links.

ElderCare
www.eldercare-info.com
Private, nonprofit no-cost referral agency.

Emotional Support Guide
http://asa.ugl.lib.umich.edu/chdocs/support/emotion.html
Links to Griefnet and Caregiver Information, chronic illness resources and bereavement resources.

Family Caregiver Alliance
www.caregiver.org/text/index/html
Assistance to caregivers of persons with Alzheimer's, Parkinson's and other brain disorders. Interesting links to other resource centers.

Gay and Lesbian Retirement Communities
www.ourtownvillages.com/ or
www.gylesbianretiring.org/ or
www.prideworks.com/palms.htm.
Information regarding retirement communities for gay adults.

GriefNet
http://rivendell.org
Resources related to death, dying, bereavement, and major emotional and physical losses. Very good site.

Guide to Nursing Homes in Florida
http://www-wane-leon.scri.fsu.edu/AHCA/NURSDAT/index-frame.html
Tips on finding a nursing home; good resource even for the non-Floridian.

HOMECARE ON LINE
National Association for Home Care
www.nahc.org
Information about state organizations, consumer information, legislative information.

Institute of Gerontology
http://www.iog.wayne.edu
Features GERO WEB, resource for researchers, educators, practitioners. Numerous links to related sites.

Internet Resources for Caregivers
Gopher://152.160.1.32/00/resources/caregivers/careint.txt
Central listing on personal and professional caregiving.

Living Wills
http://www.twoscan.com/2s...iam/wills/main2.html
Information on living wills, legal assistance and directories and associations on advance directives.

MedAccess
www.medacces.com
Health and wellness information; Link to guide to choosing a nursing home.

MedWeb: Geriatrics
http://www.cc.emory.edu/WHSCL/medweb.geriatrics.html
From the Health Sciences Library at Emory University; links.

Mental HealthNet
www.cmhc.com
Over 4,200 individual resources on mental health issues. Worth a visit.

National Aging Information Center
www.ageinfo.org
Eldercare Locator can be obtained from this site.

National Center for Elder Abuse
(see also Elder Abuse)
www.interine.com/NCEA/indexnf.html
Information and statistics about elder abuse; links and publications listing.

National Coalition for the Homeless
http://nch.ari.net/
Online library, Internet resources of government, legislation, advocacy, and politics.

National Hospice Organization
http://nho.org
Good site; wide range of links including How to Find a Hospice.

National Senior Citizens Law Center
(see also Senior Law)

www.nsclc.org
Information on Social Security, SSI, Medicare, Medicaid, age discrimination, and mandatory retirement; Older Americans Act.

Office of Ombudsman
www.ombud.gov.bc.ca/index.html
What an Ombudsman is and how to use one; other links.

Pysch Central
www.coil.com/grohol/web.htm
Mental health information; lengthy list of support resources links.

Senior Law Home Page
www.seniorlaw.com
Specialists in elder law.

Senior Link Online
www.seniorlink.com
Elder care resource; referral and consultation for older adults, families, care providers.

Social Security Online
www.ssa.gov
Comprehensive site; visitors can request earnings record, review statistical information about benefits and beneficiaries and review information on history and legislation on Social Security.

Seniors-Site
www.seniors-site.com
Aging concerns and financial information.

U.S. Census Bureau
http//www.census.gov
U.S. Census bureau links including subjects A-Z listing

U.S. Department of Housing and Urban Development
www.hud.gov
Information about housing policy or programs.

U.S. Department of Labor
www.dol.gov
Resources and link to pension information.

Additional Internet Resources on Aging
http://lexis.pop.upenn.edu/aging/agingres.html
Listing of organizations, resources, publications, and demographic data on aging.

www.aoa.dhhs.gov/aoa/pages/jpost/st.html
Listing of Internet resources on aging

References

Abbott, D. W.; deZwaan, M.; Mussell, M. P.; Raymond, N. C.; Seim, H. C.; Crow, S. J.; Crosby, R. D.; & Mitchell, J. E. (1998). Onset of binge eating and dieting in overweight women: Implications for etiology, associated features and treatment. *Journal of psychosomatic research, 44* (3/4), 367-374.

Abel, E. K., & Sankar, A. (1995). The uses and evaluation of qualitative research: It's not what you do when you don't have data or don't know statistics. *Research on aging, 17* (1), 3-7.

Abel, S. A. (1998). Social Security retirement benefits: The last insult of a sexist society. *Family and conciliation courts review, 36* (1), 54-64.

Achenbaum, W. A., & Bengtson, V. L. (1994). Re-engaging the disengagement theory of aging. *Gerontologist, 34* (6), 756–763.

Adami, S.; Passerl, M.; & Ortolani, S. (1995). Effects of oral alendronate and intranasal salmon calcitonin in bone mass and biochemical markers of bone turnover in postmenopausal women with osteoporosis. *Bone, 17*, 383-390.

Adams, R. G. (1986). Friendship and aging. *Generations, 10,* 40-43.

Adams, R. G., & Blieszner, R. (1994). An integrative conceptual framework for friendship research. *Journal of social and personal relationships, 11,* 163-184.

Adams, R. G., & Blieszner, R. (1995). Aging well with family and friends. *American behavioral scientist, 38* (2), 209-224.

Adams, T. (1996). Informal family caregiving to older people with dementia: Research priorities for community psychiatric nursing. *Journal of advanced nursing, 24*, 703-710.

Aday, R. H., & Kano, Z. M. (1997). Attitudes toward caring for aging parents: A comparison of Laotian and US students. *Educational gerontology, 23,* 151-167.

Aday, R. H.; Sims, C. R.; & Evans, E. (1991). Youth's attitudes toward the elderly: The impact of intergenerational partners. *The journal of applied gerontology, 19* (3), 372-384.

Aday, R. H.; Sims, C. R.; McDuffie, W.; & Evans, E. (1996). Changing children's attitudes toward the elderly: The longitudinal effects of an intergenerational partners program. *Journal of research in childhood education, 10* (2), 143-151.

Adelman, R. (1987, April). A community-oriented geriatric rehabilitation unit in a nursing home. *Gerontologist, 27,* 143-146.

Ade-Ridder, L., & Kaplan, L. (1993). Marriage, spousal caregiving, and a husband's move to a nursing home. *Journal of gerontological nursing, 19* (10), 13-23.

Adkins, G.; Martin, P.; & Poon, L. W. (1996). Personality traits and states as predictors of subjective well being in centenarians, octogenarians, and sexagenerians. *Psychology and aging, 11* (3), 408-416.

Administration on Aging. (1997). *Profile of older Americans: 1997.* Program Resources Department, American Association of Retired Persons and the Administration on Aging, U.S. Department of Health and Human Services.

Aiken, L. (1994). *Dying, death, and bereavement* (3rd ed.). Boston: Allyn and Bacon.

Akiyama, H.; Elliott, K.; & Antonucci, T. C. (1996). Same-sex and cross-sex relationships. *Journal of gerontology: psychological sciences, 51B* (6), P374-382.

Alexy, B., & Belcher, J. (1997). Rural elderly present need for nursing continuity. *Nursing economics, 15* (3), 146-150.

Allain, T. J.; Matenga, J. A.; Gomo, Z.; Adamchak, D. J.; & Wilson, A. O. (1997). Determinants of happiness and life satisfaction in elderly Zimbabweans. *Central African journal of medicine, 42* (11), 308-311.

Allan, M. A. (1998). Elder abuse: A challenge for home care nurses. *Home healthcare nurse, 16* (2), 103-110.

Amenta, E.; Carruthers, B. G.; & Zylan, Y. (1992). A hero for the aged? The Townsend movement, the political mediation model, and US old-age policy, 1934-1950. *American journal of sociology, 98* (2), 308-339.

American Association of Retired Persons. (1990). *Using the experience of a lifetime.* Booklet #D13353. Washington, DC: American Association of Retired Persons.

American Association of Retired Persons. (1995). *Women's issues.* [Online]. Available at *http://www.aarp/webplace* [1997. March 30].

American Association of Retired Persons. (1997). *Profile of older Americans: 1997.* Administration on Aging, US Department of Health and Human Services, Washington, DC.

American Cancer Society. (1996). *Cancer facts and figures.* Atlanta, GA: American Cancer Society.

American Psychiatric Association. (1994). *Diagnostic and statistical manual for mental disorders (DSM-IV)* (4th ed.). Washington, DC: American Psychiatric Association.

American Psychiatric Association. (1997). Practice guidelines for the treatment of patients with schizophrenia. *American journal of psychiatry, 15* (supplement), 1-63.

American Psychological Association. (1997). *The graying of America: An aging revolution in need of a national research agenda.* Cavanaugh, J. C. & Park, D. C., co-chairs, Division 20, Vitality for Life Committee. Washington, DC.

Amir, Y. (1969). Contact hypothesis in ethnic relations. *Psychological bulletin, 71*, 319-342.

Anderson, D. C. (1997, July 13). Aging behind bars. *New York Times,* pp. 28-32.

Antonucci, T. C., & Akiyama, H. (1987). Social networks in adult life: A preliminary examination of the convoy model. *Journal of gerontology: Social sciences, S42,* 512-527.

Antonucci, T. C., & Akiyama, H. (1995). Convoys of social relations: Family and friendships within a life span context. In R. Blieszner & V. H. Bedford (Eds.), *Handbook of aging and the family.* Westport, CT: Greenwood.

Antonucci, T. C.; Fuhrer, R.; & Dartigues, J.-F. (1997). Social relations and depressive symptomatology in a sample of community-dwelling French older adults. *Psychology and aging 12* (1), 189-195.

Apple, D. D. (1956). The social structure of grandparenthood." *American anthropologist, 58,* 656–663.

Apt, N. A. (1995). Health care of the elderly in Africa: Focus on Ghana. *Caring magazine, 14* (1), 42-49.

Aquino, J. A.; Russell, D. W.; Cutrona, C. E.; & Altmaier, E. M. (1996). Employment status, social support, and life satisfaction among the elderly. *Journal of counseling psychology, 43* (6), 480-489.

Archbold, P. (1983). Impact of parent caring on women. *Family relations, 32,* 39-45.

Ardelt, M. (1997). Wisdom and life satisfaction in old age. *Journal of gerontology: Psychological sciences, 52B,* P15-P27.

Arnold, S. E., & Trojanowski, J. Q. (1996). Cognitive impairment in elderly schizophrenia: A dementia (still) lacking distinctive histopathology. *Schizophrenia bulletin, 22* (1), 5-9.

Associated Press. (1987, September 20). Elderly unpersons. *Santa Rosa Press Democrat,* pp. 1, A11.

Atchley, R. (1973). *The sociology of retirement.* Cambridge, MA: Schenkman.

Austad, S. N. (1997). *Why we age: What science is discovering about the body's journey through life.* New York: Wiley

Baba, S. (1993). The super-aged society. *World health, 46* (3), 9-11.

Bahr, Sr. R.T. (1994). An overview of gerontological nursing. In M.O. Hogstel (Ed.), *Nursing care of the older adult* (3rd ed., pp. 2-25). Albany. NY: Delmar.

Baltes, P. (1991). The many faces of human aging: Toward a psychological culture of old age. *Psychological medicine, 21,* 827-854.

Baltes, P. (1993). The aging mind: Potential and limits. *Gerontologist, 33* (5), 580–594.

Baltes, P. B., & Horgas, A. L. (1996). Long-term care institutions and the maintenance of competence. In S. L. Willis, K. W. Schaie, & M. Hayward

(Eds.), *Social mechanisms for maintaining competence in old age.* New York: Springer.

Baltes, P. B., & Lindenberger, U.(1988). Emergence of a powerful connection between sensory and cognitive functions across the adult life span: A new window to the study of cognitive aging? *Psychology and aging, 12,* 12-21.

Baltes, P. B., & Smith, J. (1990). The psychology of wisdom and its ontogenesis. In R. J. Sternberg (Ed.), *Wisdom: Its Nature, Origins, and Development* (pp. 87-120). New York: Cambridge University Press.

Bank, S. P. (1995). Before the last leaves fall: Sibling connections among the elderly. *Journal of geriatric psychology, 28* (2), 183-195.

Barazan, M. (1994). Fear of crime and its consequences among urban elderly individuals. *International journal of aging and human development, 38* (2), 99-116.

Barbato, C. A., & Freezel, J. D. (1987). The language of aging in different age groups. *Gerontologist, 27,* 527–531

Baringa, M. (1991). How long is the human life span? *Science, 254,* 936-941.

Barker, W. H. & Mullooly, J. P. (1997). Stroke in a defined elderly population, 1967-1985: A less lethal and disabling but no less common disease. *Stroke, 28* (2), 284-290.

Barrow, G. M. (1994a*). College student attitudes toward older people.* Unpublished report. Santa Rosa Community College, CA.

Barrow, G.M. (1994b). *Personal reactions to growing old.* Unpublished. Santa Rosa, CA: Santa Rosa Junior College.

Bartels, S. J.; Muester, K. T.; & Miles, K. M. (1997). Functional impairments in elderly patients with schizophrenia and major affective illness in the community: Social skills, living skills, and behavior problems. *Behavior therapy, 28,* 43-63.

Barusch, A. S. (1997). Self-concepts of low-income older women: Not old or poor, but fortunate and blessed. *International journal of aging and human development, 44* (4), 269-282.

Bash, A. (1995, February 17). Field wields clout within "Means." *USA Today*, p. 24.

Bazargan, M. (1994). The effects of health, environmental, and socio-psychological variables on fear of crime and its consequences among urban black elderly individuals. *International journal of aging and human development, 38* (2), 99-115.

Beard, B. B. (1991). *Centenarians: The new generation.* Westport, CT: Greenwood Press.

Beauvoir, S. de (1973). *The coming of age.* New York: Warner Communications Co.

Bechara, A.; Damasio, H.; Tranel, D.; & Anderson, S. W. (1998). Dissociation of working memory from decision making within the human prefrontal cortex. *The journal of neuroscience, 18* (1), 428-437.

Beck, M. (1990, July 16). Trading places. *Newsweek,* 48-54.

Beck, J. G., & Stanley, M. A. (1997). Anxiety disorders in the elderly: The emerging role of behavior therapy. *Behavior therapy, 28,* 83-100.

Bekey, M. (1991, April/May). Special report on fraud. *Modern Maturity*, 31–64.

Bellandi, D. (1997, August 25). Seniors on patrol. *Modern healthcare,* 44-45.

Belliveau, F., & Richter, L. (1970). *Understanding human sexual inadequacy.* New York: Bantam Books.

Bengtson, V.L., & Achenbaum, W.A. (1993). *The changing contract across generations.* New York: Aldine de Gruyter, Inc.

Bengtson, V. L.; Burgess, E. O.; & Barrott, T. M. (1997). Theory, explanation, and a third generation of theoretical development in social gerontology. *Journal of gerontology: Social sciences, 52B* (2), S72-S88.

Bengtson, V. L., & Dowd, J. J. (1981). Sociological functionalism, exchange theory and life-cycle analysis: A call for more explicit theoretical bridges. *International journal of aging and human development, 12* (2), 55-73.

Beresford, L. (1997). The good death. *Hospitals and health networks, 71* (12), 60-62.

Berger, M. (1987, June 15). The rush is on: Mine the "silver generations." *Business week, 52-53.*

Binstock, R. (1983). The aged as scapegoats. *Gerontologist 23,* 136–143.

Blazer, D. (1990). *Emotional problems in later life.* New York: Springer.

Blieszner, R., & Bedford, V. H. (1995). The family context of aging: Trends and challenges. In R. Blieszner & V. H. Bedford (Eds.), *Handbook of aging and the family.* Westport, CT: Greenwood.

Blouin, A. S., & Brent, N. J. (1996). Downsizing and potential discrimination based on age. *Journal of nursing administrators, 26* (11), 3-5.

Boise, L. (1991, February). *Family care of the aged in Sweden.* New York: Swedish Information Service.

Bould, S. (1989). *Eighty-five plus: The oldest old.* Belmont, CA: Wadsworth.

Bowen, J.; Teri, L.; Kukull, W.; McCormick, W.; McCurry, S. M.; & Larson, E. B. (1997). Progression to dementia in patients with isolated memory loss. *Lancet, 349,* 763-765.

Bowling, A. (1997). The effects of illness on quality of life: Findings from a survey of households in Great Britain. *Journal of epidemiology and community health, 50,* 149-155.

Bowling, A.; Grundy, E.; & Farquhar, M. (1995). Changes in network composition among the very old living in inner London. *Journal of cross-cultural gerontology, 10,* 331-347.

Boxer, A. M. (1997). Gay, lesbian, and bisexual aging into the twenty-first century: An overview and introduction. *Journal of gay, lesbian, and bisexual identity,* 2 (3/4), 187-193.

Boynton, S. (1993). Aging boomers! The graying of a generation. *Santa Rosa Press Democrat,* March 22, p. B1.

Brackley, M. H. (1994). The plight of American family caregivers: Implications for nursing. *Perspectives in psychiatric care, 30* (4), 14-20.

Braus, P. (1994, June). Groceries over grandchildren. *American demography,* 33.

Brecher, E. (1984). *Love, sex and aging: A Consumers' Union report.* Boston: Little, Brown.

Brecht, S. B. (1996). Trends in the retirement housing industry. *Urban land, 55* (11), 32-39.

Bretschneider, J., & McCoy, N. (1988). Sexual interest and behavior in healthy 80 to 102 year olds. *Archives of sexual behavior, 17* (2), 102-129.

Brignolo, D. (1998, March 10). Investment fiasco ends in sentencing. *San Jose Mercury News,* 1B.

Brody, E. (1984). Caregivers, daughters and their local siblings: Perceptions, strains, and interactions. *Gerontologist, 29* (4), 529-538.

Brody, E. (1985). *Women in the middle: Their parent care years.* New York: Springer.

Brown, A. S. & Nix, L. A. (1996). Age-related changes in tip-of-the-tongue experience. *American journal of psychology, 109* (1), 79-91.

Brown, R. (1993). Do health maintenance organizations work for Medicare? *Health care financing review, 15* (1), 7-24.

Bryant, H., & Fernald, L. (1997). Nursing knowledge and use of restraint alternatives: Acute and chronic care. *Geriatric nursing, 18* (2), 57-60.

Buckwalter, J. A. (1997). Decreased mobility in the elderly: The exercise antidote. *The physician and sportsmedicine, 25* (9), 127-133.

Buckwalter, J. A.; Woo, S. L.; & Goldberg, V. M. (1993). Current concepts review: Soft-tissue aging and musculoskeletal function. *Journal of bone and joint surgery, 75* (10), 1533-1548.

Buhrich, N. & Teesson, M. (1996). Impact of a psychiatric outreach service for homeless persons with schizophrenia. *Psychiatric services, 47* (6), 644-646.

Bureau of Justice Statistics. (1992). *Criminal victimization in the United States, 1991.* Washington, DC: US Government Printing Office.

Burger, J. M.; Horita, M.; Kinoshita, L.; Roberts, K.; & Vera, C. (1997). Effects of time on the norm of reciprocity. *Basic and applied social psychology 19* (1), 91-100.

Burke, J. L. (1981). Young children's attitudes and perceptions of older adults. *International journal of aging and human development, 14,* 205-221.

Burkhauser, R. V. (1996). Editorial. Touching the third rail: Time to return the retirement age for early social security benefits to 65. *The gerontologist, 36* (6), 726-727.

Burkhauser, R. V.; Couch, K. A.; & Phillips, J. W. (1996). Who takes early Social Security benefits? The economic and health characteristics of early beneficiaries. *The gerontologist, 36* (6), 789-799.

Burkhauser, R. V.; Duncan, G. J.; & Hauser, R. (1994). Sharing prosperity across the age distribution: A comparison of the United States and Germany in the 1980s. *The gerontologist, 34* (2), 150-160.

Burl, M. R. (1993). *Hunger among the elderly: Local and national comparisons.* Washington, DC: The Urban Institute.

Burn, T. (1997). But seniors have the hardest time. *Insight on the news, 13* (41), 43.

Burnette, D. (1998). Grandparents rearing grandchildren: A school-based small group intervention. *Research on social work practice, 8* (1), 10-27.

Busan, T. (1991). *Use your perfect memory.* New York: Plume Division, Penguin Books.

Butler, R. N. (1981). Ageism: A forward. *Journal of social issues, 36,* 8-11.

Butler, S. S., & DePoy, E. (1996). Rural elderly women's attitudes toward professional and governmental assistance. *AFFILIA, 11* (1), 76-94.

Butler, R., & Lewis, M. I. (1991). *Aging and mental health.* New York: Macmillan.

Calabrese, R. L. & Barton, A. M. (1995). Mexican-American male students and Anglo female teachers: Victims of the policies of assimilation. *The high school journal, 78* (3), 115-123.

Calasanti, T. M. (1996). Incorporating diversity: Meaning, levels of research and implications for theory. *The gerontologist, 36* (2), 147-156.

California law firm settles age-bias suit. (1997, August 7). *Wall Street Journal,* p. A4(W).

Camp, C., & Camp, G. (1996). *The corrections yearbook*. South Salem, NY: Criminal Justice Institute.

Campbell, J. (1992). *How policies change: The Japanese government and the aging society.* Princeton, NJ: Princeton University Press.

Carr, M. (1997). Not at your age! *Accountancy—International Edition, 41.*

Carstensen, L.; Mason, S.E.; & Caldwell, E. C. (1982). Children's attitudes toward the elderly: An intergenerational technique for change. *Educational gerontology, 8*, 291-301.

Cassel, C. K. (1996). Overview on attitudes of physicians toward caring for the dying patient. In American Board of Internal Medicine (Ed.), *Caring for the dying: Identification and promotion of physician competency*. Washington, DC: AMA.

Cavanaugh, J. (1993). *Adult Development*. Pacific Grove, CA: Brooks/Cole.

Census Population Statistics (1996). *Annual demographic survey, March supplement.* US Bureau of the Census. Washington, DC: US Government Printing Office.

Centers for Disease Control and Prevention (1996). *Suicide among older persons—United States, 1980-1992.* US Department of Health and Human Services *MMWR, 45* (1), 3-6.

Ceridian, Control Data Systems settle age bias lawsuits (1997, March 6). *Wall Street Journal,* P13.

Chappell, N. (1991). Living arrangements and sources of caregiving. *Journals of gerontology, 46* (1), S1-S8.

Chatard, J.-C.; Boutet, C.; Tourny, C.; Garcia, S.; Berthouze, S.; & Guezennec, C.-Y. (1998). *European journal of applied physiology, 77* (1/2), 157-163.

Chestnut, C. H.; McClung, M. R.; & Ensrud, K. E. (1995). Alendronate treatment of the postmenopausal osteoporotic woman: Effect of multiple dosages on bone mass and bone remodeling. *American journal of medicine, 99,* 144-152.

Chew, S. C. (1962). *The pilgrimage of life*. New Haven, CT: Yale University Press.

Chodzko-Zajko, W. (1997). Translating theory in practice—a formidable challenge for the future. *Journal of aging and physical activity, 5,* 283-284.

Choi, N. G. (1994a). Changes in labor force activities and income of the elderly before and after retirement: A longitudinal analysis. *Journal of sociology and social welfare, 21* (2), 5-26.

Choi, N. G. (1994b). Pattern and determinants of social service utilization: Comparison of the childless elderly and elderly parents living with or apart from their children. *The gerontologist, 34* (3), 353-362.

Choi, N. G. (1996). Changes in the living arrangements, work patterns, and economic status of middle-aged single women: 1971-1991. *Affilia, 11* (2), 164-178.

Choi, N. G., & Wodarski, J. S. (1996). The relationship between social support and health status of elderly people: Does social support slow down physical and functional deterioration? *Social work research, 20* (1), 52-63.

Cicirelli, V. G. (1981). Kin relationships of childless and one-child elderly in relation to social services. *Journal of gerontological social work, 4* (1), 19-33.

Clark, D. E.; Knapp, T. A.; & White, N. E. (1996, Summer). Personal and location-specific characteristics and elderly interstate migration. *Growth and change, 27,* 327-351.

Cloninger, S. C. (1996). *Theories of personality: Understanding persons* (2nd ed.). Upper Saddle River, NJ: Prentice Hall.

Cohen, E., & Kruschwitz, A. (1990). Old age in America represented in nineteenth and twentieth century popular sheet music. *The gerontologist, 30* (3), 354-354.

Cohen, H. J. (1997). Cancer and the functional status of the elderly. *Cancer, 80* (10), 1883-1886.

Cohen, L. D., & Adler, N. E. (1992). Female and male perceptions of ideal body shapes. *Psychology of women quarterly, 16, 69-79.*

Cole, T. (1992). *The journey of life: A cultural history of aging in America.* New York: Cambridge University Press.

Collins, C., & Frantz, D. (1994, June). Let us prey: Cults and the elderly. *Modern maturity,* 22–26.

Colsher, P. (1992, June). Health status of older male prisoners. *American journal of public health, 82* (6), 881.

Comfort, A. (1976, November/December). Age prejudice in America. *Sociology policy, 17,* 3-8.

Commonwealth Fund (1993, November). *The untapped resource: Americans over 55 at work.* New York: Commonwealth Fund.

Computer World (1997, October 20). Silicon shame, *31* (42), 36.

Connidis, I. (1994). Sibling support in old age. *Journal of gerontology, 49,* 5309–5317.

Connidis, I., & Campbell, L. D. (1995). Closeness, confiding, and contact among siblings in middle and late adulthood. *Journal of family issues, 16* (6), 722-745.

Cook, E. A. (1997). The effects of reminiscence on psychological measures of ego integrity in elderly nursing home residents. *Archives of psychiatric nursing, 5* (5), 292-298.

Cooper, M. H. (1998). Caring for the elderly. *Congressional quarterly, 8* (7), 147-166.

Corbin, D. E.; Metal-Corbin, J.; & Barg, C. (1989). Teaching about aging in the elementary school: A one-year follow-up. *Educational gerontology, 15*, 103-110.

Corder, E. H.; Saundres, A. M.; & Strittmatter, W. J. (1993). Gene dose of apolipoprotein E type 4 allele and the risk of Alzheimer's disease in late onset families. *Science, 261*, 921-923.

Costa, P. T., & McCrae, R. R. (1987). The case for personality stability. In G. Maddox & E. Busse (Eds.), *Aging, the universal human experience.* New York: Springer.

Costa, P. T.; Metter, E. J.; & McCrae, R. R. (1994). Personality stability and its contribution to successful aging. *Journal of gerontological psychology, 27* (1), 41-59.

Council on Scientific Affairs, American Medical Association (1996). Council report: Alcoholism in the elderly. *Journal of the American medical association, 275* (10), 797-801.

Courneya, K. S. (1995). Understanding readiness for regular physical activity in older individuals: An application of the theory of planned behavior. *Health psychology, 14* (1), 80-87.

Courtenay, B. C.; Poon, L. W.; Martin, P.; Clayton, G. M.; & Johnson, M. A. (1992). Religiosity and adaptation in the oldest-old. *International journal of aging and human development, 34* (1), 47-56.

Covey, H. C. (1988). Historical terminology used to represent older people. *Gerontologist, 28*, 291-297.

Covey, H. C. (1991). Old age and historical examples of the miser. *The gerontologist, 31* (5), 573-678.

Coward, R. T., Cutler, S. J., Lee, G. R., Danigelis, N. L., & Netzer, J. (1996). Racial differences in the household composition of elders by age, gender, and area of residence. *International journal of aging and human development, 42* (3), 205-227.

Cowgill, D. & Holmes, L. (1972). *Aging and modernization.* New York: Appleton-Century-Crofts.

Cowley, M. (1980). *The view from eighty.* New York, Viking Press.

Cox, H. (1990). Roles for the aged individuals in post-industrial societies. *International journal of aging and human development, 3* (1), 55-62.

Crandall, R. C. (1980). *Gerontology: A behavioral approach.* Reading, MA: Addison Wesley.

Crane, M. (1994). Elderly homeless people: Elusive subjects and slippery concepts. *Aging and society, 14*, 631-640.

Crenshaw, A. (1992, September 27). Living trusts lure some people not to be trusted. *Washington Post,* pp. H3.

Crispell, D. (1993, September 13). Rank of older wives swell in work force. *Wall Street Journal*, pp. B1 (W), B11 (E).

Crockett, W., & Hummert, M. L. (1987). Perceptions of aging and the elderly. In B. A. Maher (Ed.), *Progress in experimental personality research, Vol. 2* (pp. 217-241). New York: Academic Press.

Cronk, M. (1998, March 21). Thief poses as Cupertino City worker, steals cash. *San Jose Mercury News,* p. 2B.

Crystal, S., & Beck, P. (1992, October). A room of one's own: The SRO and the single elderly. *Gerontologist, 32* (5), 684-692.

Crystal, S., & Shea, D. (1990). Cumulative advantage, cumulative disadvantage, and inequality among elderly people." *The gerontologist, 30* (4), 437–443.

Cumming, E., & Henry, W. E. (1961). *Growing old: The process of disengagement.* New York: Basic Books.

Cummins, R. A. (1996). The domains of life satisfaction: An attempt to order chaos. *Social indicators research, 38*, 303-328.

Cunningham, C. M.; Callahan, C. M.; Plucker, J. A.; Roberson, S. C.; & Rapkin, A. (1998). Identifying Hispanic students of outstanding talent: Psychometric integrity of a peer nomination form. *Exceptional children, 645* (2), 197-209.

Cutler, N. (1997). *Generations, 21* (2), 5-8.

Cyr, D. (1996). Lost and found: Retired employees. *Personnel journal, 75* (11), 40-46.

Dai, Y.-T., & Dimond, M. F. (1998). Filial piety: A cross-cultural comparison and its implications for the well-being of older parents. *Journal of gerontological nursing, 24* (3), 13-18.

D'Augelli, A. R., & Garnets, L. D. (1995). Lesbian, gay, and bisexual communities. In A. R. D'Augelli & C. J. Patterson (Eds.), *Lesbian, gay and bisexual identities over the lifespan: Psychological perspectives.* New York: Oxford University Press.

Daniels, W. (1997). "Derelicts," recurring misfortunate, economic hard times and lifestyle choices: Judicial images of homeless litigants and implications for legal advocates. *Buffalo law review, 45* (3), 687-736.

Davidson, M.; Harvey, P. D.; Powchick, P.; Parrella, M.; White, L.; Knobler, H. Y.; Losonczy, M. F.; Keefe, R. S.; Katz, S.; & Frecska, E. (1995). Severity of symptoms in chronically institutionalized geriatric schizophrenic patients. *American journal of psychiatry, 152,* 197-207.

Dawson, K. (1982). *Serving the older community.* Sex Education and Information Council of the United States, Report No. SIECUS Report.

Day, N. E. (1993). Performance in salespeople: The impact of age. *Journal of managerial issues, 5,* 254-278.

Debats, D. L.; van der Lubbe, P. M.; & Wezeman, F. R. A. (1993). On the psychometric properties of the Life Regard Index (LRI): A measure of meaningful life. An evaluation in three independent samples based on the Dutch version. *Personality and individual differences, 14,* 337-345.

Deets, H. B. (1993). The media and the marketplace: A new vision of aging. *Vital speeches, 50* (5), 134.

Delany, S. L., with Hearth, A. H. (1997). *On my own at 107: Reflections on life without Bessie.* San Francisco: Harper.

Denis, M. (1996). Implications of offering early retirement benefits in exchange for a release from employment claims. *Employment relations today, 23* (3), 65-69.

Denney, N. W., & Palmer, A. A. M. (1987). Adult age differences in traditional and practical problem solving measures. *Psychology and aging, 4,* 438-442.

DeParle, J. (1994). Build single room occupancy hotels. *The Washington monthly,* 52-53.

Department of Health and Human Services (DHHS) (1997). *An overview of nursing homes and their current residents: Data from the 1995 national nursing home survey.* Public Health Service 97-1250, Report 280.

D'Epiro, N. W. (1996, November). Treating Alzheimer's disease: Today and tomorrow. *Patient care,* 62-83.

de Rijk, M. C.; Breteler, M. M. B.; Graveland, G. A.; Ott, A.; Grobbee, D. E.; van der Meche, F. G. A.; & Hofman, A. (1995). Prevalence of Parkinson's disease in the elderly: The Rotterdam study. *Neurology, 45,* 2143-2146.

DeSpelder, L. A., & Strickland, D. L. (1991). *The last dance.* Mountain View, CA: Mayfield Press.

Devitt, T. (1991, September/October). Staying young. *On Wisconsin magazine,* 21-26.

Devlin, S. J., & Arye, L. (1997). The Social Security debate: A financial crisis or a new retirement paradigm? *Generations, 21* (2), 27-33.

Devons, C. A. J. (1996). Suicide in the elderly: How to identify and treat patients at risk. *Geriatrics, 51* (3), 67-72.

DeVries, H. (1991, December 8). An interview with Cher. *San Francisco Chronicle,* p. 37 (Datebook).

Diamond, T. H.; Thornley, S. W.; Sekel, R.; & Smeraely, P. (1997). Hip fracture in elderly men: Prognostic factors and outcomes. *Medical journal of Australia, 167* (8), 412-415.

Dolliver, R. H. (1994). Classifying the personality theories and personalities of Adler, Freud, and Jung with introversion/extraversion. *Individual psychology, 50* (2), 192-202.

Dolnick, E. (1991, July 16). The mystery of superwoman. *San Francisco Chronicle,* pp. 3-8.

Dorfman, R. (1994). *Aging into the 21st century: The exploration of aspirations and values.* New York: Brunner/Mazel.

Dowd, J. J. (1975). Aging as exchange: A preface to theory. *Journal of gerontology, 30,* 584-594.

Dowd, J. (1984). Beneficence and the aged. *Journal of gerontology, 39,* 102-108.

Downe-Wamboldt, B. L. & Melanson, P. M. (1990). Attitudes of baccalaureate student nurses toward aging and the aged: Results of a longitudinal study. *Educational gerontology, 16,* 49-57.

Drench, M. E. & Losee, R. H. (1996). Sexuality and sexual capacities of elderly people. *Rehabilitation nursing, 21* (3), 118-123.

Drozdiak, W. (1994, May 3). Elderly Dutch reach for political power in "granny revolution." *Washington Post,* p. A16

Duffield, P. & Podzamsky, J. E. (1996). The completion of advance directives in primary care. *The journal of family practice, 42* (4), 378-383.

Duffy, J. M. (1987). *The measurement of service productivity and related contextual factors in long-term care facilities.* Unpublished doctoral dissertation, University of Texas, Austin.

Dychtwald, K. (1989). *Age wave.* Los Angeles, CA: Tarcher.

Ekstrom, M. (1994). Elderly people's experiences of housing renewal and forced relocation: Social theories and contextual analysis in explanations of emotional experiences. *Housing studies, 9* (3), 369-391.

Elder, G., & Liker, J. (1982). Hard times in women's lives: Historical influences across forty years. *American journal of sociology,* 241-267.

Encandela, J. A. (1997). Social construction of pain and aging: Individual artfulness within interpretive structures. *Symbolic interaction 20* (3), 251-273.

Ensrud, K. E.; Lipschutz, R. C.; Cauley, J. A.; Seeley, D.; Nevitt, M. C.; Scott, J.; Orwoll, E. S.; Genant, H. K.; & Cummings, S. R. (1997). Body size and hip fracture risk in older women: A prospective study. *The American journal of medicine, 103* (4), 274-280.

Erikson, E. (1963). *Childhood and society* (2d ed.). New York: Norton.

Erikson, E. (1966). Eight ages of man. *International journal of psychiatry, 2,* 281–297.

Erikson, E. (1982). *The life cycle completed.* New York: W. W. Norton.

Estes, C. L. (1993). The aging enterprise revisited." *The gerontologist 33* (3), 292–298.

Estes, C. L., & Binney, E. (1989). The biomedicalization of aging," *Gerontologist 29,* 586–589.

Estrada, L. (1994, May 9). At the dawn of assisted living centers. *Washington Post,* p. WB11.

Ettner, S. (1997). Medicaid participation among the eligible elderly. *Journal of policy analysis and management, 16* (2), 237-255.

Euler, B. (1992). A flaw in gerontological assessment: The weak relationship of elderly superficial life satisfaction to deep psychological well being. *International journal of aging and human development, 34,* 299-310.

Evans, M. (1998, March 27). Caregiving daughters suffer stress. *Santa Rosa Press Democrat,* p. A13.

Evans, W., & Rosenberg, I. H. (1991). *Biomarkers: The 10 determinants of aging you can control.* New York: Simon & Schuster.

Featherman, D. L.; Smith, J.; & Peterson, J. G. (1990). Successful aging in a 'post-retired' society. In P. B. Baltes & M. M. Baltes (Eds.), *Successful aging: Perspectives from the behavioral sciences* (pp. 50-93). New York: Cambridge University Press.

Feder, J.; Lambrew, J.; & Huckaby, M. (1997).Medicaid and long-term care for the elderly: Implications of restructuring. *The milbank quarterly, 75* (4), 425-459.

Fehring, R. J.; Miller, J. F.; & Shaw, C. (1997). Spiritual well-being, religiosity, hope, depression, and other mood states in elderly people coping with cancer. *Oncology nursing forum, 24* (4), 663-671.

Feldman, P. (1993). Work life improvements for home care workers: Impact and feasibility. *The gerontologist,* 47-54.

Feldstein, I. (1970). *Sex in later life.* Baltimore, MD: Penguin Books.

Feldstein, M. (1997). The case for privatization. *Foreign affairs,* 24-38.

Ferraro, K. F. (1992). Cohort changes in images of older adults, 1974-1981. *The gerontologist, 32,* 296-304.

Field, D. (1991). Continuity and change in personality in old age—evidence from five longitudinal studies: Introduction to a special issue. *Journal of gerontology: Psychological sciences, 46* (6), P271-274.

Field, D. (1993, November). *Looking back, what period of your life brought you the most satisfaction?* Paper presented to the Annual Gerontological society meeting, New Orleans, LA

Finch, C. E. & Pike, M. C. (1996). Maximum life span predictions from the Compartz mortality model. *Journal of Gerontology: Biological Sciences, 51B,* B183-B194.

Fischer, D. H. (1977). *Growing old in America.* New York: Oxford University Press.

Fisk, J. E., & Warr, P. (1996). Age and working memory: The role of perceptual speed, the central executive, and the phonological loop. *Psychology and aging, 11* (2), 316-323.

Fiske, M., & Chriboga, D. (1990). *Change and continuity in adult life.* San Francisco, CA: Jossey-Bass.

Fleeson, W., & Heckhausen, J. (1997). More or less "me" in past, present, and future: Perceived lifetime personality during adulthood. *Psychology and aging, 12* (1), 125-136.

Foley, K.T., & Mitchell, S. J. (1997). The elderly driver: What physicians need to know. *Cleveland clinic journal of medicine, 64* (8) 423-428.

Foner, A. (1996). Age norms and the structure of consciousness: Some final comments. *The gerontologist, 36* (2), 221-223.

Forrester, J. S., & Shah, P. (1997). Using serum cholesterol as a screening test for preventing coronary heart disease: The five fundamental flaws of the American College of Physicians' guidelines. *The American journal of cardiology, 79* (6), 790-792.

Fowles, D. G. (1995). *A profile of older Americans, 1995.* Washington, DC: American Association of Retired Persons and US Department of Health and Human Services Administration on Aging.

Frolik, L. A. (1996). The special housing needs of older persons: An essay. *Stetson law review, 26* (2), 647-666.

Frost, J. C. (1997). Group psychotherapy with the aging gay male: Treatment of choice. *Group, 21* (3), 267-285.
Fuller-Thomson, E.; Minkler, M.; & Driver, D. (1997). A profile of grandparents raising grandchildren in the United States. *The gerontologist, 37* (3), 406-411.
Fullmer, H. T. (1984). Children's descriptions of an attitude toward the elderly. *Educational gerontology, 10*, 22-107.
Gall, T. L.; Evans, D. R.; & Howard, J. (1997). The retirement adjustment process: Changes in the well-being of male retirees across time. *The journal of gerontology: Psychological sciences, 52B* (3), P110-P117.
Garber, A. M.; Browner, W. S.; & Hulley, S. B. (1996). Cholesterol screening in asymptomatic adults, revisited. *Annals of internal medicine, 1224*, 518-531.
Garfein, A. J. & Herzog, R. A. (1995). Robust aging among the young-old, old-old, and oldest-old. *Journal of gerontology, 50B* (2), 577-587.
Garrard, J.; Cooper, S. L.; Goertz, C. (1997). Drug use management in board and care facilities. *The gerontologist, 37* (6), 748-756.
George, L. K. (1997). Choosing among established assessment tools: Scientific demands and practical constraints. *Generations, 21* (1), 32-36.
Gerstner, C. R. & Day, D. V. (1997). Meta-analytic review of leader-member exchange theory: Correlates and construct issues. *Journal of applied psychology, 82* (6), 827-844.
Gibson, R. (1993). Reconceptualizing retirement for black Americans. In E. Stoller & R. Gibson (Eds.), *Worlds of difference*. Thousand Oaks, CA: Pine Forge Press.
Gilleard, C., & Gurkan, A. (1987). Socioeconomic development and status of elderly men in Turkey: A test of modernization theory. *Journal of gerontology, 42* (7), 353-357.
Glasheen, L. (1994, June). Mobile homes. *Bulletin of the American association of retired persons*, 1-16.
Glass, J. C., Jr., & Jolly, G. R. (1997). Satisfaction in later life among women 60 or older. *Educational gerontology* 23, 297-314.
Glazer, B., & Strauss, A. (1996). *Awareness of dying*. Chicago: Aldine Publishing.
Glen, N. D, & Weaver, C. N. (1983-1984). Enjoyment of work by full-time workers in the US: 1955-1980. *Public opinion quarterly, 46*, 459-470.
Gliksman, M. D.; Lazarus, R.; Wilson, A.; & Leeder, S. R. (1995). Social support, marital status and living arrangement correlates of cardiovascular disease risk factors in the elderly. *Social science and medicine, 40* (6), 811-814.
Goering, P.; Wasylenki, D.; Lindsay, C.; Lemire, D.; & Rhodes, A. (1997). Process and outcome in a hostel outreach program for homeless clients with severe mental illness. *American journal of orthopsychiatry, 67* (4), 607-617.
Golant, S. M. (1994). Housing quality of U.S. elderly households: Does aging in place matter? *Gerontologist, 34* (6), 803-814.
Golant, S. M., & LaGreca, A. J. (1994). Differences in the housing quality of white, black, and Hispanic US elderly households. *The journal of applied gerontology, 13* (4), 413-437.
Gold, D. (1990, March). Relationship classification: A typology of sibling relationships in later life. *Journal of gerontology, 45* (2), S43-S51.
Golberg, L.; Gallagher, T. C.; Anderson, R. M.; Koegel, P. (1997). Competing priorities as a barrier to medical care among homeless adults in Los Angeles. *American journal of public health, 87*, 217-221.
Gold, D. P.; Andres, D.; Etezadi, J.; Arbuckle, T.; Schwartzman, A.; & Chikelson, J. (1995). Structural equation model of intellectual change and continuity and predictors of intelligence in older men. *Psychology and aging, 10* (2), 294-303.
Goldbourt, U. (1997). Physical activity, long-term CHD, mortality and longevity: A review of studies over the last 30 years. *World review of nutrition and dietetics, 82*, 229-239.
Goldman, N.; Korenman, S.; & Weinstein, R. (1995). Marital status and health among the elderly. *Social science and medicine, 40* (12), 1717-1730.
Goldman, R. J. & Goldman, J. D. (1981). How children view old people and aging: A developmental study of children in four countries. *Australian journal of psychology, 33* (3), 405-418.
Goldstein, K. (1980). *Language and language disturbances*. New York: Grune & Stratton.
Goldstein, M. (1983). Social and economic forces affecting intergenerational relations in extended families in a third world country: A cautionary tale from South Asia. *Journal of gerontology, 38* (11), 716-724.
Goldstein, M. Z.; Pataki, A.; & Webb, M. T. (1996). Alcoholism among elderly persons. *Psychiatric services, 47* (9), 941-943.
Gouldner, A. (1960). The norm of reciprocity: A preliminary statement. *American sociological review, 25*, 161-178.

Graham, J. E.; Rockwood, K.; Beattie, B. L.; Eastwood, R.; Gauthier, S.; Tukko, H.; & McDowell, I. (1997). Prevalence and severity of cognitive impairment with and without dementia in an elderly population. *Lancet, 349,* 1793-96.

Greco, A. J. & Swayne, L. E. (1992, September/October). Sales response of elderly consumers to point-of-purchase advertising. *Journal of advertising research,* 43-53.

Greenberg, J. (1993). Aging parents of adults with disabilities: gratifications and frustrations. *The gerontologist, 32,* 542-550.

Gruen, R. J.; Silva, R.; Ehrlich, J.; Schweitzer, J. W.; & Friedhoff, A. J. (1997). Vulnerability to stress: Self-criticism and stress-induced changes in biochemistry. *Journal of personality, 65* (1), 33-47.

Gubrium, J. F. (1975). *Living and dying at Murray Manor.* New York: St. Martin's Press.

Gubrium, J. F. & Holstein, J. A. (1995). Life course malleability: Biographical work and deprivatization. *Sociological inquiry, 65* (2), 207-223.

Guilford, J. P. (1966). Intelligence: 1965 model. *American psychologist, 21,* 20-26.

Guillemard, A.-M. & Rein, M. (1993). Comparative patterns of retirement: Recent trends in developed societies. *Annual review of sociology, 19,* 469-503.

Gutmann, D. L. (1987) *Reclaimed powers: Toward a new psychology of men and women in later life.* New York: Basic Books.

Gutmann, D. L. (1992). Toward a dynamic geropsychology. In J. Birren, M. Eagle, and D. Welitzky (Eds.), *Interface of psychoanalysis and psychology*, Washington, DC: American Psychological Association.

Gutmann, D. L. (1997). The cross-cultural perspective: Notes toward a comparative psychology of aging. In J. E. Birren and K. W. Schaie (Eds.), *Handbook of the psychology of aging.* New York: Van Nostrand Reinhold.

Guyotte, R. L. (1997). Generation gap: Filipinos, Filipino Americans and Americans, here and there, then and now. *Journal of American ethnic history, 17* (1), 64-70.

Haber, C. (1983*). Beyond sixty-five: The dilemma of old age in America's past.* New York: Cambridge University Press.

Hagenaars, A., & de Vos, K. (1988). The definition and measurement of poverty. *Journal of human resources, 23,* 211-221.

Haight, B. K. (1996). Suicide risk in frail elderly people relocated to nursing homes. *Geriatric nursing, 16* (5), 104-107.

Hardy, M. A. ; Hazelrigg, L. E.; & Quadagno, J. S. (1996)*. Ending a career in the auto industry: Thirty and out.* New York: Plenum.

Hardy, M. A., & Quadagno, J. S. (1995).Satisfaction with early retirement: Making choices in the auto industry. *Journal of gerontology: social sciences, 50* (4), S217-228.

Harman, D. (1995). Free radical theory of aging: Alzheimer's disease pathogenesis. *Age, 18* (3), 97-119.

Harper, L. (1994, June 28). Young-at-heart retirees work at amusement parks. *Wall Street Journal,* pp. A1 (W), A1 (E).

Harris, M. B. (1994). Growing old gracefully: Age concealment and gender. *Journal of gerontology: Psychological sciences, 49,* 149-158.

Harris, P. (1993) The misunderstood caregiver? A qualitative study of the male caregiver. *The gerontologist, 32, 551-556.*

Hashimoto, A. (1992). Aging in Japan. In D. Phillips (Ed.), *Aging in East and Southeast Asia.* London: Edward Arnold Publishing.

Hashizume, Y., & Kanagawa, K. (1996). Correlates of participation in adult day care and quality of life in ambulatory frail elderly in Japan. *Public health nursing, 13* (6), 404-415.

Hass, C., & Selkoe, D. J. (1998). A technical KO of amayloid-B peptide. *Nature, 391 (2),* 339-340.

Hassell, B. L. & Perrewe, P. (1995). An examination of beliefs about older workers: Do stereotypes still exist? *Journal of organizational behavior, 16* (5), 457-468.

Havighurst, R. J. (1972). *Developmental tasks and education* (3rd ed.). New York: McKay.

Hawkins, B. A.; Kim, K.-a.; & Eklund, S. J. (1995). Validity and reliability of a five dimensional life satisfaction index. *Mental retardation, 33* (5), 294-303.

Haynor, P. (1998). Meeting the challenge of advance directives. *American journal of nursing, 98* (3), 26-32.

Hays, J. C.; Gold, D. T.; Pieper, C. F. (1997). Sibling bereavement in late life. *Omega, 36* (1), 25-42.

Health Care Financing Administration. (1990). *Program statistics: Medicare and Medicaid data book.* Publication No. 03314. Washington, DC: Health Care Financing Administration.

Health Care Financing Administration. (1996). *1996 HCFA statistics.* Publication No. 03394. Washington, DC: Health Care Financing Administration.

Heath, J. M. (1993). Outpatient management of chronic bronchitis in the elderly. *American family physician, 48* (5), 841-848.

Heckhausen, J.; Dixon, R. A.; & Baltes, P. B. (1989). Losses in development throughout adulthood as perceived by different adult age groups. *Developmental psychology, 25*, 109-21.
Hedin, B. (1993). *Growing old in Sweden.* Stockholm: The Swedish Institute.
Heidrich, S. L., & Ryff, C. D. (1993). The role of social comparisons processes in the psychological adaptation of elderly adults. *Journal of gerontology: Psychological sciences, P48,* 127-136.
Hein, H. O.; Suadicani, P.; Sorensen, H.; & Gyntelberg, F. (1994). Changes in physical activity level and risk of ischemic heart disease. *Scandinavian journal of medicine and science in sports, 4,* 52-64.
Hendricks, J. (1995). Exchange theory in aging. In G. Maddox (Ed.), *The encyclopedia of aging* (2nd ed.). New York: Springer.
Herdt, G.; Beeler, J.; & Rawls, T. (1997). Understanding the identities of older lesbians and gay men: A study in Chicago. *Journal of gay, lesbian, and bisexual identity,* 2 (3/4), 231-245.
Hevesi, D. (1994, March 27). Anger wins out over fear of a gang. *New York Times,* p. 31 (L).
Heynen, J. (1990). *One hundred over 100.* Golden, CO: Fulcrum Publishing.
Hickey, N. (1990, October 20). Its audience is aging...So why is TV still chasing the kids? *TV Guide*, pp. 22-24.
Hillman, J., & Stricker, G.(1996). Predictors of college students' knowledge of an attitudes toward elderly sexuality: The relevance of grandparental contact. *Educational gerontology, 22,* 539-555.
Hilt, M. L., & Lipschultz, J. H. (1996). Broadcast news and elderly people: Attitudes of local television managers. *Educational gerontology, 22,* 669-682.
Hinrichsen, G. (1985). The impact of age-concentrated, publicly-assisted housing on older people's social and emotional well-being. *Journal of gerontology, 40,* 758-760.
Hobbs, F. B., with Damon, B. L. (1996). *65+ in the United States.* [Online]. Available at ***http://www.census.gov/prod/1/pop/p23-190/p23190-k.pdf.***
Hoefler, J. (1994). *Deathright: Culture, medicine, politics and the right to die.* Boulder, CO: Westview Press.
Hogan, R., & Nicholson, R. A. (1988). The meaning of personality test scores. *American psychologist, 43*, 621-626.
Holden, K. C. & Kuo, H.-H. D. (1996). Complex marital histories and economic well-being: The continuing legacy of divorce and widowhood as the HRS cohort approaches retirement. *The gerontologist, 36* (3), 383-390.
Holding, R. (1991, September 12). 'Help! I've fallen' firm sued. *San Francisco Chronicle,* p. A19.
Holliday, R. (1996). The current status of the protein error theory of aging. *Experimental gerontology, 31* (4), 449-452.
Holliday, S. G., & Chandler, M. J. (1986). Wisdom: Explorations in adult competence. In J. A. Meacham (Ed.), *Contributions to human development (vol. 17),* (pp. 1-96).
Holmes, T., & Rahe, R. (1967). The Social Readjustment Rating Scale. *Journal of psychosomatic research*, 213-218.
Holstein, M. (1995). Qualitative gerontology: Methodology and meaning. *Research on aging, 17* (1), 114-116.
Hong, L. K. & Duff, R. W. (1997). Relative importance of spouses, children and friends in the life satisfaction of retirement community residents. *Journal of clinical geropsychology, 3* (4), 275-282.
Hooker, K. (1994). Personality and coping among caregivers of spouses with dementia. *The gerontologist,* 386-392.
Hooyman, N., & Kiyak, H. A. (1996). *Social Gerontology: A multidisciplinary perspective.* Boston: Allyn and Bacon.
Hope, T. (1997). Aging, research and families. *Journal of medical ethics, 23*, 267-268.
Horgan, J. (1997, May). Seeking a better way to die. *Scientific American,* 100-105.
Hosen, R. (1996). The benign comparison scale and its relevance to subjective well-being research. *Psychology: A journal of human behavior, 33* (2), 63-67.
Hostetler, A. J., & Cohler, B. J. (1997). Partnership, singlehood, and the lesbian and gay life course: A research agenda. *Journal of gay, lesbian, and bisexual identity,* 2 (3-4), 199-230.
Hoyert, D. L., & Rosenberg, H. M. (1997). Alzheimer's disease as a cause of death in the United States. *Public health reports, 112,* 497-505.
Huang, B.; Rodreiguez, B. L.; Burchfiel, C. M.; Chyou, P.-H; Curb, J. D.; & Sharp, D. S. (1997). Associations of adiposity with prevalent coronary heart disease among elderly men: The Honolulu heart program. *International journal of obesity and research, 21* (5), 340-348.
Hubbard, P. (1992, December). Seniors for justice. *Gerontologist, 32* (6), 856-858.
Hueston, W. J.; Mainous, A. G. III; Schilling, R. (1996). Patients with personality disorders: Functional status, health care utilization, and

satisfaction with care. *The journal of family practice, 42* (1), 54-60.
Hugo, G. (1992). Aging in Indonesia. In D. Phillips (Ed.), *Aging in East and South-East Asia.* London: Edward Arnold Publishing.
Hummert, M. L. (1993). Age and typicality judgments of stereotypes of the elderly: Perceptions of elderly vs. young adults. *International journal of aging and human development, 37,* 217-26.
Hummert, M. L. (1995). Judgments about stereotypes of the elderly: Attitudes, age associations, and typicality ratings of young, middle-aged, and elderly adults. *Research on aging, 17* (2), 168-189.
Hummert, M. L.; Garetka, T. A.; Shaner, J. L.; & Strahm, S. (1994). Stereotypes of the elderly held by young, middle-aged and elderly adults. *Journal of gerontology: Psychological sciences, P49,* P240-49.
Humphry, D. (1985). *Let me die before I wake.* Los Angeles: The Hemlock Society and Grove Press.
Humphry, D. (1991). *Final exit.* New York: Dell Trade.
Humphry, D. (1993). *Dying with dignity.* New York: St. Martin's Press.
Hwang, S. W.; Orav, E. J.; O'Connell, J. J.; Lebow, J. M.; & Brennan, T. A. (1997). Causes of death in homeless adults in Boston. *Annuals of internal medicine, 126,* 625-628.
IMSC—The Italian Multicentric Study on Centenarians. (1997). Epidemiological and socioeconomic aspects of Italian centenarians. *Archives of gerontology and geriatrics, 25,* 149-157.
Intrieri, R. C.; Kelly, J. A.; Brown, M. M.; & Castilla, C. (1993). Improving medical students' attitudes toward and skills with the elderly. *The gerontologist, 33,* 373-378.
Jacob, M., & Guarnaccia, V. (1997). Motivational and behavioral correlates of life satisfaction in an elderly sample. *Psychological reports, 80,* 811-818.
Jacobs, D. (1998, February 8). Laid off? Dismissed? To sue or not to sue. *New York Times,* 47 (3), BU11.
Jacobs, J. (1975). *Older persons and retirement communities: Case studies in social gerontology.* Springfield, IL: Charles C. Thomas.
Jacobs, R. (1994). *Be an outrageous older woman: ARASP.* Manchester, CT: Knowledge, Ideas and Trends Publishing.
Jail doctor wins age-bias settlement (1998, January 5). *New York Times,* p. A13.
James, G. (1994). Man is held in swindles of elderly. *New York Times,* 29, B3 (L).
James, J. B.; Lewkowicz, C.; Libhaber, J.; & Lachman, M. (1995). Rethinking the gender identity crossover hypothesis: A test of a new model. *Sex roles, 32,* 314, 185-207.
Jazwinski, S. M. (1996). Longevity, genes, and aging. *Science, 273,* 54-59.
Job, E. (1983). Retrospective life span analysis: A method for studying extreme old age. *Journal of gerontology, 38,* 367-374.
Johansen, H. C. (1987, August). Growing old in an urban environment. *Continuity and change, 2,* 297-305.
Johansson, C.; Mellstrom, D.; Rosengren, K.; & Rundgren, A. (1993). A prevalence of vertebral fractures in 85 year olds. Radiological examination. *Acta orthopedics of Scandinavia, 64,* 25-27.
John, R. (1991a). The state of research on American Indian Elders. In *Minority elders.* Washington, DC: Gerontological Society of America.
John, R. (1991b). Family support networks among elders in a Native American community: Contact with children and siblings among the Prairie Band Potawatomi. *Journal of aging studies, 5* (1), 45-59.
Johnson, C. L. (1996). Cultural diversity in the late-life family. In R. Blieszner & V. H. Bedford (Eds.), *Aging and the family: Theory and research.* Westport, CT: Praeger.
Jones, P. S. (1995). Paying respect: Care of elderly parents by Chinese and Filipino American women. *Health care for women international, 16,* 385-398.
Joseph, J. (1997). Fear of crime among black elderly. *Journal of black studies, 27* (5), 698-717.
Jung, C. (1916/1955). *Two essays on analytical psychology.* New York: Meridian.
Kahana, E.; Redmond, C.; Hill, G. J.; Kercher, K.; Kahana, B.; Johnson, J. R.; & Young, R. F. (1995). The effects of stress, vulnerability and appraisals on the psychological well-being of the elderly. *Research on aging, 17* (4), 459-489.
Kalish, R. A. (1985). *Death, grief, and caring relationships* (2nd ed.). Belmont, CA: Brooks/Cole Publishing.
Kalish, R. A. (1987). Death and dying. In G. Busse (Ed.), *Elderly as pioneers* (pp. 360-385). Bloomington: Indiana University Press.
Kalymun, M. (1992). Board and care vs. assisted living. *Adult residential care journal, 6* (1), 35-44.
Kanacki, L. S.; Jones, P. S.; & Galbraith, M. E. (1996). Social support and depression in widows

and widowers. *Journal of gerontological nursing, 22* (2), 39-45.

Kane, D. (1996). A comparison of job satisfaction and general well-being for job sharing and part-time female employees. *Guidance and counseling, 11* (3), 27-30.

Kane, R. (1992). The literature lives: Generations of applied gerontological research. *Gerontologist, 32* (6), 724-725.

Kant, G. L.; D'Zurilla, T. J.; & Maydeu-Olivares, A. (1997). Social problem solving as a mediator of stress-related depression and anxiety in middle-aged and elderly community residents. *Cognitive therapy and research, 21* (1), 73-96.

Karp, D. A. (1988). A decade of reminders: Changing age consciousness between fifty and sixty years old. *Gerontologist, 28* (6), 727-738.

Karpinski, J. (1997). Engaging and treating the self-neglecting elder. *Journal of geriatric psychiatry, 42*, 133-151.

Karr, A. (1993, February 4). Imperiled promises: risk to retirees rises as firms fail to fund pensions they offer. *Wall Street Journal*, p. A1.

Kastenbaum, R. (1992). Death, suicide, and the older adult. In A. Leenaars (Ed.), *Suicide and the older adult.* New York: Guilford Press.

Kaufman, A. S., & Horn, J. L. (1996). Age changes on tests of fluid and crystallized ability for women and men on the Kaufman adolescent and adult intelligence test (KAIT) at ages 17-94 years. *Archives of clinical neuropsychology, 11* (2), 97-121.

Kaufman, S. (1987). *The ageless self: Sources of meaning in later life.* Madison, WI: University of Wisconsin Press.

Kaufman, S. (1994). Reflections on the ageless self. *Generations, 17*, 13-16.

Kausler, D. H. & Kausler, B. C. (1996). *The graying of America.* Chicago, IL: University of Illinois Press.

Kaye, R. A. (1993). Sexuality in the later years. *Aging and society, 13*, 415-426.

Keeton, K. (1992). *Longevity.* New York: Viking.

Keil, K. L. (1998). An intimate profile of generation X. *The American enterprise, 9* (1), 49-51, 59.

Keith, P. M. (1983). Patterns of assistance among parents and the childless in very old age: Implications for practice. *Journal of gerontological social work, 6* (1), 49-59.

Kelley, P. (1997). Grandparents raising grandchildren in the inner city. *Families in society, 78* (5), 492.

Kemnitz, J. W.; Weindruck, R.; Roecker, E. B.; Crawford, K.; Kaufman, P. O.; & Ershler, W. B. (1994). Dietary restriction of adult male rhesus monkeys: Design, methodology, and preliminary findings from the first year of study. *Journals of gerontology, 48* (10), B17-B26.

Kendig, H. L. (1988, April). Confidants and family structure in old age. *Journal of gerontology, 43*, 531-540.

Kennedy, G. E. (1996). Grandparenthood literature for family life educators: Updating for curriculum development. *Journal of family and consumer sciences education, 14* (2), 4.

Kerr-Layton, D. (1993, November). Gray panthers discrimination update. *Network newsletter*, 1.

King, V., & Elder, G. H. (1997). The legacy of grandparenting: Childhood experiences with grandparents and current involvement with grandchildren. *Journal of marriage and the family, 59*, 848-859.

Kinoshita, Y., & Kiefer, C. (1992). *Refuge of the honored.* Berkeley: University of California Press.

Kirkland, R. I. (1994, February 21).Why we will live longer...and what it will mean. *Fortune*, 66-77.

Kitano, H. (1991). *Race relations.* Upper Saddle River, NJ: Prentice Hall.

Kleemeier, R. W. (1962). Intellectual change in the senium. *Proceedings of the social statistics section of the American statistical association, 1*, 290-295.

Klemmack, D., & Roff, L. L. (1984). Fear of personal aging and subjective well-being in later life. *Journal of gerontology, 39*, 756-758.

Kleyman, P. (1974). *Senior power: Growing old rebelliously.* San Francisco: Glide Publications.

Klitgaard, H.; Zhou, M.; & Schiaffino, S. (1990). Aging alters the hyosin heavy chain composition of single fibers from human skeletal muscle. *Acta physiology Scandinavia, 140* (1), 55-62.

Knight, B. (1993). A meta-analytic review of interventions for caregiver distress. *The gerontologist, 32*, 249-257.

Koenig, H. G.; Wildman-Hanlon, D.; & Schmader, K. (1996). Attitudes of elderly patients and their families toward physician-assisted suicide. *Archives of internal medicine, 156* (9), 2240-2248.

Kolata, G. (1992, February 2). Elderly become addicts to drug-induced sleep. *New York Times*, p. E4.

Kramer, D. A. (1987). Cognition and aging: The emergence of a new tradition. In P. Silverman (ed.), *Elderly as Modern Pioneers* (pp. 45–58). Bloomington: Indiana University Press.

Kratch, P.; DeVaney, S.; DeTurk, C.; Zink, M. H. (1996). Functional status of the oldest-old in a home setting. *Journal of advanced nursing, 25,* 456-464.

Krause, N. (1988). Stressful life events and physician utilization. *Journal of gerontology: Social sciences, 43,* S53-61.

Krause, N. (1991). Stress and isolation from close ties in later life. *Journal of gerontology: Social sciences, 46,* S183-194.

Krause, N. (1995). Negative interaction and satisfaction with social support among older adults. *Journal of gerontology: Psychological sciences, 50B,* P59-P73.

Kruk, E.. *(1994).* Grandparent visitation disputes: Multigenerational approaches to family mediation. *Mediation quarterly, 12* (1), 37-53.

Kubler-Ross, E. (1969). *On death and dying.* New York: Macmillan.

Kutty, N. (1998). The scope for poverty alleviation among elderly home-owners in the United States through reverse mortgages. *Urban studies, 35* (1), 113-129.

Kwong, P.,& Guoxuan, C. (1992). Aging in China. In D. Phillips (Ed.), *Aging in east and south-east Asia.* London: Edward Arnold Publishing.

Lachs, M. S.; Williams, C.; O'Brien, S.; Hurst, L.; & Horwitz, R. (1997). Risk factors for reported elder abuse and neglect: A nine-year observational cohort study. *The gerontologist,* 37 (4), 469-474.

Lamb, H.; Christie, J.; Singelton, A.B.; Leake, A.; Perry, R.H.; Ince, P.G.; McKeith, I.G.; Melton, L.M.; Edwardson, J.A.; & Morris, C.M. (1998). Apolipoprotein E and alpha-1 antichymotrypsin polymorphism genotyping in Alzheimer's disease and in dementia with Lewy bodies. *Neurology, 50,* 388-391.

Lambert, W., & Woo, J. (1994, April 29). CBS settlement. *Wall Street Journal,* pp. B5 (W), B4 (E).

Lamme, S.; Dykstra, P. A.; & van Groenou, M. I. B. (1996). Rebuilding the network: New relationships in widowhood. *Personal relationships, 3,* 337-349.

Landau, J. C. & Werbel, J. D. (1995). Sales productivity of insurance agents during the first six months of employment: Differences between older and younger hires. *Journal of personal selling and sales management, 15* (4), 33-43.

Landers, A. (1998, March 22). Ann Landers' column: Sweepstakes' fine print tells all. *San Jose Mercury News,* p. 4G.

Lanza, M. L. (1996). Divorce experienced as an older woman. *Geriatric nursing, 17,* 166-170.

Larson, R. A. (1997). The emergence of solitude as a constructive domain of experience in early adolescence. *Child development, 68* (1), 80-93.

Laumann, E.; Michaels, M. R.; & Gagnon, J. (1994). *The social organization of sexuality.* Chicago: University of Chicago Press.

Lavie, C. J. & Milani, R. V. (1997). Benefits of cardiac rehabilitation and exercise training in elderly women. *The American journal of cardiology, 79* (5), 664-666.

Laws, G. (1995). Understanding ageism: Lessons from feminism and postmodernism. *Gerontologist, 35* (1), 112-118.

Lawton, M. P. (1997). Measures of quality of life and subjective well-being. *Generations, 21* (1), 45-47.

Leavitt, K. R.; Lazenby, H. C.; & Sivarajan, L. (1996). National health expenditures, 1994. *Health care financing review, 17,* 205-242.

Lee, I.-M.; Hseih, C.-c.; Pfaffenbarger, R., Jr. (1995). Exercise intensity and longevity in men: The Harvard alumni health study. *Journal of the American medical association, 273* (15), 1179-1184.

Lee, J.; Hanna, S. D.; Mok, C. F. J.; & Wang, H. (1997). Apparel expenditure patterns of elderly consumers: A life-cycle consumption model. *Family and consumer sciences research journal, 26* (2), 109-140.

Lehman, H. (1953). *Age and achievement.* Princeton, NJ: Princeton University Press.

Lemming, M. R. & Dickinson, G. E. (1994). *Understanding dying, death, and bereavement* (3rd ed.). Orlando, FL: Harcourt Brace & Company.

Lempinen, E. W. (1998, July 15). Disabled care study hushed up. *San Francisco Chronicle,* p. A1.

Lester, D., & Savlid, A. C. (1997). Social psychological indicators associated with the suicide rate: A comment. *Psychological reports, 80,* 1065-1066.

Levinson, D. (1977). *The seasons of a man's life.* New York: Knopf.

Levinson, D. (1996). *The seasons of a woman's life.* New York: Knopf.

Levy, B., & Langer (1994). Aging free from negative stereotypes: Successful memory in China and among the American deaf. *Journal of personality and social psychology, 66* (6), 989-997.

Lewinsohn, P. M.; Seeley, J. R.; Roberts, R. E.; & Allen, N. B. (1997). Center for eipdemiologic studies depression scale (CES-D) as a screening instrument for depression among community-residing older adults. *Psychology and aging, 12* (2), 277-287.

Liang, J.; Bennett, J.; Akiyama, H.; & Maeda, D. (1992). The structure of PGC morale scale in American and Japanese aged: A further note. *Journal of cross-cultural gerontology, 7,* 45-68.

Liang, J. (1984). Dimensions of the life satisfaction index A: A structural formulation. *Journal of Gerontology, 39,* 613-622.

Liberto, J. G.; Oslin, D. W.; & Ruskin, P. E. (1992). Alcoholism in older persons: A review of the literature. *Hospital community psychiatry, 43,* 975-983.

Lichtenstein, P.; Gatz, M.; Pedersen, N. L.; Berg, S.; & McClearn, G. E. (1996). A co-twin control study of response to widowhood. *Journal of gerontology: Psychological sciences, 51B* (5), P279-P289.

Lieberman, M. S., & Tobin, S. (1983). *The experience of old age: Stress, coping, and survival.* New York: Basic Books.

Linville, P. W. (1982). The complexity-extremity effect and age-based stereotyping. *Journal of personality and social psychology, 42,* 183-211.

Liu, X.; Liang, J.; & Gu, S. (1995). Flows of social support and health status among older persons in China. *Social science and medicine, 41* (3), 1175-1184.

Lofland, L. H. (1979). *The craft of dying: The modern face of death.* Beverly Hills, CA: Sage Publications

Losyk, B. (1997). Generation X: What they think and what they plan to do. *Public management, 79* (12), 4-9.

Lovenheim, B. (1990). *Marriage odds: When you are smart, single, and over 35.* New York: William Morrow Co.

Luborsky, M. R. (1993). The romance with personal meaning in gerontology: Cultural aspects of life themes. *The gerontologist, 33* (4), 445-452.

Luborsky, M., & Sankar, A. (1993, August). Extending the critical gerontology perspective: Cultural dimensions. *Gerontologist, 33* (4), 440-454.

Luszcz, M. A.; Bryan, J.; & Kent, P. (1997). Predicting episodic memory performance of very old men and women: Contributions from age, depression, activity, cognitive ability, and speed. *Psychology and aging, 12* (2), 340-351.

Luszcz, M. A. & Fitzgerald, K. M. (1986). Understanding cohort differences in cross-generational, self, and peer perspectives. *Journal of gerontology, 41,* 234-40.

Maas, H. S., & Kuypers, J. A. (1977). *From thirty to seventy.* San Francisco: Jossey-Bass.

Madden, M. M. (1997). Strengthening protection of employees at home and abroad: The extraterritorial application of Title VII of the civil rights act of 1964 and the age discrimination in employment act. *Hamline law review, 20* (3), 739-768.

Maeda, D. (1993). Japan. In E. Palmore (Ed.), *Development and research on the aging: An international handbook.* Westport, CT: Greenwood Press.

Magno, J. (1990). The hospice concept of care: Facing the 1990s. *Death studies, 14,* 109-119.

Malmberg, B., & Zarit, G. (1993). Group homes for people with dementia: A Swedish example. *Gerontologist, 33* (5), 682-686.

Manchester, J. (1997). Aging boomers and retirement: Who is at risk? *Generations, 21* (2), 19-22.

Mangen, D., & Westbrook, G. (1988). Measuring intergenerational norms. In D. Mangen (Ed.), *Measurement of intergenerational relationships.* Newbury Park, CA: Sage.

Mannheim, K. (1952). The problem of generations. In D. Kecskemeti (Ed.), *Essays on the sociology of knowledge* (2nd ed., pp. 276-322). London: Oxford University Press.

Mannheim, K. (1993). The sociology of intellectuals. *Theory, culture and society, 10,* 69-80.

Manson, M., & Gutfeld, G. (1994, May). Losing the final five. *Prevention magazine, 46* (5), 22-24.

Marcellini, F.; Sensoli, C.; Barbini, N.; & Fioravanti, P. (1997). Preparation for retirement: Problems and suggestions of retirees. *Educational gerontology, 23,* 337-388.

Markides, K. S., & Mindel, C. H. (1987). *Aging and ethnicity.* Newbury Park, CA: Sage.

Marrone, R. (1996). *Death, mourning, and caring.* Pacific Grove, CA: Books/Cole Publishing.

Martin, J. D. (1971, May). Power, dependence, and the complaints of the elderly: A social exchange perspective. *Aging and human development, 2,* 108-112.

Martin, L. (1989, July). The graying of Japan. *Population bulletin, 44* (2), 13-39.

Martin, L. R.; Friedman, H. S.; Tucker, J. S.; Schwartz, J. E.; Criqui, M. H.; & Tomlinson-Keasey, C. (1995). An archival prospective study of mental health and longevity. *Health psychology, 14* (5), 381-387.

Masters, W. M., & Johnson, V. E. (1966). *Human sexual response.* Boston: Little Brown.

Masters, W. M., & Johnson, V. E. (1970). *Human sexual inadequacy.* Boston: Little Brown.

Matloff, N. (1998, January 28). Now hiring if you're young. *New York Times,* pp. 147, A19 (L), A21 (N).
Matthews, S. H. (1979). *The social world of old women: Management of self-identity.* Newbury Park: Sage.
Matzo, M. L. (1997). The search to end suffering: A historical perspective. *Journal of gerontological nursing, 23* (3), 11-17.
Mayeux, R.; Saunders, A.; Shea, S.; Mirra, S.; Evans, D.; Roses, A.; Hyman, B.; Crain, B.; Tang, M.-X.; & Phelps, C. (1998). Utility of the apoliproprotein E genotype in the diagnosis of Alzheimer's disease. *The New England journal of medicine, 338,* 506-511.
McAdams, D. P. & de St. Aubin, E. (1994). A theory of generativity and its assessment through self-report, behavioral acts, and narrative themes in autobiography. *Journal of personality and social psychology, 62* (6), 1003-1015.
McCarty, E. F. (1996). Caring for a parent with Alzheimer's disease: Process of daughter caregiver stress. *Journal of advanced nursing, 23,* 792-803.
McCoy, H. V.; Wooldredge, J. D.; Cullen, F. T.; Dubeck, P. J.; & Browning, S. L. (1996). Lifestyles of the old and not so fearful: Life situation and older persons' fear of crime. *Journal of criminal justice, 24* (3), 191-205.
McCulloch, J. & Kivett, V. R. (1995). Characteristics of and survivorship among the very old. *Family relations, 44,* 87-94.
McGarry, K. (1996). Factors determining participation of the elderly in supplemental security income. *The journal of human resources, 31* (2), 331-358.
McGue, M.; Vaupel, J.W.; Holm, N.; & Harvald, B. (1993). Longevity is moderately heritable in a sample of Danish twins born 1870-1880. *Journal of gerontology: Biological sciences, 48B,* B237-B244.
McIntosh, J. (1992). Epidemiology of suicide in the elderly. In A. Leenaars (Ed.), *Suicide and the older adult* (pp. 15–35). New York: Guilford Press.
McMorris, F. A. (1997, February 20). Age-bias suits may become harder to prove. *The Wall Street Journal,* p. B1.
Mead, M. (1972, January). Dealing with the aged. *Current.*
Mehta, K. (1997). Respect redefined: Focus group insights from Singapore. *International journal of aging and human development, 44* (3), 205-219.
Meyer, D. R., & Bartolomei-Hill, S. (1994). The adequacy of supplemental security income benefits for aged individuals and couples. *The gerontologist, 34* (2), 161-172.
Meyer, M. J. (1995). Dignity, death and modern virtue. *American philosophical quarterly, 32* (1), 45-55.
Michaels, S. (1996). The prevalence of homosexuality in the United States. In R. P. Cabaj & T. S. Stein (Eds.), *Textbook of homosexuality and mental health.* Washington, DC and London: American Psychiatric Press.
Miller, B. & Kaufman, J. E. (1996). Beyond gender stereotypes: Spouse caregivers of persons with dementia. *Journal of aging studies, 10* (3), 189-204.
Mills, C. W. (1959). *The sociological imagination.* New York: Oxford University Press.
Minda, G. (1997). Aging workers n the postindustrial era. *Stetson law review, 26* (2), 561-597.
Minkler, M. (1996). Critical perspectives on ageing: New challenges for gerontology. *Aging and society, 16,* 467-487.
Minker, M., & Estes, C. L. (1991). *Critical perspectives on aging.* New York: Baywood.
Minkler, M., & Roe, K. (1993). *Grandmothers as caregivers: Raising children of the crack cocaine epidemic.* Newbury Park, CA: Sage.
Mintz, H. (1998, February 19). Trial opens for thrift accused of elder fraud. *San Jose Mercury News,* p. 1B.
Mittelman, M. S.; Ferris, S. H.; Shulman, E.; Steinberg, G.; Ambinder, A.; Mackell, J. A.; & Cohen, J. (1995). A comprehensive support program: Effect on depression in spouse-caregivers of AD patients. *The gerontologist, 35* (6), 792-802.
Moody, H. (1992). *Ethics in an aging society.* Baltimore: Johns Hopkins University Press.
Morgan, D. (1989, February). Adjusting to widowhood: Do social networks make it easier? *Gerontologist, 29* (1), 101-107.
Morgan, L., & Kunkel, S. (1998). *Aging: The social context.* Thousand Oaks, CA: Pine Forge Press.
Morgan, D. L.; Neal, M. B.; & Carder, P. C. (1997). Both what and when: The effects of positive and negative aspects of relationships on depression during the first 3 years of widowhood. *Journal of clinical geropsychology, 3* (1), 73-91.
Mori, N.. (1997). Molecular genetic approaches to the genes of longevity, aging and neurodegeneration in mammals. *Mechanisms of aging and development, 98* (3), 223-230.

Morley, J. E., & Kaiser, F. E. (1989). Sexual function with advancing age. *Medical clinics of North America, 73* (6), 1483-1495.

Morris, J. N. (1994). Exercise in the prevention of coronary heart disease: Today's best buy in public health. *Medicine and science in sports and exercise, 26,* 807-814.

Morris, J. N.; Heady, J. A.; & Raffle, P.A.B. (1953). Coronary heart disease and physical activity at work. *Lancet, 265,* 1053-1105.

Morris, P. L.; Robinson, R. G.; & Samuels, J. (1993). Depression, introversion and mortality following stroke. *Australian and New Zealand journal of psychiatry, 23,* 443-449.

Morris, R., & Caro, F. G. (1995). The young-old, productive aging, and public policy. *Generations, 19* (3), 32-37.

Morton, J. (1992). *An administrative overview of the older inmate.* Washington, DC: US Department of Justice and National Institute of Corrections.

Mudrick, Peter E. (1997). Protestant work-ethic dimensions and work orientations. *Personality and individual differences, 23* (2), 217-225.

Mui, A., & Burnette, D. (1994). Long-term care service used by frail elders: Is ethnicity a factor? *The gerontologist, 34* (2), 190-198.

Mullen, F. (1996). Public benefits: Grandparents, grandchildren, and welfare reform. *Generations, 20* (1), 61-64.

Mulroy, T. M. (1996). Divorcing the elderly: Special issues. *American Journal of Family Law, 10,* 65-70.

Mundorf, N., & Brownell, W. (1990). Media preferences of old and younger adults. *Gerontologist, 30,* 685-691.

Murer, M. J. (1997). Assisted living: The regulatory outlook. *Nursing homes: Long term care management, 46* (7), 24-29.

Murray, C. J. L. & Lopez, A. D. (1997). Regional patterns of disability-free life expectancy and disability-adjusted life expectancy: Global burden of disease study. *The lancet, 349* (5), 1347-1352.

Mutchler, J. E.; Burr, J. A.; & Pienta, A. M. (1997). Pathways to labor force exit; Work transitions and work instability. *Journal of gerontology: social sciences, 52B* (1), S4-S12.

Mutter, S. A., & Goedert, K. M. (1997). Frequency discrimination vs. frequency estimation: Adult age differences and the effect of divided attention. *Journal of gerontology: Psychological sciences, 52B* (6), P319-P328.

Mykyta, L. J. (1997). The consequences of osteoporosis in the elderly. *Australian family physician, 26* (2), 115-121,

National Center for Health Statistics. (1994). *Vital statistics of the United States, 2* (A). Washington: US Public Health Service.

National Center for Health Statistics. (1995). *Healthy people 2000: Review, 1994.* Hyattsville, MD: US Public Health Service.

National Center for Health Statistics. (1996). *Births and Deaths: United States 1995.* US Department of Health and Human Services, 45 (3), supplement 2. Washington, DC.

National Institute on Aging. (1993). *Profiles of America's elderly: Racial and ethnic diversity.* Washington, DC: US Department of Health and Human Services.

National Institutes of Health, National Institute on Aging. (1993). *In search of the secrets of aging* (NIH Publication No. 93-2756). Bethesda, MD: National Institutes of Health.

National Safety Council. (1993). *Accident facts.* Chicago: National Safety Council.

Neimeyer, R. (1994). *Death anxiety handbook.* Washington, DC: Taylor and Francis, 1994.

Nelson, H. L., & Nelson, J. L. (1995). *The patient in the family: An ethics of medicine and families.* New York: Routledge.

Nelson, L.; Brown, R.; Gold, M.; Ciemnecki, A.; & Docteur, E. (1997). Access to care in Medicare HMOs, 1996. *Health affairs, 16* (2), 148-156

Neugarten, B. L. (1977). Personality and aging. In J.E. Birren & K.W. Schaie (Eds.), *Handbook of the psychology of aging.* New York: Academic Press.

Neugarten, B. L. (1985). Interpretive social sciences and research on aging. In A. Rossi (Ed.), *Gender and the life course.* New York: Aldine.

Neugarten, B. L.; Havighurst, J.; & Tobin, S. (1961). The measurement of life satisfaction. *Gerontology, 16,* 134-143.

Neugarten, B. L., & Neugarten, D. N. (1986). Age in the aging society. *Daedalus issue: The aging society, 115,* 31–50.

Newbold, K. B. (1996). Determinants of elderly interstate migration in the United States, 1985-1990. *Research on aging, 18* (4), 451-476.

Newman, E. (1984). *Elderly criminals.* Cambridge, MA: Oelgeschlager, Gunn, and Hain.

Niederehe, G. (1997). Future directions for clinical research in mental health and aging. *Behavior therapy, 28,* 101-108.

Nolan, D. C. (1997). Assisted living: Moving its availability down the income scale. *Nursing homes: Long term care management, 46* (7), 29-31.

Nugent, J. (1990). Old age security and the defense of social norms. *Journal of cross-cultural gerontology, 5* (5), 243-254.

Nuland, S. (1994). *How we die: Reflections on life's final chapter.* New York: Alfred A. Knopf, 1994.

Nye, W. (1993, March). Amazing grace: Religion and identity among elderly black individuals. *International journal of aging and human development, 36* (2), 103-105.

Oates, B.; Shufeldt, L.; & Vaught, B. (1996). A psychographic study of the elderly and retail store attributes. *Journal of consumer marketing, 13* (6), 14-27.

O'Bryant, S. (1991, January). Older widows and independent lifestyles. *International journal of aging and human development, 32* (1), 41-51.

O'Connell, L. J. (1994). The role of religion in health-related decision making. *Generations, 18* (4), 27-30.

O'Connor, G. T.; Buring, J. E.; & Yusuf, S. (1989). An overview of randomized trials of rehabilitation with exercise after myocardial infarction. *Circulation, 80,* 234-244.

Ogg, J., & Bennett, G. (1992). Elder abuse in Britain. *British medical journal, 305,* 988-898.

Ohuche, N., & Littrell, J. (1989). Igbo students' attitudes toward supporting aged parents. *International journal of aging and human development 29* (4), 259-267.

Olshansky, S. J. (1995). Introduction: New developments in mortality. *The gerontologist, 35,* 563-587.

Olson, S. (1998). Senior housing: A quiet revolution. *Architectural record, 186* (1), 103-106.

Onega, L. L., & Tripp-Reimer, T. (1997). Expanding the scope of continuity theory: Application to gerontological nursing. *Journal of gerontological nursing, 23* (6), 29-35.

Opatrny, S. (1991, March 3). Women who stay vital past seventy. *San Francisco Examiner,* p. A1-A3.

Orchard, T. J., & Strandness, D. B. (1993). Assessment of peripheral vascular disease in diabetes: Report and recommendations of an international workshop sponsored by the American Diabetes Association and the American Heart Association. *Circulation, 88,* 819-828.

Orwoll, L., & Achenbaum, W. A. (1993). Gender and the development of wisdom. *Human development, 36,* 274-296.

Osgood, N. (1991). *Suicide among the elderly in long-term care facilities.* Westport, CT: Greenwood Press.

Paffenbarger, R. S., Jr.; Hyde, R. T.; Wing, A. L.; & Steinmetz, C. H. (1985). A natural history of athleticism and cardiovascular health. *Journal of the American medical association, 252,* 491-495.

Paffenbarger, R. S., Jr., & Lee, I.-M. (1996). Physical activity and fitness for health and longevity. *Research quarterly for exercise and sport, 67* (3), 11-28.

Palmore, E. (1975). *The honorable elders.* Durham, NC: Duke University Press.

Palmore, E. (1985, March). Predictors of function among the old-old: A ten-year follow-up. *Journal of gerontology, 40,* 244-250.

Palmore, E. (1988). *The Facts of Aging* Quiz. New York: Springer.

Palmore, E. (1990). *Ageism: Negative and Positive.* New York: Springer Publishing.

Parker, L. D.; Cantrell, C.; & Demi, A. S. (1997). Older adults' attitudes toward suicide: Are there race and gender differences? *Death studies, 21,* 282-289.

Parker, R. (1995). Reminiscence: A continuity theory framework. *The gerontologist, 35* (4), 515-525.

Pascual-Leone, J. (1990). An essay on wisdom: Toward organismic processes that make it possible. In R. J. Sternberg (Ed.), *Wisdom: Its nature, origins, and development* (p. 244-278). Cambridge, UK: Cambridge University Press.

Pascucci, M. A., & Loving, G. L. (1997). Ingredients of an old and healthy life: A centenarian perspective. *Journal of holistic nursing, 15* (2), 199-213.

Pearlman, M. (1993). Late mid-life astonishment: Disruptions to identity and self-esteem. In N. David (Ed.), *Faces of women and aging.* Binghamton, NY: Haworth Press.

Perkins, K. (1994, July 12). Older women forced back to work. *Santa Rosa Press Democrat,* p. A1.

Perlmutter, M. (1990). *Later life potential.* Washington, DC: The Gerontological Society of America.

Perls, T. T. (1995, January). The oldest old. *Scientific American,* 70-75.

Peterson, B. E. & Klohnen, E. C. (1995). Realization of generativity in two samples of women at midlife. *Psychology and aging, 10* (1), 20-29.

Peto, R. & Doll, R. (1997). There is no such thing as aging. *British medical journal, 315* (7115), 1030-1032.

Phone swindlers dangle prizes to cheat elderly out of millions. (1997, June 29). *New York Times,* p. D18.

Pickens, J. (1998). Formal and informal care of people with psychiatric disorders: Historical perspectives and current trends. *Journal of psychosocial nursing, 36* (1), 37-43.

Pillemer, K., & Moore, D. (1989, June). Abuse of patients in nursing homes: Findings from a survey of staff. *The gerontologist, 29* (3), 314–320.

Plumb, J. D. (1997). Homelessness: Care, prevention, and public policy. *Annals of internal medicine, 126* (12), 973-975.

Podkieks, E. (1992). National survey on abuse of the elderly in Canada. *Journal of elder abuse and neglect, 4,* 5-58.

Poon, L. W. (1992). *The Georgia centenarian study.* Amityville, NY: Baywood Publishing.

Posner, R. A. (1995). *Aging and old age.* Chicago: University of Chicago Press.

Preston, D. B. (1995). Marital status, gender roles, stress, and health in the elderly. *Health care for women international, 16,* 149-165.

Puentes, W. J. (1998). Incorporating simple reminiscence techniques into acute care nursing practice. *Journal of gerontological nursing, 24* (2), 14-20.

Quadagno, J. S. (1982). *Aging in early industrial society.* New York: Academic Press.

Quadagno, J. S. (1991, August). Falling into the Medicaid gap: The hidden long-term care dilemma. *Gerontologist, 31* (4), 521-526.

Quadagno, J. S., & Meyer, M. (1993). Gender and public policy. In E. Stoller & R. Gibson (Eds.), *Worlds of difference.* Thousand Oaks, CA: Pine Forge Press.

Quinnan, E. J. (1997). Connection and autonomy in the lives of elderly male celibates: Degrees of disengagement. *Journal of aging studies, 11* (2), 115-130.

Rahe, R. H. (1995). Stress and coping in psychiatry. In H. I. Kaplan & B. J. Sadock (Eds.), *Comprehensive textbook of psychiatry* (6th ed., pp. 1545-1559). Baltimore: Williams and Wilkins.

Rando, T. A. (1995). Grieving and mourning: Accommodating to loss. In H. Wass & R. A. Niemeyer (Eds.), *Dying: Facing the facts.* Washington, DC: Taylor & Francis.

Rantz, M. J.; Mohr, D. R.; Popejoy, L.; Zwygart-Stauffacher, M.; Hicks, L. L.; Grando, V.; Conn, V. S.; Porter, R.; Scott, J.; & Maas, M. (1998).Nursing home care quality: A multidimensional theoretical model. *Journal of nursing care quality, 12* (3), 30-46.

Rathbone-McCuan, E. (1996). Self-neglecting in the elderly: Knowing when and how to intervene. *Aging*, 44-49.

Ray, D. (1987). Differences in psychologists' ratings of older and younger clients. *Gerontologist, 27,* 82-86.

Reday-Mulvey, G. (1996, May 16). Why working lives must be extended. *People magazine,* pp. 24-29.

Redfoot, D., & Gaberlavage, G. (1991). Housing for older Americans: Sustaining the dream. *Generations,* 35-38.

Reich, K., & Morrison, P. (1986, October 1). Deception in insurance mailers. *Los Angeles Times,* p. 3.

Reker, G. T. (1997). Personal meaning, optimism, and choice: Existential predictors of depression in community and institutional elderly. *The gerontologist, 37* (6), 709-716.

Rempel, J. (1985). Childless elderly: What are they missing? *Journal of marriage and the family, 47,* 343-348.

Rhodes, E. (1984). Reevaluation of the aging and modernization theory: The Samoan evidence. *The gerontologist, 24* (6), 243-250.

Riabowol, K.; Harley C.; & Goldstein, S. (1995). The maintenance of the accuracy of protein synthesis and its relevance to aging. *Experimental gerontology, 30,* 5-6.

Richardson, C. A. & Hammond, S. M. (1996). A psychometric analysis of a short device for assessing depression in elderly people. *British journal of clinical psychology, 35* (4), 543-551.

Richardson, J. P. & Lazur, A. (1995). Sexuality in the nursing home patient. *American family physician, 51,* (1), 10-14.

Richman, J. (1995). From despair to integrity: An Eriksonian approach to psychotherapy for the terminally ill. *Psychotherapy, 32* (2), 317-322.

Ricklefs, R. E. and Finch, C. E. (1995). *Aging: A natural history.* New York: Scientific American Library W. H. Freeman & Company.

Riley, M., & Riley, J. (1994). Age integration and the lives of older people. *Gerontologist*, 110-115.

Roan, S. (1993, January 17). The Ponce de Leon study. *Sunday Punch section of the San Francisco Chronicle,* p. 2.

Roan, C. L. & Raley, R. K. (1996). Intergenerational coresidence and contact: A longitudinal analysis of adult children's response to their mother's widowhood. *Journal of marriage and the family, 58,* 708-717.

Roberto, K. A. (1997). Qualities of older women's friendships: Stable or volatile? *International journal of aging and human development, 44* (1), 1-14.

Roberto, K. A., and Scott, J. (1984/85). Friendship patterns among older women. *International journal of aging and human development, 19,* 1–9.

Roberts, P. (1995, February 20). It's time to privatize social security. *Business week,* p. 22.

Robinson, B. E. (1997). Guideline for initial evaluation of the patient with memory loss. *Geriatrics, 52* (12), 30-39.

Robinson, J. D., & Skill, T. (1995). The invisible generation: Portrayals of the elderly on prime-time television. *Communication Reports, 8* (2), 111-119.

Robinson, L., & Mahon, M. M. (1997). Sibling bereavement: A concept analysis. *Death studies, 21,* 477-499.

Roha, R. R. (1998, January). Medigap: One size doesn't fit all. *Kiplinger's personal finance magazine,* 107-111.

Rosen, M.; Simon, E. W.; & McKinsey, L. (1995). Subjective measure of quality of life. *Mental retardation, 33,* 31-34.

Rosenkoetter, M. M. (1996). Changing life patterns of the resident in long-term care and the community-residing spouse. *Geriatric nursing, 17* (6), 267-272.

Ross, D. W. (1996).Biology of aging. *Archives of pathological laboratory medicine, 120* (12), 114-116.

Rossi, A. S., & Rossi, P. H. (1990). *Of human bonding.* New York: Aldine de Gruyter.

Rowe, J. W. (1997). The new gerontology. *Science, 278* (5337), 367-369.

Rowland, V. T. & Shoemake, A. (1995). How experiences in a nursing home affect nursing students' perceptions of the elderly. *Educational gerontology, 21,* 735-748.

Ryan, M. (1993, July 18). Undercover among the elderly. *Parade magazine,* p. 8.

Salili, F.(1995). Age, sex, and cultural differences in the meaning and dimensions of achievement. *Personality and social psychology bulletin, 20* (6), 695-648.

Saluter, A. F. (1992). Marital status and living arrangements: March, 1991. *Current population reports: Population characteristics.* Series P-20, No. 461. Washington, DC.

Sandell, S. H., & Iams, H. M. (1997). Reducing women's poverty by shifting Social Security benefits from retired couples to widows. *Journal of policy analysis and management, 16* (2), 279-297.

Sanders, G.F.; Montgomery, J.E.; Pittman, J.F., Jr.; & Blackwell, C. (1984). Youth attitudes toward the elderly. *Journal of applied gerontology, 3,* 59-70.

Savage, R. D.; Britton, P.; Bolton, N.; & Hall, E. H. (1973). *Intellectual functioning in the aged.* London: Methuen.

Sawyer, C. H. (1996). Reverse mortgages: An innovative tool for elder law attorneys. *Stetson law review, 26* (2), 617-646.

Schaie, K. W. (1996). *Intellectual development in adulthood: The Seattle longitudinal study.* New York: Cambridge University Press.

Schaie, K. W. & Willis, S. (1996). *Adult development and aging.* HarperCollins: NY.

Schick, F., & Schick, R. (1994). *Statistical handbook of aged Americans.* Phoenix, AZ: Onyx Press.

Schideler, K. (1994, August 8). Everybody gets osteoporosis. *Santa Rosa Press Democrat,* p. D2.

Schmidt, K. (1993, March 8). No purpose in dying: Staying young longer. *U. S. News and World Report,* 66-73.

Schoonmaker, C. (1993). Aging lesbians: Bearing the burden of triple shame. In N. Davis, E. Cole, & C. Rothblum (Eds.), *Faces of women and aging.* New York: Haworth Press.

Schuchter, S. R., & Zisook, R. (1993). The course of normal grief. In M. S. Stroebe, W. Stroebe, & R. O. Hansson (Eds.), *Handbook of bereavement: Theory, research, and intervention.* Cambridge, UK: Cambridge University Press.

Schulz, J.; Borowski, A.; & Crown, W. (1991). *Economics of population aging: The 'graying' of Australia, Japan, and the United States.* Chicago: Auburn House Greenwood.

Schutter, M. E; Scherman, A.; & Carroll, R. S. (1997). Grandparents and children of divorce: Their contrasting perceptions and desires for the postdivorce relationship. *Educational gerontology, 23,* 213-231.

Schwald, S. J. & Sedlacek, W. E. (1990). Have college students' attitudes toward older people changed? *Journal of college student development, 31,* 127-23.

Seals, J. D. R.; Hagberg, J. M.; & Hurley, B. F. (1984). Endurance training in older men and women. Cardiovascular responses to exercise. *Journal of applied physiology, 57* (4), 1024-1029.

Seelye, K. Q. (1997, March 27). US of future: Grayer and more Hispanic. *New York Times,*

Segell, M. (1993, September). How to live forever. *Esquire magazine,* 125-132.

Selzer, M. M. (1989). The three R's of life cycle sibships: Rivalries, reconstructions, and relationships. *American behavioral scientist, 33,* 107-115.

Serafini, M. W. (1997). Brave new world. *National Journal, 29* (33), 163-165.

Seshadri, S.; Wolf, P.A.; Beiser, A.; Au, R.; McNulty, K.; White, R.; & D'Agostino, R.B. (1997). Lifetime risk of dementia and Alzheimer's disease. The impact of mortality on risk estimates in the Framingham study. *Neurology, 49,* 1498-1504.

Settersten, R. A., & Hagestad, G. O. (1996). What's the latest? Cultural age deadline for family transitions. *The gerontologist, 36* (2), 178-188.

Severance offers change to teach (1991, November 26). *USA today,* p. 4B.

Sharpley, C. F. (1997). Psychometric properties of the self-perceived stress in retirement scale. *Psychological reports, 81,* 319-322.

Sheehy, G. (1976). *Passages.* New York: Dutton.

Shelton, A. J. (1972). The aged and eldership among the Igbo. In D. O. Cowgill & L. D. Holmes (Eds.), *Aging and modernization.* New York: Appleton-Century-Crofts.

Shephard, R. J.; Rhind, S.; & Shek, P. N. (1995). The impact of exercise on the immune system: NK cells, interleukins 1 and 2, and related responses. In J. O. Holloszy (Ed.), *Exercise and sports sciences reviews, 23,* 214-241.

Shepherd, M.D., & Erwin, G. (1983). An examination of students' attitudes toward the elderly. *American journal of pharmaceutical education, 47,* 35-38.

Sheppard, D. (1997). Informed consent issues in home care. *CARING magazine, 16* (3), 46-49.

Sherrard, C. (1997). Subjective well-being in later life. *Aging and society, 17,* 609-613.

Shimizu, M. (1992). Depression and suicide in late life. In M. Gergener, K. Hasegawa, S. I. Finkel, & T. Nishimura (Eds.), *Aging and mental disorders: International perspectives* (p. 91-101). New York: Springer.

Shmotkin, D., & Hadari, G. (1996). An outlook on subjective well-being in older Israeli adults: A unified formulation. *International journal on aging and human development.* 42 (4), 271-289.

Shock, N. W.; Greulich, R. C.; Andres, R.; Arenburg, D.; Costa, P. T.; Lakatta, F. G.; & Tobin, J. D.(1989). *Normal human aging: The Baltimore longitudinal study of aging.* NIH Publication No. 84-2450. Washington, DC: US Government Printing Office.

Shoemake, A.F., & Rowland, V.T. (1993). Do laboratory experiences change college students' attitudes toward the elderly? *Educational gerontology, 19,* 295-309.

Siegel, J. (1996). *Aging into the 21st century.* National Information Center Special Report. Washington, DC: U.S. Administration on Aging.

Siegel, S. R. (1993). Relationships between current performance and likelihood of promotion for old versus young workers. *Human resources development quarterly, 4* (1), 39-50.

Silverman, E.; Range, L.; & Overholser, J. (1995). Bereavement from suicide as compared to other forms of bereavement. *Omega, 30,* 41-51.

Simmons, L. W. (1945). *The role of the aged in primitive society.* New Haven, CT: Yale University Press.

Simmons, L. W. (1960). Aging in preindustrial societies. In C. Tibbitts (Ed.), *Handbook of social gerontology.* Chicago: University of Chicago Press.

Small, J. P. (1995). Recent scientific advances in the understanding of memory. *Helios, 22* (2), 156-162.

Smith, D. W. (1996). Cancer mortality at very old ages. *American cancer society, 77* (7), 1367-1372.

Smith, D. W. (1997). Centenarians: Human longevity outliers. *The gerontologist, 37* (2), 200-207.

Smyer, T.; Gragert, M. D.; & LaMere, S. (1997). Stay sate! Stay healthy! Surviving old age in prison. *Journal of psychosocial nursing, 35* (9), 10-17.

Soldo, B. J.; Hurd, M. D.; Rodgers, W. L.; & Wallace, R. B. (1997). Asset and health dynamics among the oldest old: An overview of the AHEAD study. *The journals of gerontology, 52B* (special issue), 1-20.

Sonnichsen, A. C.; Ritter, M. M.; Mohrle, W.; Richter, W. O.; & Schwandt, P. (1993). The waist-to-hip ratio corrected for body mass index is related to serum triglycerides and high-density lipoprotein cholesterol but not to parameters of glucose metabolism in healthy premenopausal women. *Clinical investigation, 71,* 913-917.

Stafford, R. S., & Cyr, P. L. (1997). The impact of cancer on the physical function of the elderly and their utilization of health care. *Cancer, 80* (10), 1973-1980.

Stallings, M. E.; Dunham, C. C.; Gatz, M.; Baker, L. A.; & Bengtson, V. L. (1997). Relationship among life events and psychological well-being: More evidence for a two-factor theory of well-

being. *Journal of applied gerontology, 16* (1), 104-119.
Starr, B., & Weiner, M. (1981). *The Starr-Weiner Report on sex and sexuality in the mature years.* Briarcliff Manor, NY: Stein & Day.
Starr, K. (1996). *Endangered dreams: The great depression in California.* New York: Oxford University Press.
Stein, M. B.; Chartier, M. J.; Hazen, A. L.; Kozak, M. V.; Tancer, M. E.; Lander, S.; Furer, P.; Chubaty, D.; & Walker, J. R. (1998). A direct-interview family study of generalized social phobia. *American journal of psychiatry, 155* (1), 90-97.
Steinberg, D. (1993, March 13). Seniorities: How fairy tales help perpetuate ageist mythology. *San Francisco Examiner*, p. C7.
Steinweg, K. K. (1997). The changing approach to falls in the elderly. *American family physician, 56* (7), 1815-1822.
Stern, M. R. (1987, April). At 93, Blessings and Memories. *Washington Post,* p. 23.
Sternberg, R. J. (1990). *Wisdom: Its nature, origins, and development.* Cambridge University Press: New York.
Stevens, N. (1995). Gender and adaptation to widowhood in later life. *Aging and society, 15,* 37-58.
Still, J. S. (1980). Disengagement reconsidered: Awareness of finitude. *Gerontologist, 20,* 457-462.
Stolberg, S. (1994, July 27). Many elderly too medicated, study finds. *Los Angeles Times,* p. A1.
Stolk, R. P.; Lamberts, S. W.; Breteler, M.; Grobbee, D.; Hoffman, A.; Ott, A.; & Pols, H. (1997). Insulin and cognitive function in an elderly population. *Diabetes care, 20* (5), 792-795.
Stoller, E. (1990). Males as helpers: The role of sons, relatives, and friends. *The gerontologist, 30,* 228-236.
Stolley, J. M., & Hoenig, H. (1997). Religion/spirituality and health among elderly African Americans and Hispanics. *Journal of psychosocial nursing, 35* (11), 32-38.
Stone, P. (1993). Just another con job on the elderly?" *National journal, 25* (36), 2141–2144.
Stone, R., & Keigher, S. (1994). Toward equitable universal caregiver policy: The potential of financial supports for family caregivers. *Aging and social policy, 6,* 57-76.
Strawbridge, W. J.; Wallhagen, M. I.; Shema, S. J.; & Kaplan, G. A. (1997). New burdens or more of the same? Comparing grandparent, spouse, and adult-child caregivers. *The gerontologist, 37* (4), 505-510.
Stroebe, M. (1993). *Handbook of bereavement.* New York: Cambridge University Press.
Strom, R. D.; Buki, L. P.; & Strom, S. K. (1997). Intergenerational perceptions of English speaking and Spanish speaking Mexican American grandparents. *International journal of aging and human development, 45* (1), 1-21.
Sundstrom, G. (1986, August). Intergenerational mobility and the relationship between adults and their aging parents in Sweden. *Gerontologist, 26,* 367-371.
Sung, K.-T. (1994). A cross-cultural comparison of motivations for parent care: The case of Americans and Koreans. *Journal of aging studies, 8* (2), 195-209.
Szinovacz, M. (1996). Couples' employment/retirement patterns and perceptions of marital quality. *Research on aging, 18* (2), 243-268.
Szulc, T. (1988, May 29). How can we help ourselves age with dignity. *Santa Rosa Press Democrat,* pp. 4-7.
Talamantes, M. A.; Cornell, J.; Espino, D. V.; Lichenstein, M. J.; & Hazuda, H. P. (1996). SES and ethnic differences in perceived caregiver availability among young-old Mexican Americans and non-Hispanic whites. *The gerontologist, 36* (1), 88-99.
Tandemar Research (1988). *Quality of life among seniors.* Toronto, Ontario: Tandemar Research.
Tanenbaum, L. (1997, March/April). Changing the images makes a big difference. *Extra!* pp. 22-23.
Tauer, L. (1995). Age and farmer productivity. *Review of agricultural economics, 17*, 63-69.
Thapa, P. B.; Gideon, P.; Brockman, K. G.; Fought, R. L.; & Ray, W. A. (1996). Clinical and biomechanical measures of balance as fall predictors in ambulatory nursing home residents. *Journals of gerontology, 51A* (5), M239-M246.
The Top Ten Health Frauds (1990, February). *Consumer's research magazine,* pp. 34–36.
Thomas, J. (1992). *Adult and aging.* Boston, MA: Allyn and Bacon.
Thomas, W. I. (1923). *The unadjusted girl.* Boston: Little, Brown.
Tiberti, C.; Sabe, L.; Kuzis, G.; Cuerva, A. G.; Leiguarda, R.; & Starkstein, S.E. (1998). Prevalence and correlates of the catastrophic reaction in Alzheimer's disease. *Neurology, 50,* 546-548.
Tillman, R. A. (1997). The President's page: Elderly—advanced in years or past middle age. *The journal of the medical association of Georgia, 86* (2), 73-74.

Tinker, A. (1991). Granny flats—the British experience. *Journal of housing for the elderly, 7* (2), 421-456.

Tobin, S. (1991). *Personhood in advanced old age.* New York: Springer.

Toughill, E.; Jason, D. J.; Beck, T. L.; & Christopher, M. A. (1993). Health, income, and postretirement employment of older adults. *Public health nursing, 10* (2), 100-107.

Townsend, A. L. & Franks M. M. (1997). Quality of the relationship between elderly spouses: Influence on spouse caregivers' subjective effectiveness. *Family relations, 46,* 33-39.

Tracy, K. R. (1996). Diversifying into adult day care: A learning experience. *Nursing homes: Long term care management, 45* (10), 39-41.

Tracy, M. (1991). *Social policies for the elderly in the third world.* Westport, CT: Greenwood Publishing Group.

Troll, L. E. (1986). *Family issues in current gerontology.* New York: Springer.

Troll, L. E., & Skaff, M. M. (1997). Perceived continuity of self in very old age. *Psychology and aging, 12* (1), 162-169.

Tuckman, J., & Lorge, I. (1953). Attitudes toward old people. *Journal of Gerontology* 32, 227–232.

Turjanski, N.; Lees, A. J.; & Brooks, D. J. (1997). In vivo studies on striatal dopaminen D_1 and D_2 site binding in L-dopa-treated Parkinson's disease patients with and without dyskinesias. *Neurology, 49,* 717-723.

Turner, L. (1996). Time out with half-time: Job sharing in the nineties. *Canadian journal of counseling, 30* (2), 104-113..

Uehara, E. S. (1995). Reciprocity reconsidered: Gouldner's 'moral norm of reciprocity' and social support. *Journal of social and personal relationships, 12* (4), 483-502.

Uhlenberg, P. I. (1996). Mortality decline over the twentieth century and supply of kin over the life course. *Gerontologist, 36,* 681-685.

U.S. Bureau of the Census. (1990). *Marital status and living arrangement.* Current population reports (Series P20, No. 455). Washington, DC: U.S. Government Printing Office.

U.S.Bureau of the Census. (1991). *Statistical abstract of the United States, 1990.* Washington, DC: Department of Commerce, Bureau of the Census.

U.S. Bureau of the Census. (1993). *Statistical abstract of the United States,* 113th edition. Washington, DC: U.S. Government Printing Office.

U.S. Bureau of the Census. (1994). *1990 Census of population and housing: special tabulation on aging* (CD90-AoA-USA). Washington, DC: U.S. Department of Commerce.

U.S. Bureau of the Census. (1996). Income, poverty and valuation of noncash benefits. *Current Population Reports,* P60-189. Washington, DC: U.S. Government Printing Office.

U.S. Bureau of the Census. (1997). *Sixty-five plus in the US.* Current Population Reports. Series P23-190. US Department of Commerce.

Usdansky, M. L. (1992, November 10). Nation of youth growing long in the tooth. *USA Today,* p. 10A.

U.S. Department of Health and Human Services. (1997). *Healthy people 200 review, 1995-97.* Center for Disease Control National Center for Health Statistics. Washington, DC.

U. S. Department of Labor. (1998). Women gaining in pay but still lag behind men according to US Department of Labor report. *Department of Labor Press Release.* [Online]. Available, U.S. Department of Labor, Women's Bureau, http://www.dol.gov

U.S. Department of Labor Statistics (1996). *Facts on US working women. Caring for elderly family members.* Fact Sheet No. 86-4, Women's Bureau, Washington, DC.

US News Bulletins (1997, September 21). Kevorkian assists in suicide of Canadian from British Columbia. [Online] Available at *http://www.rights.org/deathnet/Usnews_9709.html*

US News Bulletins (1998, March 1). Kevorkian says: "Charge me – or leave me alone!" [Online] Available at *http://www.rights.org/deathnet/Usnews_9803.html.*

Van Boxtel, M. P. J.; Paas, F. G. W. C.; Houx, P. J.; Adam. J. J.; Teeken, J. C.; & Jolles, J. (1997). Aerobic capacity and cognitive performance in a cross-sectional aging study. *Medicine and science in sports and exercise, 29* (10), 1357-1365.

van den Hoonaard, D. (1997). Identity foreclosure: Women's experiences of widowhood as expressed in autobiographical accounts. *Aging and society, 17,* 533-551.

van Ranst, N., & Marcoen, A. (1997). Meaning in life of young and elderly adults: An examination of the factorial validity and invariance of the Life Regard Index. *Personality and individual differences, 22* (6), 877-884.

Vasavada, T.; Masand, P. S.; & Nasra, G. (1997). Evaluations of competency of patients with organic mental disorder. *Psychological reports, 80* (2), 107-113.

Vasil, L. & Wass, H. (1993). Portrayal of the elderly in the media: A literature review and implications for educational gerontologists. *Educational gerontology, 19*, 71-85.
Verbrugge, L. M.; Gruber-Baldini, A. L.; & Fozard, J. L. (1996). Age differences and age changes in activities: Baltimore Longitudinal Study on Aging. *Journal of gerontology: Social sciences, 51B* (1), S30-S41.
Vertinsky, P. (1991). Old age, gender and physical activity: The biomedicalization of aging. *Journal of sport history, 18* (1), 64-80.
Verwoerdt, A.; Pfeiffer, E.; & Wang, H. S. (1969). Sexual behaviorism in senescence. *Geriatrics, 24*, 137-153.
Vogt, M. T.; Wolfson, S. K.; & Kuller, L. H. (1992). Lower extremity arterial disease and the aging process: A review. *Journal of clinical epidemiology 45*, 529-542.
Wacker, R. R.; Roberty, K. A.; & Piper, L. E. (1998). *Community resources for older adults: Programs and services in an era of change*. Thousand Oaks, CA: Pine Forge Press.
Walford, R. L. (1983). *Maximum life span*. New York: Norton & Co.
Wallace, B. (1992, February 10). Elderly cheated out of homes by scam artists. *San Francisco Chronicle*, p. A13.
Wallis, C. (1995, March 6). How to live to be 120. *Time*, p. 85.
Walls, C. & Zarit, S. (1991).Informal support from black churches and the well-being of elderly blacks. *The gerontologist, 31* (4), 490-495.
Walter, P. (1997). Effects of vegetarian diets on aging and longevity. *Nutrition reviews, 55* (1), S61-S65.
Ward, R. A. (1984). The marginality and salience of being old. *Gerontologist, 24*, 227-232.
Ware, J. M. (1996). Differences in four-year health outcomes for elderly and poor, chronically ill patients treated in HMO and fee-for-service systems: Results from the medical outcomes study. *Journal of the American medical association, 276* (13), 1039-1047.
Watson, K. (1997, Fall). *Current trauma in the lives of older adults: Surviving and healing the wounds of a changing self-concept and self-neglect*. Unpublished manuscript, Gerontology of Aging, Rohnert Park, CA: Sonoma State University.
Weaver, C. N. (1997). Has the work ethic in the USA declined? Evidence from nationwide surveys. *Psychological report, 81*, 491-495.
Weber, M. (1958). *The Protestant ethic and spirit of capitalism* (T. Parsons, Trans.). New York: Scribner. [original work published 1904-1905].
Welch, J. (1997, June 26) Intel faces fight over "termination quotas." *People management*, p. 9.
Wellman, N. S.; Weddle, D. O.; Krantz, S.; & Brain, C. T. (1997). Elder insecurities: Poverty, hunger, and malnutrition. *Journal of the American dietetic association, 97* (10), 120-122.
Wells, R. M. (1997, March 1). Subsidies for Section 8 program are on the chopping block. *Congressional quarterly*, 539-541.
Westinghouse Electric, Northrop settle suits on age discrimination (1997, November 3). *Wall Street Journal*, p. A2.
Whaley, D. E., & Ebbeck, V. (1997). Older adults' constraints to participation in structured exercise classes. *Journal of aging and physical activity, 5* (3), 190-213.
White, N., & Cunningham, W. R. (1988). Is terminal drop pervasive or specific? *Journals of gerontology, 42*, P141-P144.
Whitehead, C., & Finucane, P. (1997). Malnutrition in elderly people. *Australian and New Zealand journal of medicine, 27* (1), 68-74.
Wicclair, M. (1993). *Ethics and the elderly*. New York: Oxford University Press.
Wick, G., & Grubeck-Loebenstein, B. (1997). The aging immune system; Primary and secondary alterations of immune reactivity in the elderly. *Experimental gerontology, 32* (4/5), 401-413.
Wilcox, S. (1997). Age and gender in relation to body attitudes: Is there a double standard of aging? *Psychology of women quarterly, 21* (4), 549-565.
Wildavsky, B. (1997). Social insecurity. *National journal, 29* (41), 201-203.
Willett, W. C. (1994). Diet and health: What should we eat? *Science, 264*, 532-537.
Williams, A.; Coupland, J.; Folwell, A.; & Sparks, L. (1997). Talking about Generation X: Defining them as they define themselves. *Journal of language and social psychology, 16* (3), 251-277.
Williams, L. J.; Gavin, M. B.; & Williams, M. L. (1996). Measurement and nonmeasurement processes with negative affectivity and employee attitudes. *Journal of applied psychology, 81*, 88-101.
Willis, S. L. (1987). Cognitive training and everyday competence. *Annual review of gerontology and geriatrics, 7*, 159-188.

Wise, L. (1990, June). Partial and flexible retirement: The Swedish system. *Gerontologist, 30* (3), 355-361.

Witkin, G. (1994, January 17). Ten myths about sex. *Parade Magazine, Santa Rosa Press Democrat.*

Wolf, D. A.; Freedman, V.; & Soldo, B. J. (1997). The division of family labor: Care for elderly parents. *The journals of gerontology, 52B* (special issue), 102-109.

Wolfson, C. (1993).Adult children's perceptions of their responsibility to provide care for dependent elderly parents. *The gerontologist,* 315-323.

Wolters, G., & Prinsen, A. (1997). Full versus divided attention and implicit memory performance. *Memory and cognition, 25* (6), 764-771.

Woman, 73, battles intruder and foils rape in apartment. (August 14). *New York Times,* p. A12(N).

World Health Organization. (1991). *World health statistics annual.* Geneva, Switzerland: WHO.

World Health Organization. (1997). *The world health report 1997: Conquering suffering... enriching humanity.* Geneva, Switzerland: Health Communications and Public Relations.

Worsley, R. (1996, January 11). Only prejudices are old and tired. *People management,* 18-20.

Worsnop, R. I. (1997). Caring for the dying. *Congressional quarterly researcher, 7* (33), 769-792.

Wurtzel, A. (1992). *The changing landscape of network television.* ABS Television network, 77 West 66th Street, New York, NY.

Yancik, R. (1993). Ovarian cancer. *Cancer, 71,* 517-523.

Yashin, A. I., & Iachine, I. A. (1995). Genetic analysis of durations: Correlated family model applied to survival of Danish twins. *Genetic epidemiology, 12,* 529-538.

Zeiss, A. M., & Breckenridge, J. S. (1997). Treatment of late life depression: A response to the NIH consensus conference. *Behavior therapy, 28,* 3-21.

Photo Credits

2 (right): Reuters/ Corbis-Bettmann; 2 (left): UPI/ Corbis-Bettmann; 4: © Jean-Claude Lejeune/ Stock Boston; 6: © Elizabeth Crews/ Stock Boston; 11: AP Photo Wide World/ Francois Mori; 22: Agence France Presse/ Corbis-Bettmann; 29: © Alan Carey/ The Image Works; 35: © Harry Cutting; 44: Shizuo Kambayashi, A/P Wide World; 50: © Glen Korenbold/ Stock Boston; 60: © Mike Malyszko/ Stock Boston; 63: © Jim Harrison/ Stock Boston; 73: © Joel Gordon; 75: © Gary Walts/ The Image Works; 78: James L. Shaffer; 82: © Spencer Grant/ Stock Boston; 97: © Harry Cutting; 102: © Peter Menzel/ Stock Boston; 105: © Larry Kolvcoro/ The Image Works; 113: Joel Gordon; 120: James L. Shaffer; 123: © M. Greenlar/ The Image Works; 129, 141: James L. Shaffer; 149: © Carl Glassman/ The Image Works; 154: © Jim Harrison/ Stock Boston; 164: James L. Shaffer; 168: © Alan Carey/ The Image Works; 178: Joel Gordon; 186: © L. Eber/ The Image Works; 193: © K. Preuss/ The Image Works; 201: © Arthur Grace/ Stock Boston; 214: Anestis Diakopoulos/ Stock Boston; 220: Alan Oddie/ PhotoEdit; 234: San Francisco Chronicle; 238: James L. Shaffer; 250: AP Photo/ J. Terrill; 266: James L. Shaffer; 271: © Joel Gordon Photography; 284: © Bob Daemmrich/ The Image Works; 287: © Harry Cutting; 295: © George Gardner/ The Image Works; 303: Mark Lennihan, A/P Wide World; 307: Deborah Kahn Kalas/ Stock Boston; 319: © David Strickler/ The Image Works; 328: © Joel Gordon; 333: Richard Sheinwald, A/P Wide World; 340: Joel Gordon; 350: Lionel Delevingne/ Stock Boston; 351: © Lisa Law/ The Image Works; 356: © Joel Gordon; 359: UPI/ Corbis-Bettmann; 363: James L. Shaffer; 374: © Lee Snider/ The Image Works; 377: UPI/ Corbis-Bettmann; 380: Spencer Grant III/ Stock Boston; 384: © Joel Gordon.

Name Index

Page numbers printed in *italic* refer to illustrations

Subject Index

Page numbers printed in *italic* type refer to tables, figures, or illustrations